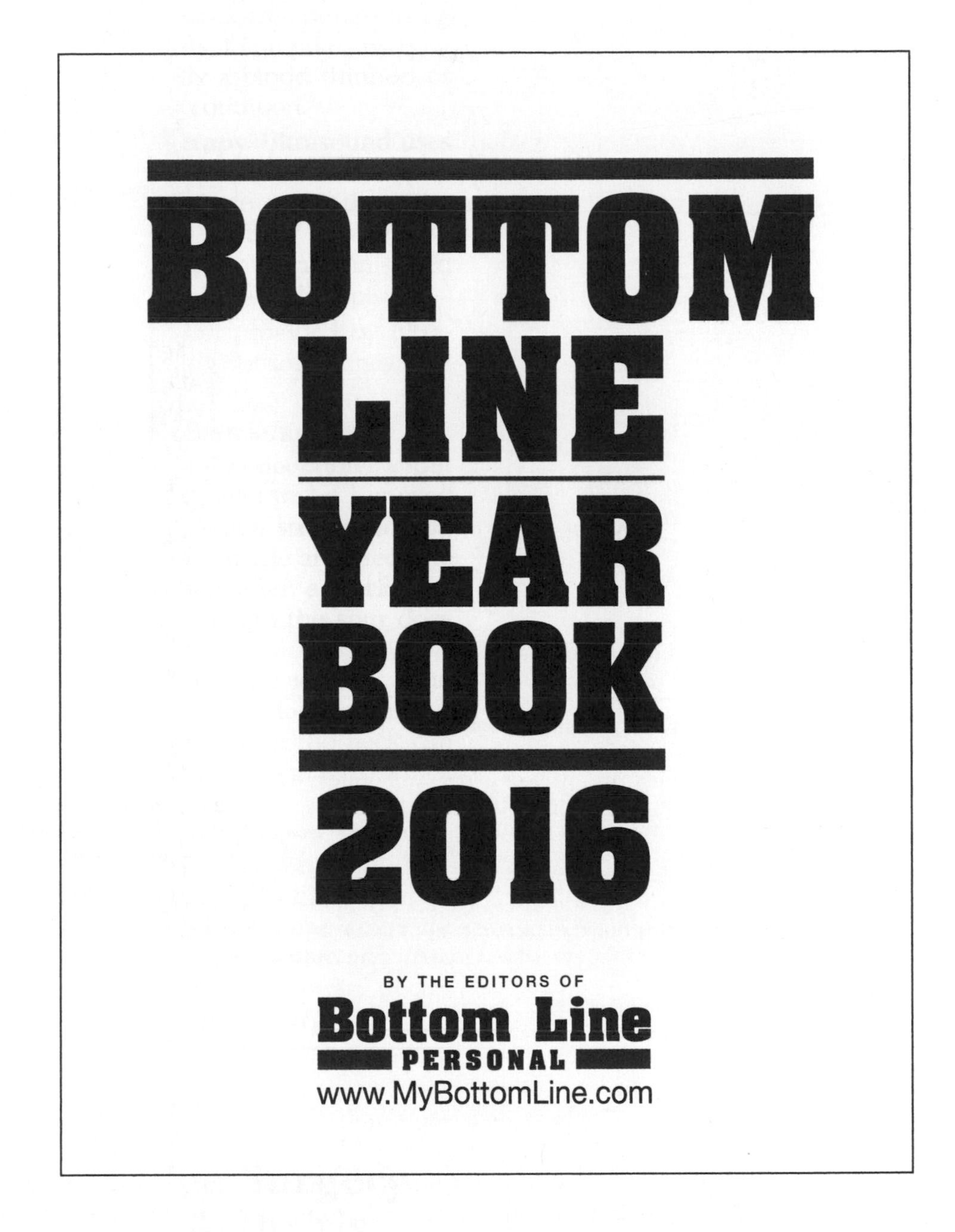
BOTTOM
LINE
YEAR
BOOK
2016
BY THE EDITORS OF
Bottom Line
PERSONAL
www.MyBottomLine.com

Bottom Line Year Book 2016

10 9 8 7 6 5 4 3 2 1

ISBN 0-88723-731-2

Bottom Line Books® publishes the advice of expert authorities in many fields. These opinions may at times conflict as there are often different approaches to solving problems. The use of a book is not a substitute for legal, accounting, investment, health or any other professional services. Consult competent professionals for answers to your specific questions.

Offers, prices, rates, addresses, telephone numbers and websites listed in this book are accurate at the time of publication, but they are subject to frequent change.

Bottom Line Books® is a registered trademark of
Boardroom® Inc.
281 Tresser Boulevard, Stamford, CT 06901

www.MyBottomLine.com

Bottom Line Books® is an imprint of Boardroom® Inc., publisher of print periodicals, e-letters and books. We are dedicated to bringing you the best information from the most knowledgeable sources in the world. Our goal is to help you gain greater wealth, better health, more wisdom, extra time and increased happiness.

Printed in the United States of America

Contents

3 • FAST FIXES FOR COMMON CONDITIONS

4 • FOCUS ON FITNESS & DIET

5 • NATURAL NEWS

6 • PRIVATE & PERSONAL

PART TWO: YOUR MONEY

7 • MONEY MANAGER

8 • INSURANCE INSIGHTS

9 • TAX TUNE-UP

PART THREE: YOUR FINANCIAL FUTURE

12 • RETIREMENT RUNDOWN

PART FOUR: YOUR LEISURE

13 • TRAVEL TALK

14 • FUN FINDS

PART FIVE: YOUR LIFE

15 • CAR CARE

16 • FAMILY FIRST

17 • HOUSEHOLD HELPERS

18 • LIFE LESSONS

19 • BUSINESS BRAINSTORM

20 • SAFETY SURVEY

Preface

We are happy to bring you our *Bottom Line Year Book 2016*. Here you will find numerous helpful and practical ideas for yourself and for everyone in your family.

At Bottom Line Books, it is our mission to provide all of our readers with the best information to help them gain better health, greater wealth, more wisdom, extra time and increased happiness.

The *Year Book 2016* represents the very best and the most useful Bottom Line articles from the past year. Whether you are looking for ways to get the most from your money or how to grow your business...lower your blood pressure naturally or avoid misdiagnosis at the doctor...keep your marriage strong or deal with those difficult people in your life, you'll find it all in this book...and a whole lot more.

Over the past 30 years, we have built a network of thousands of expert sources.

When you consult the *2016 Year Book*, you are accessing a stellar group of authorities in fields that range from natural and conventional medicine...to shopping, investing, taxes and insurance...to cars, travel, security and self-improvement. Our advisers are affiliated with the premier universities, financial institutions, law firms and hospitals. These experts are truly among the most knowledgeable people in the country.

As a reader of a Bottom Line book, you can be assured that you are receiving reliable, well-researched and up-to-date information from a trusted source.

We are very confident that the *Bottom Line Year Book 2016* can help you and your family have a healthier, wealthier, wiser life. Enjoy!

The Editors, *Bottom Line/Personal*
Stamford, CT

Health Hotline

Butter Is Bad for You... and Other Lies About Fat

Fat is one of the most misunderstood foods. And there are a lot of myths about fat that just won't die. *Here we separate what is true from what's not...*

***True or False:* Saturated fat causes heart disease.**

False: An analysis of about 80 studies that involved more than 500,000 people found that saturated fat does not increase heart disease risk. The analysis was conducted by a team of international scientists and published in *Annals of Internal Medicine*.

Even though a diet high in saturated fat raises blood levels of LDL (the so-called "bad" cholesterol), it simultaneously increases levels of beneficial HDL. The ratio of LDL to HDL is more significant than LDL alone.

But isn't a high-fat diet bad for your weight? Wrong again. Fats may contain more than twice the calories of carbohydrates and protein, but they're less likely to cause weight gain than, say, a diet high in refined carbohydrates.

This is partly due to satiety—high-fat foods fill you up more quickly than other foods, so you tend to eat less overall. Also, people who cut back on fat tend to replace it with something—and that something typically is carbohydrates that can really pack on the pounds.

***True or False:* Oils are more healthful than butter.**

False: Olive, canola, soybean and other vegetable oils are good for the heart, but that

Tonia Reinhard, MS, RD, a registered dietitian and professor at Wayne State University in Detroit. She is program director for the Coordinated Program in Dietetics, course director for clinical nutrition at Wayne State University School of Medicine and a past president of the Michigan Academy of Nutrition and Dietetics. She is author of *Superfoods: The Healthiest Foods on the Planet* and *Superjuicing: More Than 100 Nutritious Vegetable and Fruit Recipes*.

doesn't mean that small amounts of butter—or lard, for that matter—are harmful.

The saturated fat in butter and lard doesn't seem to be a problem, particularly because most people don't use a lot. Besides, butter and lard have unique cooking qualities. A flaky piecrust? You can't beat lard or butter!

True or False: **Olive oil is the healthiest fat.**

Partly true: Olive oil is high in monounsaturated fatty acids, which reduce both total and LDL cholesterol. Olive oil also contains antioxidants and anti-inflammatory compounds that can help prevent heart disease and cancer.

Olive oil may be somewhat healthier than polyunsaturated fats (such as soybean oil and canola oil), but the difference isn't dramatic.

True or False**: Heated olive oil can be toxic.**

True: You never want to heat oil beyond its smoke point—the temperature at which an oil starts to smoke. Overheated oils produce *acrolein*, a compound that has been linked to cancer and other chronic diseases, including heart disease. The best oils for high-heat cooking—searing meats and in stir-fries, for example—are corn, soybean, peanut, palm and sesame oils. Olive, canola and grape-seed oils can handle the moderately high heat used for sautés. The lower smoke-point oils, such as walnut and flaxseed, are mainly used for seasoning salads and other cold dishes.

True or False: **Low-fat dairy helps with weight loss.**

Probably false: Whole-milk and full-fat cheeses have more calories than their leaner counterparts, but they are less likely to be associated with weight gain. A study published in the *European Journal of Nutrition* found that people who consumed whole-milk dairy actually were less likely to be obese than those who avoided it. There also is evidence that some of the bioactive substances in whole milk, such as *sphingolipids*, protect against cancer and diabetes.

True or False: **Coconut oil is a superfood.**

False: Despite claims that coconut oil strengthens immunity, improves thyroid function and prevents heart disease and cancer, there is little evidence to support it. Coconut oil is higher in saturated fat than any other food on the planet (including butter). It is so high in saturated fat that it actually is a solid at room temperature.

Until more studies are in, limit coconut oil to small amounts. In small amounts, it is a good choice for curries and other dishes that benefit from a light, slightly sweet flavor.

True or False: **Grilled meat can be harmful to your health.**

True: The smoke caused by the combustion of fat dripping onto the coals contains *polycyclic aromatic hydrocarbons* (PAHs), chemical compounds that have been linked to cancer. That char on meats contains *heterocyclic amines*, another class of cancer-causing compounds.

Helpful: Dry rubs that contain rosemary and thyme. They reduce the formation of cancer-causing compounds. Also, a recent study found that marinating meat in beer before cooking reduces the formation of PAHs.

Coffee: The Good News... and the Bad News

Wilkie A. Wilson, Jr., PhD, a neuropharmacologist and research professor of prevention science at the Social Science Research Institute at Duke University, where he is also a faculty fellow at the Center for Child and Family Policy, both in Durham, North Carolina. Dr. Wilson is coauthor, with Cynthia Kuhn, PhD, and Scott Swartzwelder, PhD, of *Buzzed: The Straight Facts About the Most Used and Abused Drugs from Alcohol to Ecstasy.*

Here is a shocking statistic for you—90% of Americans need a drug just to get through the day. If they don't get it, many suffer withdrawal symptoms. That may sound like an exaggeration, but think about the caffeine that nearly all American adults get in their coffee, tea and soda each day. Caffeine is a drug—and a potent one.

It is true that caffeine increases energy and alertness—and may even help fight certain chronic diseases (see next page). In large amounts, however, caffeine can often lead to nervousness and agitation—along with high blood pressure, rapid heartbeats and even panic attacks.

The facts about caffeine...

IT'S EVERYWHERE!

With caffeine now included in so many different beverages and foods, it's easy to consume much more than you realize.

Do the math: The average US adult drinks about three cups of coffee a day, with anywhere from 75 milligrams (mg) to 200 mg of caffeine in an eight-ounce cup (decaf has about 12 mg or less per cup).

Tea drinkers get 67 mg in an eight-ounce cup of generic black tea brewed for three minutes and 43 mg from the same size generic green tea with an equal brewing time (the caffeine content increases the longer it's brewed).

And do you have a soft drink now and then? A Coke or Pepsi (regular or diet) has about 35 mg of caffeine per 12-ounce serving. Some energy drinks have more than double that amount.

The dark chocolate you may enjoy—in part for its health benefits—has about 20 mg per ounce (the darker the chocolate, the more caffeine it will contain).

Meanwhile, the Excedrin that you may take for headaches adds another 65 mg per tablet.

What you may not realize: The Food and Drug Administration (FDA) advises getting no more than 400 mg of caffeine a day, but you could be getting a lot more than that.

HOW CAFFEINE HELPS

An increasing body of evidence shows that caffeine—whether it's from coffee, tea, colas or some other source—has positive health effects. *Key examples...*

- **Less cognitive decline.** In a 2012 study, 124 participants with mild cognitive impairment (which often precedes Alzheimer's disease) had memory tests at the start of the study and again two to four years later. Those who had caffeine levels consistent with three daily cups of coffee did not develop Alzheimer's, while those who developed dementia had caffeine levels that were, on average, 51% lower.

The study did not prove that caffeine is protective. Coffee, for example, contains other chemical compounds that might protect brain cells. But it's possible that the increased alertness from caffeine could make people more likely to pursue social and intellectual activities that improve brain health.

- **Fewer gallstones.** Two important studies found that coffee drinkers were less likely to develop gallstones (20% less likely in women and 40% in men) than people who don't drink coffee. The reason is not yet known, but it's possible that gallbladder contractions triggered by caffeine reduce buildups of stone-forming cholesterol and bile pigments. Drinkers of decaf didn't get the same benefit.
- **Less Parkinson's disease.** Caffeine intake has been linked to lower incidence of Parkinson's disease, and recent research found that symptoms, such as tremors and stiffness, eased in people with Parkinson's who consumed 100 mg to 200 mg of caffeine twice a day (roughly two to four cups of coffee).
- **Headache relief.** A strong cup of coffee or tea can help ward off a migraine by constricting blood vessels in the brain. Caffeine also offsets the widening of blood vessels that occurs during migraines. Not surprisingly, you'll see caffeine listed on the labels of painkillers, including not only Excedrin but also Anacin and Midol.
- **Better workouts.** Caffeine helps mobilize fatty acids for endurance, so it could improve a workout. But be sure to drink water before, during and after exercise because caffeine can cause dehydration.

THE NOT-SO-GOOD NEWS

Even though it's almost impossible for an adult to overdose on coffee, tea or other beverages with caffeine, the FDA has warned consumers to avoid any powdered form of caffeine sold on the Internet. One teaspoon of the powder, which was recently linked to the death of a teenager, contained the equivalent of 25 cups of coffee.

You probably know that even "safe" amounts of caffeine, such as that found in a few cups of coffee, can lead to sleep problems (especially when consumed within six hours of bedtime)

CAFFEINE ALERT...

How Big a Buzz?

Americans get most of their caffeine from coffee, but it's tricky to predict how much you'll actually get. The exact amount depends on the coffee variety, how it's roasted and even how it's prepared. *Some surprising facts...*

- **The inexpensive bulk coffees in supermarkets,** made from robusta beans, can have double the caffeine of the more expensive arabica beans (used in specialty coffees from Costa Rica and Sumatra, for example).
- **Dark-roasted coffees** have a strong taste but actually have less caffeine than lighter varieties.
- **Drip coffee** has more caffeine than percolated or coffee made with a French press. A "cup" of espresso has about the same amount of caffeine as a cup of percolated coffee, but the espresso cup is only about two ounces. The higher concentration causes the caffeine to be absorbed more quickly, giving an "espresso buzz."

Wilkie A. Wilson, Jr., PhD, Duke University, Durham, North Carolina.

and can cause unpleasant effects, such as jitteriness, in some people. *Caffeine also may increase risk for...*

- **High blood pressure.** Caffeine from a cup or two of coffee can temporarily increase the heart rate by as much as 10 to 20 beats per minute in sensitive individuals. This isn't a problem in healthy adults but could be dangerous for those with hypertension. An increased heart rate also can trigger heartbeat irregularities (*arrhythmias*) in some people.
- **Impaired glucose regulation.** Some studies have found that people with type 2 diabetes who consume two to three cups of coffee may have higher-than-expected surges in glucose (blood sugar) after meals. People with diabetes should talk to their doctors about their use of caffeine, especially if they are having trouble regulating blood glucose.

But just to show you how complicated caffeine research can be, a recent study found that coffee consumption reduced risk for type 2 diabetes. Is it the caffeine or something else in the coffee? Research is ongoing.

- **Stress.** Caffeine increases *adrenaline*, a hormone that's already elevated during times of stress. The effect can be magnified if you happen to drink even more coffee during stressful times.

There is some evidence that caffeine also can trigger panic attacks in people who have had them previously. Even if you don't have a history of panic attacks, large amounts of caffeine (more than 300 mg, or about three cups of coffee) at one time can trigger them.

- **Incontinence.** Caffeine increases urine production, and studies have linked coffee intake to urinary incontinence.

Takeaway for everyone: To minimize your risk for caffeine-related health problems, consider spreading your coffee intake out over several hours or alternate it with decaf or water.

The Dark Side of Superfoods

Jamison Starbuck, ND, a naturopathic physician in family practice and a guest lecturer at the University of Montana, both in Missoula. She is also a past president of the American Association of Naturopathic Physicians and a contributing editor to *The Alternative Advisor: The Complete Guide to Natural Therapies and Alternative Treatments.*

It's no secret that I believe eating nutritious foods is one of the best ways to protect your health. But when the talk about certain foods doesn't give both sides of the story, then it's time for me to weigh in with the facts. We've always known that whole, nutritious food functions as medicine. But advertisers have now gotten in on the action by co-opting the term "superfood" for one-sided campaigns to sell grocery items—and not in a way that's always healthful! While there's certainly plenty of truth to the health benefits conferred by superfoods, it's only fair that any downsides of these highly touted foods get equal airtime. *Some not-so-super facts about four enormously popular superfoods...*

•**Kale.** This slightly bitter, leafy green is rich in vitamin K, folic acid and calcium. It also contains *indole-3-carbinol*, a compound thought to lower cancer risk. All that sounds great. But there can be some problems if certain people consume too much kale. If you take a blood thinner, such as *warfarin* (Coumadin), all that vitamin K will interact with the drug. Kale also contains *oxalates* that may contribute to kidney stones, and raw kale can act as a *goitrogen*, meaning it reduces thyroid function. Additionally, when eaten raw, kale can cause intestinal gas and bloating in some people.

Bottom line on kale: If you are on a blood thinner or you have had oxalate-type kidney stones, avoid kale. If you have hypothyroidism (low thyroid function), don't consume concentrated, juiced kale. Cooking kale deactivates some of its goitrogenic properties, so it's OK to enjoy a couple of servings per week. For everyone else, it's safe and healthy to eat kale once a day.

•**Goji berry.** Goji is believed to improve physical stamina, promote sleep and help confer a longer life. The downside? Well, goji isn't all that unique from a nutritional standpoint—in fact, it's similar to many red-colored fruits and berries. Goji is rich in vitamins, particularly beta-carotene and vitamin C, and it's a good source of calcium. However, there have recently been reports of pesticide-laden goji being imported from Asia. That's why you must read labels and inquire about sources when you purchase goji. To play it safe, avoid goji from Asia—it may contain pesticides. Buy organic goji from the US or grow it yourself. Enjoy goji as you would raspberries or blackberries.

•**Chia seeds.** Rich in fiber, antioxidants and calcium, chia seeds (like flaxseeds) have a mild, nutty flavor. They are a good plant source of omega-3s and make a nice addition to oatmeal, baked goods and protein-rich snack bars. The problem with chia seeds? Some promoters sell chia seeds as a weight-loss aid, but this has not been proved.

•**Quinoa.** Gluten-free and high in protein, quinoa is often called the superfood of grains. However, quinoa contains *saponins*, foamy, bitter chemical compounds that can create indigestion in some people. Food manufacturers know this and often prewash quinoa before processing it to be sold to consumers. Even so, some saponins slip through. So if you like quinoa but it gives you indigestion, be sure to rinse it thoroughly before cooking.

Beware the Red Check Mark on Food Packages!

Foods with the red heart–check mark from the American Heart Association (AHA) can be high in sodium. The check mark means that the food meets the criteria for fat and cholesterol content and other nutrients important for heart health.

But: Foods can get the check mark even if each serving contains as much as 480 milligrams (mg) of salt—nearly one-third the total recommended daily limit.

And: Some foods may be packaged in a way that leads people to consume even more salt.

Example: Canned soup may have a portion size of one cup, but consumers may eat an entire two-serving can.

University of California, Berkeley Wellness Letter. BerkeleyWellness.com

---

6 Dangerous Myths About Your Blood Pressure

Mark C. Houston, MD, an associate clinical professor of medicine at Vanderbilt University School of Medicine in Nashville and director of the Hypertension Institute of Nashville at Saint Thomas Hospital. He is also a member of the American Heart Association Council on Arteriosclerosis, Thrombosis and Vascular Biology and author of *What Your Doctor May Not Tell You About Hypertension* and *What Your Doctor May Not Tell You About Heart Disease*.

About one of every three adults in the US has high blood pressure (hypertension). But only about half of these people have it under control. This unfortunate statistic is due, in part, to some common misconceptions about hypertension.

SIX MYTHS—AND THE FACTS...

MYTH #1: In-office blood pressure tests are the gold standard. The automated devices in most doctors' offices are convenient, but they are not as precise as the manual (mercury) blood pressure kits. It's common for automated office blood pressure machines to give readings that are off by several points. The old-fashioned monitors tend to give more precise measurements, since doctors use a stethoscope to listen to the sound of blood flowing.

To get an accurate blood pressure reading, the patient should have rested in a seated position for at least five minutes, and his/her arm should be supported on a table or held by the person giving the test.

Important: Both types of monitors can give a skewed reading due to "white-coat hypertension," higher readings that result from anxious feelings during a doctor's visit.

Fact: You can get accurate blood pressure readings at home as long as you use an automatic, cuff-style monitor that properly fits over your upper arm (not over your wrist or finger) and follow the instructions. The device should be approved by the Association for the Advancement of Medical Instrumentation (AAMI). This ensures that the device has undergone extensive studies to validate its accuracy. To tell if a monitor has AAMI approval, check the label on the device's package.

MYTH #2: It's fine to check your blood pressure now and then. Checking your blood pressure every few days or just once a week is fine for maintaining good blood pressure readings but not for achieving good control in the beginning.

New approach: 24-hour ambulatory blood pressure monitoring (ABPM). It's done routinely in the UK but is still a novelty in the US. That's likely to change because studies show that it's the most effective way to measure blood pressure.

With ABPM, patients wear a device (usually around the waist) that controls a blood pressure cuff that measures *brachial pressure* (inside the arm at the elbow crease). ABPM, which takes readings every 15 to 60 minutes over a 24-hour period, allows your doctor to choose medications and doses more precisely. The test costs $100 to $350,* but it is usually covered by insurance with proper diagnostic coding (such as labile, or "episodic," hypertension or resistant hypertension).

My advice: Have the test once when diagnosed with hypertension, and repeat it once or twice a year to see how treatment is working.

MYTH #3: It's OK to take blood pressure medication at your convenience. Blood pressure normally drops 10% to 20% during sleep. But about 25% of blood pressure patients (known as nondippers) don't experience this nighttime drop. Their blood pressure is always elevated, and they need to time their medications accordingly.

If a 24-hour test shows that you're a nondipper, your doctor will probably advise you to take medications at night. Taking medications at night—say, at about 9 pm—can reduce the risk for cardiovascular events (such as a heart attack) by 61% compared with taking them in the morning. Nighttime medications can also help lower the surge in blood pressure that occurs in the morning.

MYTH #4: Sodium isn't a big deal for everyone. Much of what we hear or read about blood pressure these days includes references to "salt sensitivity." For people who are salt-sensitive, even small amounts of sodium can cause a rapid rise in blood pressure. But don't assume that you're safe just because your blood pressure doesn't seem to rise when you consume sodium.

Fact: Excessive salt causes vascular damage even in people without hypertension...and it increases the risk that you'll eventually develop high blood pressure.

The recommended daily limit for sodium is 1,500 milligrams (mg) for adults age 51 and over. People who are salt-sensitive should get even less. People who cut back on salt usually see a drop in *systolic* (top number) blood

*Prices subject to change.

pressure of six to seven points and a drop in *diastolic* (bottom number) pressure of three to four points.

Also: Don't assume that sea salt is safe. It has only slightly less sodium chloride than table salt.

MYTH #5: You need drugs to control blood pressure. If your blood pressure is 140/90 or higher, your doctor will probably prescribe one or more medications.

But certain nutritional supplements can help boost the effectiveness of those drugs. One study found that 62% of patients who used the DASH 2 diet, exercised, lost weight and took specific supplements for six months were able to reduce or stop their use of blood pressure medications.** *Supplements to discuss with your doctor…*

- **Coenzyme Q10 (CoQ10)** reduces blood pressure by an average of 15/10 points. About half of people who take it can eventually discontinue blood pressure medications.

Typical dose: 120 mg to 225 mg daily.

- **Taurine,** an amino acid, can lower blood pressure by 9/4.1 points.

Typical dose: 2 grams (g) to 3 g daily. Larger doses may be needed in some cases.

- **Lycopene** is an antioxidant in tomatoes, grapefruit and other fruits. It reduces blood pressure, blood fats and inflammatory markers such as C-reactive protein. Consider taking this supplement if you don't consume a lot of lycopene-rich foods.

Typical dose: 10 mg to 20 mg daily.

MYTH #6: Food won't help your blood pressure. Foods rich in potassium can reduce blood pressure. Try to get at least two-and-a-half times more potassium than sodium in your diet—the ratio that blocks sodium's negative effects.

Good high-potassium foods: A medium-sized potato with skin has 926 mg of potassium, and a medium-sized banana has 422 mg.

**For additional details on the DASH 2 diet, go to *HypertensionInstitute.com* and search under "Nutritional Services."

BETTER WAYS…

More Effective BP Monitoring

Office blood pressure testing is not enough to diagnose hypertension. People who have a slightly elevated reading at one doctor visit should not be rushed onto medication. To be sure that a patient has hypertension that needs treatment, blood pressure should be measured over a longer period outside the doctor's office, either by wearing a 24-hour-a-day pressure cuff or using a device to monitor blood pressure at home.

Samuel Joseph Mann, MD, hypertension specialist and professor of clinical medicine at Weill Cornell Medical College, New York City.

Valuable Clue for Cardiac Risk

Different blood pressure readings in each arm indicate cardiac risk. A difference of more than 10 points in *systolic pressure* (the top number) indicates 38% higher risk for a cardiac event.

Study of 3,390 people without cardiovascular disease, age 40 or older, over an average of 13 years, by researchers at Massachusetts General Hospital, Boston, published in *The American Journal of Medicine.*

Puzzling Palpitations? What These Unusual Heartbeats Really Mean…

Robert Stark, MD, an internist and a cardiologist who is the medical director of the Cardiovascular Prevention Program at Greenwich Hospital/Yale New Haven Health and a clinical faculty member at New York Medical College in Valhalla. *RobertStarkMD.com*

Chances are, you hardly ever notice the steady rhythm of your heart, even though it beats approximately 100,000 times a day. But there may be times when you can feel your heart beating. Perhaps it's racing, even though you haven't done anything strenuous. Or maybe you notice a fluttering sensation...an abrupt thump...or a flip-flop feeling.

Is this a sign that something is seriously wrong with your heart or just a harmless "glitch" in your normal heartbeat?

LISTENING TO YOUR HEART

Most people think of heart palpitations as a racing or pounding sensation in the heart, but the term actually applies whenever you have any unpleasant awareness of your own heartbeat. Palpitations can be normal—when you exercise, for example, you'll feel your heart pounding.

Heart palpitations also can be caused by *arrhythmias*, heartbeat irregularities that may (or may not) be harmless. For example, when you're under a lot of stress, drink too much coffee or use a cold medicine with a stimulating ingredient (such as *pseudoephedrine)*, you may experience arrhythmias.

When there may be a problem: If palpitations are repetitive or recurrent over the course of a day, this could be a sign of heart damage or disease. So could palpitations that last more than a few seconds or are accompanied by dizziness, shortness of breath or other symptoms. These palpitations should always be checked by a physician (in some cases, on an emergency basis). You might need tests—including blood work and an *electrocardiogram* (EKG or ECG)—to analyze the heartbeat and identify likely problems. *Unusual heart sensations—and what they could mean...*

***Sensation*: Skipped beats.**

What it could be: *Premature atrial contractions* (PACs), which occur in the heart's upper chambers, or atria...or *premature ventricular contractions* (PVCs), which affect the lower chambers, or ventricles. These are the most common types of palpitations—and usually the least serious.

With these palpitations, the heart simply beats earlier than it should. You might feel a "pause" in your heartbeat, followed by a strong "thump" as the heart compensates for the delayed beat.

Most individuals have occasional PVCs. PACs are also common. If you don't have a history of heart disease (including atherosclerosis), your doctor will probably tell you not to worry.

Exception: When PVCs are repetitive, with one following right after the other for seconds or minutes. This pattern increases the risk for a more serious arrhythmia called *ventricular tachycardia* (see next page).

Treatment options: For frequent premature heartbeats, you may need an antiarrhythmic medication. There are many such drugs, including *disopyramide* (Norpace), *propranolol* (Inderal) and *sotalol* (Betapace).

Helpful: Cutting back or avoiding alcohol, caffeine, smoking and emotional stress often can reduce the frequency of PVCs and PACs and may prevent the need for medication.

***Sensation*: Racing (as with a very fast pulse) and/or fluttering.**

What it could be: *Atrial fibrillation*. It's a serious arrhythmia that you may or may not feel—and it might occur with sudden sweating or chest pain that feels like a heart attack. It also can cause dizziness, weakness and/or shortness of breath. With atrial fibrillation, the heart's upper chambers beat too erratically to efficiently pump blood to the lower chambers.

Result: Blood pools in the atria and may form clots. Each year, about 8% of people with untreated atrial fibrillation have a stroke.

If you have racing and/or fluttering sensations in your heart, go to a hospital emergency department. If your heart turns out to be healthy, you might have had lone atrial fibrillation, a onetime event that's unlikely to be dangerous. But if you keep having these sensations, or they last a long time (or never go away), you're going to need treatment.

Treatment options: If you are experiencing atrial fibrillation, your doctor will try to convert the heartbeat back to a normal rhythm, which can sometimes be done using antiarrhythmic drugs or with *electrical cardioversion*, in which an electrical shock is delivered to restore the heart's normal rhythm.

If this treatment doesn't work, you might be given a prescription for a beta-blocker, a calcium channel blocker or other drugs that prevent the heart from racing or fluttering, along with blood-thinning medications to prevent clots. You'll probably need to take the drugs for life. Another approach, known as *radiofrequency ablation*, uses electricity to permanently damage (ablate) the cells in the heart that are causing abnormal rhythms. This is usually done only when medications and other approaches haven't helped.

***Sensation:* A sudden burst of rapid beats lasting seconds to hours.**

What it could be: *Ventricular tachycardia* (V tach). Get to an emergency department! V tach usually occurs in people with a history of heart disease. The lower chambers of the heart can start beating faster than 170 times a minute. It can lead to ventricular fibrillation, a dangerous arrhythmia that causes the heart to quiver instead of pump. It's the main cause of sudden cardiac arrest, which is usually fatal.

How can you distinguish a racing heart from V tach? You can't. You must be treated at a hospital emergency department, particularly if you're dizzy or have actually lost consciousness—both of these are symptoms of insufficient blood flow.

Treatment options: Patients with V tach are often treated in an emergency department with antiarrhythmic medications. They might be given a strong electrical shock to restore the heart's normal rhythm.

Once the heart has stabilized, you might need long-term care to prevent future attacks.

Possibilities: An *implantable cardioverter defibrillator* (ICD), a surgically implanted device that analyzes the heartbeat and administers shocks to prevent ventricular fibrillation...or radiofrequency ablation, which, as mentioned above, purposely damages the parts of the heart that cause abnormal beats.

New Heart Disease Test

Recently approved by the FDA, the *PLAC* blood test measures the activity of *Lp-PLA2*, an enzyme that is a marker for vascular inflammation. Elevated levels indicate a greater risk for heart disease and heart attack. The test is recommended for people with heart disease risk factors, such as high blood pressure or elevated cholesterol, and may be covered by insurance.

Robert Stark, MD, medical director, Cardiovascular Prevention Program, Greenwich Hospital/Yale New Haven Health, Connecticut. *RobertStarkMD.com*

Double Whammy for Heart Attack and Stroke

A combination drug prevents heart attack and stroke better than a statin alone. *Vytorin*, which contains the statin *simvastatin* plus *ezetimibe*, a drug that prevents the body from absorbing cholesterol, brought down levels of LDL (bad) cholesterol more than simvastatin did on its own. Vytorin had no more side effects than taking a statin alone. Patients who took Vytorin had 6.4% reduced risk for cardiac events. Vytorin should be considered when a statin alone leaves the patient with LDL greater than 70 milligrams per deciliter (mg/dL) or when the patient cannot take a full dose of a statin because of a side effect.

Robert M. Califf, MD, vice-chancellor for clinical and translational research and director of the Duke Translational Medicine Institute, Durham, North Carolina. He led a study presented at a recent meeting of the American Heart Association.

TAKE NOTE...

Running Does *Not* Make for a Healthy Heart

A recent study measured the levels of coronary-artery plaque in men who had run at least one marathon a year for 25 years and compared them with a group of sedentary men. Surprisingly, the runners had higher levels of plaque.

Theory: Maintaining a well-balanced diet of nutritious foods is necessary for heart health. Long-distance runners often assume that they can eat anything they want.

Study of 73 men led by researchers from Minneapolis Heart Institute and Foundation, published in *Missouri Medicine*.

Antibiotic Alert for Heart Patients

A popular antibiotic can be dangerous for people with heart conditions. Respiratory infections often are treated with the antibiotic *clarithromycin*, but in a recent study, clarithromycin was associated with a 76% greater risk for cardiac death than penicillin.

Why: Clarithromycin can affect the heart's electrical activity.

Among the safest antibiotics for heart patients: *Penicillin*, *amoxicillin* and related drugs.

Suzanne Steinbaum, DO, director of Women's Heart Health, Heart and Vascular Institute, Lenox Hill Hospital, New York City, and author of *Dr. Suzanne Steinbaum's Heart Book. SRSHeart.com*

20-Second Stroke-Risk Test

Balance on one leg for at least 20 seconds. Difficulty balancing may mean that tiny strokes or bleeds have already occurred, increasing your risk for more serious strokes.

Recent finding: Among those who had two or more tiny strokes, about one-third had trouble balancing.

Yasuharu Tabara, PhD, associate professor, Center for Genomic Medicine, Kyoto University Graduate School of Medicine, Japan, and lead author of a study published in *Stroke*.

Overlooked Stroke Risk

People with the most stress, depression, anger and/or hostility were up to twice as likely to suffer a stroke or *transient ischemic attack* (TIA), also known as a "ministroke," as those with the lowest levels of those traits, according to a recent 11-year study.

Why: Chronic psychological problems are just as significant as traditional stroke risk factors, such as smoking and high blood pressure.

Susan Everson-Rose, PhD, MPH, associate professor of medicine, University of Minnesota, Minneapolis.

MRI Predicts Risk of Stroke

An MRI of the carotid artery is better than ultrasound (the test most often used for this purpose) for predicting whether a person will have a stroke or heart attack. In fact, a recent study shows that MRI scans are 7% more accurate in predicting stroke over a five-year period than ultrasound or traditional risk factors alone, such as family history.

Reason: MRI can help determine the thickness of the artery wall and identify deposits of calcium or fat within plaque—all are linked to increased risk for stroke.

Note: MRI for this purpose may not be covered by insurance.

David Bluemke, MD, director of radiology and imaging sciences, National Institutes of Health Clinical Center, Bethesda, Maryland.

INTERESTING FINDING...

Only About 4% of Stroke Patients Get a Drug That Could Save Their Lives

Tissue plasminogen activator (tPA) was shown 20 years ago to dissolve stroke-related clots that can cause brain damage, but most patients don't receive it. The drug must be given within three hours of a stroke, according to the package insert. If you are having possible stroke symptoms, seek medical attention immediately.

Study done by researchers at University of Cincinnati, presented at the American Heart Association/American Stroke Association's annual International Stroke Conference 2014 in San Diego.

Better Stroke Recovery

When hospitalized after an *ischemic stroke* (the most common type, caused by a blood clot), patients should lie as flat as possible to keep blood flowing to the brain.

Recent research: The head of the bed should be *raised* if brain swelling is suspected, to improve blood drainage and reduce intracranial pressure.

If a loved one suffers a stroke: Talk to the doctor about the most beneficial positioning of the patient's bed.

Murray Flaster, MD, PhD, associate professor of neurology, Stritch School of Medicine, Loyola University Chicago.

Beware: Signs of an Abdominal Aortic Aneurysm

Christopher J. Abularrage, MD, assistant professor of surgery, division of vascular surgery and endovascular therapy, The Johns Hopkins Hospital, Baltimore. He has published several articles on aortic aneurysms in *Journal of Vascular Surgery*, *Annals of Vascular Surgery* and other medical journals.

A pulsating sensation in the abdomen can be a sign of many health problems, such as a hernia or an enlarged spleen. However, the most serious cause is an *abdominal aortic aneurysm.*

This type of aneurysm is an enlargement of the abdominal aorta, the large blood vessel that extends from the heart to the legs. As the aneurysm enlarges, there is a greater risk for rupture, which is often fatal.

Aneurysms usually develop gradually over many years and often have no symptoms. Signs that an aneurysm may be starting to rupture include severe, sudden, persistent pain in the abdomen or back...dizziness...nausea...and a rapid heart rate. If you have any of these symptoms, get to a hospital emergency department. If your only symptom is a pulsating sensation in the abdomen, your doctor can screen for an aneurysm with an ultrasound (this procedure should be covered by insurance).

Depending on the size of the aneurysm and your overall health, the aneurysm may need to be repaired with traditional open surgery or with a minimally invasive procedure that uses a stent.

Painkillers Linked to Blood Clots

A meta-analysis of six studies of *venous thromboembolism*—a type of clot that includes deep vein thrombosis and pulmonary embolism—showed an 80% higher clot risk in people who use *naproxen*, *ibuprofen* and other *nonsteroidal anti-inflammatory drugs* (NSAIDs) compared with nonusers. For patients known to have increased risk for venous thromboembolism because of genetic factors or extended immobility, *acetaminophen* may be a safer pain reliever. Talk to your doctor.

Patompong Ungprasert, MD, an instructor in the department of rheumatology at Mayo Clinic, Rochester, Minnesota, and leader of an analysis published online in *Rheumatology.*

Aspirin for DVT

Aspirin for blood clot prevention may be an alternative to *warfarin* for *deep vein thrombosis* (DVT) patients. DVT often is treated with the anticoagulant drug warfarin.

But: Long-term use of warfarin to prevent clots may require frequent blood tests and dosage adjustments, and it may cause bleeding in some patients.

Newer drugs such as *dabigatran* (Pradaxa) and *rivaroxaban* (Xarelto) are effective, but they can be expensive and some patients can't tolerate them. An inexpensive daily aspirin reduces risk for clots by 42% without causing excessive bleeding.

Caution: Do not switch from warfarin to aspirin unless you speak to your doctor first.

Study of 1,224 people by researchers at University of Sydney, Australia, published in *Circulation*.

The Shocking Diabetes Trigger That Can Strike *Anyone*

Hyla Cass, MD, a board-certified psychiatrist and nationally recognized expert on integrative medicine based in Los Angeles. She is also author of numerous books, including *8 Weeks to Vibrant Health* and *The Addicted Brain and How to Break Free. CassMD.com*

Everyone knows about high blood sugar and the devastating effects it can have on one's health and longevity. But low blood sugar (*hypoglycemia*) can be just as dangerous—and it does not get nearly the attention that it should.

Simply put, hypoglycemia occurs when the body does not have enough glucose to use as fuel. It most commonly affects people with type 2 diabetes who take medication that sometimes works too well, resulting in low blood sugar.

Who gets overlooked: In other people, hypoglycemia can be a precursor to diabetes that is often downplayed by doctors and/or missed by tests. Having low blood sugar might even make you think that you are far from having diabetes...when, in fact, the opposite is true.

Hypoglycemia can also be an underlying cause of anxiety that gets mistakenly treated with psychiatric drugs rather than the simple steps (see the next page) that can stabilize blood sugar levels. That's why anyone who seems to be suffering from an anxiety disorder needs to be seen by a doctor who takes a complete medical history and orders blood tests. When a patient comes to me complaining of anxiety, hypoglycemia is one of the first things I test for.

What's the link between hypoglycemia and anxiety? A sudden drop in blood sugar deprives the brain of oxygen. This, in turn, causes the adrenal glands to release *adrenaline*, the "emergency" hormone, which may lead to agitation, or anxiety, as the body's fight-or-flight mechanism kicks in.

THE DANGERS OF HYPOGLYCEMIA

Hypoglycemia has sometimes been called carbohydrate intolerance, because the body's insulin-releasing mechanism is impaired in a manner similar to what occurs in diabetics. In people without diabetes, hypoglycemia is usually the result of eating too many simple carbohydrates (such as sugar and white flour). The pancreas then overreacts and releases too much insulin, thereby excessively lowering blood sugar.

The good news is that hypoglycemia—if it's identified—is not that difficult to control through diet and the use of specific supplements. Hypoglycemia should be considered a warning sign that you must adjust your carbohydrate intake or risk developing type 2 diabetes.

Caution: An episode of hypoglycemia in a person who already has diabetes can be life-threatening and requires prompt care, including the immediate intake of sugar—a glass of orange juice or even a sugar cube can be used.

Common symptoms of hypoglycemia include: Fatigue, dizziness, shakiness and faintness...irritability and depression...weakness or cramps in the feet and legs...numbness or tingling in the hands, feet or face...ringing in the ears...swollen feet or legs...tightness in the chest...heart palpitations...nightmares and panic attacks..."drenching" night sweats (not menopausal or perimenopausal hot flashes)...constant hunger...headaches and migraines...impaired memory and concentration...blurred vision...nasal congestion...abdominal cramps, loose stools and diarrhea.

A TRICKY DIAGNOSIS

Under-the-radar hypoglycemia (known as "subclinical hypoglycemia") is difficult to diagnose because symptoms may be subtle and irregular, and test results can be within normal ranges. Technically, if your blood sugar drops below 70 milligrams per deciliter (mg/dL), you are considered hypoglycemic. But people without diabetes do not check their blood sugar levels on their own, so it is important to be aware of hypoglycemia symptoms.

If you suspect that you may have hypoglycemia, talk to your physician. Ideally, you should arrange to have your blood glucose levels tested when you are experiencing symptoms. You will then be asked to eat food so that your blood glucose can be tested again. If this approach is impractical for you, however, talk to your doctor about other testing methods.

THE RIGHT TREATMENT

If you have been diagnosed with diabetes, hypoglycemia may indicate that your diabetes medication dose needs to be adjusted. The sugar treatment described earlier can work in an emergency but is not recommended as a long-term treatment for hypoglycemia. Left untreated, hypoglycemia in a person with diabetes can lead to loss of consciousness and even death.

In addition to getting their medication adjusted, people with diabetes—and those who are at risk for it due to hypoglycemia—can benefit from the following...

- **A high-protein diet and healthful fats.** To keep your blood sugar levels stabilized, consume slowly absorbed, unrefined carbohydrates, such as brown rice, quinoa, oatmeal and sweet potatoes. Also, get moderate amounts of healthful fats, such as those found in avocado, olive oil and fatty fish, including salmon...and protein, such as fish, meat, chicken, soy and eggs.

Recommended protein intake: 10% to 35% of daily calories. If you have kidney disease, get your doctor's advice on protein intake.

- **Eat several small meals daily.** Start with breakfast to give your body fuel for the day (if you don't, stored blood sugar will be released into your bloodstream) and then have a small "meal" every three to four waking hours.

- **Avoid tobacco and limit your use of alcohol and caffeine,** all of which cause an excessive release of *neurotransmitters* that, in turn, trigger the pancreas to deliver insulin inappropriately.

The supplements below also help stabilize blood sugar levels (and can be used in addition to a daily multivitamin)...*

- **Chromium and vitamin B-6.** Chromium helps release accumulated sugars in the liver, which can lead to a dangerous condition called fatty liver. Vitamin B-6 supports chromium's function and helps stabilize glucose levels.

Typical daily dose: 200 micrograms (mcg) of chromium with 100 milligrams (mg) of vitamin B-6.

- **Glutamine.** As the most common amino acid found in muscle tissue, glutamine plays a vital role in controlling blood sugar. Glutamine is easily converted to glucose when blood sugar is low.

Typical daily dose: Up to four 500-mg capsules daily...or add glutamine powder to a protein drink or a smoothie that does not contain added sugar—these drinks are good options for your morning routine. Glutamine is best taken 30 minutes before a meal to cut your appetite by balancing your blood sugar.

*Consult your doctor before trying any supplements, especially if you take prescription medication and/or have a chronic medical condition, including diabetes.

Why Artificial Sweeteners May *Increase* Diabetes Risk

Studies in mice and people show that some users of artificial sweeteners have different gut bacteria from those of nonusers—and have higher glucose intolerance, which puts them at increased risk for diabetes.

Eran Segal, PhD, a professor in the department of computer science and applied mathematics, Weizmann Institute of Science, Rehovot, Israel. He is coauthor of a study published in *Nature*.

How Often Should You Get Screened for Diabetes?

Everyone over age 45 should be screened for type 2 diabetes and prediabetes every three years, according to the US Preventive Services Task Force. People who are found to have abnormal blood sugar—a precursor to diabetes—can then take aggressive measures to prevent the disease, such as eating healthier and exercising.

US Preventive Services Task Force in Rockville, Maryland.

If You Need to Pee a Lot at Night...

Frequent trips to the bathroom at night may indicate diabetes or heart failure. Try limiting beverages close to bedtime. If that doesn't help, keep a diary for three days, noting all of the times you urinate. If one-third or more of your bathroom trips occur at night, talk to your doctor.

Tiffany Sotelo, MD, assistant professor of urology, George Washington University School of Medicine & Health Sciences, Washington, DC, quoted in *Woman's Day.*

Statins May Help Diabetes

In addition to lowering risk for heart attack and stroke, statins lowered risk for diabetes complications, according to a recent finding. People with diabetes taking statins were 34% less likely to be diagnosed with diabetes-related nerve damage (*neuropathy*)...40% less likely to develop diabetes-related damage to the retina...and 12% less likely to develop gangrene than diabetics not taking statins.

Børge G. Nordestgaard, MD, DMSc, chief physician at Copenhagen University Hospital, Herlev, Denmark, and leader of a study of 60,000 people, published in *The Lancet Diabetes Endocrinology.*

New Weekly Diabetes Drug Gets FDA Nod

Recently approved by the FDA, *dulaglutide* (Trulicity) is a once-a-week injectable, single-dose pen that has been shown to safely improve blood sugar levels in six separate trials of more than 3,300 people with type 2 diabetes. The medication, which requires no mixing (as do competing drugs), can be used alone or in combination with other diabetes medication, including *metformin* and mealtime insulin. Possible side effects can include nausea, diarrhea and abdominal pain. People at risk for thyroid or endocrine gland tumors should not take dulaglutide.

Ralph A. DeFronzo, MD, deputy director, Texas Diabetes Institute, San Antonio.

Prediabetes Increases Cancer Risk

A review of nearly 900,000 adults found that those with prediabetes had a 15% greater risk for cancer, particularly liver, stomach, colorectal, endometrial, breast and pancreatic cancers. Prediabetes is a condition in which blood glucose levels are higher than normal but not high enough to be classified as type 2 diabetes—above 100 milligrams per deciliter (mg/dL) but below 126 mg/dL.

If you have prediabetes: Talk to your doctor about more frequent glucose and cancer screenings.

Yuli Huang, MD, PhD, professor, The First People's Hospital, Foshan, China.

TAKE NOTE...

The Nose Knows

Sense of smell predicts longevity. People who have difficulty identifying common smells, such as rose, leather, orange, fish and peppermint, are more likely to die within five years than people who can identify those smells. An inability to smell indicates that the body is not regenerating cells in the nose—and that may not be happening elsewhere in the body as well.

Study of 3,005 people by researchers at University of Chicago, published in *PLOS ONE*.

Thyroid Cancer—Epidemic...or Overdiagnosis?

Juan Pablo Brito, MBBS, assistant professor and health-care delivery scholar in the division of endocrinology, diabetes, metabolism and nutrition at the Mayo Clinic, Rochester, Minnesota, where he also is coinvestigator of the Knowledge and Evaluation Research Unit. He is lead author of "Thyroid Cancer: Zealous Imaging Has Increased Detection and Treatment of Low Risk Tumours," which appeared in *BMJ*.

Any increase in cancer is worrisome, but the dramatic rise in thyroid cancer is particularly troubling. In just 30 years, the incidence in the US has more than tripled, from 3.6 cases per 100,000 people in 1973 to 11.6 per 100,000 in 2009.

It is among the fastest-growing diagnoses in the US. This is an alarming trend—but not for the reason you might think.

Experts have concluded that the vast majority of thyroid cancers were there all along. Better imaging tests such as *ultrasound* and *magnetic resonance imaging* (MRI) now make it possible to detect minuscule cancers that would have been missed before. What looks like an increase in disease actually is an increase in diagnosis.

Isn't it good to detect cancers when they're still small? Not in this case. The most common type of thyroid cancer grows slowly—if it grows at all. Most patients would never have symptoms or need treatment. But once you know you have cancer, you want that thing out of there. Unfortunately, the treatments often cause more problems than they solve.

MORE SCREENING, MORE CANCER

There's a saying in medicine, "When you have a new hammer, everything looks like a nail."

In the 1980s, ultrasound was the new hammer. Endocrinologists used it routinely during office visits. Even if you came in with vague symptoms that could be caused by just about anything, such as fatigue from insomnia, you would likely be given a neck ultrasound and possibly an MRI or a *computerized tomography* (CT) scan. These tests can detect nodules as small as 2 millimeters (mm) in diameter.

In many cases, tests that were ordered for other conditions happened to detect a growth in the thyroid. More cases of thyroid cancer are diagnosed incidentally than when doctors actually are looking for them. Doctors call these unexpected findings "incidentalomas."

Does finding small cancers save lives? Despite the tremendous increase in diagnosed thyroid cancers, the death rate has scarcely budged—it was 0.5 per 100,000 people a generation ago, and it is virtually the same today. All that has changed is the ability to detect them.

THE RISK OF KNOWING

About 90% of diagnosed thyroid cancers are small *papillary cancers*. They usually are indolent—cancers that are unlikely to grow or cause problems. Two Japanese studies and one American study have tracked nearly 1,500 patients who did not receive active treatment for papillary cancers less than one centimeter. After an average of five years, none of these patients has died.

Yet most people who are diagnosed with papillary thyroid cancers opt for treatment—generally a complete *thyroidectomy*, the removal of the thyroid gland. Once the gland is removed, patients require lifelong treatment with thyroid-replacement medications. Some suffer nerve damage that causes permanent voice changes. When surgery is followed by radioactive iodine therapy, patients face additional risks.

TAKE NOTE...

Symptoms of Thyroid Cancer

Thyroid cancer typically doesn't cause any signs or symptoms early in the disease. *As thyroid cancer grows, it may cause...*

• **A lump that can be felt through the skin on your neck**

• **Changes to your voice,** including increasing hoarseness

• **Difficulty swallowing**

• **Pain in your neck and throat**

• **Swollen lymph nodes in your neck**

MORE DANGEROUS THYROID CANCERS

There are other types of thyroid cancer—*follicular*, *medullary* and *anaplastic*—that are more serious. These typically require surgery, usually the total removal of the thyroid gland and sometimes the removal of lymph nodes in the neck. Patients with these cancers typically are given postsurgical radioactive iodine to destroy remaining parts of the gland and any cancer cells that were left behind during surgery.

WHAT TO DO

Experts do not recommend widespread screening for thyroid cancer. A neck ultrasound is recommended only for specific patients—people who have a family history of thyroid cancer...had previous exposure to head/neck radiation...or a nodule that can be felt during an exam. If a test reveals a nodule that is one centimeter or more in diameter, a biopsy often is performed to determine the seriousness of the growth.

Also important...

• **Question the ultrasound.** If your doctor recommends neck ultrasonography during a routine checkup or because you're experiencing somewhat vague symptoms (such as fatigue), ask if you really need it and what the benefits and risks are if you do the test or don't do the test. You should clearly understand the goal of doing the test and how you will benefit.

• **Consider a second opinion before agreeing to surgery.** According to data from the US National Cancer Institute, death rates in patients who didn't have immediate surgery for papillary cancers were virtually the same as for those who did have surgery. Watchful waiting—forgoing treatment but getting checkups every six months at the beginning and then every year after that to see if a tumor has grown—usually is the best approach for these cancers.

• **Keep your emotions in check.** It is emotionally difficult to know that you have a cancer and not do something about it. You will want it gone whether it poses a threat or not. But most thyroid cancers—like the majority of slow-growing prostate cancers—are simply not dangerous. Some experts believe that they should not even be called cancer. An alternative, less frightening term that has been proposed is *papillary lesions of indolent course* (PLIC).

• **Get the treatment that fits you.** If you have a papillary cancer that does need treatment, ask your doctor if you can have a partial rather than a total thyroidectomy. The partial procedure is safer and, for most papillary cancers, just as effective.

• **Don't agree to postsurgical treatment with radioactive iodine unless your doctor insists that you need it.** It usually is not recommended for low-risk thyroid cancers because it can cause serious side effects, including an altered sense of taste and inflamed salivary glands. The treatment also has been linked to a 5.7-fold increase in the risk for leukemia.

Better Way to Detect Pancreatic Cancer

Pancreatic cancer has an overall five-year survival rate of 6%, partly because it produces few symptoms in the early stages.

Recent study: Genetic biomarkers for pancreatic cancer were found in 90% of adults in the early stages of the disease but not in those who did not have it.

Until the new test becomes available in a few years, be sure your doctor knows if you're at increased risk for pancreatic cancer due to family history, obesity and/or smoking.

Nita Ahuja, MD, associate professor of surgery at The Johns Hopkins University School of Medicine in Baltimore.

---

5 Sunburns = More Cancer Risk

If you had five or more blistering sunburns before age 20, watch out. This increases lifetime risk for melanoma by 80%, according to a recent study of nearly 109,000 Caucasian women.

Why: Sudden, massive amounts of sun exposure may damage pigment cells in the skin.

If you had many bad sunburns in your youth: Be particularly vigilant about further sun exposure and having annual skin exams, which should be performed by a board-certified dermatologist.

Abrar Qureshi, MD, MPH, professor and chair of dermatology, Warren Alpert Medical School, Brown University, Providence.

Little-Known Skin Cancer Sign

Pain or itching can be signs of skin cancer. People often are told to be on the lookout for visual changes to their skin, but it is important not to overlook changes in how skin feels.

Recent findings: More than one-third of skin cancer lesions itch—these can be a sign of *basal cell carcinoma.* Approximately 30% are painful, and these can indicate *squamous cell carcinoma.*

Gil Yosipovitch, MD, chair of dermatology at Temple University School of Medicine and director of Temple Itch Center, both in Philadelphia, and leader of a study published in *JAMA Dermatology.*

Popular Wrinkle Reducer Slows Cancer Growth

Tumor growth was slowed and survival rates improved after animals with stomach cancer (which is typically fatal) were injected with Botox, commonly used to smooth wrinkles. Botox may block nerve signals needed for tumor growth.

Science Translational Medicine.

Got Cancer? Here's a Program That Gives You the Help You Need

Mitch Golant, PhD, senior consultant for strategic initiatives at the Cancer Support Community and a clinical psychologist in Los Angeles. He helped develop the Open to Options counseling program. Dr. Golant is also coauthor of *The Total Cancer Wellness Guide: Reclaiming Your Life After Diagnosis.*

"You have cancer" are three of the most frightening words a person can hear.

A hidden challenge: While cancer patients are still reeling from the emotions of a potentially life-threatening diagnosis, they are asked to make some of the most important decisions of their lives. Even with the support of loved ones, all the treatment decisions that must be made can feel overwhelming.

Good news: There's now a unique approach that can help cancer patients feel less alone.

WHERE TO START

Most cancer-treatment decisions are made within a few weeks of the initial diagnosis. Patients who aren't thinking clearly are expected to understand what's happening and make difficult decisions.

A resource worth trying: A free, evidence-based counseling program, called Open to Options, is available nationwide. Developed by the Cancer Support Community (CSC), a nonprofit group based in Washington, DC, the program matches cancer patients with paid professional counselors (psychologists, social workers and marriage and family therapists) throughout the country. They are specially trained to help patients better communicate with their doctors by formulating questions about their treatment options during that difficult period between diagnosis and treatment.

What research shows: Studies of nearly 200 patients have found that those who worked with Open to Options' counselors were more informed during meetings with their doctors and were less likely to have second thoughts after treatment decisions were made.

HOW IT WORKS

To find professional counselors in their areas, newly diagnosed cancer patients can use the CSC website, *CancerSupportCommunity.org*, or call the Cancer Support Helpline at 888-793-9355. They can meet with counselors face-to-face or communicate by phone or e-mail.

Counselors in this program do not answer medical questions or give medical advice. Rather, the counselors are trained to help patients decide what issues are most important to them and should be discussed with their doctors.

After the counselor and patient meet, the counselor creates a one-page summary *agenda* that the patient will share with his/her doctor. (The agenda can be faxed or e-mailed to the doctor before the patient's appointment.)

WHAT THE PROGRAM COVERS

When working with a counselor, a patient creates a list of all his questions: Will I suffer from the mental fog ("chemo brain") that sometimes goes along with chemotherapy? How long will I be treated? How can I minimize side effects? When can I return to work? Will my concentration or ability to travel be affected?

When a patient speaks with a counselor, he'll be guided through a series of steps to answer questions such as...

- **What's your situation?** You already know you have cancer, and your doctor probably has a good sense of how he will recommend treating it. But your personal situation and values will also influence your decisions.

Example 1: Your doctor might be inclined to treat your cancer with a particular form of chemotherapy, one that sometimes causes hand neuropathy as a side effect. If you mention that you're an artist and can't make a living without the use of your hands, he might choose another treatment instead.

Example 2: Your doctor tells you about a new effective oral chemotherapy that costs $20,000 a month. Your insurance covers only 80%. What are the possibilities for payment, financial assistance and therapy?

- **What are your options?** These will depend on your health history and the type of cancer. The counselor will help you formulate some of the most important questions.

Example: You might want to continue working for the next several years. Will you do better with surgery, chemotherapy or radiation? Are the survival rates similar with each treatment? How long will it take to recover from each? What will the side effects be?

Important: Don't forget to ask the doctor whether a clinical trial (a study of a new treatment) is appropriate. Many people avoid clinical trials because they assume that they might be assigned to a "control" group that receives no treatment. However, in a typical clinical trial, participants are assigned to different groups—one is given the current standard care, and the other is given the new treatment being studied. Placebos are never given in place of treatment.

- **What are your goals?** This goes beyond "surviving" or "being healthy." Other factors are equally important—or even more important for some people.

Example: You might want to treat your cancer aggressively but not before you've attended your daughter's wedding. Your objective might be simply to wait a bit before starting treatment. You'll ask your doctor what the ramifications might be.

• **Who is in your support network?** Think about everyone who might be involved in your care—health professionals, your spouse, friends, helpful neighbors, etc.

Will you have someone to help you on the days of your scheduled treatments? Maybe your spouse is available only on certain afternoons. Let your doctor know this—most cancer centers or hospitals have social-work departments that can help you solve logistical problems.

• **What comes next?** You'll probably have many questions as your treatment progresses. Write them down as you go. If you're not sure how to formulate your questions—or you're not even sure what you should know—ask your counselor for help. Even though most patients use the Open to Options program immediately following their diagnoses, they can rely on it anytime a treatment decision must be made. If they like, patients can also work with a specific counselor each time they ask for help.

Important: Even though you may feel inclined to act immediately if you've just gotten a cancer diagnosis, research shows that patients have better treatment outcomes and less anxiety when they are well-informed and partner with their doctors in determining the best treatments for them. This may take a bit longer, but the benefits far outweigh the risks.

DID YOU KNOW THAT...

Lung Cancer Can Go Undetected for Many Years

In fact, it can lie dormant for *more than 20 years* and then become aggressive. In a small study of smokers, former smokers and people who never smoked, researchers found that the initial genetic errors that cause cancer can go undetected for many years, and the cancer can become active when triggered by new mutations.

Study by researchers at Cancer Research UK, published in *Science*.

Is Your "Arthritis Pain" Really a Bone Spur?

Harris H. McIlwain, MD, a pain specialist board-certified in internal medicine, rheumatology and geriatric medicine. With a private practice in Tampa, Florida, Dr. McIlwain is author of 28 books on topics including arthritis, osteoporosis, back pain and fibromyalgia. He has been the principal investigator in numerous clinical trials on rheumatoid arthritis, osteoarthritis, lupus, gout and more.

That stabbing, aching pain in your joints may mean that you just have a touch of garden-variety osteoarthritis. Or so you tell yourself.

What most people don't realize: When osteoarthritis wears down the cartilage covering the ends of your bones, it can lead to bony growths known as *osteophytes*, an often undetected source of severe joint pain.

Commonly known as bone spurs, these smooth or pointed growths on normal bone tissue also can form in response to stress on a joint—as may occur from repetitive motion activities, such as running or typing. Regardless of the trigger, bone spurs can rub against other bones, ligaments, tendons or nerves and are marked by painful inflammation.

Why this matters: It's important to distinguish bone spurs from run-of-the-mill arthritis so that you can take the necessary steps to stay ahead of potentially debilitating joint inflammation. If not dealt with in the right way (and at the right time), bone spurs often require powerful additional treatment to control the pain, and this treatment can have bad side effects. You want to deal with bone spurs early.

What you need to know to determine if you have bone spurs—and the therapies that help most...

MORE THAN ARTHRITIS

How do you tell whether your joint pain is partly or completely due to bone spurs?

Clues to watch for: Osteoarthritis pain tends to come and go gradually—like the general stiffness that affects a large area of your body, such as your lower back, in the morning but eases by afternoon.

A bone spur, on the other hand, may cause chronic localized pain that's bad enough to make you not want to move your back, neck, hip, finger or some other joint that may be affected. You may have bone spurs in more than one place, but one spur could cause more pain, depending on its location and the amount of physical activity in that area.

The more sudden and severe the pain, the more likely that a bone spur is the culprit. Numbness, tenderness and weakness may also occur. If a parent or sibling has suffered from bone spurs, you're at increased risk, too—research suggests there is a genetic component.

HOT SPOTS FOR BONE SPURS

Any joint can develop a bone spur, but here are the most common locations and how the pain and other symptoms may vary in each part of your body...

- **Knees.** Bone spurs in the knee—a common location for those that occur with osteoarthritis—often resemble a pointy bird's beak on X-rays. The resulting discomfort is typically a blend of arthritis and bone spur pain—both sore and sharp.

- **Feet and/or heels.** Acute pain that occurs with every step—the kind that makes you want to avoid walking—can signal bone spurs in the feet and/or heels (often called "heel spurs"). Corns and calluses may also build up over heels or toes as the body tries to protect the area by providing added padding. Therefore, if you have pain along with corns and/or calluses, ask your doctor to check for a bone spur.

- **Hips.** Arthritis in the hips generally produces a deep aching and stiffness that occurs when you stand or walk. Bone spurs at the side of the hip—where the bony prominence can sometimes be felt—trigger pain when the hip is flexed, such as when riding a bike.

- **Hands and/or shoulders.** Jabbing pain (rather than a dull throb) is the telltale sign.

- **Neck and/or spine.** Bone spurs at these locations usually do not cause pain unless accompanied by arthritis, but they can pinch the spinal cord and irritate surrounding nerves.

GETTING DIAGNOSED

If you have one or more bone spurs, the typical arthritis treatments—including *nonsteroidal anti-inflammatory drugs* (NSAIDs), like *ibuprofen* (Motrin) or *naproxen* (Aleve)... stretching...and warm heat—often don't make a dent in your joint pain.

Because bone spurs usually are not large enough to feel externally, an X-ray is the easiest way to diagnose them. In certain areas, such as the neck, more advanced imaging tests, such as MRI or CT scans, may be needed to diagnose them.

My advice: If your joint pain doesn't respond to the therapies described earlier and you suspect that you may have bone spurs, you don't need a definitive diagnosis provided by an X-ray. Ask your physician whether you may have bone spurs, and get his/her OK to promptly try the approaches below. If you don't start treatment quickly, the serious pain that bone spurs typically cause may limit your use of the joint, progressively weakening muscles surrounding it and creating an even worse problem.

FINDING THE BEST TREATMENT

Among the best therapies for joint pain due to bone spurs...

- **Alternate heating pads and ice packs in 20-minute intervals.** Use ice first to ease acute pain, then moist heat to penetrate inflamed areas. Do this twice a day.

- **Get acupuncture.** Acupuncture has been shown to reduce pain and improve functional mobility. Your acupuncturist will tailor a treatment plan for your bone spur.

- **Eat inflammation-fighting foods.** Processed foods promote inflammation, while certain whole foods, such as salmon, nuts, beets, leafy greens, olive oil and berries, fight it. Include as many of these foods in your daily diet as possible.

- **Use targeted supplements.** These include fish oil, turmeric and ginger. There is strong research showing that these supplements help fight painful inflammation.

My advice: You can take one or all of these supplements, depending on the intensity of your pain. Daily dosages are up to 3 grams (g) of fish oil...three 400-milligram (mg) to 600-mg tablets or capsules of turmeric...and two 500-mg to 1,000-mg capsules of ginger, taken with food. It usually takes about two months for turmeric to work.

Caution: Talk to your doctor before using any of these supplements if you take any type of medication (especially a blood thinner) or have a chronic medical condition.

- **Try ultrasound therapy.** Ultrasound uses sound waves that can penetrate more than two inches into the body to reach the painful area. Often used for shoulder or heel pain caused by bone spurs, it can be administered by a medical doctor or physical therapist.

Caveat: The pain relief provided by ultrasound may be long-lasting but sometimes lasts only a few weeks.

WHEN TO CONSIDER SURGERY

One of the biggest misconceptions about bone spurs is that they need to be removed surgically. The truth is, when strategies such as those described in this article are used, the inflammation may lessen after a period of weeks or months even though the spur does not go away.

In determining the need for surgery, location of the bone spurs is the key factor. For example, bone spurs located in the neck can press on nerves or even the esophagus, which can interfere with swallowing.

In general, however, risks associated with surgery, such as infection, outweigh the benefits for most bone spurs. If you have tried the regimen described above for bone spurs for about a year but still have not gotten adequate pain relief, then ask your primary care doctor for a referral to an orthopedic surgeon.

Common Knee Surgery May Lead to Arthritis

In a recent study, all 31 knees operated on to repair tears of the *meniscus* (cartilage that stabilizes the knee joint) developed arthritis within one year, compared with 59% of the 165 knees that didn't have surgery. Talk to your doctor about whether surgery is really necessary and whether physical therapy, including targeted muscle exercises, is a better option for you.

Frank Roemer, MD, associate professor of radiology, Boston University School of Medicine and University of Erlangen–Nuremburg, Germany. His study was presented at a meeting of the Radiological Society of North America.

Men Get Osteoporosis, Too!

Up to one in four men over age 50 will break a bone due to osteoporosis.

Problem: A recent analysis that looked at 439 patients' medical records found that men are less likely than women to be screened for osteoporosis and far less likely to be treated for the condition after a fracture.

Why it matters: Treating the fracture but not the underlying cause puts patients at risk for future breaks.

Tamara D. Rozental, MD, associate professor of orthopedic surgery, Harvard Medical School, Boston.

TAKE NOTE...

Texting Can Hurt Your Spine

An adult head weighs 10 to 12 pounds. Tilting the head forward to look at a phone increases stress on the spine. Over time, this can lead to "text-neck syndrome," which causes early wear and degeneration of the spine and may require surgery.

Self-defense: Stay as close to upright as possible when texting or otherwise using your smartphone.

Study by researchers at New York Spine & Rehabilitation Medicine, New York City, published in *Surgical Technology International*.

Fibromyalgia: Unraveling the Mystery

Anne Louise Oaklander, MD, PhD, an associate professor of neurology at Harvard Medical School and director of a diagnostic and research laboratory at Massachusetts General Hospital that studies neurological causes of chronic pain and itch, both in Boston. Dr. Oaklander serves on the editorial board for the journal *PAIN* and serves on panels for the National Institutes of Health, the FDA and the Institute of Medicine.

For the roughly 5 million American adults with fibromyalgia, the muscle soreness, body aches and telltale painful "tender points" on the shoulders, neck, back, hips, arms and legs are all too familiar.

But until very recently, the condition was a much maligned mystery illness. In fact, some doctors told patient after patient that the condition was "all in your head" because no cause could be identified.

Now: The medical naysayers are rethinking fibromyalgia because of recent research showing that the condition does have an identifiable cause in some patients. Substantial numbers of people with fibromyalgia have been found to have a little-known—but testable—condition that triggers faulty signals from tiny nerves all over the body, possibly causing the symptoms of fibromyalgia.

In addition to chronic widespread pain, sufferers often have various other symptoms, such as fatigue, insomnia, digestive problems (including constipation and nausea), and memory and concentration difficulties commonly known as "fibro fog." People with fibromyalgia also may experience numbness, tingling and/or burning in the hands, arms, feet and/or legs, chronic headaches, depression and even frequent urges to urinate.

WHAT RECENT RESEARCH HAS UNCOVERED

Even though the American College of Rheumatology has recognized fibromyalgia as an illness since 1990, most doctors have been uneasy about diagnosing it because there has been no way to test for the condition. X-rays and blood tests can rule out other conditions, such as rheumatoid arthritis, but fibromyalgia has been a diagnosis based on symptoms alone. The recent research findings may change that.

What important recent studies have uncovered: According to several studies published in 2013, one conducted by researchers at Massachusetts General Hospital, nearly half of people with fibromyalgia have evidence of a disease known as *small-fiber polyneuropathy* (SFPN).

A form of *peripheral neuropathy*, SFPN involves damage to specific nerve cells that can trigger pain and the digestive problems that often accompany fibromyalgia.

How was this discovery made? Skin biopsies were the key tests that uncovered abnormalities in the nerve cells of 40% of SFPN sufferers who were tested.

Meanwhile, researchers at Albany Medical College found another interesting piece of the puzzle—excessive nerve fibers lining the blood vessels within the skin of people with fibromyalgia. Since these fibers control the flow of blood, oxygen and nutrients to muscles during exercise, this abnormality might explain the deep muscle pain of fibromyalgia.

These recent findings do not mean that the name has been changed—fibromyalgia (*fibro*, the Latin term for fibrous tissue...and the Greek words *myo*, meaning muscle...and *algia*, meaning pain) perfectly describes the condition's primary symptoms of chronic, widespread muscle pain.

Even though the discoveries described above don't apply to all fibromyalgia patients, they give researchers some clues to follow toward cracking the disease's formidable mystery.

NEW HOPE FOR BETTER TREATMENTS

Scientists may be intrigued by this new evidence, but what does it mean for people who suffer from fibromyalgia? The most immediate—and significant—implication has to do with testing. Fibromyalgia symptoms can vary widely, so the diagnosis can be challenging even for experienced rheumatologists.

Now that fibromyalgia has been linked to SFPN, people with fibromyalgia symptoms may want to ask their doctors about testing for SFPN. A skin biopsy from the lower leg is currently the best way to diagnose SFPN.

The sample can be mailed to an accredited lab—for example, at Massachusetts General Hospital—for analysis. It is usually covered by insurance.

In the meantime, the following medications (in addition to the nondrug approaches described below) can help relieve symptoms of fibromyalgia...

• **FDA-approved medications.** *Pregabalin* (Lyrica), an anticonvulsant...and *duloxetine* (Cymbalta) and *milnacipran HCI* (Savella), both *serotonin and norepinephrine reuptake inhibitors* (SNRIs), have been shown to reduce pain and improve function for some people with fibromyalgia. Researchers do not know exactly why these drugs work, but some data suggest that they affect pain signaling in the brain and spinal cord.

• **Nortriptyline (Pamelor).** An older tricyclic antidepressant that has also been proven effective for chronic pain relief, *nortriptyline* is not specifically FDA-approved for fibromyalgia. But it and several other off-label medications, including the anticonvulsant *gabapentin* (Neurontin)—available cheaply as generic drugs—have strong research supporting their use for fibromyalgia.

NONDRUG APPROACHES

Medication isn't the only treatment for fibromyalgia symptoms. *Other good options...*

• **Exercise.** Don't think this is just another plug for exercise. The research showing exercise's effect on fibromyalgia pain is very strong. Whether it's walking, strength training or stretching, exercise improves emotional well-being and lessens muscle wasting, an unfortunate consequence of avoiding exercise due to pain.

• **Vitamin D.** This inexpensive vitamin supplement has just begun to prove its mettle for some people with fibromyalgia. A study published in the journal *PAIN* indicates that vitamin D supplements may reduce chronic pain linked to fibromyalgia for those whose blood tests show a low level of the nutrient. The optimal vitamin D dose depends on the level of deficiency.

Conquer Pain Safely: 4 Pain Fighters You've Probably Never Tried

Vijay Vad, MD, a sports medicine physician and researcher specializing in minimally invasive arthritis therapies at the Hospital for Special Surgery in New York City. Dr. Vad is an assistant professor at Weill Medical College of Cornell University and founder of the Vad Foundation, an organization that supports medical research on back pain and arthritis. He is author of *Stop Pain: Inflammation Relief for an Active Life. VijayVad.com*

What's the first thing you do when you're hurting? If you're like most people, you reach for aspirin, *ibuprofen* (Advil, Motrin), *naproxen* (Aleve) or a similar *nonsteroidal anti-inflammatory drug* (NSAID). Each day, more than 30 million Americans take these popular medications. Another roughly 7 million take a different class of painkiller, *acetaminophen* (Tylenol) each day (see the next page).

The risks most people don't think about: Even though NSAIDs are as common in most American homes as Band-Aids and multivitamins, few people realize that these medications often cause stomach and intestinal bleeding that leads to up to 20,000 deaths every year in the US. And while previous studies have suggested that these drugs also threaten heart health, an important recent meta-analysis found that the risks are more significant than once thought. In fact, ibuprofen and other NSAIDs—taken in doses that many people consider normal—increased the risk for "major vascular events," including heart attacks, by about one-third.

SAFER PAIN RELIEF

The good news is, it's still fine to take an NSAID for arthritis, a headache or other types of short-term pain up to two or three times a week. It is also safe, with your doctor's approval, to take a daily low-dose aspirin—81 milligrams (mg)—to prevent heart attacks and stroke.

What not to do: It is never a good idea to depend on these drugs to relieve chronic pain. As a doctor who specializes in treating arthritis pain, I rarely recommend these medications for long-term use because there are safer analgesics that are just as effective.

My favorite alternatives to oral NSAIDs (ask your doctor which might work best for your pain)...

ANALGESIC CREAMS

You've probably seen over-the-counter pain-relieving creams, such as Zostrix and Capzasin. These products contain *capsaicin*, which causes a mild burning sensation and appears to reduce *substance P*, a neurotransmitter that delivers pain signals to the brain. Capsaicin products work well for some people suffering from osteoarthritis or rheumatoid arthritis, back pain, shingles and diabetic nerve pain (*neuropathy*). *Many people, however, get better results from...*

- **Voltaren Gel.** In the heart study mentioned earlier, oral *diclofenac* (Voltaren) was one of the riskiest NSAIDs. But a topical version, Voltaren Gel, which is available by prescription, is less likely to cause side effects, even though it's just as effective as the tablets. Voltaren Gel is good for pain in one joint, but if your pain is in several joints, supplements (see below) will offer more relief.

How it's used: Apply the gel (up to four times a day) to the area that's hurting—for example, your knee or wrist.

Helpful: Apply it after a bath or shower, when your skin is soft. More of the active ingredient will pass through the skin and into the painful area. Voltaren Gel should not be combined with an oral NSAID.

PAIN-FIGHTING SUPPLEMENTS

If you need even more pain relief, consider taking one or more of the following supplements. Start with the first one, and if pain has not decreased after eight weeks, add the second, then wait another eight weeks before adding the third, if necessary.

Important: Be sure to check first with your doctor if you take blood thinners or other medications because they could interact.

- **Curcumin.** There's been a lot of research on the anti-inflammatory and painkilling effects of curcumin (the compound that gives the curry spice turmeric its yellow color). One study found that it reduced pain and improved knee function about as well as ibuprofen.

Typical dose: 1,000 mg, twice daily.

- **Fish oil.** A huge amount of data shows that the omega-3 fatty acids in fish oil have analgesic and anti-inflammatory effects.

Scientific evidence: One study found that 60% of patients with neck, back and joint pain who took fish oil improved so much that they were able to stop taking NSAIDs or other medications.

Typical dose: 2,000 mg daily.

- **Boswellia.** Boswellia (or frankincense) is an herbal medicine that can reduce both pain and inflammation. It's effective for all types of joint pain, including osteoarthritis and rheumatoid arthritis.

Scientific evidence: In one study, patients with knee arthritis took boswellia or a placebo for two months, then switched to the opposite treatment for another two months.

Results: The people taking boswellia had less pain and more knee mobility than those taking placebos.

Typical dose: 300 mg to 400 mg, three times daily.

HOW TO USE TYLENOL FOR PAIN

If you prefer an oral medication over the options in the main article, ask your doctor about switching from NSAIDs to acetaminophen. It's not an anti-inflammatory, but it's an effective pain reliever that doesn't cause stomach upset or bleeding—or trigger an increase in cardiovascular risks. I've found that people who limit the dosage of acetaminophen are unlikely to have side effects.

Caution: Taking too much of this drug can lead to liver damage, particularly if it's used by someone who consumes a lot of alcohol or has underlying liver disease, such as hepatitis.

My recommendation: No more than 2,000 mg daily of acetaminophen (this dosage is lower than the limits listed on the label).

Important: In calculating your total daily dose, be sure to factor in all sources of acetaminophen. More than 600 prescription and over-the-counter drugs, including cold and flu medications and allergy drugs, contain the active ingredient acetaminophen. For a partial list of medications that contain acetaminophen, go to *KnowYourDose.org/common-medications*.

To be safe: Get a liver function test (usually covered by insurance) every six months if you regularly take acetaminophen.

New Help for Sleep Apnea

People who have obstructive sleep apnea stop breathing for very short intervals during the night, disrupting sleep and increasing the risk for diabetes, heart attack and stroke. In addition to conventional treatments such as *continuous positive airway pressure (CPAP) machines* and oral mouthpieces that advance the jaw, newer treatments include Provent Sleep Apnea Therapy (*ProventTherapy.com*), which is a small disposable patch that fits over each nostril. A central valve produces pressure in the airway so that it remains open during sleep. Another new treatment, The Winx Sleep Therapy System (*Apnicure.com*), uses a soft mouthpiece that is connected to a small vacuum console. The device creates suction to open the throat.

David Rapoport, MD, professor of medicine and director of the Sleep Disorders Center, New York University Medical Center, New York City.

Alternative to an Overnight Sleep Study

A device known as the WatchPAT is FDA-approved to diagnose sleep apnea, a condition in which you stop breathing repeatedly during sleep. Studies have found that, for most patients, results from the portable device are as accurate as sleep tests that are performed overnight in a sleep center.

The WatchPAT, which is worn on the wrist while sleeping, measures oxygen levels in the blood, body movement, respiratory disturbances, snoring and other indicators of sleep apnea. The test typically is covered by insurance.

Gal Ifergane, MD, head of neurology, Soroka University Medical Center, Ben-Gurion University of the Negev, Be'er-Sheva, Israel.

Sleep Deprivation Can Cause Brain Damage!

In a recent finding, after one night without sleep, blood samples of study participants showed increased concentrations of molecules that are known to spike when brain damage is present.

Theory: Pulling an all-nighter deprives the brain of the restorative time it needs to clean out these toxic molecules.

Study led by researchers at Uppsala University in Sweden, published in *Sleep*.

BREAKTHROUGH...

Headband That Relieves Migraines

Cefaly is a headbandlike device that delivers electrical pulses to stimulate the nerves just above the eyes that are involved in migraine pain.

Recent discovery: Migraine patients who wore the device for 20 minutes a day had significantly fewer migraines and reduced their use of antimigraine medication.

The device is less effective than the most widely used migraine medications, but it does not cause the unpleasant side effects, such as nausea, skin tingling and fatigue. Cefaly was approved by the FDA in 2014.

Study by researchers at Headache Research Unit, University of Liège, Belgium, published online in *Neurology*.

Statins Stave Off Barrett's Esophagus

Statins may reduce risk for *Barrett's esophagus*, a precursor to esophageal cancer. Barrett's esophagus is mainly caused by long-term *gastroesophageal reflux disease* (GERD), obesity and/or a family history of GERD.

Recent finding: In older men, the use of statins—mainly *simvastatin*—was associated with a 43% lower risk for Barrett's esophagus.

But first-line prevention involves controlling GERD, maintaining a normal weight and eating a balanced diet.

Hashem B. El-Serag, MD, a professor of medicine at Baylor College of Medicine, Houston, and leader of a study of 1,212 men, published in *Gastroenterology*.

Dangerous Naps!?

Adults who napped every day for an hour or more had a 32% higher risk of dying from a respiratory illness, compared with those who did not take naps or nap as long. Researchers are studying whether sleeping during the day triggers inflammation in the body or signals that someone already has a lung disease, such as pneumonia, bronchitis or emphysema.

Study of more than 16,000 people by researchers at Cambridge University, England, published in *American Journal of Epidemiology*.

"Senior Moments" Don't Necessarily Mean Dementia

Only about 20% of people who experienced memory lapses and/or showed poor judgment went on to develop Alzheimer's, dementia or other serious brain-related disorders in a recent study.

Three-year study of 357 people, ages 75 and older, led by researchers at Institute of Primary Medical Care, Kiel, Germany, published in *Annals of Family Medicine*.

DEMENTIA DANGERS...

Distrust Harms the Brain

People who habitually distrust others, believing that others act mainly in their own self-interest, are three times more likely to develop dementia than those who do not. That was the finding of an eight-year study of older adults (average age 71).

Why: Chronic negative emotions can impair cognitive function.

Anna-Maija Tolppanen, PhD, development director of neurology, University of Eastern Finland, Kuopio.

Alzheimer's Tied to Meds

People who take *benzodiazepines*, commonly used for insomnia and anxiety, for three months or longer are up to 51% more likely to get Alzheimer's disease, a recent study has found. The strength of this association grew the longer the drugs (such as Xanax and Restoril) were taken.

If you are prescribed a benzodiazepine drug: Tell your doctor that you'd like to follow the recommended medication limits (less than three months for anxiety and no more than one month for sleep problems).

Antoine Pariente, MD, associate professor, University of Bordeaux, France.

Concussion/Dementia Link

Even a mild concussion after age 65 can boost risk for dementia. The older brain appears to be particularly vulnerable to traumatic brain injury.

To reduce the risk for dementia once you've recovered from a concussion: Exercise, be mentally active and maintain an active social life.

Raquel Gardner, MD, clinical research fellow, San Francisco Veterans Affairs Medical Center, and leader of a study published in *JAMA Neurology*.

An MRI May Reveal Alzheimer's Risk

By using *arterial spin labeling* (ASL), which can be done by all modern MRI scanning machines, it may be possible to detect very subtle blood flow changes in parts of the brain linked to memory. Early detection could make it possible to start medicines to slow decline.

Sven Haller, MD, a senior physician in clinical neuroradiology at Geneva University Hospital, Switzerland, and leader of a study published online in *Radiology*.

ALZHEIMER'S ALERT...

The Peanut Butter Test for Alzheimer's

One of the first areas of the brain to be affected by Alzheimer's is the one that controls the sense of smell. People with Alzheimer's couldn't smell a teaspoon of peanut butter until it was five centimeters (about two inches) away. People without Alzheimer's could smell it when it was 17 centimeters (about seven inches) away, on average.

Study by researchers at McKnight Brain Institute Center for Smell and Taste, University of Florida, Gainesville, published in *Journal of the Neurological Sciences*.

Chemical Caution

The brain may never recover from chemical fumes. In a study of more than 2,000 retired industrial workers, those who had high exposure to benzene, petroleum, paint, glue, chlorinated solvents and other chemicals scored worse on tests for cognitive functioning—and impairment was detected in people whose exposure dated back 50 years.

Explanation: Industrial solvents may permanently damage brain cells, so if you are around them, be sure to wear a face mask and keep the area ventilated.

Erika Sabbath, ScD, assistant professor, Boston College Graduate School of Social Work, Chestnut Hill, Massachusetts.

Promising Drug for Parkinson's

An experimental drug, dubbed *AT2101*, improved symptoms in mice within four months. The drug, originally developed for a rare genetic disease, appears to protect dopamine-producing cells in the brain.

Neurotherapeutics.

MS May Be Slowed by a Cholesterol Med

In a recent finding, high doses of the statin drug *simvastatin* slowed brain atrophy in some patients with advanced multiple sclerosis (MS). A very early Phase II trial found that some MS patients who were given 80 milligrams (mg) of simvastatin a day for two years had less neural degeneration.

Patricia K. Coyle, MD, professor of neurology and director of the Multiple Sclerosis Comprehensive Care Center, Stony Brook University Medical Center, East Setauket, New York.

Pasta and Meat Add Up to More Depression

Women who consumed these foods that are linked to inflammation and infrequently consumed wine, coffee, olive oil and vegetables were 29% to 41% more likely to be diagnosed with or treated for depression during a 12-year period. The women also had higher blood indicators for biomarkers associated with the kind of inflammation that has been linked to heart disease, stroke, diabetes and cancer.

Michel Lucas, PhD, researcher, department of nutrition, Harvard School of Public Health, Boston, and lead author of a study of 43,685 women, published in *Brain, Behavior, and Immunity.*

Botox Bonus

Botox fights depression. A single injection decreased depression symptoms by 47%

in people who had a shot of the wrinkle eraser between their brows.

Possible reason: Smoothing the muscles between the eyebrows may reduce distress signals to the brain, boosting mood.

Eric Finzi, MD, PhD, dermatologist in private practice, Chevy Chase, Maryland, and leader of a study published in *Journal of Psychiatric Research.*

New Nasal Spray for Severe Depression

A new nasal spray rapidly relieves severe depression. A 50-milligram (mg) dose of the intranasal spray *ketamine*, an FDA-approved anesthetic, was found to alleviate depressive symptoms within hours with few side effects in people with treatment-resistant major depressive disorder.

Study by researchers at Icahn School of Medicine at Mount Sinai, New York City, published in *Biological Psychiatry.*

New Treatment for Bipolar Depression

Bipolar depression is often hard to treat. But the antipsychotic medication Latuda (*lurasidone*), provides another valuable treatment option. Latuda can be used on its own for patients who respond well to it. Other patients may experience only a partial response, in which case Latuda can be combined with medications including *lithium* or *valproate.* Latuda is well-tolerated by most people who take it. However, some patients taking it develop side effects such as restlessness, nausea, drowsiness, muscle twitching and slowed movements.

Robert Rowney, DO, a psychiatrist in the department of psychology and psychiatry at the Cleveland Clinic.

The Germiest Spots in Public Places

Philip M. Tierno, Jr., PhD, a microbiologist and director of clinical microbiology and diagnostic immunology at New York University Langone Medical Center and a clinical professor in the departments of microbiology and pathology at New York University School of Medicine, both in New York City. He is author of *The Secret Life of Germs.*

You're not paranoid—germs really are out to get you. But not from the much publicized diseases such as Ebola. The real risk comes from mundane microbes lurking where you might not expect them. *Here's where they are and what to do about them...*

LYING IN WAIT

About 80% of all infections are caused by touch—either from direct contact or from touching a contaminated surface. And when you're in a public place, just about every surface is contaminated.

When researchers at the University of Arizona applied a noninfectious virus to an office door—a virus that was not naturally present in the office—the virus was detected on more than half of the office surfaces (and on the hands of office workers) within just four hours.

Don't count on people washing their hands. Researchers observed the hand-washing habits of nearly 4,000 people in public restrooms. They found that about 10% didn't wash at all. Among those who did, about two-thirds didn't use soap, and only 5% washed long enough to thoroughly remove harmful organisms.

PUBLIC OFFENDERS

Bacteria and viruses can survive on hard surfaces for anywhere from a few hours to several days—and sometimes longer when they're protected by a sheen of hand lotion or residue from a greasy meal. *Watch out for...*

• **Coffee-cup lids.** A University of Arizona professor found that about 17% of disposable coffee-cup lids placed on cups by coffee shop workers were contaminated with fecal bacteria.

Solution: Skip the lid, or pour the coffee into your own thermos cup.

• **Office coffeepot handles.** The pots usually get rinsed out, but the handles are rarely cleaned.

Solution: Wash your hands after pouring your coffee, or use a disposable wipe to wipe down the handle before using.

• **ATM machines.** A British study found that ATM machines were heavily contaminated with bacteria at the same levels as nearby public toilets.

Solution: Bring a disposable wipe to wipe the keypad or touch screen, or clean your hands with a disposable wipe immediately after using the machine.

• **Supermarket checkout conveyor belts.** Juices from raw poultry and beef, which may be contaminated with dangerous bacteria, including *salmonella* and *E. coli*, may leak onto the belts. Other food-related bacteria end up there, too. A study by Michigan State University tested 100 belts in 42 grocery stores. All 100 belts were found to have mold, yeast, the disease-causing bacteria *Staphylococcus aureus* (staph) and other bacteria.

Solution: When you get home, wash your hands before opening cabinets and the refrigerator. Wash them again when you're done unpacking your groceries. Put packaged raw meat and poultry in plastic bags before you refrigerate or freeze it. Wash off the tops of cans before you open them.

• **Public telephones.** Though pay phones have all but disappeared, you still find telephones for public use in office lobbies, conference rooms, hotel lobbies, etc. They are rarely cleaned.

Solution: Use a disposable wipe to clean the mouthpiece...the part that presses against your ear...and the buttons before using public phones.

HOTELS

• **Bathtubs.** Don't be fooled by the gleaming white porcelain and legions of bustling hotel maids. When we took cultures from hundreds of apparently clean bathtubs, about 60% were contaminated with staph.

Rinsing a tub doesn't help because staph survives in biofilm, an invisible coating that forms in tubs and keeps the bacterium moist and viable.

Solution: You need mechanical action to remove biofilm. If you know that you'll want to take a bath in your hotel, bring a small scrub brush and a few ounces of bleach. A solution of one part household bleach to nine parts water and a few drops of soap (such as the shampoo or shower gel at the hotel) will kill most microbes within a few seconds, and the brush will remove them.

• **Pillows.** Pillows are rarely laundered. When I travel, I always bring protective covers (look for antiallergy pillow casings). I wash them each time I return home.

Also: Just about everyone knows (or suspects) that the bedspreads used in most hotels aren't laundered anywhere near as often as the sheets.

Solution: Remove the bedspread and toss it in a corner. To stay warm, request additional blankets, which are laundered more often than bedspreads.

• **Carpets.** The carpets in public places can harbor some 200,000 bacteria per square inch—thousands of times more than live on the average toilet seat. Since carpets aren't deep-cleaned very often, they provide a veritable buffet for bacteria and other organisms.

Solution: Higher-end hotels often provide a pair of disposable scuffs or slippers. Wear them! Or be sure to bring your own slippers or flip-flops.

RESTAURANTS

• **Tables.** Does the server wipe your table before you sit down?

Bad news: The damp wiping cloths should be sanitized between uses but often aren't. They can harbor astonishing amounts of bacteria. One study found that 70% of wiped restaurant tables were contaminated with E. coli and other fecal bacteria.

Solution: When you go to a restaurant, wipe the table yourself with a sanitizing wipe.

• **Toilets.** The top of the toilet seat might be sparkling clean, but most germs are underneath. Your fingertips are contaminated when you raise or lower the seat.

Solution: Use a disposable wipe or a thick layer of toilet tissue to lift the seat.

Also important: Close the lid, if the toilet has one, before you flush. Flushing an old-style toilet can spray bacteria-laden droplets up to 20 feet—the newer, low-flush toilets will spray no more than one foot.

Better Way to Clean Moldy Coffeemakers

Coffeemakers often contain mold, yeast and even *coliform* bacteria, which can form a biofilm that is resistant to cleaning products.

To keep your coffeemaker germ-free: Scrub the reservoir and basket with a clean brush, and disinfect with undiluted white vinegar or a solution that the owner's manual recommends.

Robert Donofrio, PhD, director of NSF International's Applied Research Center, Ann Arbor, Michigan, quoted in *Men's Health*.

More Bad News on Secondhand Smoke

Secondhand smoke makes the air in a house as dangerous as the air in a polluted city. Nonsmokers living with smokers are typically exposed to more than three times the World Health Organization's recommended safe levels of harmful air particles.

Study of the air in 110 homes by researchers at University of Aberdeen, Scotland, published in *Tobacco Control*.

Medical Matters

3 Questions You *Must* Ask Your Doctor

Approximately a year before my mother-in-law passed away from cancer, her oncologist said nothing more could be done to treat her illness. He did not volunteer how much longer she might live, nor did he indicate how the remaining course of her disease would likely unfold.

Here's the surprising part: This doctor's omissions were perfectly legal in the state in which he practiced. That's because there is no law in that state that required him to disclose such information unless the patient specifically asked for it or he was proposing a treatment that required the patient to either accept or reject it.

This is just one of the thorny issues related to "informed consent." Simply put, informed consent is when a doctor must tell you what he/she wants to do about your medical problem...explain the treatment or procedure in a detailed, yet understandable way (including what might go wrong)...and get your permission to proceed. *To avoid confusion regarding your care, always ask your doctors these questions before you make a medical decision requiring your consent...*

QUESTION #1: What is my prognosis? State laws and courts have ruled that doctors must give you a prognosis if asked for one or if you have to make a decision about a treatment that might have a direct effect on your health. This includes surgery and treatments such as radiation and the use of prescribed drugs.

Action alert: Because disclosure rules are governed by state laws, which vary from state

Charles B. Inlander, a consumer advocate and health-care consultant based in Fogelsville, Pennsylvania. He was founding president of the nonprofit People's Medical Society, a consumer advocacy organization credited with key improvements in the quality of US health care, and is author or coauthor of more than 20 consumer-health books.

to state, always ask for a prognosis if you have to make a major treatment decision. Do this even if you plan on forgoing all treatment. All state laws give you the right to ask and get an answer.

QUESTION #2: What experience do you have performing this procedure? I have never seen an informed consent form that describes the doctor's experience performing the proposed procedure. Again, a doctor is not required to disclose experience unless you ask for it. However, studies show that choosing a practitioner experienced in providing the treatment you need greatly improves your chances of a successful outcome. A key question is how many times the doctor has performed the procedure in the past year.

Action alert: Consent forms are designed to convince you to say "yes" to the proposed treatment, so make sure you ask questions about undisclosed treatment issues.

Questions to include: "How long is the recovery time?" and "How might the procedure affect other conditions I have?"

QUESTION #3: Could I get this in writing? Surprisingly, doctors are generally not required to get your consent for medical treatment in writing. It's legal for doctors to give you treatment information verbally, and by saying "yes," you have given consent. But you do have the right to ask for the information (including the purpose of the treatment, risks and chances for success) in writing.

Action alert: To avoid any confusion later on, ask for all your options in writing. Even if you have given written consent, you may be asked to approve a change of plan during treatment. This also can be done in writing (unless it's an emergency) to spell out exactly what will happen. When it comes to your medical care, you don't want to be surprised!

Beware of Medical Apps

A study published in *The Journal of the American Medical Association Dermatology* by researchers from University of Pittsburgh Medical Center looked at four apps that claimed to diagnose melanoma. Three misread actual melanomas as "unconcerning" 30% of the time. Another study looked at all cancer-related apps and found that almost half did not contain scientifically validated data. The only apps that now require FDA approval are those that meet the definition of a medical device—for example, a mobile app that can be used as an electrocardiography machine.

Analysis by IMS Institute for Healthcare Informatics, based in Danbury, Connecticut.

Better Time for Doctor Appointments

In a recent study involving 21,867 patients with acute respiratory infections, doctors were 26% more likely in the fourth hour of their shifts to give patients an antibiotic prescription—whether it was needed or not—than in the first hour.

Takeaway: Doctors are human, too, and may experience "decision fatigue" over the course of the day.

What to do: Schedule doctor appointments early in the day whenever possible, and always be sure to ask your doctor if an antibiotic is really needed.

Jeffrey Linder, MD, associate professor of medicine, Harvard Medical School, Boston.

BETTER WAYS...

Helpful Symptom Checker

Before calling your doctor when you develop a new set of symptoms, check out possible diagnoses with a web tool called Isabel Symptom Checker (*IsabelHealthCare.com*). Enter your symptoms, and Isabel uses medical research to produce a list of possible diagnoses, indicating which are common and which are rare. The idea is to help you ask your doctor better questions about tests and treatments.

Money. Money.com

How to Go Online to Find a Doctor

Charles B. Inlander, a consumer advocate and health-care consultant based in Fogelsville, Pennsylvania. He was founding president of the nonprofit People's Medical Society, a consumer advocacy organization credited with key improvements in the quality of US health care, and is author or coauthor of more than 20 consumer-health books.

These days, there aren't many things you can't shop for online. But a doctor? Yes, you can even find a good doctor online—if you know what information is trustworthy (and what might not be). The appeal of sites such as *HealthGrades.com*, *RateMDs.com* and *Vitals.com* is that they offer the kind of firsthand feedback that we used to get only from family, friends or neighbors sharing stories over the back fence. How's a doctor's bedside manner? Is it tough to get an appointment? The problem is, even though these sites provide some good information, they do have their limits. *Here are the advantages and disadvantages of using such websites...*

PRO: The basics are all in one place. Most doctor-rating sites give helpful biographical information, such as the doctor's age...where he/she went to school...if he is board-certified in a particular specialty...and how long he's been in practice. In fact, these sites are the best resources to find all of this biographical information in one place for most licensed doctors in every state. Some sites also list the hospitals where the doctor has admitting privileges or is employed.

Excellent feature: Most doctor-rating sites let you search doctors by specialty anywhere in the US. This is a great service if you're looking for a doctor for a family member in another locale.

CON: High ratings don't always mean good medical care. While the actual reviews provided by patients give some telling details about a doctor's willingness to answer questions and other aspects of his patient care, remember these are only opinions. A patient may write a negative review simply because a doctor wouldn't prescribe an antibiotic for a cold or held off on ordering an MRI in favor of another test. Meanwhile, a good review might have been submitted by a practitioner's relative or friend (even though some sites have systems to screen phony reviews). That's why I advise trying to find multiple reviews of a doctor (which may mean checking more than one site) in case the feedback is skewed for one of these reasons. But you must realize that these sites don't review a doctor's medical competence. In fact, studies show that patients tend to give higher ratings to doctors who prescribe more drugs and tests and run up more costs.

To find out about a physician's skill level: You need to consult resources beyond doctor-rating websites. If you are looking for a skilled orthopedic surgeon, for example, go to *US News & World Report's* well-respected hospital ratings (*USNews.com/best-hospitals*) to find the best hospital in your region that is known for its orthopedic department. Check that hospital's website to review its roster of doctors. You can even check the rosters of nationally ranked hospitals outside your region and call one of the top doctors there. It's been my experience that those doctors often can refer patients to highly skilled doctors in other locales. In addition, many states, such as California, Massachusetts, New York, Pennsylvania and Texas, have their own physician outcome data for certain procedures and make it available to the public. Contact your state's Health Department for information. Medicare also has information on physician outcomes on its website. Go to *Medicare.gov/physiciancompare*.

New Ways to "See" a Doctor

Charles B. Inlander, a consumer advocate and health-care consultant based in Fogelsville, Pennsylvania. He was founding president of the nonprofit People's Medical Society, a consumer advocacy organization credited with key improvements in the quality of US health care, and is author or coauthor of more than 20 consumer-health books.

If you think that seeing a doctor could be simpler and more convenient than the current setup, then the emerging field of telemedicine may be just for you. Telemedicine, which is destined to radically change the way health care is delivered in this country, broadly refers to patients' use of two-way video, text messaging, e-mail and even smartphones to interact with medical professionals. To get the best care from telemedicine, you just need to know the benefits—and possible traps. *Key pros and cons of this approach...*

PRO: You don't have to leave home. With telemedicine, you can use your own doctor (if he/she offers the service) or one affiliated with one of many telemedicine practices. These practices retain licensed physicians, nurse practitioners and other health professionals and make them available directly to patients—sometimes 24/7. Whether you are dealing with your own doctor or one from a telemedicine practice, you can communicate via such services as secure video, e-mail or phone without leaving your home or office. Telemedicine consults can be used to discuss test results, follow up on a course of treatment, monitor vital signs and even determine if you need care in a doctor's office.

PRO: Telemedicine is widely available. Thousands of US employers have added telemedicine services such as Teladoc (*Teladoc.com*) and MDlive (*MDlive.com*) to their employees' traditional health coverage. These employers have found that employees who use telemedicine practices miss less work, since they spend less time going to doctors' appointments. For those with private insurance, companies such as WellPoint, Aetna and Blue Cross/Blue Shield affiliates offer similar services. If you're interested in using a doctor from a telemedicine practice but your employer doesn't pay for it or your individual policy doesn't cover it, you can buy coverage directly from a telemedicine provider for about $15 to $50 per month.* Without coverage, each electronic "conversation" (such as e-mail or video) with a medical provider can cost $40 to $75. Medicare and Medicaid also have telemedicine programs, but they are currently focused in rural or underserved areas.

*Prices subject to change.

PRO: No more waiting! A televisit eliminates those long waits at the doctor's office. With electronic health records, you can arrange to have your medical history stored or made accessible to any provider you use. That means it will be available electronically as the doctor or nurse speaks with you via video, text and/or phone.

CON: You may need an in-person visit. No matter how sophisticated the technology, a face-to-face physical is often vital to a correct diagnosis—for example, when you have multiple or severe symptoms such as dizziness, chest tightness or high fever. And if your connection via the Internet is slow, you may not get the ultimate value of telemedicine.

CON: Privacy isn't guaranteed. Even though telemedicine interactions must comply with federal HIPAA privacy laws, you still need to be careful. Ask your doctor or telemedicine provider if his Internet lines are encrypted and secure before sharing personal information or transferring medical history. General telephone lines and Skype are NOT secure.

Doctor House Calls Are Back!

Thomas Cornwell, MD, president of the American Academy of Home Care Medicine based in Edgewood, Maryland. Dr. Cornwell has made 31,000 house calls during his 20 years in practice. Based in Wheaton, Illinois, he specializes in family medicine and geriatrics. *AAHCM.org*

The image of a doctor visiting sick patients at home, black bag in hand, is no longer a part of our past.

What's new: Advances in portable medical equipment, a rapidly aging population and increased payments from Medicare for in-home doctor visits mean that house calls are back. In fact, the number of house calls made to Medicare patients more than doubled in recent years, and private insurers are beginning to cover them as well.

To find out more about the recent upswing in house calls and how they can benefit you, we spoke with Thomas Cornwell, MD, a national leader in home-care medicine who has made 31,000 in-home visits throughout his career.

WHY THE COMEBACK?

Until recently, most major tests, like X-rays and ultrasounds, required a visit to a hospital or other medical facility. Now, technology makes possible diagnostic and therapeutic equipment that's portable and accurate. Even a chest X-ray can be done in the comfort of the home. And house-call physicians currently have an arsenal of tools that they can use on the road—such as an ultrasound machine that fits in a pocket...a smartphone case that turns into an EKG machine...and an app for checking drug interactions.

Another driving factor: Most older adults would prefer to remain in their homes as they age and avoid expensive nursing homes. For many, this would simply not be possible without house calls.

What's more: Studies have shown that doctors visiting patients in the home reduce hospital admission rates, readmission rates and overall costs. In fact, a recent study of Medicare patients found that those cared for at home had 17% lower health-care costs.

The types of doctors most likely to make house calls include family physicians, internists, geriatricians and palliative-care doctors.

THE MANY BENEFITS

Some patients are too sick to come into the doctor's office but don't need to go to an emergency room. Or they simply refuse to go to the doctor's office...or don't have anyone to take them.

Additionally, house calls are typically much longer than the usual office doctor visit. By going into the home, the doctor can assess much more than the current health issue affecting a patient. If the patient is frail, the need for in-home medical equipment, such as grab bars in a shower or bath, can be identified. Plus, safety risks like electrical cords or rugs can be pointed out to help prevent falls.

Patients are encouraged to bring all of their medicines to a doctor appointment, but this is not always done, and often a drug or supplement is forgotten. A home visit is more likely to uncover all the prescriptions and supplements that are being taken. And by investigating other factors like diet and living conditions, a physician can better treat chronic conditions, such as diabetes or heart disease, or determine if the patient should be getting additional at-home assistance.

Finally, by remaining in their homes for medical care, patients are not exposed to the viruses and bacteria common in doctors' offices. This is particularly helpful for those who have weakened immunity.

WHO SHOULD CONSIDER HOUSE CALLS

- **Frail older patients.** For older patients who have difficulty getting out of the house, a home visit can be a literal lifesaver. Home-based primary care for frail older patients can help delay institutionalization or admission to the hospital and allow physicians to assess the quality of help caregivers are able to provide. For patients who are terminally ill, home visits provide palliative care and reduce the chances of dying in a hospital.
- **Patients who have certain disorders/diseases.** Among patients of all ages, house calls are extremely helpful for those who suffer from neuromuscular diseases like muscular dystrophy, Lou Gehrig's disease or paralysis. With these conditions, getting to an appointment can be an arduous task, and home visits keep the doctor up-to-date on the patient's needs.

OTHER HOUSE-CALL OPTIONS

Some doctors' offices now offer medical concierge services (the patient pays an annual fee or retainer to a primary care doctor). These services may include house calls. Costs range from less than one hundred to several thousand dollars a year. Some employers also offer home visits as part of their employee insurance.

HOW TO ARRANGE A HOUSE CALL

For Medicare recipients and many with private insurance, there needs to be a medically necessary reason for the house call. The patient must also find it physically difficult to leave his/her home in order for Medicare or private insurance to cover some portion of the visit. Medical concierge services may not have this requirement.

To find a doctor who makes house calls: First, check with your primary care doctor to see if he can provide this service or give you a referral. You can also go to the website of the American Academy of Home Care Medicine, *AAHCM.org*, and click on "Locate a Provider."

GETTING THE MOST OUT OF YOUR HOUSE CALL

The length of a house call depends on the patient's specific needs and whether it's a first-time visit or a follow-up.

How to prepare...

- **As with any doctor appointment,** write down all your questions and concerns beforehand.
- **Before the doctor arrives,** arrange all of your prescription medications, over-the-counter medications and supplements in one place so that they can be reviewed by the doctor.
- **Make sure any family members who help out with your care are present** so the doctor can get an accurate picture of the home environment.

Also: Don't be afraid to reach out to your doctor between visits. Doing so, even if the problem seems minor, such as a lingering cough, may prevent an unnecessary ER visit or hospitalization down the road.

BETTER WAYS...

Protect Yourself from Germy Doctors

Physicians wash their hands before examining their patients (or certainly should!). But what about their stethoscopes? In a recent study, the parts of stethoscopes used to examine 71 patients were found to be contaminated with more bacteria (including dangerous *MRSA*) than every part of the physician's hand except the fingertips.

Before your doctor uses a stethoscope: Ask him/her to clean it with an alcohol wipe.

Didier Pittet, MD, director, infection control program, University of Geneva Hospitals, Switzerland.

Medical Tests That Can Cause More Harm Than Good

Reid B. Blackwelder, MD, FAAFP, president of the American Academy of Family Physicians. He is also a practicing family physician in Johnson City, Tennessee, and professor of family medicine at Quillen College of Medicine at East Tennessee State University, also in Johnson City. In 2000, Dr. Blackwelder was honored with the prestigious Humanism in Medicine Award from the Healthcare Foundation of New Jersey.

Are you receiving cookie-cutter medical care? Too many people are—and one glaring example of this is the number of tests and procedures that are being prescribed regardless of the individual's specific health situation.

In fact, there's more and more evidence that many of the tests that are given so routinely are causing more harm than good.

Here are some popular tests that are often not necessary...*

CT SCANS FOR LOW-BACK PAIN

If your low back is giving you fits, your doctor may order an X-ray or even a more detailed test such as a CT scan to see what's going on.

Problem: Americans are receiving doses of radiation from X-rays and CT scans (not to mention spending enormous amounts of money) to diagnose a problem that will likely go away on its own in a few weeks. In some cases, an incidental finding that's not even related to the pain leads to unnecessary back surgery.

New thinking...

- **Unless you are experiencing worsening nerve damage** (such as loss of bladder or bowel control or loss of sensation or muscle power in your legs) or have cancer (which could possibly spread to your back), you

*The tests in this article are evaluated at *ChoosingWisely.org*, a website that advises patients and doctors on a wide range of tests and procedures. Developed by more than 50 medical specialty societies, such as the American Academy of Family Physicians and the American College of Surgeons, the information is based on the most current scientific evidence. Remember to check with your doctor for advice that's tailored to your specific needs.

probably don't need an imaging test within the first six weeks of your back pain.

Also: There is no medical or legal reason to get X-rays as a "baseline" for work-related back injuries.

BONE-DENSITY TESTS

For years, physicians have been routinely recommending bone-density tests using *dual-energy X-ray absorptiometry* (DXA). The test estimates the amount of bone in the hip and spine, which is a marker for osteoporosis. Until recently, women have often been advised to have a "baseline" DXA screening at menopause...then periodically after that.

Problem: Being labeled with "preosteoporosis" (commonly known as *osteopenia*) can start you on a medical journey of repeated DXA testing and use of medications that may be harmful. For example, osteoporosis drugs known as *bisphosphonates—risedronate* (Actonel), *ibandronate* (Boniva) and *alendronate* (Fosamax)—have been shown, in rare cases, to cause an unusual fracture of the thighbone when one of these medications is taken for longer than five years.

And evidence shows that this test is not always a reliable predictor of fractures even in high-risk patients who are already receiving drug therapy for osteoporosis.

New thinking...

- **Unless you are a woman age 65 or older or a man age 70 or older**—or you have a special risk factor for osteoporosis, such as family history, smoking or alcohol abuse or use of corticosteroid drugs—you probably don't need DXA screening.
- **If your DXA test results show that you have normal bone mass,** you don't need to be tested again for up to 10 years, provided you don't break a bone or show other signs of osteoporosis, such as losing more than an inch in height.

CAROTID ARTERY IMAGING

Your carotid arteries carry blood from your heart through the neck to your brain. If those arteries become narrowed from a buildup of plaque (a condition known as *carotid artery stenosis*, or CAS), your blood flow is slowed and your risk for stroke increases. Doctors can use ultrasound, *magnetic resonance angiography* (MRA) or *computed tomography angiography* (CTA) scans to check for plaque in these arteries.

Problem: If testing does show a blockage, you may be advised to take medication that won't necessarily improve your life expectancy. You may even be urged to undergo surgery (*endarterectomy*) to clear the artery. However, this is a difficult and complex operation that in rare cases leads to stroke, heart attack or even death.

New thinking...

- **Unless you are experiencing symptoms,** such as stroke, *transient ischemic attack* (a so-called "ministroke") or unexplained dizziness, you probably do not need to be screened for CAS. Evidence shows that the harms of screening (and subsequent treatment) in people without symptoms usually outweigh the benefits.

If you do undergo screening for CAS, surgery is generally not recommended unless you have more than 70% blockage in one or both of your carotid arteries and you have had a stroke or ministroke in the previous six months.

EKG AND STRESS TEST

During your routine physical, your doctor may have ordered an *electrocardiogram* (EKG or ECG) to measure your heart's electrical activity and/or a cardiac stress test to check the same functions but under conditions where you are "stressed" via exercise or medication.

Problem: Unnecessary stress testing can lead to false-positive tests—indicating that something is wrong when you are actually healthy. This can mean more follow-up tests, including CT scans or *coronary angiography*, both of which expose you to radiation. And in rare cases, an angiography actually leads to a heart attack in people who have the test. Sometimes, after a "bad" EKG or stress test, a doctor may also prescribe unnecessary heart medication.

New thinking...

- **If you don't have any heart-related symptoms** (such as chest pain or shortness of breath), the evidence shows that an annual EKG or other cardiac screening is unlikely to prevent a heart attack, catch a hidden heart problem or otherwise make you any healthier than you already are.

• **If you are getting noncardiac thoracic surgery** (for example, on the lungs, esophagus or other organs in the chest), you do not need to have stress testing before the operation unless you have a history of heart problems. In healthy patients, testing rarely changes how they are treated, so it's generally not necessary.

---

4 Secrets to Avoiding a Misdiagnosis

Trisha Torrey, a Baldwinsville, New York–based patient advocacy consultant, also known as "Every Patient's Advocate" and author of *You Bet Your Life! The 10 Mistakes Every Patient Makes*. She is also founder and director of the Alliance of Professional Health Advocates and lectures across the country on the best ways to navigate the health-care system. *EveryPatientsAdvocate.com*

Ten years ago, I noticed a golf ball–sized lump on my torso. My family doctor sent me to a surgeon, who removed the lump and sent it to a lab for testing.

A few weeks later, I got the news from my doctor: "You have a very rare type of lymphoma." I froze with fear. The second blow came when an oncologist told me that if I didn't start chemotherapy right away, I'd be dead within months.

But I didn't feel sick, and my intuition told me that something was off with the diagnosis. So I sought a second opinion from another oncologist, who reviewed my case and had the biopsy analyzed again. As it turned out, I didn't have cancer. The lump was simply an inflamed bundle of fat cells. I didn't need chemo, and 10 years later I'm fine.

So how do you make sure that you or a loved one never experiences a misdiagnosis nightmare? It happens a lot. Twelve million Americans are misdiagnosed each year.

For the past decade, I have dedicated my life to helping people become smarter patients and, in the process, avoid misdiagnoses. Some of what I've learned may sound a little unconventional, but I know from my experience and that of other patients that the steps below work. *How to avoid a misdiagnosis...*

SECRET #1: Track your symptoms. You probably know to write down your questions before seeing a doctor, but I suggest that you first spend at least a little time tracking your symptoms. Medical symptoms can be vague, inconsistent and wax and wane unexpectedly, so patients often don't give their doctors enough facts to ensure a correct diagnosis. Without such details, it's easy for physicians to jump on the most obvious—though sometimes incorrect—diagnosis.

What to do: If you're not dealing with an emergency, keep a diary of your symptoms before you see your doctor. Include a clear description of all your symptoms and when they started. Also, be sure to include any triggers—anything that makes the symptoms worse... or better.

Of course, don't let your symptom tracking become an excuse to delay going to the doctor. Even if your appointment is the next day or so, you can use that time to organize your notes on what you've observed so far. And once you've tracked your symptoms, you'll be better prepared to write down your questions for the doctor.

SECRET #2: Make a list of possible diagnoses. If you've got an unexplained symptom, most doctors tell you to avoid the Internet. You will just confuse yourself, they reason. I disagree. If you've got a weird symptom, you want to know what may be causing it so you can ask the doctor intelligent questions.

When doing research online, just make sure you don't jump to conclusions. And skip websites that are sponsored by pharmaceutical companies or businesses trying to sell you something. Also, disregard comments and forums populated by non–health professionals. Up-to-date and reliable health information is available at such sites as *MedlinePlus.gov... HealthFinder.gov*...and *UptoDate.com* (used by many doctors around the world).

In my own situation, using the Internet helped me to realize that cancer wasn't the

TAKE NOTE...

TV Doctors Often Give Wrong Advice

Only 43% of recommendations on the *Dr. Oz Show* are supported by evidence...and only 63% of those on *The Doctors*. And 15% of the *Dr. Oz* recommendations—along with 14% of those given on *The Doctors*—contradict available medical evidence.

Study of 80 major recommendations made on the two shows by researchers at University of Alberta, Canada, published in *BMJ*.

only possible diagnosis, and it compelled me to ask many more questions.

Important: Don't try to diagnose yourself...and don't talk yourself out of going to the doctor.

SECRET #3: Ask this crucial question. Your doctor has just given you a diagnosis. Now what? Rather than launching into a discussion about the best treatments for the diagnosis you've just received—as most often occurs—I suggest that you stop and ask the doctor, "What else could it be?"

Specifically, ask the doctor for the "differential diagnosis"—that is, the conditions he/she ruled out. Then ask how he ruled them out. Listen carefully—if there are any gaps in the case he makes for your diagnosis, they are likely to come up at this time. After this explanation, ask about anything you don't understand. Be concise and stay focused. If you start to ramble, your doctor won't stay engaged.

SECRET #4: Don't be afraid of your doctor. There are ways to get what you need and ask your questions without offending anyone.

What you need to know: A good, ethical doctor won't be upset by your desire for additional medical opinions. Getting more than one opinion is crucial, especially if your doctor has recommended any invasive type of treatment such as chemotherapy, surgery or a long-term drug prescription.

Ask for your own medical records and take them to additional opinion appointments. Your goal is to find at least two doctors who give you the same diagnosis, maximizing your odds of getting a correct one. Let new doctors draw their own conclusions about your diagnosis rather than sharing previous opinions they can simply agree with.

If your online research doesn't jibe with what your doctor has told you, don't be confrontational. Instead, ask questions like, "I recently read about this (diagnosis or treatment). Can you tell me why you ruled that out?" This acknowledges your doctor's extensive education but puts him on notice that you've done your homework and need to know more.

What Your Eye Exam Can Reveal

You may know that a good eye exam can reveal more than just your eye health. But did you know that it can detect signs of multiple sclerosis, diabetes, high blood pressure, rheumatoid arthritis, high cholesterol and Crohn's disease? In a study of insurance claims, 6% of these conditions were first detected by eye doctors.

Why: The eyes contain blood vessels, nerves and other structures that can be affected by chronic illness.

If you're over age 40, get an eye exam at least every two years.

Linda Chous, OD, chief eye-care officer, UnitedHealthcare, Minneapolis.

Simple Way to Save on Expensive Imaging!

Save $600 on an MRI by having it done at an independent radiologic facility. Many charge only half the typical $1,200 cost of having the procedure done at a hospital.

Holly Phillips, MD, internist and medical contributor for *CBS News*, quoted in *AARP Bulletin*.

INTERESTING FINDING...

Fasting Before Blood Tests May Not Be Necessary

Guidelines from the National Institutes of Health recommend that patients fast for nine to 12 hours before a cholesterol test.

But: A recent study shows that readings taken from fasting and nonfasting blood tests showed no difference in their predictive value for cardiovascular problems or all-cause mortality.

Study of more than 16,000 people by researchers at New York University Langone Medical Center, New York City, published in *Circulation*.

How to Supercharge Your Medications

Thomas Kruzel, ND, a naturopathic physician at the Rockwood Natural Medicine Clinic in Scottsdale, Arizona. He is the former vice president of clinical affairs and the chief medical officer at the Southwest College of Naturopathic Medicine & Health Sciences in Tempe, Arizona, and a past president of the American Association of Naturopathic Physicians. Dr. Kruzel is author of *The Homeopathic Emergency Guide. RockwoodNatural Medicine.com*

When you get a new prescription, most doctors don't talk about dietary supplements. If a conversation does take place, it probably focuses on the potentially dangerous interactions that can occur when people take a prescription medication and a supplement.*

The other side of the story: While some supplements can cause dangerous interactions with certain drugs, the reverse is also true—certain supplements can actually boost the effectiveness of a prescription drug and/or reduce its side effects. In some cases, this beneficial effect may allow you to take a lower dose of the drug...or even discontinue it at some point.

DRUG-BOOSTING SUPPLEMENTS

If you are interested in using a supplement as part of a medication regimen, always discuss this with your doctor. Medical supervision is necessary to ensure that you are using the combination safely.

Medication-supplement pairings that often work well...

• **Diabetes medication and alpha-lipoic acid.** *Alpha-lipoic acid* is an *endogenous* (it is made in the body) antioxidant that helps transform blood sugar (glucose) into energy. It is found in foods such as red meat and liver, though it is difficult to get enough from food to work effectively with your medication for type 2 diabetes.

When it's taken in the larger doses that are found in supplements, alpha-lipoic acid lowers blood sugar and may reduce pain, itching and other symptoms caused by diabetes-related nerve damage (*neuropathy*). For diabetic neuropathy, I typically recommend 400 milligrams (mg) to 500 mg of alpha-lipoic acid, twice daily. For general antioxidant benefit, 100 mg to 300 mg daily is usually sufficient.

If you're taking a diabetes medication that lowers blood sugar, such as *metformin* (Glucophage) or *glyburide* (DiaBeta), the addition of alpha-lipoic acid may allow you to use a smaller drug dose. If your glucose levels are stabilized through diet and regular exercise (without medication), you may want to take alpha-lipoic acid indefinitely.

Caution: Taking too much alpha-lipoic acid with a diabetes drug could lead to excessively low blood sugar, which can trigger anxiety, sweating, shakiness and/or confusion. Alpha-lipoic acid also may interact with chemotherapy drugs and thyroid medication such as *levothyroxine* (Synthroid). Talk to your doctor before taking alpha-lipoic acid with any prescription medication.

• **Cholesterol medication and CoQ10.** *Coenzyme Q10* (CoQ10) is a critical component of the energy-producing mitochondria of the cells in your body. It is found in foods such as meat and fish. CoQ10 levels decline as we

*To see if a drug you have been prescribed may interact with a supplement you are taking, ask your doctor. You can also go to *NLM.NIH.gov/medlineplus*, and click on "Drugs & Supplements."

grow older. Cholesterol-lowering statin drugs also deplete CoQ10.

Food generally does not provide a therapeutic amount of CoQ10. When taken in supplement form, CoQ10 (100 mg to 200 mg daily) helps prevent the muscle pain that can occur as a side effect of statin medication. Research shows that CoQ10 itself has a mild cholesterol-lowering effect and may reduce the risk for cardiovascular disease.

Caution: CoQ10 may increase bleeding risk when taken with aspirin, *warfarin* (Coumadin) and other blood thinners. Talk to your doctor before taking CoQ10 with any prescription medication.

- **Antidepressant medication and vitamin B-12.** Vitamin B-12 is required for red blood cell formation and neurological function. This vitamin is naturally present in animal foods, such as clams, beef liver, red meat and eggs.

It's well-known that vitamin B-12 levels decline with age—largely due to a loss of the stomach acid that is needed to absorb this vitamin. Strict vegetarians also tend to have low levels of B-12.

In a recent study, patients with a vitamin B-12 deficiency who took an injectable form of the vitamin—1,000 micrograms (mcg) weekly for six weeks—while also taking an oral antidepressant reported a significantly greater reduction in depression symptoms than those taking the oral medication alone.

Oral vitamin B-12 supplements (100 mcg daily for adults under age 50) or sublingual (under-the-tongue) tablets (1,000 mcg daily for adults over age 50) can be used to help make antidepressants more effective. No adverse effects have been linked to excess vitamin B-12 intake from food or supplements in healthy adults. However, when higher doses than those described above are used (to treat a severe B-12 deficiency or anemia, for example), the treatment should be supervised by a doctor.

- **Blood pressure medication and magnesium.** *Magnesium* is an extremely versatile mineral. It promotes the health of your heart and blood vessels and regulates the effects of calcium and other important nutrients in the body. Healthy adults can usually get plenty of magnesium from nuts, green vegetables and whole grains.

However, in order to get enough magnesium to help lower blood pressure, people with hypertension usually need a supplement (400 mg to 500 mg, twice daily). *Magnesium citrate* is the most absorbable form of the mineral.

Many blood pressure drugs relax and dilate the arteries, which allows blood to circulate with less force. Combining magnesium with a blood pressure–lowering medication can result in even lower blood pressure, which may allow you to take a reduced dose of the drug. When adding magnesium to a blood pressure medication regimen, check your blood pressure daily at home until your doctor says it's stable.

Caution: Taking too much magnesium with a blood pressure drug may lead to low blood pressure. Symptoms include fatigue and lightheadedness. Magnesium supplements can also cause diarrhea, so you may need a lower dose.

A Shocking Side Effect of Everyday Drugs: These Meds Can Mess with Your Mind

Jack E. Fincham, PhD, RPh, professor of pharmacy administration at Presbyterian College School of Pharmacy in Clinton, South Carolina. He serves as a panel member of the FDA Nonprescription Drugs Advisory Committee and is a former special emphasis panel member who evaluated proposals for the Agency for Healthcare Research and Quality's Centers for Education and Research on Therapeutics. Dr. Fincham also serves as a consultant to the Canadian Institutes of Health Research.

You wouldn't be surprised if a narcotic painkiller made you feel a little sleepy or you developed an upset stomach after taking an aspirin-like painkiller for a few days.

What most people don't know—and their doctors don't talk about—is that popular prescription and over-the-counter (OTC) drugs can affect your body and your mind.

A hidden risk: Let's say that you start taking a new drug. Weeks or even months later, you begin to feel depressed or suffer some other psychiatric symptom. You might assume that something's wrong with you when, in fact, the drug could be to blame. Common offenders you need to know about—psychiatric side effects can occur with any dose, but the greater the drug amount, the greater the risk...

PAINKILLERS

• **Naproxen** (Aleve, Naprosyn and others). It's one of the most popular pain relievers because it's less likely to cause stomach upset than other *nonsteroidal anti-inflammatory drugs* (NSAIDs), such as aspirin or *ibuprofen* (Motrin). But it's more likely than other OTC painkillers to cause depression.

How it hurts: The exact mechanism isn't clear, but naproxen affects the central nervous system in ways that other NSAIDs do not. Some people who take naproxen every day—for chronic arthritis, for example—have reported drowsiness, reduced concentration and/or depression.

My advice: Be aware of your mood when using naproxen. Even though this drug is less likely to cause stomach upset than other NSAIDs, you should watch for signs of depression while taking naproxen. If depression develops, ask your doctor for advice.

BLOOD PRESSURE DRUGS

• **Beta-blockers,** such as *propranolol* (Inderal) and *sotalol* (Betapace), work by blocking the effects of *epinephrine* (also known as adrenaline), thus slowing the heart rate.

How they hurt: Damping down the heart's action can cause fatigue and depression. Because these drugs affect many different body systems, including the brain, they've also been linked to mania and other mood problems in some people.

My advice: Beta-blockers are typically used to treat serious conditions such as high blood pressure and cardiac arrhythmias, so never stop taking this medication without consulting your physician. You may be able to switch to a different drug (such as a calcium channel blocker) for high blood pressure.

If you must take a beta-blocker, use nondrug approaches to improve your energy levels and mood. Be sure to exercise regularly, rely on positive thinking and get enough sunlight, which the body uses to produce vitamin D (low levels have been linked to depression).

COLD REMEDIES

• **Guaifenesin.** This is one of the most common ingredients in OTC decongestants and cold remedies, such as Robitussin and Mucinex. As an expectorant, *guaifenesin* thins mucus, making it easier to cough it up.

How it hurts: Guaifenesin has wide-ranging effects on the central nervous system. In some people, these changes can lead to fatigue and/or depression. When guaifenesin is combined with other ingredients such as *pseudoephedrine* (a common decongestant), side effects can also include anxiety.

My advice: For most individuals, drinking water helps to thin mucus about as well as any pharmaceutical expectorant does. When you're stuffed up, drink a few more glasses of water—or tea or juice—than you usually consume during an average day.

ALLERGY DRUGS

• **Nonsedating antihistamines.** Don't believe the labels—so-called "nonsedating" allergy drugs may have less noticeable side effects than older antihistamines (such as Benadryl), but they are sedating.

Some people with seasonal or year-round allergies who use drugs such as *loratadine* (Claritin) or *cetirizine* (Zyrtec) complain about drowsiness—and depression.

How they hurt: All antihistamines have *anticholinergic effects* (caused by blocking a neurotransmitter in the central nervous system). While some people have no side effects, others notice that they're agitated and/or confused. For some people, these antihistamines also may lead to depression or concentration problems.

My advice: Since unwanted sedation is the most common side effect, take antihistamines at bedtime. Pollen counts and allergy symptoms tend to be worse in the morning, so taking an antihistamine at night will also help you feel better when you wake up.

Worth a try: Break the tablets in half (assuming the medication is not timed-release).

Many people get the same allergy relief with fewer side effects from a lower dose.

HEARTBURN MEDICATIONS

• **H2 blockers.** Some patients who take these heartburn drugs, including *cimetidine* (Tagamet) and *ranitidine* (Zantac), have reported suffering from depression, confusion and even hallucinations. These and other side effects usually occur in older adults, who tend to accumulate higher drug levels in the body.

How they hurt: Ironically, the psychiatric side effects of H2 blockers are probably related to lower stomach acidity—the effect that these drugs provide to fight heartburn. Too much stomach acid (or a weak esophageal muscle that allows acid reflux) is obviously a problem, but reduced acid may have its own risks. For example, people who take these drugs every day tend to absorb smaller amounts of folate and other nutrients—an effect that can lead to mood problems.

My advice: Most people can reduce—or even eliminate—heartburn without the daily use of potent drugs. Simple approaches that work include not eating within a few hours of bedtime...and avoiding "trigger" foods such as chocolate or alcohol. If you need more relief, you may be able to get by with the occasional OTC antacid, such as Mylanta or Maalox.

Is Your Medication Dose Wrong for You? Biggest Dangers...

Heather Whitley, PharmD, an associate professor in the Auburn University Harrison School of Pharmacy in Auburn, Alabama. She is also associate affiliate professor at The Institute for Rural Health Research at The University of Alabama, Tuscaloosa, and the lead author of "Sex-Based Differences in Drug Activity," which appeared in the journal *American Family Physician*.

If you are a man and take a sleeping pill in the middle of the night, you may fall asleep quickly and wake up feeling refreshed. If you're a woman and take the same pill, you may fall asleep just as fast but find that you are slogging through the morning with a drug-powered hangover.

Just a fluke? Absolutely not.

An under-recognized problem: While scientists have long suspected that men and women don't respond in the same ways to certain drugs, a growing body of research shows that these differences are more significant than previously thought.

Why this matters: You may be taking a drug—or be prescribed one in the future—in a dose that's not right for you...or in a class that is not the most effective for your condition. *What you need to know...*

HOW GENDER SLIPPED UNDER THE RADAR

Since 1992, when the sedative *zolpidem* (Ambien) was first introduced in the US, the recommended maximum dose for men and women has been the same—10 milligrams (mg).

A startling finding: Recently, evidence came to light that women who took the same dose of zolpidem as men had blood levels that were 45% higher. The "standard" dose, in other words, was essentially an overdose for women.

Meanwhile, zolpidem has also been implicated in cases of so-called "sleep driving," in which people who have taken the drug drive their cars while not fully awake.

Now the Food and Drug Administration (FDA) has stepped in and cut the recommended dose of zolpidem for women in half, to 5 mg. The daily dose for the extended-release version is up to 12.5 mg for men and 6.25 mg for women.

But it's not just sleeping pills that affect men and women differently. Entire classes of medications—including beta-blockers, opioid painkillers and heart medications—have sex-specific effects.

Why haven't we heard more about this?

Until the early 1990s, women of childbearing age were excluded from most drug-based research. The majority of drugs were tested only in men. Based on these results, doctors assumed that any research that cleared a medication as being safe and effective for men would also apply to women—but they didn't really know.

Today, medications are routinely tested in roughly equal numbers of men and women—but there are still hundreds, maybe thousands, of drugs on the market whose outcomes have never been analyzed based on gender. What's more, data do not always separate outcomes based on age, ethnicity and other factors. So the recommended dose may not be the optimal amount for certain people.

WHICH DRUGS ARE SUSPECT?

You'd expect that a small woman would require a lower dose of medication than a large man. But size is only one difference.

Because women have a higher percentage of body fat, on average, drugs that are *lipophilic*—that is, accumulate in fatty tissue—cause longer-lasting effects in women than in men. On top of that, women tend to metabolize (break down) some medications more slowly than men, so women can be more likely to accumulate higher-than-expected concentrations of those drugs in their bodies.

A woman's digestive process is also generally slower than a man's, which means that women may have to wait for a longer time after meals in order to take some medications "on an empty stomach."

Trust your gut: If you start taking a new medication and your instincts tell you that something's wrong, pay attention. You may need a different drug or dose.

The research on sex-based drug effects is still in the early stages. There are probably hundreds, if not thousands, of drugs that affect men and women differently.

Among the drugs that women should use with caution…

SEDATIVES

• **Benzodiazepine sedatives,** such as *diazepam* (Valium), accumulate in fat and have longer-lasting effects in women. Women may find themselves feeling drowsy the next day…less alert than usual…and having slower reaction times. (Zolpidem, the medication discussed earlier, has similar effects.)

My advice: If you are a woman taking one of these medications for anxiety, back spasms or any other condition, ask your physician, "Could I take a lower dose because I'm a woman?"

BLOOD PRESSURE DRUGS

• **Beta-blockers,** such as *metoprolol* (Lopressor), *atenolol* (Tenormin) and *propranolol* (Inderal), have stronger effects on women. For example, women who take them tend to have a greater drop in blood pressure and heart rate than men, particularly during exercise.

My advice: All patients should be started on the lowest possible dose, then gradually adjusted (titrated) every few weeks until the desired effects are achieved.

Let your doctor know if you're experiencing dizziness, fatigue or other symptoms—this could signal that you're taking a dose that's too high for you.

• **Calcium channel blockers,** including *amlodipine* (Norvasc) and *felodipine* (Plendil), are among the most commonly used drugs for high blood pressure. One potential side effect of these drugs is edema (fluid accumulation in the body)—and women tend to experience more of this edema than men.

My advice: Rather than taking a diuretic to manage edema, women (and men) who have this side effect might do better without a calcium channel blocker at all.

They can frequently switch to an ACE inhibitor such as *lisinopril* (Zestril), which also provides blood pressure–lowering effects—and does not cause edema. Alternatively, adding an ACE inhibitor to the calcium channel blocker can reverse edema.

PAINKILLERS

• **Opiate analgesics,** such as *morphine, oxycodone* (OxyContin) and *hydromorphone* (Dilaudid), have a greater analgesic effect in women.

In fact, women usually get pain relief from a 30% to 40% lower dose than that required for men. Women who do not take the lower dose are also more likely than men to experience side effects, including unwanted sedation.

My advice: Tell your doctor that you want the lowest effective dose. It can always be increased if you need more relief.

BREAKTHROUGH...

No More Pills or Shots!

Experimental drug-loaded microchips could safely deliver daily doses of medication, possibly for years. Doses can be changed or stopped by remote control.

Massachusetts Institute of Technology.

HEART MEDICATION

- **Low-dose aspirin** is routinely recommended to prevent heart attacks and/or strokes. This benefit has been shown to occur in both men and women who have already had a heart attack or stroke but is less clear-cut in those who have not had these issues. Clinical studies have found that low-dose aspirin helps prevent stroke in healthy women ages 55 to 79 and heart attack in healthy men ages 45 to 79. Preventive low-dose aspirin may be especially beneficial for men and women with cardiovascular risk factors, such as high blood pressure, high cholesterol, diabetes, family history or smoking.

My advice: Men and women should discuss with their doctors whether they need low-dose (81-mg) aspirin to prevent a heart attack or stroke, especially since even small doses of aspirin increase the risk for gastric bleeding. Unlike some other drugs in which side effects are amplified for women, low-dose aspirin is less likely to cause gastric bleeding in women than in men.

Drugs That Work Against Each Other: Are Your Drugs Making You Sicker?

David Lee, PharmD, PhD, assistant professor in the College of Pharmacy at Oregon State University in Portland. Dr. Lee is also a coauthor of a recent paper on therapeutic competition that was published in the journal *PLOS ONE*.

Most people who have a chronic health problem such as osteoarthritis, high blood pressure or diabetes are accustomed to taking medication to help control their symptoms. But if you have more than one chronic condition—and take medication for each of them—you could be setting yourself up for other problems.

The risk that often goes undetected: Taking medication prescribed for one disease may actually worsen another health problem. This situation, known as "therapeutic competition," has received surprisingly little attention from the medical profession.

ARE YOU AT RISK?

Therapeutic competition can occur at any time in a person's life. But the risk increases with age—the older we get, the more likely we are to have chronic medical conditions and use more medications. Because our bodies metabolize medication less efficiently as we age, we're also more likely to develop side effects that can worsen other health problems.

Modern medicine has not done very much to help the situation. For one thing, *polypharmacy*—the use of multiple medications—has become more common than ever before.

For people with more than one chronic medical condition, frequent conflicts occur if you have...

HIGH BLOOD PRESSURE

If you also have *chronic obstructive pulmonary disease* (COPD), drugs that you take to ease your breathing, such as the beta-adrenergic agonist *albuterol* (Proventil) or a corticosteroid, may raise your blood pressure.

If you are also being treated for depression, an antidepressant such as *venlafaxine* (Effexor) or *duloxetine* (Cymbalta) could push your blood pressure higher. COX-2 inhibitors such as *celecoxib* (Celebrex), commonly used for osteoarthritis, also may increase blood pressure.

DIABETES

Corticosteroids taken for COPD can raise blood sugar levels, worsening diabetes. If you have an enlarged prostate and take an alpha-blocker such as *tamsulosin* (Flomax) or a beta-blocker such as *atenolol* (Tenormin) for high blood pressure, the drug can mask symptoms of low blood sugar, such as shakiness.

COPD

If you also have high blood pressure or angina and take a nonselective beta-blocker such as *propranolol* (Inderal), the drug could worsen lung symptoms.

HEART DISEASE

COPD drugs, including *albuterol*...tricyclic antidepressants such as *imipramine* (Tofranil), taken for depression...and COX-2 inhibitors for osteoarthritis also can make heart disease worse.

ATRIAL FIBRILLATION

Osteoporosis drugs, including bisphosphonates such as *alendronate* (Fosamax)...and Alzheimer's drugs, including cholinesterase inhibitors such as *donepezil* (Aricept), may worsen atrial fibrillation.

OSTEOPOROSIS

Corticosteroids used for treating COPD often lead to significant bone loss. Glitazones taken for diabetes and proton pump inhibitors such as *omeprazole* (Prilosec), commonly prescribed for *gastroesophageal reflux disease* (GERD), can accelerate bone loss.

GERD OR PEPTIC ULCERS

Warfarin (Coumadin) or *clopidogrel* (Plavix), often prescribed for atrial fibrillation or heart disease, as well as nonsteroidal anti-inflammatory drugs (NSAIDs), can cause bleeding that worsens GERD and ulcers. Bisphosphonates taken for osteoporosis may aggravate esophageal damage that commonly occurs with GERD and ulcers.

HOW TO PROTECT YOURSELF

If you have more than one chronic condition and take two or more medications to treat them, it is crucial that you watch for signs of therapeutic competition, such as new symptoms that are unexplained or begin soon after a new medication is started. Any new health condition actually may be an adverse effect of medication. *To avoid therapeutic competition...*

• **Try to cut back on the drugs you take.** The less medication you're on, the less likely one of your drugs will adversely affect another condition. Ask your doctor whether it's advisable to reduce the overall number of prescriptions you take. A drug you have been taking for years may no longer be necessary. And lifestyle changes—such as getting more exercise—may allow you to cut back on blood pressure or diabetes medication.

• **Get the right medication.** If it seems that a drug is worsening another condition, ask your doctor about less harmful alternatives. Some medications are more selective—that is, their effects on the body are more focused on the target illness, making unintended consequences for other conditions less of a danger.

Example: The nonselective beta-blockers, such as propranolol, often worsen COPD symptoms, but medications with more selective action, such as *metoprolol* (Lopressor), are usually just as effective for the heart problem they're prescribed for without adversely affecting your lungs.

GET A YEARLY MEDICATION CHECK

If you suffer from multiple ailments, you need to tell all your doctors about the medications you take. Also, talk to your pharmacist each time you pick up a new prescription to make sure your drugs aren't working against each other.

To ensure that no drug-related problems develop: Once a year, have a pharmacist (ask one at your drugstore) review all your medications. This service includes a discussion of side effects, interactions and alternatives. For many people, Medicare Part D and some private health plans will pay for this service. If not, it usually costs less than $100 (price subject to change).

Misuse of Antibiotics

Antibiotics are most commonly misused for the following conditions—eye infections and pinkeye...respiratory infections... sinus infections...urinary-tract infections in older people...and wounds from skin surgery. Antibiotics should be prescribed only if the infection is bacterial...lasts longer than just a few days...or is accompanied by pain, burning and/or swelling.

Compilation from several medical organizations by *Consumer Reports on Health.*

Antibiotic Treats Skin Infections in One Dose!

Potentially dangerous skin and soft-tissue infections, including MRSA (*methicillin-resistant Staphylococcus aureus*), often require a week or more of twice-daily antibiotic infusions at a health-care facility. The new IV drug *oritavancin* (Orbactiv) is equally effective—but it is so fast-acting, potent and long-lasting that it needs to be given only once.

William Schaffner, MD, professor of preventive medicine and professor of medicine in infectious diseases at Vanderbilt University School of Medicine, Nashville. He is a board member and former president of the National Foundation for Infectious Diseases. *NFID.org*

TAKE NOTE...

Common OTC Meds with Scary Side Effects

In one recent finding, common over-the-counter (OTC) sinus medicines—including Tylenol Sinus, Sudafed PE Sinus, Benadryl Allergy Plus Sinus and Excedrin Sinus Headache—that have both *phenylephrine* and *acetaminophen* could cause high blood pressure, dizziness and tremors.

Reason: Acetaminophen increases the effects of phenylephrine.

Take one or the other but not both.

Jane C. Ballantyne, MD, professor (retired) of anesthesiology and pain medicine, University of Washington, Seattle.

Dangerous Painkiller Gets FDA Approval

G. Caleb Alexander, MD, MS, codirector of the Johns Hopkins Center for Drug Safety and Effectiveness, Baltimore. He is a practicing general internist and pharmacoepidemiologist and an ad hoc member of the FDA Drug Safety and Risk Management Advisory Committee.

The US Food and Drug Administration (FDA) recently approved a new painkiller called Zohydro ER (*hydrocodone* extended-release), even though its own expert advisory committee voted 11 to two against it.

Zohydro ER is the first hydrocodone therapy without *acetaminophen* and thus has a lower risk for liver injury. But Zohydro ER and its fellow "opioid" painkillers are extremely addictive, even compared with other pain medications. Opioids caused more than 16,600 overdose deaths in the US in 2010—that's more than 75% of the total number of deaths from pharmaceutical drugs. In fact, it's more than 43% of all overdose deaths, including those from illegal drugs—and Zohydro ER is even more powerful than most of the previous opioids on the market.

Patients can build up a tolerance to opioids over time, diminishing the drugs' effectiveness. Some patients even develop *opioid-induced hyperalgesia*, a condition that causes opioids to increase pain rather than reduce it. And opioids can cause unpleasant side effects including constipation and drowsiness.

Opioids can be a painkilling option for a short-term problem, such as after the removal of wisdom teeth—and some patients have chronic and debilitating pain, making opioids a reasonable choice. But opioids should be prescribed only as a last resort.

Expired Drugs Are Still Good

Sharon Horesh Bergquist, MD, a physician with the Emory Clinic in Atlanta. She's assistant professor of medicine at Emory University, Atlanta. *EmoryHealthcare.org*

Do not throw away prescription and over-the-counter drugs just because they are past their expiration dates. These dates are not when the drugs will go bad—they are merely the dates beyond which the drugmakers no longer guarantee full potency. While there is a lot of variability among different drugs, drugmakers tend to be overly conservative with these potency guarantees because they don't want to go to the expense of testing drug longevity over longer periods.

A 20-year Food and Drug Administration (FDA) study found that 88% of the 122 medicines that were properly stored and tested still were perfectly fine a full year after their expiration dates, and the average expiration date could be extended by five-and-a-half years.

Expired drugs do not "spoil" as some expired foods do. There has not been a single confirmed case of an expired medication becoming toxic. The only potential risk from using an expired medication is that the drug might have lost some of its potency. A past-its-use-by-date pain medication might retain only 90% or 95% of its original potency, for example.

But using expired drugs is not worth the risk for lower potency when your life depends on the potency of the medication.

Examples: Replace your EpiPen when it reaches its expiration date if you have a potentially lethal allergy. Replace your nitroglycerine pills when they reach their expiration date if you have them for a serious heart condition.

Store medications in a cool, dry place out of direct sunlight. A bedroom drawer or kitchen cabinet can be a good spot (though not the kitchen cabinet above the stove). Do not store medications in the bathroom, where heat and humidity can reduce their useful life.

Medicine is especially likely to remain effective if it is in tablet or capsule form. Ointments, creams, liquid medications and any medications requiring refrigeration are significantly less likely to remain viable long after their expiration dates.

BETTER WAYS...

Before Going to the Hospital...

One in every 25 patients in the US gets an infection in the hospital. And of the 648,000 patients who develop an infection each year, 11% die as a result.

Before a hospital stay: Check your hospital's infection-control records at *Medicare.gov/hospitalcompare*, a Medicare website.

"Multistate Point-Prevalence Survey of Health Care–Associated Infections," a report from the Centers for Disease Control and Prevention, Atlanta, published in *The New England Journal of Medicine*.

Don't Let What Happened to Joan Rivers Happen to You: Safer Outpatient Surgery

David Sherer, MD, an anesthesiologist and former physician-director of risk management for a major HMO in the metropolitan Washington, DC, area. His research interests include the use of anesthesia in starting intravenous lines, the effects of obesity on health and health care, and the importance of patient autonomy for hospital and outpatient care. He is author, with Maryann Karinch, of *Dr. David Sherer's Hospital Survival Guide* and *The House of Black and White*, a memoir of growing up in a medical family. *DrDavidSherer.com*

Ever since Joan Rivers died after a routine surgical procedure at an outpatient center in Manhattan, people have been wondering if they're better off having surgery in a hospital.

The reality is that the vast majority of outpatient procedures go off without a hitch. But you can reduce your risk by getting involved before the procedure. *Important steps...*

CHECK YOUR PHYSICAL STATUS

Ask your doctor about your "physical status classification." The American Society of Anesthesiologists uses a numerical scale to assess a patient's surgical risks. Patients with higher *physical status* (PS) scores (four or five) because of health problems should have procedures done in hospitals because their risk for complications is higher.

Example: A patient who needs a knee replacement also might have poorly controlled diabetes, kidney insufficiency and nerve damage. His/her PS might be rated as four—too high to safely have a major procedure at an outpatient center.

In general, patients with PS scores of one through three—with one meaning generally healthy and three indicating that they have serious diseases that aren't life-threatening—are good candidates for outpatient procedures.

PICK YOUR SURGEON CAREFULLY

Don't assume that every surgeon in an outpatient center has the same experience—or the same credentials.

Suppose that you're planning to get Botox or Restylane injections. These are not as simple as most people think. For the best results—and the lowest risk for complications—you should have the procedure done by a physician who is board-certified in plastic and reconstructive surgery.

Caution: In many states, many procedures can be done by any physician who has undergone minimal training in these procedures, such as a weekend course or three-day seminar. These doctors might be board-certified in something but not necessarily in the field that concerns you.

Also important: The amount of experience. Studies have clearly shown that doctors who do a lot of procedures have better results, with fewer complications, than those who do them less often.

Example: If I were planning to have LASIK eye surgery, I wouldn't feel comfortable seeing a surgeon who had done the procedure 50 times. I would want someone whose total cases numbered in the hundreds or even thousands.

INSIST ON PAIN CONTROL

Most people assume that their surgeons will do everything possible to minimize postoperative pain. Not true. Some doctors are reluctant to order strong painkillers on an ongoing basis because they worry that the patient will become addicted. Or they mainly use narcotics (*opioids,* such as *codeine* and *morphine*) that dull pain but can cause unpleasant and sometimes dangerous side effects, including impaired breathing, constipation, itching, nausea and vomiting.

Poorly controlled pain is among the most serious postoperative complications. It impairs immunity and increases the risk for infection...slows healing times...and can increase the risk for blood clots when patients hurt too much to move normally.

My advice: Tell your surgeon that you're terrified of pain. Ask what he/she plans to use to relieve your pain—and emphasize that you would like to avoid narcotics if at all possible.

Also, ask about *bupivacaine* (Exparel), a nonnarcotic anesthetic that was recently approved by the Food and Drug Administration (FDA). The active ingredient is encapsulated in *liposomal* (fat-based) particles and slowly released over 72 hours. When injected into the surgical area, it relieves pain as effectively as narcotics with fewer side effects.

BEWARE OF SUPPLEMENTS

Tell your doctor about everything that you're taking. Surgeons and anesthesiologists routinely ask patients about medications that they're using. They don't always think to ask about supplements.

This is a dangerous oversight because many supplements—along with garden-variety over-the-counter medications such as aspirin—can interact with the drugs that are used during and after surgery.

Examples: Garlic supplements increase the risk for excessive bleeding, particularly when they are combined with aspirin. The herbs ephedra and kava can interfere with anesthetics.

Patients who are taking natural remedies—including vitamin E, echinacea, ginseng, valerian and St. John's wort—should ask their doctors if they need to quit taking them. You may need to stop two weeks or more before the procedure. Aspirin should be discontinued two to three days before.

PLAN FOR THE WORST

Even routine procedures sometimes go south. Most outpatient surgical centers are equipped with crash carts (used for cardiac emergencies) and other equipment and drugs for handling serious complications—but some don't have these on hand.

Ask the surgeon if a crash cart will be available. *Also ask...*

- **Is there *dantrolene* (Dantrium)?** It can reverse a rare but deadly complication from anesthesia known as *malignant hyperthermia.* The drug is always stocked in hospitals, but an outpatient center might not have it.

- **Is there *succinylcholine* (Anectine, Quelicin)?** It's a fast-acting paralytic agent that assists doctors in quickly intubating patients who can't breathe—one of the most dangerous complications of anesthesia. It has been reported that Joan Rivers might have lived if this drug had been available.

DON'T PUT UP WITH NAUSEA

It is estimated that 30% of all postsurgical patients will experience nausea, retching or vomiting. These are among the most common surgical complications.

My advice: Tell your anesthesiologist/surgeon if you've suffered from surgery-related nausea in the past. He/she can administer *granisetron* (Kytril) or *ondansetron* (Zofran), which helps prevent nausea in most patients.

GET MOVING

Try to get moving as soon as you can. Surgeons used to recommend lengthy bed rest for postsurgical patients. They now know that it's better to move around as soon as possible to prevent constipation, urinary retention and muscle weakness, among other common postsurgical complications.

As soon as you're able, get up and walk (with your doctor's permission, of course). If you can't stand right away, at least move in bed. Stretch your legs. Move your arms. Roll over, sit up, etc. Any kind of physical movement increases blood flow and improves recovery times. It also improves the movement of your lungs, which can help prevent postsurgical pneumonia.

EASY-TO-DO...

Drug-Free Ways to Reduce Nausea After Surgery

Nausea is a common problem after surgery. *Here are some natural ways to relieve it...*

Stimulate the P6 acupoint on the wrist—located three finger widths up from the inside of the wrist joint...use aromatherapy—try essential oil of ginger or the nonprescription product QueaseEASE, an aromatherapy mixture formulated to calm nausea associated with surgery and anesthesia...or try mind-body therapies, such as guided imagery through meditation and deep breathing.

HealthLetter. MayoClinic.com

"You Need to Go to an ER!"

Rebecca Shannonhouse, editor, *Bottom Line/Health*, 281 Tresser Blvd., Stamford, Connecticut 06901. *BottomLineHealth.com*

What if you're convinced that someone needs to go to the ER, but that person refuses to go?

Personal story: A neighbor suddenly got a severe headache. His wife begged him to go to the ER, but he resisted for several minutes—and died a few days later of a brain hemorrhage. Getting to the ER quickly might not have saved him, but it certainly couldn't have hurt.

You can't make someone go to the ER. Even if you could, doctors can't force treatment if the person doesn't want it. So how can you persuade someone to go to an ER? Learn the warning signs of an emergency—and tell the person that you know something is wrong, says Bill Benda, MD, an emergency physician in Big Sur, California.

Red flags: Shortness of breath...any sudden or severe pain...sudden dizziness or weakness...and suicidal feelings. For other warning signs, go to *NLM.NIH.gov* and search "Recognizing Medical Emergencies."

Additional advice...

- **Stay calm.** Becoming frantic will only make things worse.
- **Appeal to the person's emotions.** You might say something like, "Your grandkids really need you, so please get checked out."
- **Call the ER at the nearest hospital**—or your family doctor—and describe the symptoms. Ask if the problem can be handled at an urgent-care center. If not, let the sick person know.

Last resort: Call an ambulance. Paramedics will take reluctant patients to the ER if it's clear that they're incapable of making sound decisions.

Fast Fixes for Common Conditions

What a Top Naturopath Has in His Own Medicine Cabinet for Common Problems

Sometimes you really do need a powerful, fast-acting medication. But prescription and over-the-counter drugs alike can present serious risks. It is estimated that more than 2 million adverse drug reactions occur in the US every year and are responsible for more than 100,000 deaths annually.

I strongly recommend and use natural remedies. They contain lower doses of chemically active agents. They're less likely than drugs to cause dangerous side effects. And they often work just as well, sometimes better. All are available at health-food stores and online.

Important: Always check first with your physician before taking any new medication or supplement.

LESS JOINT PAIN

Aspirin and related painkillers often irritate the stomach and increase the risk for ulcers. Natural analgesics are much gentler and just as effective.

- **Boswellia,** a tree found in India, Africa and the Middle East, has a milky resin that inhibits the body's production of inflammatory molecules. A study that looked at patients with osteoarthritis of the knee found that boswellia extract relieved pain and stiffness as effectively as the drug *valdecoxib* (Bextra), which has been withdrawn from the market

Mark Stengler, NMD, a naturopathic medical doctor and founder of Stengler Center for Integrative Medicine, Encinitas, California. He has served on a medical advisory committee for the Yale University Complementary Medicine Outcomes Research Project and has been an associate clinical professor at the National College of Naturopathic Medicine in Portland, Oregon. He is coauthor of *The Natural Physician's Healing Therapies*.

because of side effects. A small percentage of boswellia users experience digestive upset. If that happens, reduce the amount. If you don't start to feel better within 48 hours, stop taking it. If you are taking it for chronic pain, give it two weeks.

Dose: 750 milligrams (mg), two to three times daily during flare-ups.

• **Curcumin** is the active ingredient found in the spice turmeric. In a study, rheumatoid arthritis patients reported that it helped relieve morning pain and stiffness.

Caution: Taking curcumin with blood thinners can increase the risk for bleeding.

Dose: 500 mg, three times daily. You can take it every day to keep pain and inflammation down or just take it during flare-ups.

LESS STRESS AND ANXIETY

Chamomile tea is a gentle relaxant that has traditionally been used as a "nerve tonic." Other herbs have similar effects. *One of my favorites...*

• **Passionflower.** Despite the name, passionflower is more relaxing than arousing. It increases brain levels of *gamma-aminobutyric acid* (GABA), a neurotransmitter that dampens activity in the part of the brain that controls emotions, making you feel more relaxed. In one study, participants drank either passionflower tea or a placebo tea before going to bed. Those who drank passionflower tea slept better and were more likely to wake up feeling refreshed and alert.

How to use it: Steep one teaspoon of dried passionflower in three ounces of just-boiled water. Drink it two to three times daily when you're stressed. Or take passionflower capsules or tinctures, following the label directions.

MIGRAINE RELIEF

There are many drugs for treating migraines, but they're rife with side effects—and may increase the risk for liver damage or even a heart attack.

• **Butterbur,** a member of the daisy family, is an effective alternative. It contains two potent anti-inflammatory compounds, *petasin* and *isopetasin,* which may help blood vessels in the brain dilate and contract more normally.

A study published in *Neurology* found that people who used butterbur had a 48% reduction in the frequency of migraines. You also can use butterbur to reduce migraine intensity.

Dose: For prevention, take 50 mg of Petadolex (a butterbur extract) three times daily, with meals, for one month. Then reduce the dose to twice daily. For treating a migraine, take 50 mg three times daily until the migraine is gone.

EASE MUSCLE SORENESS

For an aching back or sore arms, apply an ice pack or a heating pad...or alternate cold and warmth. *Also helpful...*

• **Arnica** is a plant in the daisy family that reduces muscle soreness and swelling. It also helps bruises heal more quickly.

A recent study from the Australian Institute of Sport in Canberra, Australia, published in *European Journal of Sport Science*, found that the topical application of arnica reduced the level of achiness for up to three days after a vigorous workout. The participants included men who ran in five bouts of eight-minute bursts on a treadmill, followed by two minutes of walking on a flat surface. They applied arnica gel or a placebo gel every four hours.

How to use it: Apply a small amount of cream or tincture to the sore areas. Repeat every hour as necessary. Don't apply if the skin is broken.

Helpful: If a large area is sore, you can take arnica orally instead. Take two pellets of a 30C potency three times daily for one to two days.

REDUCE HEARTBURN

I advise patients to start with all-natural approaches, including sleeping on their left side (sleeping on the right side makes heartburn worse)...avoiding "trigger" foods, such as onions and chocolate...and maintaining a healthy weight (excess weight makes stomach acid more likely to enter the esophagus and cause heartburn). *Also helpful...*

• **Melatonin,** a supplement that is often used for insomnia, also is effective for heartburn. A study published in *Journal of Pharmacology* found that melatonin reduces the amount of acid produced in the stomach without blocking it altogether. This is important because you need stomach acid for good digestion—you just don't want too much of it.

Dose: 3 mg to 6 mg, taken daily at bedtime.

INFLUENZA FIGHTERS

A healthy immune system is the best way to protect against flu. *Starting at the beginning of flu season (typically early October), take...*

- **Influenzinum,** a homeopathic remedy that I've recommended for more than 15 years. The makers of influenzinum reformulate it annually based on the flu viruses that are expected to predominate that year.

Dose: Three pellets (of a 9C potency) dissolved under the tongue, once a week for six weeks.

- **N-acetylcysteine (NAC),** an antioxidant, reduces both the chance that you will get the flu and the severity of symptoms if you do get sick. An Italian study found that only 25% of older people who were injected with flu virus after taking NAC for six months experienced flu symptoms, versus 79% who took a placebo.

Dose: 1,000 mg daily in tablet form for prevention during the flu months (typically October through April). If you get the flu, increase the dose to 4,000 mg daily until you recover.

Also helpful: 2,000 international units (IU) of vitamin D daily. During the peak flu months, increase the dose to 5,000 IU.

COLD RELIEF

Don't waste your money on often ineffective over-the-counter cold medicines. *Instead...*

- **Pelargonium sidoides,** a South African plant, has been tested in more than 20 clinical studies. It relieves congestion, sore throat and other cold symptoms. It is available in syrups, lozenges, capsules and tablets. Follow the dosing instructions on the label.

Pinch Here...Poke There: 17 Natural Remedies You Always Have with You

Joan Wilen and Lydia Wilen, health investigators based in New York City who have spent decades collecting "cures from the cupboard." They are authors of *Bottom Line's Treasury of Home Remedies & Natural Cures* and the free e-letter *Household Magic Daily Tips* at *HouseholdMagicDailyTips.com.*

Here are 17 quick fixes for common health problems that all have one thing in common—you always have these simple remedies with you!

- **Dry mouth.** When it's important for you to seem calm and sound confident, don't let your dry mouth get in the way. Gently chew on your tongue. Within about 30 seconds, you will manufacture all the saliva you need to end this uncomfortable condition. If people notice, they will just think that you're chewing gum or sucking a candy.

- **Burned fingertips.** If you get a minor burn on your fingertips, simply hold your earlobe—it's an acupressure point. Place your thumb on the back of the lobe and the burned fingertips on the front of the lobe. Stay that way for one minute. It works like magic to relieve the pain.

- **Hiccups.** *Here are two remedies...*
  - Pretend that your finger is a mustache. Place it under your nose, and press in hard for 30 seconds. That should do it, but if not...
  - Take a deep breath. Without letting any air out, swallow. Breathe in a little bit more, then swallow. Keep inhaling and swallowing until you absolutely can't inhale or swallow anymore. Then, in a controlled way, slowly exhale.

- **Motion sickness.** Pull out and pinch the skin in the middle of your inner wrist, about one inch from your palm. Keep pulling and pinching, alternating wrists, until you feel better. It shouldn't take too long.

- **Leg cramps.** The second you get a cramp in your leg, "acupinch" it away. Use your thumb and your index finger to pinch your *philtrum*—the skin between your nose and upper lip. Pinch it for about 20 seconds until the pain and the cramp disappear.

• **Stomachache.** This remedy came to us from an Asian massage therapist. If you are having stomach discomfort, massage the acupressure points at the sides of your knees, just below the kneecaps. This will relieve your stomachache.

• **Warts.** First thing each morning, dab some of your own spittle on the wart (but do not lick the wart). "First thing" means before you brush your teeth. We don't know why it works—it just does.

• **Hemorrhoids.** Edgar Cayce, who is often called the father of holistic medicine, recommended this exercise for the treatment of hemorrhoids...

• Stand with your feet about six inches apart, hands at sides.

• Then raise your hands up to the ceiling, and if balance isn't a problem for you, gradually rise up on your toes at the same time.

• Bend forward, and bring your hands as close to the floor as you can get them.

• Go back to the first position, and do it again. Perform this exercise for two or three minutes twice every day, one hour after breakfast and one hour after dinner, until your hemorrhoids are relieved.

• **Choking cough.** When you're not actually choking on something but you just are coughing as though you are, raise your hands as high as you can and the choking cough will stop.

• **Tension headache.** Tense all the muscles in your face, neck, jaw, scalp and shoulders. Hold that tension for at least 30 seconds. Then, suddenly, relax completely, letting go of all the tension, and your headache along with it.

• **Gas.** Try this yoga pose called the wind-relieving pose. Lie on your back with your legs and arms extended. As you exhale, draw both knees to your chest. Clasp your hands around them. While holding only your right knee with both hands, release your left leg and extend it along the floor. Hold this pose for one minute. Draw your left knee back in toward your chest, and clasp your hands around both knees again. Then while holding only your left knee, release your right leg and extend it along the floor. Hold this pose for up to a minute. Finally, draw both knees to your chest. Then with an exhalation, release and extend both legs.

• **Fatigue.** If you are having a hard time staying awake or paying attention, here are five energizing strategies. *Try the one that is doable in your situation...*

• Chinese theory is that "tiredness" collects on the insides of your elbows and the backs of your knees. Wake up your body by slap-slap-slapping those areas.

• Run in place for about two minutes.

• Energy lines directly connected to internal organs and body functions run through your earlobes. Use your thumbs and index fingers to rub your earlobes for about 15 seconds. This should wake up your entire nervous system.

• This visualization exercise will help you overcome drowsiness. Sit back, close your eyes, and let all the air out of your lungs. Imagine a bright blue-white energizing light entering and filling your entire body as you inhale slowly through your nostrils. Then open your eyes. You will feel refreshed.

• Boost your energy by belting out a few bars of a favorite cheerful song. Inhale deeply as you sing to bring more energizing oxygen into your lungs and increase circulation in your body.

Is It Really Sinusitis? Simple Self-Test Plus Remedies That Work

Murray Grossan, MD, an otolaryngologist and head-and-neck surgeon with the Tower Ear, Nose and Throat Clinic at Cedars-Sinai Medical Center in Los Angeles. He is author of *Free Yourself from Sinus and Allergy Problems Permanently. GrossanInstitute.com*

Don't assume that it's merely a bad cold when you're stuffed up and feeling lousy for more than the usual seven to 10 days. It could be something worse—and much harder to get rid of. It could be *sinusitis.*

Sinusitis is a condition where the nasal passages become inflamed and swollen. It's usually caused by a cold, but it could be triggered by allergies or a bacterial or fungal infection.

Here's how to tell if you have sinusitis and what to do about it if you do...

STEP 1: Make the diagnosis. Long-lasting congestion, accompanied by tenderness around the eyes, forehead and/or cheeks, is the hallmark of sinusitis. Mucus will probably be yellow or greenish rather than clear.

Sinusitis can persist for weeks, months or even years. Colds never last that long. Another hint is when you get sick. If your symptoms are predictable—they occur only in the spring or summer, for example, or when you eat certain foods—you might have sinusitis triggered by allergies.

Most people with sinusitis have slow-moving *cilia,* microscopic filaments in the respiratory tract that propel mucus out through the nose or down the back of the throat. After an allergy or a cold, the cilia slow down. Also, some people with certain conditions such as cystic fibrosis have chronic slow-moving cilia. Impaired mucus transport is what causes congestion, which can become a breeding ground for infection.

Step 2: **Irrigate the nasal cavities.** Irrigation is the best treatment for congestion-related conditions, including sinusitis, colds and allergies. It thins and flushes away mucus and helps the sinuses drain. It also washes out allergens and infection-causing bacteria.

Mix about one teaspoon of salt and one-half teaspoon of baking soda in two cups of warm *sterile* water or use store-bought saline solution, and pour it into a sterile squeeze bottle or sterile neti pot. (Or you could buy squeeze bottles already filled with saline or try a system I invented called the Hydro Pulse Nasal and Sinus Irrigation System, available online—it applies the low, steady pressure needed to create suction and pull out mucus.)

Keeping the head centered, put the solution into one nostril. Keep it flowing until the solution begins to flow out the other nostril. Gently blow your nose, then repeat on the other side.

Caution: If you're using a squeeze bottle, try to maintain steady pressure. A University of Pennsylvania study found that infected mucus can backflow into squeeze bottles and cause a reinfection.

STEP 3: Shrink the swelling. Much of the discomfort of sinusitis comes from swollen mucous membranes. To reduce swelling, apply moist heat to the sinus area. Soak a washcloth in warm-to-hot water, and drape it over the nose and cheeks. When it cools, resoak and reapply it several times a day.

Another way to reduce swelling and congestion is to lift the tip of your nose. It sounds (and looks) silly, but it works because a downward-dipping nose (common in older adults) can block the nasal openings. At night, loop a piece of one-half-inch-wide medical-grade tape under the end of the nose...pull the ends slightly upward...and stick them between the eyes. It will keep the nasal passages open while you sleep.

Also helpful: My Clear-ease natural fruit enzyme tablets. Follow the label directions. Fruit-based enzymes such as *bromelain* and *papain* reduce sinus swelling.

STEP 4: Clean your home. Pollens, molds and dust mites, along with plain old dust, can cause sinusitis.

You don't have to give your home the "white-glove treatment." But do wash bedding weekly in hot water to kill dust mites and their eggs. Also consider dust mite–proof mattress and pillow covers. Vacuum carpets once a week, preferably with a vacuum equipped with a HEPA filter. It's also a good idea to keep dogs and cats out of the bedroom to minimize nighttime exposure to dust and dander from their coats.

STEP 5: More vitamin C. Vitamin C can reduce the intensity and duration of coldlike symptoms, including congestion. It's a mild antihistamine that reduces mucus production and sinus swelling. When sinusitis flares, increase your dietary intake of vitamin C by eating plenty of salads, leafy green vegetables, citrus, etc.

Caution: Some fresh fruits such as strawberries contain high levels of natural histamines, but canned or cooked do not. If you

EASY-TO-DO...

Sweet Self-Test for Sinusitis

Open a package of saccharin, and put a few of the granules inside your nostrils. See how long it takes before you taste sweetness. If you taste the saccharin in about five minutes, you probably don't have sinusitis. If it takes 20 to 30 minutes, sinusitis is likely.

Murray Grossan, MD, Cedars-Sinai Medical Center, Los Angeles.

notice an increase in congestion and/or head pain after eating certain foods, avoid them until you're feeling better.

STEP 6: Use a decongestant. I don't recommend decongestants before trying drug-free treatments. But if you've had sinusitis for a few weeks or longer, your body's defenses are probably exhausted. Using a decongestant spray once or twice will provide relief and give your natural defenses a chance to catch up.

Any decongestant spray, tablet or liquid can help, but I like Patanase Nasal Spray. It's a prescription spray that quickly clears congestion and doesn't contain a corticosteroid. Menthol inhalers such as Vicks and Benzedrex also can provide relief.

STEP 7: De-stress. Doctors have known for a long time that emotional stress can dampen immunity and increase the risk for infection. It also tends to increase the incidence (and discomfort) of colds, allergies and sinusitis.

Stress creates a cycle known as anxiety reinforcement. The more stress you experience, the more likely you are to get sick—and the more you'll notice the discomfort.

My advice: Practice biofeedback. It's easy—and effective. Once or twice a day, sit in front of a mirror. Slowly inhale for a count of four, then exhale for a count of six. As you exhale, consciously relax the muscles in the face, jaw and shoulders. It's physiologically impossible to feel anxiety when your muscles are relaxed.

People who practice this technique soon learn that they can reduce stress-related symptoms at any time, not just when they're in front of the mirror.

WHEN TO SEE YOUR DOCTOR

By taking the steps in this article, you might be able to avoid a trip to the doctor's office, which could save you $100 or so. However, if you still have sinusitis symptoms after several weeks, do see your doctor. He/she may recommend other treatments including an antibiotic (usually *amoxicillin*) if you have a bacterial infection.

Hugs Fight Colds

In a recent study, more than 400 healthy adults were exposed to a cold virus and quarantined.

Finding: Those who reported getting the fewest hugs in their daily lives were more likely to suffer from severe cold symptoms. While greater conflict was also linked to a greater likelihood of infection for those getting few hugs, those who were hugged the most were protected from infection even when they had conflicts.

Theory: Hugs boost immunity by buffering stress.

Sheldon Cohen, PhD, director, Laboratory for the Study of Stress, Immunity and Disease, Carnegie Mellon University, Pittsburgh.

Sweet Drink Beats Lingering Cough

In a recent study, a warm honey-coffee drink relieved persistent coughing better than corticosteroids or cough syrups.

To make: Mix one-half teaspoon of instant coffee granules with two-and-a-half teaspoons of honey. Stir into seven ounces of warm water. Drink three servings a day.

Honey is a well-known remedy for cough, and caffeine dilates bronchi and stimulates breathing. If your cough hasn't eased after a few weeks of using this remedy, see your doctor.

Neda Raeessi, MD, researcher, Baqiyatallah University of Medical Sciences, Tehran, Iran.

Flu Prevention Smarts

Even though most flu germs are transmitted through airborne droplets when people sneeze, cough or talk, they also are transmitted if your fingers come in contact with the virus and you touch your eyes, nose or mouth. In fact, the flu virus can survive on your fingers for up to 30 minutes.

Self-defense: Wash your hands often with soap and water or use a hand sanitizer, and avoid touching your face.

Study by researchers at University Hospitals of Geneva, Kantonales Laboratorium, Basel, and Federal Office of Public Health, Bern, Switzerland, published in *Clinical Microbiology and Infection.*

Homemade Flu-Fighting Electrolyte Punch

Store-bought electrolyte drinks, such as Gatorade and Pedialyte, are full of artificial flavors. To fight dehydration, try this homemade recipe—blend in a blender two cups of filtered water...one-half cup of fresh orange juice...one-half cup of fresh lemon juice...one-eighth teaspoon of sea salt...and two to four tablespoons of organic raw honey.

Dr. Mark Stengler's Health Revelations on the web at *HealthRevelations.com.*

Shot-Free Allergy Relief

The FDA has recently approved Oralair, an under-the-tongue medicine, for people allergic to grass pollens. The first dose is taken at a doctor's office, in case of any adverse reaction. Then patients take one pill each day at home. Oralair does not relieve symptoms immediately—it needs time to build up, just as with allergy shots.

Dean Mitchell, MD, an allergist and immunologist in New York City and author of *Dr. Dean Mitchell's Allergy and Asthma Solution.*

More Allergy Help

The FDA has also approved a new prescription drug (Ragwitek) that helps build immunity to ragweed pollen and ease symptoms, such as sneezing and congestion. The tablet (made from ragweed extract) dissolves when placed under the tongue. Ragwitek is taken once a day, starting 12 weeks before ragweed season begins, typically mid-August (or later if you miss that timing). The drug is continued until the season ends.

Richard Firshein, DO, director, Firshein Center for Integrative Medicine, New York City.

Better Care for Allergies

Stress doesn't cause allergy attacks, but it can make them *worse*, a recent study reports.

Details: Among 179 allergy patients, those who had higher stress levels (as measured by daily online diaries) had more frequent flare-ups.

Why: Stress can disrupt the endocrine and immune systems, which could contribute to allergy episodes.

To reduce stress: Try positive thinking...eat right...get plenty of sleep...exercise regularly—and see a therapist, if necessary.

William Malarkey, MD, associate director, Institute for Behavioral Medicine Research, The Ohio State University, Columbus.

TAKE NOTE...

Most Coughs Last an Average of 18 Days

Most coughs are caused by viruses and are not relieved by antibiotics. But patients often believe that a cough should last no more than a week and ask their doctors for antibiotics. Even many doctors estimate that a cough is expected to last only seven to nine days.

Study of 493 people by researchers at University of Georgia College of Public Health, Athens, published in *Annals of Family Medicine.*

Take Control of Tension Headaches: Relieve Your Pain in Just Minutes a Day

Yacov Ezra, MD, assistant head of neurology at Soroka University Medical Center and a lecturer at Ben-Gurion University, both in Be'er Sheva, Israel. Dr. Ezra was formerly a senior neurologist at Hadassah University Medical Center in Jerusalem and served as chief neurologist for the Israel Defense Forces from 2001 to 2009, treating soldiers suffering from chronic pain with self-hypnosis techniques.

Taking a painkiller now and then may not be a problem if you have occasional tension headaches. But it's a different story if you frequently get that steady ache on both sides of your head—you probably know the feeling...it's a little like your head is being squeezed in a vise! With regular use, *nonsteroidal anti-inflammatory drugs* (NSAIDs) such as *ibuprofen* (Motrin) can lead to stomach problems and other side effects, while *acetaminophen* (Tylenol) can put the health of your liver at risk.

There is also the trap of getting "rebound" headaches—a common complication when a frequent headache sufferer overuses medication to fight the constant pain.

A missing link: In the quest to quell the pain of tension-type headaches, one crucial point often gets overlooked—up to 88% of these headaches are believed to be caused by stress. On top of that, nearly half of people who suffer from chronic tension-type headaches also have depression or anxiety disorders, which painkillers don't treat.

Many doctors prescribe *amitriptyline* (Elavil), a tricyclic antidepressant, to boost mood and help regulate pain signals. This drug helps some people with tension-type headaches, but it, like other medication, has its share of bothersome side effects—dizziness, drowsiness and dry mouth, to name just a few. What's the answer?

RESEARCH FINDS A BETTER SOLUTION

To test how tension-type headache sufferers would respond to a drug versus a nondrug approach, researchers gave 98 people with frequent or chronic tension-type headaches a choice of either using amitriptyline or trying "hypnotic-relaxation therapy," a technique that induces a deeply relaxed, focused state.

The results, published in the journal *Headache*, showed that the headache sufferers, who met with therapists to learn hypnotic relaxation, not only preferred this technique over the medication but also found it far more effective because it works as both a treatment and preventive. Specifically, after up to a year of follow-up, 74% of patients in the hypnotic-relaxation group had a 50% reduction in headache frequency, compared with 58% of patients in the amitriptyline group.

Even though this study did not include painkillers such as NSAIDs, researchers believe that hypnotic relaxation offers benefits over those medications, too. For example, with hypnotic relaxation, headache sufferers are not putting themselves at risk for the rebound headaches that so often occur with frequent use of painkilling medication.

So what does this research mean for the average sufferer of tension-type headaches? Anyone can use hypnotic relaxation. People with tension headaches who try the technique

TENSION ALERT...

Why So Many Headaches?

Up to 80% of Americans suffer from occasional tension-type headaches. About 3% struggle with these headaches almost daily. What's causing so many tension headaches?

While the reasons do vary depending on the individual, tension headaches are usually (but not always) due to tight muscles in the back of the neck and scalp. Fatigue, anxiety and emotional stress (including depression) commonly are linked to the muscle tension that can lead to these headaches.

Specific stressful situations that may trigger tension headaches include conflict at home... having too many responsibilities...dealing with a chronic illness...not getting sufficient sleep... and facing tight deadlines.

Yacov Ezra, MD, Soroka University Medical Center, Be'er Sheva, Israel.

are usually surprised by the simplicity of it. In fact, it takes just a few minutes to learn the progressive muscle relaxation and focused breathing exercises underlying the technique. *How to begin...**

- **Find a quiet, private space** that's distraction free. Turn off your cell phone.
- **Get comfortable on a chair or couch** (sitting or lying down).
- **Close your eyes and empty your mind of thoughts** (as much as possible). When intrusive thoughts return, simply acknowledge them and allow them to "drift away."
- **Breathe slowly and deeply,** visualizing tension leaving your body with each exhale. Imagine vitality entering your body with each inhale.
- **Progressively relax your body's major muscle groups,** beginning with your toes and then moving through the calves, thighs, hips, stomach, hands, arms, shoulders, neck, face and head. Stay in this relaxed state for a number of minutes, noticing the rising and falling of your chest. Now, imagine that you are at the top of a flight of 10 steps. Tell yourself that you are going to walk down the steps and count backward from 10 as you picture yourself descending each step. Feel yourself becoming more relaxed with each step.

How to create a hypnotic trance: Your next task is to self-induce a hypnotic trance using what is known as a "safe-place technique."

What to do: With your eyes closed and while breathing deeply, mentally take yourself to a place that feels calm and safe. This could be a quiet forest, a sunny beach or a serene mountaintop. What do you see, smell, hear and taste? How do you feel in this place? Engage all your senses. After a few minutes, begin repeating suggestions to yourself that reinforce a sense of well-being and lack of pain in your head.

These suggestions may include statements such as: *The muscles in my head and neck are completely relaxed...my head is completely pain-free.* The entire relaxation session takes only about 10 minutes. Ideally, headache sufferers should use hypnotic relaxation three times daily to guard against stressors that trigger tension-type headaches...it can also be used as soon as a headache starts to develop so the sufferer can quickly gain control over the pain. If pain medication is still needed, hypnotic relaxation will likely allow for a reduced dose.

*If you have difficulty with this technique, consult a trained hypnotherapist who is also a medical doctor or psychologist.

Do-It-Yourself Remedies for Dermatitis and Adult Acne

Valori Treloar, MD, a board-certified dermatologist and certified nutrition specialist of the American College of Nutrition. She is also founder and owner of Integrative Dermatology, a clinic in Newton, Massachusetts, that integrates conventional and alternative medicine, and coauthor of *The Clear Skin Diet: How to Defeat Acne and Enjoy Healthy Skin. IntegrativeDerm.com*

What is the main reason people visit their doctors? It is not heart disease, diabetes or arthritis. It's skin problems. But you can take steps on your own to control, improve and even reverse common skin conditions. *Here's how...*

Important: If you use self-care and don't see improvement within a month (or the problem worsens), see your dermatologist.

DERMATITIS (RED, ITCHY SKIN)

Dermatitis is the name for inflamed skin that can be red, itchy (sometimes severely) and swollen. There can be oozing, crusting and scaling.

The cause: Dryness and the microscopic cracks, tears and blisters that accompany it. That's why dermatitis is the main skin problem plaguing people age 50 and older. Older people produce smaller amounts of skin-lubricating oil (*sebum*).

But you can prevent, control and even reverse dermatitis by keeping your skin moist. *Here's what to do...*

- **Soak for 20 minutes.** Taking a 20-minute bath once a day helps moisturize skin, even on the face—the air above the water has high humidity. Get out of the tub when your fingertips start to prune, a sign that your skin has absorbed the maximum amount of moisture. A warm bath also reduces stress, a factor in just about every health problem, including skin problems.

Also helpful: Add a skin-soothing colloidal oatmeal product to your bathwater—such as Aveeno Eczema Therapy Bath Treatment with Colloidal Oatmeal. This can reduce the inflammation and strengthen your skin.

• **Limit the use of soap.** Soap is very drying (and it is not necessary for effective cleaning). I recommend using a nonsoap cleanser, such as Cetaphil Gentle Skin Cleanser or Eucerin Skin Calming Dry Skin Body Wash.

• **Apply a moisturizer immediately after bathing.** The moisturizer creates an evaporation barrier, helping to keep the water you absorbed in your skin.

• **Use a moisturizer that has ceramides.** The body produces a type of fat called ceramides that improves the "barrier function" of the skin—keeping moisture in and irritating factors out. Ceramides now are an ingredient in some moisturizers—and these products are among the most effective for preventing and reversing dermatitis. Some good products include Aveeo Eczema Therapy…Cetaphil Restoraderm…and CeraVe Moisturizing Lotion.

• **If necessary, use an over-the-counter 1% hydrocortisone cream.** Consider this option if your dermatitis is out of control and you are scratching like crazy, which further damages the skin, worsening the condition—leading to more itching, more scratching and more dermatitis. Dot the cream on the most irritated spots.

Red flag: Never use hydrocortisone cream on the same spot for more than one to two weeks. Extended use can thin and weaken skin.

• **Humidify your bedroom.** You spend one-third of your time there, so keeping it moist can help you tolerate dryness during the rest of the day. An ideal level of humidity is 40%. You can monitor it with a *hygrometer*, which you can buy for less than $20. I favor a steam vaporizer for humidifying—it is sterile, easy to clean and inexpensive.

• **Take vitamin D.** Among its many benefits, vitamin D helps skin cells stay healthy and reduces inflammation.

Recent research: A review study published in *Pediatric Dermatology* concluded that for people who are deficient in vitamin D, boosting the nutrient can reduce the severity of dermatitis.

Suggested dosage: 1,000 international units (IU) to 2,000 IU daily, particularly during the winter months when vitamin D–producing sun exposure may be limited.

ADULT ACNE

Women are the most common victims of adult acne, with one out of four women suffering from the problem in their 40s…and one out of seven having it in their 50s and beyond. Acne occurs when the hair follicles and ducts are plugged with oil (*sebum*) and dead skin cells, creating an environment in which bacteria can thrive.

There are countless drugs, cleansers and lotions available for treating acne. *But two simple dietary changes might prevent the problem in the first place…*

• **Try eliminating dairy products.** Many studies link dairy products with acne. Dairy

TAKE NOTE…

Secret to Youthful Skin

Exercise for youthful skin! At age 40, the top layer of skin, the *stratum corneum*, starts to thicken, making it appear drier, flakier and denser…and the second layer of skin, the *dermis*, begins to thin and lose elasticity.

Recent findings: People over age 40 who exercised regularly had thinner, healthier stratum corneums and thicker dermis layers.

And: After exercising consistently for three months, the skin of people over age 65 improved significantly—showing fewer wrinkles, crow's feet and sagging.

Study by researchers at McMaster University, Hamilton, Ontario, presented at the American Medical Society for Sports Medicine, Leawood, Kansas.

products naturally contain proteins, growth factors and hormones that may stimulate acne.

Try a simple experiment—cut all dairy except for butter out of your diet for two months. If the acne clears up, dairy was the likely cause. (It is always wise to check with your doctor before making any significant change in your diet.)

If you are worried that eliminating dairy from your diet may hurt your bones, I advise taking 400 milligrams (mg) of calcium...200 mg to 400 mg of magnesium...and 1,000 IU of vitamin D daily.

- **Stop eating a high-glycemic diet.** Studies also link a diet rich in refined carbohydrates such as sugar and white flour to acne. A high-glycemic diet boosts production of the hormone insulin, which increases inflammation and the production of sebum.

Recent research: A study published in *BMC Dermatology* compared 44 people who had acne to 44 people who did not—and those with acne had a "glycemic load" (amount of refined carbohydrates in the diet) that was 30% higher. They also ate far more ice cream and milk.

In another study, people with acne who went on a low-glycemic diet emphasizing vegetables and whole grains had significant improvements in their acne.

My advice: Eat low-glycemic meals that consist of half nonstarchy vegetables (such as greens), one-quarter protein (eggs, meat, fish, chicken) and one-quarter complex (not refined) carbohydrates. Other ways to balance insulin include regular exercise and sufficient sleep.

EASY-TO-DO...

Read the Fine Print Without Reading Glasses

To read tiny type, make a fist, leaving a small hole between your palm and your fingers. Bring your fist up to your eye, look through that small hole and focus on the fine print. The small channel of light entering your eye clears your vision.

Joan Wilen and Lydia Wilen, authors of *Bottom Line's Treasury of Home Remedies & Natural Cures* and the free e-letter at *HouseholdMagicDailyTips.com*.

A Tasty Natural Mouthwash

Using green tea as mouthwash was just as effective at reducing bad breath, dental plaque and oral bacteria as commercial products that contain *chlorhexidine gluconate* (the gold standard for plaque control), according to a recent study of volunteers who swished with either kind of mouthwash twice a day for a week.

Bonus: Those who used green tea said it tasted better than store-bought mouthwash.

Harjit Kaur, MDS, professor of periodontology, Guru Nanak Dev Dental College & Research Institute, Sunam, Punjab, India.

How to Stop an Annoying Eyelid Twitch

Samantha Brody, ND, LAc, a naturopathic physician, licensed acupuncturist and founder of the Evergreen Health Center, Portland, Oregon. *DrSamantha.com*

There can be many different reasons for eyelid twitches, and the way to get them to stop is to address the actual cause.

In some rare cases, an eyelid twitch could be a sign of an underlying condition, such as multiple sclerosis, Parkinson's disease or Sjögren's syndrome, an autoimmune disorder that causes dryness throughout the body and destroys tear glands.

It is also possible to get twitching from everyday dry eyes, pink eye or as a side effect from medication, such as antihistamines, some antidepressants and epilepsy drugs.

However, too much stress is the biggest cause of eyelid twitching. Coming up with a plan to address the factors contributing to stress is key. Some great stress-reducing tools include meditation, acupuncture and regular exercise. You may also need to get more sleep and/or cut down on alcohol and caffeine.

Magnesium citrate can help with eyelid twitches, too. I usually recommend a 150-milligram (mg) magnesium citrate supplement taken once or twice a day for two to four weeks. (Check first with your doctor if you have heart or kidney disease or take medication.) Magnesium will help relax muscles while you treat the underlying cause of the twitching. Magnesium deficiency itself can also lead to eyelid twitching.

Consult your doctor if the twitching persists.

Itchy Feet? Quick Help

Johanna S. Youner, DPM, a podiatric surgeon in private practice and an attending physician at New York–Presbyterian/Lower Manhattan Hospital, both in New York City. Dr. Youner is a board-certified foot surgeon and a Fellow of the American College of Foot and Ankle Surgeons. *HealthyFeetNY.com*

Pruritus (itching) of the feet can be extremely annoying for anyone who suffers from this problem.

It is associated with a number of different disorders. For example, it could be triggered by a simple infection, such as Athlete's foot, which is typically treated with over-the-counter (OTC) topical medication or, in more severe cases, an oral medication.

To find out what's going on, see a podiatrist. He/she can take a skin scraping to determine whether you have an infection or another skin condition such as severe foot dryness, allergies or contact dermatitis.

Once skin disorders have been ruled out, your regular doctor can then check for any underlying health problem that could be triggering severe itchiness. This may include a wide range of conditions such as liver disorders like *cholestasis* (a blockage of the flow of bile)...diabetes...lymphoma...*uremia* (an electrolyte and hormone imbalance that can develop as a result of kidney disease)...iron-deficiency anemia...and human immunodeficiency virus (HIV).

Once the underlying condition is identified, treatment will help ease the itchiness. Simple lifestyle changes, such as using a thick emollient or Benadryl cream, keeping showers brief and changing into clean socks twice a day, also can go a long way to help relieve the itching.

Fix Your Feet for Under $75

Johanna S. Youner, DPM, a podiatric surgeon in private practice and an attending physician at New York–Presbyterian/Lower Manhattan Hospital, both in New York City. Dr. Youner is a board-certified foot surgeon and a Fellow of the American College of Foot and Ankle Surgeons. *HealthyFeetNY.com*

Aching feet can be more than an annoyance. If you don't take proper care of your feet, it can throw off the alignment of your body, leading to knee, hip and back problems. Calluses can crack and turn into nasty infections. Athlete's foot can lead to thickened, painful toenails that make it difficult to even walk.

Good news: For less than $75, you can choose a handful of excellent over-the-counter (OTC) products that will relieve foot pain and keep your toenails and the skin on your feet healthy—without seeing a doctor.

Caution: If your foot pain is daily or doesn't improve with the products mentioned in this article, see a podiatrist for advice.

FOR BETTER SUPPORT

Even though shoes generally protect your feet from the surface you're walking on and from the weather, they don't always provide much support.

Fortunately, well-made, foam-padded insoles that go inside your shoes work like shock absorbers, alleviating pressure and stress on the foot. Insoles help restore balance, increase stability and reduce pain—not just in your feet but also in your knees, hips and back.

Important: If an insole does not feel comfortable in the shoe, then it's not right for you—these are not devices that are "broken in." *Before you buy expensive, custom-fit orthotics, consider trying these OTC insoles...*

• **Superfeet insoles** are now available in a variety of styles for men's and women's shoes. For example, Superfeet Delux Dress-fit insoles ($29.95,* *Zappos.com*) are slim enough to slip inside any women's shoe, but they work best in flats or shoes with heels up to one-and-a-half inches. The insole's structured cup under the heel adds shock absorption, and the support in the arch helps stabilize the foot. Superfeet Premium Blue insoles ($44.95 at *Zappos.com*), available for men and women, are designed for cleated athletic footwear and most types of casual and dress shoes.

• **Powerstep ProTech Full Length Orthotics** ($30 to $40, *Amazon.com*), also available for men and women, are especially helpful for pain in your arch or heel due, for example, to plantar fasciitis. If you have this condition, which causes inflammation of the tissue along the bottom of the feet, you'll likely benefit a lot by using these insoles.

Important: Insoles can be transferred from shoe to shoe (depending on the size of each one) but should be replaced yearly or more often if they no longer relieve pain.

TO FIGHT DRY SKIN AND CALLUSES

Dry skin can be a year-round problem for your feet. Also, corns (painful, bumpy thickenings that form on the skin) can develop on the tops and/or sides of your toes where they rub against your shoe.

Calluses (areas of dry, hard and thickened skin) can crack, especially when they are on the heel. If the cracks deepen, they can hurt, bleed and become infected.

To prevent dry skin and calluses on your feet, you need a moisturizing cream that contains a *keratolytic* (descaling) agent to strip away the layers of dead skin so the moisturizer can do its work. *To restore your feet's skin, try one of the following products with keratolytic agents...*

• **Gehwol Med Callus Cream** ($16.99 for 2.6 ounces, *Amazon.com*).

*Prices subject to change.

• **Kerasal One Step Exfoliating Moisturizer Foot Therapy** ($10.99 for one ounce, *CVS.com*).

Apply the cream after your shower, when the skin is softened a bit. Twelve to 24 hours later, rub the area gently with a pumice sponge, which is less damaging to use than a pumice stone. Be very gentle if you have cracks in your feet, especially if you've lost some of the feeling in your feet (due to neuropathy, for example). If you're using one of the moisturizing products and it stops working, switch to the other.

FOR FUNGAL INFECTIONS

These common infections—often due to athlete's foot, which can be contracted by walking barefoot in a public shower, for example—cause thickened, disfigured toenails that sometimes curl inward.

You'll need a doctor's prescription for antifungal cream, such as Ertaczo or Naftin...or maybe even oral medication, such as *terbinafine* (Lamisil). *To speed the recovery process and help prevent recurrences, try this nail cream...*

• **Kerasal Fungal Nail Renewal Treatment** ($27.49 for 0.33 ounce, *CVS.com*) contains acids and other ingredients that soften the nail, reduce its thickness and improve its appearance, usually within two weeks of nightly use.

How to Speed the Healing of Achilles Tendinitis

Johanna S. Youner, DPM, a podiatric surgeon in New York City. *HealthyFeetNY.com*

Achilles tendinitis, a painful inflammation of the tendon that runs from the lower calf to the heel, typically takes about two to three months to heal. Avoiding high-impact activities such as running will prevent further tissue damage. But, you can still stay active by doing low-impact exercise, such as walking, swimming and cycling.

"Contrast" baths increase blood flow to the area and help speed healing.

What to do: Once a day, immerse the sore area in warm water (use a bathtub or large basin) for five minutes, then cool water for five minutes. Repeat two or three times, ending with cool water. You can also do this with heating pads and ice packs. (People with diabetes should check first with their doctors, since their feet may be very sensitive to temperature changes.)

Supplements also can help heal a painful Achilles tendon.

I recommend choosing one from each of the following categories: Vitamin C, glucosamine or chondroitin sulfate to help build ligaments...fish oil, boswellia extract, devil's claw or quercetin to decrease inflammation...and the enzymes pancreatin, papain, bromelain or trypsin to relieve pain. Check with your doctor, since they could interact with medications. Follow label directions.

When You Can't Stop Burping...

Belching is your body's way of getting rid of too much air in your stomach, so you need to find out what could be causing the excess air.

Some well-known triggers: Eating or drinking too fast...talking while eating...chewing gum...sucking on hard candies...drinking with a straw...and drinking carbonated beverages.

Triggers you may be overlooking: Certain medical conditions, such as *gastroesophageal reflux disease* (GERD) or stomach inflammation, or even poorly fitting dentures, can cause burping, so consult your doctor if avoiding the more common triggers described above does not help.

Also, some people don't realize that they swallow air in response to stress. If you seem to be belching more after stressful situations, see a behavioral therapist who can help you develop techniques to reduce air swallowing.

Douglas Drossman, MD, codirector emeritus, University of North Carolina Center for Functional GI and Motility Disorders, Chapel Hill. *DrossmanGastroenterology.com*

Drug-Free Constipation Cure

Applying self-pressure to the *perineum* (the area between the anus and genitals) significantly decreased constipation for 72% of adults in a recent study. Patients also used traditional methods, such as increased fiber intake and stool softeners, but those who added this form of daily acupressure saw the most improvement.

How it works: Applying moderate pressure to the perineum for even a few seconds when you feel the urge to defecate can break up stools and relax the anal sphincter muscles.

Ryan Abbott, MD, visiting assistant professor of medicine, David Geffen School of Medicine, University of California, Los Angeles.

TAKE NOTE...

What to Do If You're Alone and Start Choking

If you start to choke and no one else is around, cough. If that doesn't work, look for a stationary object, such as the back of a chair, and push the area just above your navel against it several times. If a chair is not handy, make a fist and push in and up, just above your navel. The movement puts upward pressure on your diaphragm and, with enough force, can dislodge an object.

Also helpful: Dial 911. Most areas now have "911 ID" and can find you even if you can't talk.

Prevention. Prevention.com

How to Beat the Post-Lunch Slump

Jennifer Mielke, a certified holistic health coach at the Eleven Eleven Wellness Center in New York City. She is a graduate of the Institute for Integrative Nutrition and a certified yoga teacher who regularly works with patients seeking remedies for fatigue.

For most of us, afternoon fatigue sets in around 3 pm. You might want to down a large latte (or worse, a soda). But don't repeat a cycle of buzzing and crashing! *Use this 24-hour plan to ensure energy during the afternoon slowdown and all day long...*

Breakfast: Eat avocado at breakfast. It's rich in healthful fats, fiber and potassium, which will help energize you for hours to come. Blend it into a smoothie, or eat it with a drizzle of olive oil and tomato. If you don't like avocado, try soft-boiled eggs, which also are quick and energizing.

Midmorning: Catch up with a friendly coworker, or call a friend for a quick chat. Communicating with individuals you enjoy can be energizing. Also sneak in a revitalizing yoga stretch.

What to do: While sitting on the edge of your chair, extend your legs out straight with your heels touching the floor. Inhale and lengthen your spine. As you exhale, fold forward over your legs. In this position, take a few deep breaths. As you exhale, go deeper into the stretch. When you're ready, inhale and sit up.

Lunchtime: Take a 10-minute walk after lunch. This can lead to increased energy for up to two hours afterward, according to recent research. Or try an energizing yoga pose.

What to do: While standing, inhale and reach your arms and hands toward the sky. Exhale and then touch your toes. Take a few deep breaths, then come back up to a standing position. Repeat several times.

Avoid eating refined carbohydrates or sugar at lunch—these can cause blood sugar to spike, then crash, reducing energy.

Midafternoon: Splash cold water on your face. It can be invigorating!

Before bed: Set the stage for a restful night's sleep. Turn off all computer screens (your cell phone and TV, too!) an hour before bed. *Melatonin*, a hormone that induces sleep, is secreted in the dark. Screens can fool the body into thinking it's daytime, reducing melatonin.

Calming bedtime stretch: Lie on your back, and raise your legs up against a wall so your body forms a right angle. Breathe slowly and easily. Stay in this position for as long as is comfortable for you.

Gentle Ways to Get Better Sleep

Jamison Starbuck, ND, a naturopathic physician in family practice and a guest lecturer at the University of Montana, both in Missoula. She is also a past president of the American Association of Naturopathic Physicians and a contributing editor to *The Alternative Advisor: The Complete Guide to Natural Therapies and Alternative Treatments*.

When you're really wrestling with insomnia, it's tempting to go to your doctor and ask for one of the sleep medications we see advertised on TV—Ambien or Lunesta—or an older tranquilizing drug such as Valium. While short-term use of one of these drugs might make sense for a person who feels his/her overall health is being threatened by insomnia, I generally advise

BETTER WAYS...

Pill-Free Cure for Insomnia

Just before bed, try this acupressure trick. With your thumbs, press the soles of your feet where the heel and the arch meet. Lie on your back (on a carpeted floor is best), and bend your knees, using your right hand on your right foot and left hand on your left. Press as hard as you can for at least two minutes. You should feel the tension leaving your body.

Joan Wilen and Lydia Wilen, authors of *Bottom Line's Treasury of Home Remedies & Natural Cures* and the free e-letter at *HouseholdMagicDailyTips.com*.

against this approach. Sure, these drugs may temporarily allow you to sleep, but they don't cure insomnia. *My advice...*

• **Do some detective work.** Thinking about your own sleep issues and making some written notes can be a big help. When do you typically go to bed? How often do you have insomnia? Do you have trouble falling asleep or wake in the middle of the night? Also, look at when your problem started to determine whether it coincided with any health issues, use of new medications or habits, such as working late hours, that could lead to insomnia.

• **Get your doctor involved.** Discuss your notes with your doctor. Chronic pain, hormonal changes (including those related to hyperthyroidism and menopause) and serious illness, such as cancer and heart or lung disease, can cause insomnia. If any of these conditions is to blame, getting proper treatment may well take care of the insomnia, too.

After you've consulted your doctor, try these gentle methods...*

• **Avoid high-protein dinners.** Protein is often hard to digest. Eating a lot at dinner can lead to gastrointestinal distress that may result in insomnia. Instead, eat foods that are easy to digest (such as soup and salad) for dinner, and have larger, protein-rich meals midday.

Also helpful: Take a 2,000-milligram (mg) omega-3 supplement with your evening meal. When taken before bedtime, these healthful fats can have a calming effect on the brain, promoting sleep.

• **Try Calms Forté.** This homeopathic preparation is effective and extremely safe.

Typical dose: One tablet under the tongue at bedtime and whenever you wake up in the middle of the night (up to six tablets per 24-hour period). Calms Forté, made by Hylands, is available at natural groceries and pharmacies.

• **Add skullcap.** If the steps above don't give you relief, you may want to also try this potent herb to relax the "busy brain" experience that often keeps people awake. I recommend using skullcap in tincture form—30 to 60 drops (one-sixteenth to one-eighth teaspoon) in a cup of chamomile or spearmint tea at bedtime.

Note: Skullcap can make some people too sleepy. If you are sensitive to medication, try just 10 drops of skullcap at bedtime—or simply drink chamomile or mint tea as a sedative.

• **Use melatonin with care.** If you'd rather try this popular sleep aid, do so thoughtfully. *Melatonin* is a hormone. Taking too much can trigger irritability. Melatonin supplements may also raise women's estrogen levels, increasing overall inflammation in the body. I recommend taking no more than 3 mg of melatonin in a 24-hour period and often start my patients on a daily dose of only 1 mg. Take melatonin 30 minutes before bedtime.

*Check with your doctor before trying supplements, especially if you take medication and/or have a chronic medical condition.

Foods That Sabotage Sleep

Bonnie Taub-Dix, RDN, CDN, a registered dietitian and director and owner of BTD Nutrition Consultants, LLC, on Long Island and in New York City. She is author of *Read It Before You Eat It.* Follow her on Twitter *@eatsmartbd. BonnieTaubDix.com*

You know that an evening coffee can leave you tossing and turning in the wee hours. *But other foods hurt sleep, too...*

• **Premium ice cream.** Brace yourself for a restless night if you indulge in Häagen-Dazs or Ben & Jerry's late at night. The richness of these wonderful treats comes mainly from fat—16 grams (g) to 17 g of fat in half a cup of vanilla and who eats just half a cup?

Your body digests fat more slowly than it digests proteins or carbohydrates. When you eat a high-fat food within an hour or two of bedtime, your digestion will still be "active" when you lie down—and that can disturb sleep.

Also, the combination of stomach acid, stomach contractions and a horizontal position increases the risk for reflux, the upsurge of digestive juices into the esophagus that causes heartburn—which can disturb sleep.

• **Chocolate.** Some types of chocolate can jolt you awake almost as much as a cup of coffee. Dark chocolate, in particular, has shocking amounts of caffeine.

Example: Half a bar of Dagoba Eclipse Extra Dark has 41 milligrams (mg) of caffeine, similar to what you'd get in a shot of mild espresso.

Chocolate also contains *theobromine*, another stimulant, which is never a good choice near bedtime.

• **Beans.** Beans are one of the healthiest foods. But a helping or two of beans—or broccoli, cauliflower, cabbage or other gas-producing foods—close to bedtime can make your night, well, a little noisier than usual. No one sleeps well when suffering from gas pains. You can reduce the "back-talk" by drinking a mug of chamomile or peppermint tea at bedtime. They're *carminative* herbs that aid digestion and help prevent gas.

• **Spicy foods.** Spicy foods will temporarily speed up your metabolism. They are associated with taking longer to fall asleep and with more time spent awake at night. This may be caused by the *capsaicin* found in chile peppers, which affects body temperature and disrupts sleep. Also, in some people, spicy foods lead to sleep-disturbing gas, stomach cramps and heartburn.

FOODS THAT HELP YOU SLEEP

Carbohydrate-based meals increase blood levels of *tryptophan*, used by the body to manufacture *serotonin*, a "calming" neurotransmitter. *Also helpful...*

• **Warm milk.** It's not a myth—warm milk at bedtime really will help you get to sleep. It settles the stomach, and the ritual of drinking it can help you calm down and fall asleep more easily.

• **Cherry juice.** A study published in *Journal of Medicinal Food* found that people who drank eight ounces of tart cherry juice in the morning and eight at night for two weeks had about 17 minutes less awake time during the night than when they drank a non-cherry juice. Tart cherries are high in *melatonin*, a hormone that regulates the body's sleep-wake cycles. The brand used in the study was Cheribundi.

Helpful: Tart cherry juice has 140 calories in eight ounces, so you may want to cut back on calories elsewhere.

FDA OKs Sleeping Pill

Suvorexant (Belsomra), recently approved by the FDA, is the first drug to treat insomnia by altering the action of brain chemicals called *orexins*, which regulate the sleep-wake cycle. The new drug may be an alternative to sedative-hypnotic sleeping pills, which can be addictive. It is available in 5-milligram (mg), 10-mg, 15-mg and 20-mg doses, and the lowest effective dose should be taken within 30 minutes of bedtime.

Caution: People taking suvorexant should avoid driving the next day, since it can impair alertness.

David Rapoport, MD, director, Sleep Medicine Program, New York University School of Medicine, New York City.

Better Bedtime Reading

Adult volunteers who used electronic readers or tablets, such as iPads, for four hours before bedtime had a harder time falling asleep...got less rapid eye movement (or REM) sleep...and felt less alert and rested the next morning than when they spent the same amount of time reading a printed book.

Why: Tablets emit blue light directly into the reader's eyes, which can suppress the sleep hormone *melatonin* and disrupt the *circadian* clock.

Anne-Marie Chang, PhD, associate neuroscientist, Division of Sleep and Circadian Disorders, Brigham and Women's Hospital, Boston.

Summer Self-Defense: Stay Cool and Beat Bug Bites

Jamison Starbuck, ND, a naturopathic physician in family practice and a guest lecturer at the University of Montana, both in Missoula. She is also a past president of the American Association of Naturopathic Physicians and a contributing editor to *The Alternative Advisor: The Complete Guide to Natural Therapies and Alternative Treatments.*

Summer is meant for having fun, so there's no reason to let the usual hot-weather culprits interfere with your good times. Fortunately, the most common summer complaints are easily prevented or, if need be, treated with proper nutrition and natural medicine. *My favorite summer regimens...*

• **Use food to stay cool.** When the temperature climbs above 80°F, you must stay well hydrated to avoid *heat exhaustion*, a condition that can occur when you sweat profusely for too long, leading to fatigue, weakness and a rapid pulse. If you think you're suffering from heat exhaustion, immediately stop what you're doing...get to a cooler location...and drink cool water. Otherwise, you're setting yourself up for a more serious condition—a *heat stroke*, which can be deadly.

My advice: Drink one-half ounce of water per pound of your body weight daily. Also, during hot weather, try to limit heavy proteins and starchy foods, such as corn or potatoes—these foods require more energy to digest and increase body heat. Instead, focus on foods that are very rich in electrolytes, easy to digest and watery—fresh fruit, especially watermelon, melon and kiwi, and green salad.

A great "cooling" food: The cold soup gazpacho. This tasty blend of tomato, cucumber, fresh peppers and spices, such as garlic and parsley, is rich in electrolytes and helps with hydration. Mix the ingredients in a blender for one minute, and chill for at least one hour.

• **Fight bug bites naturally.** If you'd rather not use chemicals on your body to help guard against bugs, tweaking your diet during the summer can help reduce the frequency and severity of bites from insects such as mosquitoes, ants and flies.

My advice: Each day, consume minced garlic (one clove) and one-half teaspoon of brewer's yeast (try it in berry smoothies, on popcorn or in a vinaigrette dressing). Though research is mixed, some people find a B-1 (*thiamine*) supplement—100 milligrams (mg) daily—also helps. Check with your doctor first if you take any medications, since garlic, brewer's yeast and B-1 could interact with them.

If you do get bitten: Insects often carry bacteria that can enter your body via the bite, so clean the insect bite with mild soap and water. Then apply a tincture of *calendula*, which is an antiseptic, to the bite using a cotton ball. Reapply calendula four times daily until the bite is healed. See a doctor if you have a fever or the bite is red, tender and/or swollen.

• **Knock out food poisoning.** If you come down with food poisoning after a barbecue or picnic, the diarrhea and abdominal cramping can be brutal. For these symptoms, I usually prescribe peppermint tea, activated charcoal capsules (available at natural-food stores) and probiotics.

How to take the regimen: Every three waking hours, drink eight ounces of unsweetened mint tea (hot or cold) and take two activated charcoal capsules. Peppermint will reduce gas and cramping, while activated charcoal binds to the offending organisms, helping you to excrete them. To replenish your gut's healthy bacteria, take 1 billion to 2 billion colony-forming units (CFUs) of the probiotics *acidophilus* and *bifidus* four times daily. If symptoms from food poisoning last for more than 24 hours or include fever or severe pain, see your doctor. It could mean you have a potentially serious infection or dehydration, requiring more aggressive treatment.

Focus on Fitness & Diet

The Eat-What-You-Want Diet: It Really Takes Off the Pounds

Some people fast to "rest" the digestive tract, while others do so as part of a religious tradition. The last time you fasted may have been before a medical test, such as a colonoscopy.

But as a weight-loss technique, fasting has always been controversial. Its detractors claim that it shifts the body into a starvation mode that makes unwanted pounds even harder to drop.

What's gaining favor: More and more scientists are now studying fasting as a method for losing extra pounds and fighting disease. But does it work?

As one of the few scientists worldwide who has studied fasting in humans, I consider it to be the most effective—and healthful—method for most people to lose weight.* *How it works...*

THE SIMPLE FORMULA

With intermittent fasting, you eat a reduced number of calories every other day. Scientifically, this is called *alternate-day modified fasting.*

The principle is simple: Most people find it easier to stay on a diet in which they can eat whatever they want half of the time. In the eight clinical studies I have conducted involving about 600 people (including an ongoing three-year study funded by the National Institutes of Health), intermittent fasters typically have lost 1.5 to 3 pounds per week, depending on how much weight they had to lose.

*Check with your doctor before trying this diet—especially if you have diabetes. Fasting is not recommended for pregnant women.

Krista Varady, PhD, associate professor of kinesiology and nutrition at the University of Illinois at Chicago and the author or coauthor of 45 scientific papers that have been published in *Obesity, The American Journal of Clinical Nutrition* and many other leading medical journals. She is also coauthor of *The Every-Other-Day Diet.*

People lose weight by eating just 500 calories one day ("fast day") and all they want and anything they want the next day ("feast day")—alternating fast days with feast days until their weight-loss goal is reached. Goal weight is maintained by increasing calories on fast days to 1,000 three days a week and enjoying feast days the rest of the time.

WHY IT WORKS

Key points about using this method to lose weight...

• **Why 500 calories?** Animal studies showed that consuming 25% of the normal calorie intake on fast days produced the best results in preventing and reversing disease.

Translating this finding to people, I calculated 25% of daily recommended calories, which resulted in a general recommendation of 500 calories on fast day using foods with optimal nutrients.

Those 500 calories are consumed with one 400-calorie meal and a 100-calorie snack, since people tend to overeat if calories are broken up throughout the day. Lunch or dinner works best for the meal—if you eat your 400-calorie meal for breakfast, you'll be too hungry later in the day.

Example of a lunchtime meal: A turkey and avocado sandwich (two slices of turkey, one slice of Swiss cheese and one-quarter of an avocado on one slice of multigrain bread) and fruit (such as one-half cup of strawberries) for dessert.

Before or after your meal, you can have a snack such as a smoothie.

Tasty option: In a blender, mix one cup of unsweetened chocolate almond milk with one-half cup of unsweetened frozen cherries and one cup of ice.

• **Hunger disappears.** After two weeks of alternate-day modified fasting, hunger on fast day disappears for most people. During those two weeks, ease your fast-day hunger by drinking eight to 10 eight-ounce glasses of water and other no-cal beverages such as coffee and tea and chewing sugar-free gum. Some people reported mild constipation, weakness and irritability, which subsided after two weeks.

• **You won't overeat on feast day.** My studies show that people almost never overeat on feast day—on average, they consume 110% of their normal caloric intake. Over the two-day fast/feast cycle, that's an average of 67.5% of normal caloric intake—a perfect formula for safe, steady weight loss but without the nonstop deprivation of every-day dieting.

• **Add exercise—and lose twice as much weight.** Every-other-day fasters can exercise on fast day without feeling weak or lightheaded. Exercising before the fast-day meal is best because you'll feel hungry afterward—and can eat. *Good news:* People who go on an intermittent fast and exercise (45 minutes of brisk aerobic exercise, three times a week) will lose twice as much weight, on average, as people who only fast. You can exercise on both fast and feast days.

• **You won't lose muscle.** Five out of six conventional dieters who lose weight gain it all back. That's probably because the typical dieter loses 75% fat and 25% muscle—and never regains that calorie-burning muscle mass after the diet is over.

But people who lose weight using alternate-day modified fasting lose only about 1% muscle—a unique and remarkable result. And my one-year maintenance studies show that these alternate-day fasters maintain their weight. Longer-term studies are also needed.

AS A DISEASE-FIGHTER...

People who have followed alternate-day modified fasting not only lose weight but also improve their overall health. *In weight-loss studies of 600 people that lasted up to one year, average reductions in risk occurred for...*

• **Heart disease.** Total cholesterol dropped 21%...and LDL "bad" cholesterol dropped 20 points. Triglycerides fell from 125 milligrams per deciliter or mg/dL ("normal") to 88 mg/dL ("optimal").

• **Type 2 diabetes.** Glucose (blood sugar) levels dropped by up to 10% after eight weeks on the diet.

Animal studies have shown that intermittent fasting may help prevent...

• **Cancer.** The diet may also slow the growth of existing malignancies.

• **Cognitive decline.** Fasting intermittently helped protect the brains of mice genetically programmed to develop Alzheimer's...stopped the early development of nervous system problems in mice programmed to get Parkinson's... and helped animals recover from stroke.

Rapid Weight Loss OK

Rapid weight loss does not mean that you will regain pounds faster. Current guidelines recommend losing weight slowly to lower the chance of regaining it. But a recent study that followed participants for 144 weeks found that the speed of weight loss had no effect on the amount of weight that was regained. Both gradual-weight-loss and rapid-weight-loss participants regained similar amounts of weight.

Joseph Proietto, PhD, professor of medicine, University of Melbourne, Australia, and leader of a study of 200 overweight people, published in *The Lancet Diabetes & Endocrinology*.

Three Diet Pills That Work (They're Safe, Too)

Harry Preuss, MD, CNS, a professor in the departments of medicine and pathology at Georgetown University Medical Center, Washington, DC. He is a certified nutrition specialist and author or coauthor of more than 300 scientific papers on nutritional supplements and other topics, which have appeared in *Journal of the American College of Nutrition*, *Nutrition Journal* and many other leading medical journals. He is coauthor, with Bill Gottlieb, CHC, of *The Natural Fat-Loss Pharmacy: Drug-Free Remedies to Help You Safely Lose Weight, Shed Fat, Firm Up, and Feel Great.*

Despite what you may have heard, some diet pills can help you drop pounds safely. I've spent much of my career investigating nutritional supplements to aid weight loss. Here are three that I have found to be quite effective. Try one or all three, but always check with your doctor before taking any supplement.

TAKE NOTE...

Even Yo-Yo Dieting Can Be Good for You

People who repeatedly lose weight, then put it back on, still reduce their risk for heart disease. Losing 3% to 10% of body weight anytime keeps your heart and blood vessels healthier in the long run.

Study of more than 1,000 people by researchers at University of Glasgow, UK, published in *The Lancet Diabetes & Endocrinology*.

GARCINIA CAMBOGIA TO LOSE 10 MORE POUNDS

I started conducting scientific research on *garcinia cambogia* and its active ingredient *hydroxycitric acid* (HCA) in 2003 and wrote about it in my book *The Natural Fat-Loss Pharmacy* in 2007. But this weight-loss supplement didn't really become popular until 2012, when Dr. Oz touted it.

Garcinia cambogia is the botanical name for the Malabar tamarind, a variety of the tamarind fruit. (Tamarind, a delightfully sour spice popular in the cuisine of India, is derived from the dried rind of the fruit.) Scientific analysis of the Malabar tamarind in the 1960s and '70s showed that it is a rich source of HCA—a unique compound that lowers levels of *ATP-citrate lyase*, an enzyme that helps the body turn carbohydrates into fat. In other words, an extract of garcinia cambogia can help to reduce your body's production of fat.

Since that time, my research and the research of other scientists have confirmed that HCA can help people shed pounds. In one study designed to produce 100% compliance with the protocol, people taking HCA lost 12 pounds over two months, while those taking a placebo lost only three pounds. In a subsequent and similar study, HCA-takers lost 10 pounds, while placebo-takers lost 3.5. *What to look for...*

• **The right form.** HCA comes in two forms ("free" HCA, which is active in the body but tends to be unstable and to exhibit poor absorbability, and the more stable but inactive form, HCA "lactone"). Formulating active

HCA with certain minerals, such as potassium, magnesium and/or calcium, to create a "salt" makes the compound stable and improves absorption. The better HCA products are mixtures, such as potassium-magnesium or potassium-calcium HCA salts. For effectiveness, you also need a garcinia cambogia extract that is at least 50% HCA, with the maximum level being approximately 70%. This is why, when I have studied HCA, I mostly have used an active, stable form called HCA-SX (Super CitriMax, which includes both potassium and calcium and is 60% HCA). More recently, I studied a potassium-magnesium form of HCA with good outcomes.

Editor's note: The potassium-magnesium HCA salt that Dr. Preuss studied can be found in HCActive from Jarrow Formulas. The HCA-SX potassium-calcium HCA salt that he studied is an ingredient in several garcinia cambogia products, including those from Genesis Today, NutriGold, NutraCentials and Pure Health.

- **The right dose.** Studies show that the best single dose of the products currently on the market is 1,500 milligrams (mg)—less might not work.
- **The right time.** Take it three times a day, 30 to 60 minutes *before* breakfast, lunch and dinner, on an empty stomach. If you take HCA with food, it is poorly absorbed.
- **Realistic expectations.** The scale may not register any weight loss for two weeks or so because accumulation of water and glycogen (the form in which glucose is stored in the tissues) counteracts the fat weight loss.

Caution: People who are diabetic...taking a statin to lower cholesterol...or suffering from dementia should consult with their physician prior to taking this supplement.

CARBOHYDRATE BLOCKERS CUT CARBS WITH A PILL

If you're a typical American, a significant percentage of your calories are from refined carbohydrates such as sugar and white flour—calories that your body can easily store as fat. Cutting back on refined carbs is the best course of action, but that can be hard for some people because they are *addicted* to them. (Like other addictive substances, refined carbs stimulate the brain's pleasure centers.) To deal with carb overdosing, I recommend taking a *carbohydrate absorption blocker*, or *carb blocker*.

Made from an extract of white kidney beans (*Phaseolus vulgaris*), the supplement works by blocking the action of *alpha amylase*, a digestive enzyme secreted by the pancreas that breaks down carbs in the small intestine. Research shows that taking a carb blocker can cut carbohydrate absorption by 60% to 70%—in other words, taking a carb blocker and then eating two cups of pasta would be like eating only two-thirds of a cup.

There have been dozens of studies on carb blockers. In a study that I coauthored, dieters taking a carb blocker lost 6.5 pounds over one month, while those taking a placebo lost one pound. Carb blockers mainly work on starchy foods, such as bread, cake, cookies, chips, pasta, rice and potatoes. I personally reserve carb blockers for meals heavy in carbohydrates such as those at Italian restaurants.

Suggested dosage: The typical dosage is 1,000 mg per meal.

- **Time of intake.** Take it 15 minutes before a high-carbohydrate meal. If you don't like swallowing a large pill, you can open the capsule and sprinkle the (tasteless) carb blocker on your meal.
- **Best products.** Most of the studies on carb blockers and weight loss have been conducted using *Phase 2 carbohydrate inhibitor* from Pharmachem. (The FDA has approved this claim for Phase 2: "May assist in weight control when used in conjunction with a sensible diet and exercise program.")

Supplements with Phase 2 include: Carb-Intercept with Phase 2 from Natrol...Phase 2 Carb Controller from Swanson...and Phase 2 Starch Neutralizer from Now.

Carb blockers can cause gastrointestinal cramps and gas, but this is rare.

CHROMIUM FOR WEIGHT MAINTENANCE

When levels of this mineral are low, the hormone *insulin* does a poor job of moving blood sugar out of the bloodstream. Doctors reasoned that supplying the body with more chromium might burn up more blood sugar so that less is stored as fat. But many study results have been disappointing. In a recent review of 11 studies on chromium and weight loss published in *Obesity Reviews*, dieters who took chromium lost an average of only 1.2 pounds more than placebo-takers. So why am I recommending the nutrient?

Important scientific evidence: In 1999, I published a study in *Diabetes, Obesity and Metabolism* on 20 overweight women who were restricting calories and exercising regularly. For two months, the women took a placebo. In another two-month period, they took 600 micrograms (mcg) of chromium daily. They lost the same amount of weight on the supplement and the placebo. *But...*

When they took the placebo, they lost 92% of their weight as muscle and 8% as fat. When they took chromium, they lost 84% as fat and 16% as muscle. That is a *crucial* difference.

Pound for pound, muscle burns 60% more calories than fat. When you lose muscle during weight loss, you gain your weight back...as fat! And because you now have a fatter body, you're likely to gain back even more weight than you lost. That's exactly what happens to 90% of people who lose weight—they shed the pounds only to gain them back again (and then some). Chromium can help you not only firm your body during weight loss but also stop or at least reduce weight regain.

Suggested dosage: 200 mcg, three times a day, while dieting. After you've reached your weight-loss goal, switch to 200 mcg once a day. I have taken chromium daily for at least 15 years.

It is best to take chromium separately from meals and other supplements, which can interfere with its absorption.

Diet Pill Labels Are Misleading

A recent study by the FDA found that nine of 21 diet pill products marketed as all-natural contained *beta-methylphenethylamine*, an amphetamine-like compound that has not been tested on humans.

And: All the products' labels claimed that they included a natural ingredient called *Acacia rigidula* taken from a bushy plant in Texas and Mexico, but researchers could not find the substance in tests of the plant.

Study of 21 diet pills by scientists at the FDA, Washington, DC, published in *Journal of Pharmaceutical and Biomedical Analysis.*

Weight Loss: Men vs. Women

When it comes to weight loss, men and women are not created equal. Men have an easier time losing weight because they generally have less fat and more muscle, which burns more calories.

A recent study published in *British Journal of Nutrition* followed overweight men and women on a particular diet, such as Atkins or Weight Watchers. After two months, men had lost twice as much weight as women, but by six months, both had lost similar amounts.

Men and women can step up weight loss by making sure that strength training to build muscles is part of their exercise programs.

Barbara J. Rolls, PhD, chair of nutritional sciences, The Pennsylvania State University, University Park, and coauthor of *The Ultimate Volumetrics Diet.*

Free Weight-Loss Help

Medicare offers free weight-loss counseling, but fewer than 1% of Medicare's 50 million beneficiaries use it—even though 30% of seniors are obese and eligible for counseling.

Problem: Many of the most knowledgeable providers, such as weight-loss specialists, are not allowed to participate, because Medicare reimburses only primary-care providers, nurse practitioners and physician assistants working in doctors' offices.

Also: Medicare requires that counseling be given during a separate appointment, not when patients come in for other services.

For information, go to *Medicare.gov*.

Roundup of experts on senior obesity and Medicare requirements, reported at *MedPageToday.com*.

INTERESTING FINDING...

Most People Clean Their Plates

About 92% of adults eat *everything* that's on their plates.

Takeaway: Taking less food in the first place may help reduce calories.

Cornell University. *Cornell.edu*

New Abdominal Implant for Obesity

The Maestro Rechargeable System is a device implanted in the abdomen that sends intermittent electrical impulses to block nerve signals from the brain to the stomach, reducing hunger. In a yearlong trial, patients who received the impulses lost 8.5% more excess weight than similar patients who did not. The system is intended for people with a body mass index (BMI) of 35 to 45 and one or more obesity-related health conditions, such as type 2 diabetes. The potential adverse effects include nausea, heartburn, vomiting and complications from surgery.

Barry A. Franklin, PhD, director of preventive cardiology/cardiac rehabilitation, William Beaumont Hospital, Royal Oak, Michigan. His research includes weight management for overweight and obese individuals.

How Regular Sleep Habits Can Keep You Slim

People with the most consistent bedtimes and wake-up times had less body fat than those with the most erratic sleep habits. Sleep habits were considered to be consistent if bedtime and wake-up time varied by one hour or less.

Best amount of time to sleep: Six-and-a-half to eight-and-a-half hours a night.

Study of 330 students by researchers at Brigham Young University, Provo, Utah, published in *American Journal of Health Promotion*.

An Unusual Way to Halt Cravings

Tapping can suppress food cravings. In a recent study, 55 severely obese people were told to tap their foreheads and ears, tap a toe on the floor or stare at a blank wall. All the strategies temporarily reduced the intensity of food cravings, but the forehead tapping worked best. It blurred the mental image of the food and neutralized the craving by up to 10% more than the other exercises.

Study by researchers at Mount Sinai St. Luke's Hospital, New York City, presented at a recent conference on obesity in Boston.

Why Your Laptop May Be Making You Hungry

Smartphones, tablets and laptops make you eat more. These devices emit blue light, which can activate brain regions that regulate appetite and metabolism.

Recent finding: 15 minutes after exposure to blue light, study participants felt an increase in hunger that lasted for two hours.

Study by researchers at Northwestern University, Chicago, published in *Sleep* and presented at the 28th annual meeting of the Associated Professional Sleep Societies.

Action Movies Can Make You Fat

A recent study discovered that individuals who watched the action movie *The Island* consumed nearly two times as many snacks as people who watched the sedate *Charlie Rose* show.

JAMA: Internal Medicine.

Foods That Jump-Start Metabolism

Foods that boost metabolism and help you burn more calories...

Egg whites, which are rich in amino acids that stoke metabolism...lean meat, which contains iron (deficiencies in the mineral can slow metabolism)...cold water, which forces your body to use calories to warm up and keeps you hydrated...chili peppers, which contain the metabolism-boosting chemical capsaicin... caffeinated coffee...green tea, which contains a compound that promotes fat burning...and milk, which contains calcium that can help you metabolize fat more efficiently.

Roundup of experts in nutrition and fitness, reported in *Health.*

EASY-TO-DO...

Simple Trick to Lose Weight

To lose weight, get into daylight before noon.

Recent finding: People who spent 20 minutes outdoors in bright light in the morning had a lower body mass index (BMI) than people who got most of their light exposure later in the day.

Study of 54 people by researchers at Northwestern University Feinberg School of Medicine, Chicago, published in *PLOS ONE.* The influence of light on body weight was independent of physical activity level, caloric intake, sleep timing and age.

A Big Breakfast Spurs Weight Loss

Over a 12-week period, obese women who consumed most of their 1,400 allotted daily calories during breakfast lost an average of 17.8 pounds and three inches from their waists. Women who consumed most of their calories during dinner lost an average of 7.3 pounds and 1.4 inches from their waists. Breakfast eaters also showed better glucose control and decreased triglyceride levels.

Study of 93 obese women by researchers at Tel Aviv University, Wolfson Medical Center, Holong, Israel, and Hebrew University of Jerusalem, published in *Obesity.*

For a Healthier Lunch...

In a survey of nearly 6,000 adults, those who ate at least one sandwich daily got considerably more calories and sodium than those who didn't eat sandwiches.

Why: Typical sandwich ingredients, such as bread, cheese and processed meat, tend to be high in calories and sodium. For adults over age 50, one sandwich had about half of the daily recommended dietary allowance of sodium.

Better alternatives: Sandwiches made with healthier ingredients, such as fresh meat and vegetables...salad...fruit...or low-sodium tuna.

Rhonda Sebastian, MA, nutritionist, Beltsville Human Nutrition Research Center, Maryland.

Secret Weight-Loss Weapon

What if there were a food that had an incredible power to help you lose weight or avoid gaining weight? You'd try it, right? Well, a recent study shows exactly what that food is. It's beans and other legumes! To see exactly what benefits these nutrient-packed foods might have, researchers tracked adults who ate a daily serving (three-quarters cup) of beans, lentils, peas or chickpeas.

Result: They felt 31% fuller after meals than those who didn't eat legumes.

If you're trying to lose weight: Add legumes to your daily diet.

Cyril Kendall, PhD, nutrition researcher, University of Toronto, Canada.

Diet Soda? No Way!

Terry L. Davidson, PhD, obesity researcher at American University, Washington, DC.

A new "cure" for weight gain has been making recent headlines. Would you believe it's diet soda? The surprising announcement was based on a recent study in which half the people (weighing an average of 200 pounds) continued drinking their favorite diet sodas, while the other half drank water instead. All the participants were coached on successful weight-loss strategies. Twelve weeks later, those in the soda group had lost an average of 13 pounds, while the water group lost an average of nine pounds.

By the way, the research was paid for by the American Beverage Association. This industry-funded study, in particular, raised our eyebrows for a few reasons. First, it lasted only 12 weeks. There's no evidence that diet-soda drinkers are more successful in the long run than anyone else—in fact, some evidence suggests they do worse.

Other points not addressed...

- **Sweetness cravings.** The *non-nutritive sweeteners* (NNS) in diet sodas—such as *aspartame*—make people crave sweetness. Rather than get excess calories from soft drinks, you may be more likely to get them from, say, sugar in your coffee or more desserts.
- **Continued weight problems.** Researchers aren't certain, but there's some evidence that diet-soda drinkers may have more weight problems—and possibly more diabetes and heart disease—than those who drink other beverages.

How OJ Reduces Fat Burn

In a recent study, the rate at which participants' bodies burned fat fell by an average of 20% over the two hours after they drank orange juice.

Reason: The sugar in orange juice is a carbohydrate, and the body burns carbohydrates before it burns fat.

Best: If you drink orange juice with breakfast, give up other carbs, such as toast and cereal.

Study by researchers at Children's Hospital Oakland Research Institute, California, published in *Advances in Nutrition*.

Americans Are Making Healthier Food Choices

Fruit is now the second-most-popular food (after sandwiches) in the US—that is up from number five a decade ago. In 2003, the second-most-consumed food was carbonated soft drinks.

Harry Balzer, chief industry analyst, NPD Group, market research firm, reported in *USA Today*.

EASY-TO-DO...

Eat This at Lunch to Reduce Hunger for the Rest of the Day...

In a recent finding, overweight adults who added about one-half an avocado to their lunch reported feeling 23% more satisfied and had about 28% less desire to eat over the next five hours than people who did not eat avocado.

Study by researchers at Loma Linda University, Loma Linda, California, published in *Nutrition Journal*.

These Common Supplements Can Make You Hungry

People who took fish-based omega-3 capsules had a 20% increase in appetite—possibly because of changes in the body's level of *serotonin*, a hormone that affects appetite.

Self-defense: Add more fiber-rich foods to your diet to help counter the effect of extra hunger.

Heather R. Mangieri, RD, Academy of Nutrition and Dietetics, quoted in *Health*.

Are You Eating Too Healthfully?

Thomas M. Dunn, PhD, an associate professor in the department of psychology at University of Northern Colorado in Greeley.

Sometimes it seems as if everyone I know is on a special diet—gluten-free...dairy-free...sugar-free...vegetarian...vegan. This is good news, right?

Well, mental-health experts have recently noticed a disturbing trend—people are becoming obsessed with the perfect diet. There's even a name for the condition—*orthorexia nervosa*, which, roughly translated, means "correct eating."

At what point does the desire to eat healthier start to become an unhealthy obsession? *Some warning signs...*

- **You're often or always anxious about what you eat.** You feel shame when you don't live up to the ideal—after munching a single chip, for example.
- **Your list of "no" foods and ingredients keeps getting longer.**
- **Your social life suffers.** You think twice about going out with friends. You avoid events involving food or you bring your own.

If you think that you have orthorexia...

- **Understand that eating a "no" food now and then is OK.** Balance is what matters.
- **If you're at a restaurant or party where you think there's nothing to eat,** remind yourself that there's always a fallback position. Choose foods that you think are reasonably healthy even if they're not on your "A" list.
- **See a therapist who specializes in eating disorders.** To find a referral or support group, go to *NationalEatingDisorders.org*.

WORSE THAN OBESITY...

Physical Inactivity...

In a 12-year study of more than 330,000 people, those who didn't exercise and had a sedentary occupation were twice as likely to die prematurely from any cause as those who were obese.

Why: Physical activity benefits insulin sensitivity, glucose metabolism, blood pressure and cholesterol levels at any weight.

The good news: Just 20 minutes a day of moderate exercise, such as brisk walking, significantly cut death rates.

Ulf Ekelund, PhD, senior investigator scientist, University of Cambridge School of Clinical Medicine, UK.

Being Underweight...

In a recent study, adults with a body mass index (BMI) of less than 18.5 were 1.8 times more likely to die than those with a normal BMI (18.5 to 24.9). For people in the obese BMI range (30 or above), risk of dying was 1.2 times higher than for those with a normal BMI. The study did not include people with a chronic or terminal illness.

Takeaway: For good health, you need a reasonable amount of muscle mass and fat.

To check your BMI, log on to *NHLBI.NIH.gov* and search for "BMI Calculator."

Joel Ray, MD, associate professor, St. Michael's Hospital, Toronto, Canada.

You Can Exercise Less and Be Just as Healthy

Barry A. Franklin, PhD, director of preventive cardiology/cardiac rehabilitation at William Beaumont Hospital in Royal Oak, Michigan. He is a past president of the American Association of Cardiovascular and Pulmonary Rehabilitation and the American College of Sports Medicine. He is also coauthor, with Joseph C. Piscatella, of *109 Things You Can Do to Prevent, Halt & Reverse Heart Disease.*

Do you struggle to fit the recommended amount of exercise into your busy schedule? Well, what if we told you that the amount of exercise needed to reap health benefits might be less than you think? Maybe you could free up some of your workout time for other activities that are important to you and beneficial to your health—like playing with your kids or grandkids, volunteering for a favorite charity or cooking healthful meals.

THE LATEST IN EXERCISE RESEARCH

A recent study published in the *Journal of the American College of Cardiology* found that people lived longest when they ran, on average, for 30 minutes or more, five days a week. Surprisingly, that research also showed that people who jogged at an easy pace for as little as five to 10 minutes a day had virtually the same survival benefits as those who pushed themselves harder or longer.

Also surprising: A study recently done at Oregon State University found that one- and two-minute bouts of activity that add up to 30 minutes or more per day, such as pacing while talking on the telephone, doing housework or doing sit-ups during TV commercials, may reduce blood pressure and cholesterol and improve health as effectively as a structured exercise program.

HOW TO EXERCISE SMARTER, NOT HARDER

Here are four strategies to help you exercise more efficiently...

- **Recognize that some exercise is always better than none.** Even though exercise guidelines from the Centers for Disease Control and Prevention (CDC) call for at least 150 minutes of moderate exercise each week, you'll do well even at lower levels.

A Lancet study found that people who walked for just 15 minutes a day had a 14% reduction in death over an average of eight years. Good daily exercises include not only walking but working in the yard, swimming, riding a bike, etc.

If you're among the multitudes of Americans who have been sedentary in recent years, you'll actually gain the most. Simply making the transition from horrible fitness to below average can reduce your overall risk for premature death by 20% to 40%.

- **Go for a run instead of a walk.** The intensity, or associated energy cost, of running is greater than walking. Therefore, running (or walking up a grade or incline) is better for the heart than walking—and it's easier to work into a busy day because you can get equal benefits in less time.

For cardiovascular health, a five-minute run (5.5 mph to 8 mph) is equal to a 15-minute walk (2 mph to 3.5 mph)...and a 25-minute run equals a 105-minute walk.

A 2014 study of runners found that their risk of dying from heart disease was 45% lower than nonrunners over a 15-year follow-up. In fact, running can add, on average, three extra years to your life.

Caution: If you take running seriously, you still should limit your daily workouts to 60 minutes or less, no more than five days a week. (See the next page for the dangers of overdoing it.) People with heart symptoms or severely compromised heart function should avoid running. If you have joint problems, check with your doctor.

BETTER WAYS...

Hot Tip for Weight Loss

Animals given *capsaicin*—the substance that puts the "hot" in chili peppers—didn't gain weight, despite their high-fat diets. Capsaicin stimulates *thermogenesis,* the body's ability to burn calories. Research is under way in humans.

University of Wyoming. *UWYO.org*

• **Ease into running.** Don't launch into a running program until you're used to exercise. Make it progressive. Start by walking slowly—say, at about 2 mph. Gradually increase it to 3 mph...then to 3.5 mph, etc. After two or three months, if you are symptom-free during fast walking, you can start to run (slowly at first).

• **Aim for the "upper-middle."** I do not recommend high-intensity workouts for most adults. Strive to exercise at a level you would rate between "fairly light" and "somewhat hard."

How to tell: Check your breathing. It will be slightly labored when you're at a good level of exertion. Nevertheless, you should still be able to carry on a conversation.

Important: Get your doctor's OK before starting vigorous exercise—and don't ignore potential warning symptoms. It's normal to be somewhat winded or to have a little leg discomfort. However, you should never feel dizzy, experience chest pain or have extreme shortness of breath. If you have any of these symptoms, stop exercise immediately, and see your doctor before resuming activity.

TOO MUCH OF A GOOD THING?

Most individuals who run for more than an hour a day, five days a week, are in very good shape. Would they be healthier if they doubled the distance—or pushed themselves even harder? Not necessarily. *Risks linked to distance running include...*

• **Acute right-heart overload.** Researchers at William Beaumont Hospital who looked at distance runners before and immediately after marathon running found that they often had transient decreases in the pumping ability of the right ventricle and elevations of the same enzymes (such as *troponin*) that increase during a heart attack.

• **Atrial fibrillation.** People who exercise intensely for more than five hours a week may be more likely to develop *atrial fibrillation*, a heart-rhythm disturbance that can trigger a stroke.

• **Coronary plaque.** Despite their favorable coronary risk factor profiles, distance runners can have increased amounts of coronary artery calcium and plaque as compared with their less active counterparts.

Watch out: Many hard-core runners love marathons, triathlons and other competitive events. Be careful. The emotional rush from competition increases levels of *epinephrine* and other "stress" hormones. These hormones, combined with hard exertion, can transiently increase heart risks.

Of course, all this doesn't mean that you shouldn't enjoy a daily run...or a few long ones—just don't overdo it!

Get in Shape for *Free*

Charles B. Inlander, a consumer advocate and health-care consultant based in Fogelsville, Pennsylvania. He was founding president of the nonprofit People's Medical Society, a consumer advocacy organization credited with key improvements in the quality of US health care, and is author or coauthor of more than 20 consumer-health books.

Up until two years ago, my wife and I paid more than $900 in annual membership fees—year after year—to belong to a gym. Today, we go to the same gym and have a membership to more than 11,000 fitness centers across the country...without paying a dime out of pocket. That's because our Medicare supplemental health insurance carrier offers the SilverSneakers (*SilverSneakers.com*) fitness program as a bonus. But you don't have to be age 65 or older to access free fitness programs. Hundreds of health insurance companies (plans vary by state) offer similar no-charge fitness center memberships for any of their policyholders or through employer-sponsored plans. *Here's my advice on finding free fitness programs in your area...*

• **Just ask!** In order to get your business, or your employer's, most health insurers now offer fitness memberships and other services that are included in the regular monthly premium price. So call your insurer, or ask your employer, to find out if your insurer offers free fitness center memberships or other fitness options.

Insider tip: If you have a medical condition, such as diabetes, Parkinson's disease or arthritis, your insurer or employer may offer, or provide access to, free fitness programs that are aimed specifically at your condition. Ask when you call.

• **Look locally.** You may be surprised to learn that there are many free exercise and fitness programs right around the corner from you. Most community senior centers offer free classes. Churches often have exercise classes and fitness programs for their members and people in the neighborhood. If you belong to your local YMCA/YWCA, Jewish Community Center or similar organization, there are usually several fitness classes offered at no extra charge. Many community swimming pools, both indoor and outdoor, now offer free lap sessions for any resident or through what is now known as "Silver Splash" programs for older adults.

Insider tip: Don't forget about your community hospital. In many areas, hospitals now offer free fitness programs and fitness lectures focused on specific health-related topics, such as cancer recovery and prevention and cardiac rehab.

• **Get creative.** Of course, you can also set up your own fitness program at little or no cost. Walking is probably the easiest, most beneficial form of exercise to do economically. You can organize a walking group with friends or neighbors and use some great smartphone applications to create a fun exercise program that will keep you engaged.

What I use: *Runtastic* (available for iPhones and Android models) automatically logs in your miles, calories burned and more (check your phone's app store for fitness, walking, running or personal-trainer apps). Since many apps are free, you can try them out with little risk. There are also some excellent websites to help you set up a home workout program or walking regimen.

One of my favorites: Boston's Beth Israel Deaconess Medical Center has a comprehensive, consumer-friendly website to help you set up your own walking program (*BIDMC.org/walking*).

Tricks to Make Yourself Exercise: Simple Ways to Fall in Love with Physical Activity

Robert Hopper, PhD, a Santa Barbara–located exercise physiologist and author of *Stick with Exercise for a Lifetime: How to Enjoy Every Minute of It!*. Dr. Hopper attended The Ohio State University, where he won an NCAA swimming championship and set the American record for the 200-yard individual medley in 1965. He has served as the head water polo and swimming coach at Occidental College in Los Angeles (where he is a member of the Aquatics Hall of Fame) and has coached masters-level swimming. Follow Dr. Hopper on Twitter *@RobertHopperPhD*.

If you're like most people, those exercise resolutions you made at New Year's are just a distant memory. In fact, seven out of 10 Americans can't make exercise a habit, despite their best intentions. That's because the most common reasons for starting an exercise program—to lose weight in time for a reunion, for example—are weak long-term motivators.

But you can learn to motivate yourself to make exercise a regular part of your life. Elite athletes as well as everyday people who have made a successful commitment to lifelong fitness use these insider tips. *Here are their top secrets...*

• **Make your first experience positive.** The more fun and satisfaction you have while exercising, the more you'll want to pursue it and work even harder to develop your skills. Even if your first experience was negative, it's never too late to start fresh. Choose a sport you enjoy, and work to improve your skill level.

The key is finding a strong beginner-level coach who enjoys working with novices. For instance, the YMCA offers beginner swim lessons, and instructors are armed with strategies for teaching in a fun, nonintimidating way.

If your friends have a favorite dance class, play racquetball or practice karate, ask them for a referral to an approachable teacher. City recreation departments also often host beginner-level classes for a variety of indoor and outdoor activities. You might also try a private lesson. The confidence you gain will motivate you to try it out in a group setting next.

• **Focus on fun, not fitness.** Forcing yourself to hit the gym four times a week sounds like a chore, and you'll likely stop going before you have the chance to begin building your fitness level. But lawn bowling, dancing, Frisbee throwing, hiking, even table tennis—those all sound fun, and you'll still be getting physical activity that helps promote weight control...reduced risk for heart disease, diabetes and cancer...stronger bones...and improved mood. As you start to have more fun, you'll want to become more involved and your fitness level will improve over time.

No strategy is more crucial than this: Get hooked on the fun, and you'll get hooked on the activity for life.

• **Find your competitive streak.** We all have one, and you can tap into it, no matter what activity you choose. Jogging outside? Make it a game by spotting landmarks in the near distance, like trees or homes, and push yourself to pass them in a certain number of seconds. Swimming laps? Try to match the pace of the slightly faster swimmer in the next lane. Or keep track of the time it takes to swim 10 laps, and try to beat your time. Even riding the recumbent bicycle at the gym can be turned into a competition by moving your workout to the spin studio, where you can privately compete against other class members for pace or intensity.

• **Practice the art of the con.** If you've ever overheard a pair of weight lifters in the gym, you'll recognize this tip: The spotter encourages the lifter, "One more, just one more!" and then after the lifter completes one more lift, the spotter again urges, "Now one more!" Make this tip work for you by learning how to self-con. Let's say you're too tired to work out. Tell yourself, I'll just drive to the gym and park. If I'm still tired, I can leave. This is often enough to kick-start your workout. And while swimming laps, tell yourself you'll just do five, then two more, then just three more.

• **Cultivate a mind-set of continuous improvement.** Tennis great Jimmy Connors once shared what keeps athletes motivated—"Getting better." Lifelong exercisers have a yearning to improve that acts as both a motivator and a goal.

Help yourself get better by educating yourself about your sport. To do this, read books by and/or about professional athletes...read articles about them in magazines, newspapers and online...and even book a private lesson to have your running gait/golf swing/basketball shot analyzed.

Also, offer yourself rewards for hitting certain benchmarks. Treat yourself to a massage after your first three months of walking your dog nightly for 30 minutes...or book a trip to a luxury ski lodge to celebrate your first year of skiing. You earned it!

BETTER WAYS...

Combat Germs at the Gym

Enjoy working out at the gym but worry about germs on the equipment? Are you just being paranoid? No!

In a study in the *Clinical Journal of Sports Medicine*, cold viruses were found on 63% of equipment in fitness centers. And 80% of infectious diseases are transmitted by contact—either direct (such as kissing, coughing or sneezing) or indirect (for example, touching a contaminated surface, such as gym equipment, and then touching your eyes, nose, mouth or a wound, which are considered portals of entry for germs).

Always make sure to wash your hands with soap and water for at least 20 seconds before eating or drinking anything or before touching those portals of entry. If you're not near a sink, use a hand sanitizer that contains at least 60% alcohol.

Philip M. Tierno, PhD, clinical professor of microbiology and pathology, New York University School of Medicine, New York City.

Time to Give Yoga a Try!

I recently took up an exercise I didn't think I'd like. As a doctor, I have recommended yoga to patients many times, but I had resisted doing it myself. I thought a stiff old guy like me wouldn't have enough flexibility. My wife finally shamed me into trying it—and I was surprised to find that I liked it. I'll never be as flexible as some people in my yoga class, but I'm a lot more flexible than I was, which has helped me avoid injuries. Before I started doing yoga, I thought I would have to give up playing squash soon because of the risk for joint and muscle injuries. Now I can play without getting hurt.

David Borenstein, MD, clinical professor of medicine at The George Washington University Medical Center and a partner at Arthritis and Rheumatism Associates, both in Washington, DC. He is also author of *Heal Your Back. DrBHealth.org*

Why You Shouldn't Lift Weights Before Cardio

In a recent study, people who did upper-body exercises before cycling had a 35% decline in endurance.

Possible reason: Working the shoulders, arms, chest and back may also tire the legs as lactate and other fatigue-related substances move through the bloodstream.

Study by researchers at Nottingham Trent University, Nottingham, England, published in *Medicine & Science in Sports & Exercise.*

More Muscles, Less Risk for Premature Death

In a recent finding, people over age 55 with the lowest muscle mass had a 30% greater chance of premature death than people with the highest muscle mass. Muscle mass relative to someone's height is a better predictor of longevity than body mass index (BMI), which estimates body fat using weight and height.

To build muscle: Do a variety of strengthening exercises with dumbbells or resistance bands two to three times a week, for about 30 minutes each time.

Analysis of medical records of more than 3,500 people by researchers at the David Geffen School of Medicine at UCLA, reported in *The American Journal of Medicine.*

Better Way to Get Protein

Healthy adults whose protein intake was spread evenly throughout the day had 25% higher levels of muscle growth and repair than those who ate most of their daily protein with dinner—a typical eating pattern. The recommended dietary allowance (RDA) for protein is at least 46 grams (g) daily for women and 56 g for men. (If you have kidney disease, ask your doctor for advice on protein intake.)

Douglas Paddon-Jones, PhD, professor of nutrition, The University of Texas Medical Branch at Galveston.

Why You Can Skip the Cooldown

Cooldowns have long been advocated as a way to prevent muscle soreness, but a postworkout cooldown is not necessary.

A study found that exercisers who did a formal cooldown after a strenuous workout had the same amount or more muscle pain the next day as people who did not do a cooldown. The one benefit of a cooldown is that it prevents blood from pooling in the lower body and possibly causing dizziness, but to get that benefit, all that is needed is a few minutes of walking.

The New York Times. NYTimes.com

Natural News

4 Spices That Could Save Your Life

Certain spices have been touted as good for our health. For example, cinnamon helps to regulate blood sugar...ginger eases indigestion...and garlic can lower high blood pressure.

What most people don't realize: Several other commonly used spices are just as healthful (if not more so). *Below are four "secret" super-spices with healing powers...*

BLACK PEPPER

Black pepper is rich in *piperine*, the pungent compound that triggers a sneeze when it hits the nerve endings inside your nose. Hundreds of studies show that piperine also triggers healing—energizing and protecting nearly every organ and system in your body. *Two standout benefits...*

• **Cancer.** Cellular and animal research demonstrates that piperine helps fight cancer. In a test of 55 natural compounds, piperine scored number one in killing triple-negative breast cancer, the most virulent type. In another study, it killed aggressive HER2 breast cancer cells—and even stopped the deadly HER2 gene from activating. Other research shows that piperine can slow, stop or kill prostate, colorectal, lung, cervical, liver and stomach cancers. Piperine also slows *angiogenesis*, the growth of new blood vessels that feed tumors. It even enhances the effectiveness of radiation and chemotherapy.

• **Arthritis and gout.** Piperine is anti-inflammatory—and studies show that it can stop destructive inflammation in cartilage cells (loss

---

Bill Gottlieb, CHC, editor of *Healing Spices: How to Use 50 Everyday and Exotic Spices to Boost Health and Beat Disease*, founder and president of Good For You Health Coaching, former editor in chief of Rodale Books and Prevention Magazine Health Books and author of numerous health books that have sold more than 2 million copies. *BillGottliebHealth.com* of cartilage is the cause of osteoarthritis) and reduce inflammation associated with gout. It also reverses the symptoms of arthritis in lab animals.

How to use: For the highest level of piperine, buy whole black peppercorns and grind as needed. (Green and white peppercorns are not as rich in piperine, and once the peppercorn is ground, piperine begins to decrease.) Add freshly ground black pepper liberally and often—in cooking and at the table. Try to add freshly ground pepper at the end of cooking because the benefits break down the longer the spice is heated.

Also helpful: Studies show that just smelling black pepper (in the form of black pepper oil) can cut nicotine cravings in smokers and strengthen "postural stability" in older people (thereby helping to prevent falls). Put a drop of oil on a tissue, and inhale for two minutes, two to three times a day. Black pepper oil is available at *Amazon.com* and other online retailers.

OREGANO

Two major components of oregano—*thymol* and *carvacrol*—have been proven to have healing powers...

• **Heart disease and stroke.** In a study published in *Journal of International Medical Research,* people with high LDL (bad) cholesterol were divided into two groups—one group ingested oregano extract with every meal and one group didn't. Three months later, the oregano group had greater decreases in LDL, lower levels of *C-reactive protein* (a biomarker of artery-damaging inflammation) and greater increases in arterial blood flow.

In other studies, researchers found that oregano is more powerful than any other spice in stopping the oxidation of LDL—the breakdown of cholesterol by unstable molecules called free radicals that drives the formation of arterial plaque. Oregano also stops the activation of cytokines, components of the immune system that attack oxidized cholesterol, sparking the inflammation that worsens heart disease.

• **Infections.** Oregano is antimicrobial. It can kill the parasite *giardia* more effectively than *tinidazole*, a prescription antiparasitic drug. It decimates *Candida albicans*, a yeast that can multiply in the intestinal tract and trigger a range of health problems, such as arthritis and depression. And it can neutralize *Staphylococcus aureus*, a common hospital-acquired infection.

How to use: You can buy oregano fresh or dried. I recommend using the dried form because it concentrates the therapeutic compounds. It often is used in salad dressings, marinades, chili and in Italian and Greek dishes. For optimum benefits, try to use at least one teaspoon of dried oregano daily.

Also helpful: During the winter, consider using oregano oil in supplement form to prevent colds and flu. Follow the directions on the label.

BASIL

Basil is a traditional medicine in Ayurveda, the more than 5,000-year-old natural healing system from India, where it's used to treat diabetes, digestive disorders, skin problems and infections. The variety native to India is holy basil, and there are at least 30 more varieties worldwide. All of them contain basil's four main healing components—the antioxidants *orientin* and *vicenin* and the volatile oils *eugenol* and *apigenin*—that can help regulate blood sugar.

• **Type 2 diabetes.** In one study, people with type 2 diabetes who included more basil in their diets saw an average drop of 21 milligrams per deciliter (mg/dL) in fasting blood sugar and a 15.8 mg/dL drop in postmeal blood sugar. In a similar, smaller study, three people with type 2 diabetes had remarkable decreases in fasting blood sugar levels when they added basil to their diets three times a day for five weeks—from 250 to 110 mg/dL, from 200 to 80 mg/dL, and from 230 to 90 mg/dL (99.9 mg/dL and lower is normal...100 to 125.9 mg/dL is prediabetes...126 mg/dL and higher is diabetes).

How to use: Dried basil has a larger concentration of the health-giving volatile oils than fresh. I recommend one-quarter to one-half teaspoon daily. Use dried basil in full-flavored sauces. Fresh basil still is rich in health-giving compounds. An easy way to enjoy fresh basil is to toss a handful of leaves into your favorite hot pasta and dress with extra-virgin olive oil.

SAGE

The botanical name for sage—*Salvia officinalis*—comes from the Latin *salvare*, meaning "to save" or "to cure." *And sage lives up to its name...*

• **Memory problems.** One hour after people took a supplement of sage oil, they had better memory, more focused attention and more alertness, reported researchers in *Journal of Psychopharmacology*. In another study, people who smelled sage had a stronger memory and were in a better mood.

• **Anxiety.** In a study published in *Neuropsychopharmacology*, people who took a supplement of dried sage leaf were less anxious and felt calmer and more content than when they took a placebo.

Why it works: Sage may block the action of *cholinesterase*, an enzyme that destroys *acetylcholine*, a brain chemical that plays a role in memory, attention and alertness. Sage also might improve the functioning of *cholinergic receptors* on brain cells that receive acetylcholine.

How to use sage: Because of its robust flavor, sage is best used in hearty dishes such as pot roast, meat loaf and stuffing. It also goes well with squash, sweet potatoes and apples.

However: The amounts that improve mental and emotional functioning aren't easy to get with diet, so you may want to take a sage leaf supplement. I often recommend the herbal extract from Herb Pharm because it's made from the whole leaf that has been grown organically. Follow the directions on the label.

5 Weird Fruits with Amazing Health Benefits

Chris Kilham, an instructor of ethnobotany at University of Massachusetts, Amherst, and founder of Medicine Hunter, an enterprise that explores plant-based medicines, Leverett, Massachusetts. He is a regular contributor to *FoxNews.com*, where he also writes a weekly health column. He is author of *Kava: Medicine Hunting in Paradise. MedicineHunter.com*

Every time you read an article about "superfoods," experts always seem to trot out the same ones—such as blueberries, beans and leafy green vegetables. How much kale can one person eat?

If you crave something new and want to get the most nutritional bang for your buck, try these "weird" fruits. They often are available at natural-foods markets such as Whole Foods—and even at some "regular" supermarkets. These fruits may look a little strange—and the flavors definitely will be unfamiliar. But they have some remarkable health benefits—and you will discover some fascinating flavors that you never knew existed.

ARONIA

Even though it is native to the US, most people have never heard of aronia. Its nickname, chokeberry, suggests why it's more obscure than other berries. It's tart!

Don't let a little mouth-pucker put you off. The chokeberry has more antioxidant activity than any of the regular "superberries," including cranberries (see the next page), blueberries and strawberries. Research suggests that chokeberries may lower blood sugar and increase the body's production of insulin—helpful even for people who don't have diabetes because stabilizing blood sugar reduces the tendency for weight gain. Compounds in the berries have been linked to tumor inhibition, including tumors of the breast, colon and skin.

Chokeberries also are high in *catechins*, one of the high-powered substances in green tea. Catechins and related compounds have been shown to be very good for cardiovascular health, in part because they reduce arterial inflammation and the risk for clots.

The berries sometimes are available fresh but most often are frozen. Add them to yogurt or smoothies. If you wish, you can sweeten them with a touch of sugar, honey or agave nectar. The sugar offsets the tartness—it "opens up" the flavor and makes it more satisfying.

BURITI

This fruit is harvested from Amazonian palm trees that can tower more than 100 feet. Buriti can be peeled and eaten raw, although the firm flesh is somewhat similar to a sweet potato. It is tastier and softer when soaked in water and then put in a food processor or blender with a little water and sugar to make a creamy drink.

Buriti provides high levels of *carotenoids* that transform to vitamin A in the body, along with *tocopherols,* forms of vitamin E. Research has shown that people who get plenty of vitamin E from foods (not from supplements) tend to have lower rates of heart disease and some cancers.

DRAGON FRUIT

You might recoil the first time you see this exotic-looking fruit. It looks like a cross between a pomegranate and an iguana. Once you slice through the fleshy protrusions on the skin, you will see that the ugliness is on the surface. The flesh inside might be white, yellow or blue, freckled with generous amounts of what appear to be poppy seeds. It has a delicate taste that some compare to kiwifruit or some melons and can be eaten raw. Dragon fruit is a rich source of antioxidants, including catechins and *lycopene*. Lycopene is especially important for men because it reduces risk for prostate cancer.

GAC

Gac, which is native to Vietnam, is a mango-size fruit that has deep reddish-orange flesh. The color indicates very high levels of *beta-carotene*, the same potent antioxidant that you get from carrots—except that gac has about 10 times more. The *zeaxanthin* (another antioxidant) in gac has been linked to a reduced risk for macular degeneration, a serious eye disease. The fruit is loaded with lycopene, with about 70 times more than that in a tomato.

The flavor of the raw fruit has been compared to that of a slightly sweet cucumber. In Vietnam and other Asian countries, the pulp and seeds usually are cooked with a gelatinous form of rice and served during special events.

You can make the same dish with glutinous rice (available in Asian markets), gac fruit, coconut milk, sugar and a dash of red wine. For a recipe, search for "xoi gac" at *TheRavenousCouple.com.*

AÇAÍ BERRY

You may have heard of this one, but it is so good for you that it bears repeating. The most common form of açaí is the juice. But in Brazil, its home country, açaí (ah-sa-yee) is eaten fresh. The fruits are mashed to separate the seeds from the flesh. The mashed fruit is mixed with the Brazilian equivalent of granola, sweetened with a little sugar and served with banana slices.

Açaí is rich in *anthocyanins,* antioxidants that help reduce premature cell aging and may reduce the intestinal inflammation that goes along with inflammatory bowel disease. Anthocyanins are common in fruits with red and purple colors such as grapes and berries, but açaí has far more than any other food.

You might find fresh or frozen açaí berries in specialty stores, but if all you can find is the juice, look for one where açaí is the first ingredient on the label.

TAKE NOTE...

Not So Weird but Super-Good for You: Cranberries

Cranberries contain *proanthocyanidins* (PACs), compounds that help prevent infection-causing bacteria from adhering to tissues in the urinary tract, thereby helping to prevent infections in the urinary tract.

Men, take note: Cranberries can make life a little easier if you have *benign prostatic hyperplasia*, enlargement of the prostate gland that can make urination difficult—and way too frequent.

A study of men in their 60s found that those who were given a cranberry extract had improved urinary symptoms, including improvements in their flow rate. The men also had lower levels of *prostate-specific antigen* (PSA), an enzyme associated with prostate cancer.

Regarding drinking cranberry juice, I feel that there is not enough good data to support that the juice works for urinary tract problems or for prostate disorders. It's better to eat whole cranberries. Simmer the cranberries in a little water... add a little sugar to subdue the tartness...and continue cooking until the berries burst.

Chris Kilham, an instructor of ethnobotany at University of Massachusetts, Amherst.

Got This? Don't Eat That: Foods That Worsen Common Conditions

Michael T. Murray, ND, a naturopathic physician and leading authority on natural medicine. Dr. Murray serves on the Board of Regents of Bastyr University in Kenmore, Washington, and has written more than 30 books, including *The Encyclopedia of Natural Medicine* with coauthor Joseph Pizzorno, ND. *DoctorMurray.com*

Let's say you've got arthritis...heartburn... heart disease...or some other common health problem. You follow all your doctor's suggestions, but you still don't feel better. It could be that you're not getting the right medication or other treatment, but there's an even stronger possibility.

What often gets overlooked: Your diet. Far too many people sabotage their treatment—and actually make their health problems much worse—by consuming the wrong foods. Meanwhile, you could be helping yourself by eating certain foods that ease whatever is ailing you.

Common health problems that foods can worsen—or help...

ARTHRITIS

Both osteoarthritis and rheumatoid arthritis involve inflammation that causes joint pain and/or swelling.

What hurts: Refined carbohydrates (sugar, white bread, white rice and most pasta). They cause a spike in glucose (blood sugar) that leads to inflammation.

What helps: Raw, fresh ginger. It's a potent inhibitor of *prostaglandin* and *thromboxanes*, inflammatory compounds involved in arthritis. And unlike anti-inflammatory medications, ginger doesn't cause an upset stomach. Be sure to use fresh ginger—it's better than powdered because it contains higher levels of active ingredients. For pain relief, you need to eat only about 10 grams (g)—about a quarter-inch slice—of raw, fresh ginger a day.

Smart idea: You can add raw ginger to any fresh fruit or vegetable juice with the help of a juice extractor. Ginger mixes well with carrot, apple, pear or pineapple juice. You also can grate fresh ginger and add it to any hot tea.

CARDIAC ARRHYTHMIAS

Everyone notices occasional changes in the way the heart beats at certain times—during exercise, for example. But persistent irregularities could be a sign of *arrhythmias*, potentially dangerous problems with the heart's electrical system. The heart can skip beats or beat too slowly or too quickly—all of which can signal heart disease.

What hurts: Too much caffeine. Whether it's in coffee, tea or chocolate, caffeine stimulates the heart to beat more quickly, which triggers arrhythmias in some people.

What helps: Berries. All types of berries, including cherries, blackberries, raspberries and blueberries, are filled with *procyanidins*, plant pigments that reduce arrhythmias and improve blood flow through the coronary arteries. Aim for one cup of fresh berries daily (frozen are fine, too).

Also helpful: Concentrated extracts made from hawthorn. This herb contains the same heart-healthy compounds as berries. In Germany, it is commonly used to treat arrhythmias and congestive heart failure. If you have heart problems, a hawthorn extract containing 10% procyanidins (100 milligrams [mg] to 200 mg three times daily) is often recommended. Hawthorn can interact with heart medications and other drugs, so check with your doctor before trying it.

HEARTBURN

Also known as *gastroesophageal reflux disease* (GERD), heartburn is usually caused by the upward surge of digestive juices from the stomach into the esophagus. People who suffer from frequent heartburn can get *some* relief with lifestyle changes, such as not overeating and staying upright for a few hours after eating. But most people with heartburn don't pay enough attention to their diets.

What hurts: Alcohol and coffee are widely known to trigger heartburn. Many people, however, don't consider the effects of chocolate, fried foods and carbonated drinks, which also may weaken the *esophageal sphincter* (the muscle that prevents acids from entering the esophagus) or increase the *intra-abdominal* pressure that pushes acids upward.

What helps: Fresh (not bottled) lemon juice—two to four ounces daily in water, tea or apple or carrot juices. Lemon contains *D-limonene*, an oil-based compound that helps to prevent heartburn. Also, use the peel if you can. It's an especially good source of D-limonene.

EYE DISEASE

Age-related macular degeneration (AMD) is a leading cause of vision loss, but it (as well as cataracts) can often be prevented—or the effects minimized—by eating carefully.

What hurts: Animal fat and processed foods. A study of 261 adults with AMD found that people who ate a lot of these foods were twice as likely to have a worsening of their eye disease compared with those who ate less of the foods. Animal fat also increases risk for high cholesterol, which has been linked to increased risk for cataracts.

What helps: Cold-water fish. The omega-3 fatty acids in fish can help prevent AMD and cataracts—or, if you already have one of these conditions, help prevent it from getting worse. Try to eat three to four weekly servings of cold-water fish, such as salmon or sardines.

Also helpful: Tomatoes, watermelon and other red fruits and vegetables (such as red peppers) that are high in *lycopene*. Green vegetables are also protective. Foods such as spinach and kale are high in *lutein* and other plant pigments that concentrate in the retina to help prevent eye disease.

ROSACEA

Some 16 million Americans have *rosacea*, a chronic skin condition that causes bright-red facial flushing for at least 10 minutes per episode, along with bumps and pustules.

What hurts: Hot foods. "Hot" can mean *temperature* (a hot bowl of soup or a steaming cup of coffee or tea) or *spicy* (such as chili powder, cayenne or curry). Alcohol also tends to increase flushes.

What helps: If you have rosacea, ask your doctor to test you for *H. pylori*, the bacterium that causes most stomach ulcers and has been linked to rosacea. If you test positive, drink cabbage juice (eight to 12 ounces daily). It's not the tastiest juice, but it inhibits the growth of H. pylori. Make your own cabbage juice in a juicer (add some apples and/or carrots to improve the taste). If you have thyroid problems, check with your doctor—fresh cabbage may interfere with thyroid function.

If You Can't Eat Fish, Nuts, Soy, Dairy or Gluten—What to Eat for the Same Health Benefits

David Grotto, MS, RDN, founder and president of Nutrition Housecall, LLC, a Chicago-based nutrition consulting firm that provides nutrition communications, lecturing and consulting services and personalized, at-home dietary services. He is author of *The Best Things You Can Eat. DavidGrotto.com*

You may know about all the health benefits of fish, nuts, soy, dairy and whole wheat. But what if you're allergic to those foods or for various other reasons cannot eat them? How can you get the same nutritional benefits?

Here, common food sensitivities—and the best substitutes...

FISH

Fish is among the healthiest foods you can eat. It is high in protein and healthful fats and rich in vitamin D, selenium and zinc.

It is the healthful fats—long-chain omega-3 fatty acids—that fish is best known for. People who eat as little as three to six ounces of fish a week can reduce their risk of dying from heart disease by more than one-third.

The problem: Many people are allergic to fish.

What to eat instead: There are plenty of choices if you can't eat fish. The *alpha-linolenic acid* (ALA) in plant foods is converted to healthful omega-3s in the body.

Examples: Walnuts, flaxseeds, pumpkin seeds and canola oil contain ALA. The catch is that ALA isn't efficiently converted to long-chain omega-3s. When you eat ALA-rich plant foods, you get only about 10% to 25% of the beneficial fats that you would get from fish.

My advice: Get these fats from as many different sources as you can. Snack on nuts during the day. Cook tofu in canola oil or soybean oil. Add some ground flaxseed to your morning cereal.

NUTS

A recent study found that people who ate nuts seven or more times a week were 20% less likely to die from any cause during the study period than those who didn't eat nuts. Nuts are high in zinc as well as *phytosterols*, compounds that reduce cholesterol and may protect against cancer. Recent research suggests that they also help relieve symptoms in men with enlarged prostate glands.

The problem: You potentially can be allergic to any one type of nut or to all of them. And peanuts—which technically are a legume, not a nut—are a serious (in some cases, life-threatening) allergen for some people.

What to eat instead: Pumpkin or sunflower seeds. You can eat them raw, roasted or salted. These seeds are just as healthful as nuts, and they have the crunch, rich flavor and grab-and-go convenience of nuts. *In my house, we enjoy this recipe for roasted pumpkin seeds...*

Take one cup of seeds, rinse them off and pat dry. Melt one tablespoon of butter (or a no-trans-fat margarine spread) in a saucepan. Add one tablespoon of Worcestershire sauce. Toss the seeds and the butter sauce in a bowl. Spray a cookie sheet with nonstick cooking spray. Spread the seed mixture on the cookie sheet, and bake at 350°F for about 30 minutes, turning the seeds occasionally so that they brown on both sides.

DAIRY

There are plenty of reasons to enjoy milk, cheese and other dairy foods. The calcium is good for your bones. Dairy is high in protein. Even the fats seem to be beneficial. Studies have shown that people who eat dairy tend to lose more weight than people on low-dairy diets even when they get the same number of calories.

The problem: Millions of Americans don't produce enough *lactase* (an enzyme) to completely digest dairy. Others have a true allergy—they get symptoms such as a rash or hives when they consume one or more dairy proteins.

What to eat instead: You can buy milk and cheeses that are spiked with extra lactase. Also, research has shown that you can increase your natural supply of lactase. People who give up dairy for a few weeks and then slowly reintroduce it—say, by consuming an ounce a day for a week, then slowly adding to that amount over time—can boost their production of lactase.

It's tougher if you are allergic.

My advice: Give up cow's milk, and switch to soy milk or almond milk. These have many of the same nutrients that are found in cow's milk, and most people like the taste. Goat's milk is another possibility. People who are allergic to cow's milk usually can drink goat's milk without discomfort—but the musky taste isn't for everyone.

SOY

Tofu and other soy foods have long been the go-to protein source for people who don't eat meat. Soy also is rich in *isoflavones*, antioxidants that help balance hormones, increase bone strength and reduce the risk for some cancers.

The problem: Soy allergies are common, and they aren't limited to tofu. If you are aller-

TAKE NOTE...

Veggies Beat Fruits

Are fruits or vegetables more healthful? They're both on every health-conscious person's grocery list. But according to a recent study of 66,000 adults, vegetables are more protective, on average, than fruits.

Why: Fruits contain more natural sugar, which may increase risk for cardiovascular disease and blood sugar spikes.

However, fruits are still go-to foods. The study also found that people who ate seven or more servings of fruits and veggies a day had a 42% lower risk for death from any cause over a seven-year period.

Oyinlola Oyebode, PhD, public health researcher, University College London, UK.

gic, you have to avoid a lot of different foods, including soy sauce, miso, soy milk, tamari, edamame, etc.

What to eat instead: Other beans, such as lentils, pinto beans, kidney beans and chickpeas. All of these legumes have healthful amounts of protein, fiber and antioxidants. If you're not sensitive to gluten, try *seitan*. It's a form of wheat gluten that's popular in Asia (and in some Asian restaurants) that mimics the texture—and the protein content—of meat. Just make sure that your seitan dish isn't made with soy sauce!

IF YOU CAN'T EAT GLUTEN...

Whole grains are high in fiber, B vitamins, vitamin E and other antioxidants. A diet that includes whole wheat and other whole grains can significantly reduce your risk for diabetes, cancer, heart disease and digestive problems.

The problem: About 5% to 6% of Americans are sensitive to gluten, a protein in wheat, barley and rye. A smaller percentage suffers from celiac disease, a serious autoimmune disease triggered by gluten.

What to eat instead: Gluten-free grains, such as rice, quinoa and amaranth, have similar nutritional benefits. I recommend *teff*, an African grain that has a mildly nutty flavor and about the same amount of fiber that you would get from wheat.

Unfortunately, gluten-free breads often are dry and crumbly—they lack the chewiness and mouthfeel that comes from gluten. But manufacturers of gluten-free breads are getting better.

Example: The Udi's brand makes gluten-free bread that tastes (and feels) almost like traditional bread.

Caution: Oats don't contain gluten, but products such as oatmeal often are tainted when they are processed with the same machinery that is used for other grains or when oat crops are grown too close to wheat fields. Look for oats that are guaranteed to be gluten-free. It will be noted on the label.

The Three Supplements *Everyone* Should Take

Alan R. Gaby, MD, the contributing medical editor for *Townsend Letter,* the contributing editor for *Alternative Medicine Review*, chief science editor for *Aisle 7* and author of numerous scientific papers on nutritional medicine. His most recent book is the comprehensive textbook *Nutritional Medicine*, widely used by natural practitioners as a reference manual. *DoctorGaby.com*

Vitamin supplements have taken a beating lately. And plenty of people who use them to help ensure their good health are now left wondering whether these pills should be dumped in the trash.

But before you do that, there's another side to the vitamin question that you should know—most of the negative findings are misreported and/or the studies are flawed. After decades of research (backed by more than 26,000 medical journal articles and 19 years of clinical practice treating thousands of patients), I am confident that supplements can and often do work. The question is, which supplements?

WHAT EVERYONE NEEDS

In an ideal world, we'd get all our nutrients from foods—there's a powerful synergistic effect when vitamins and minerals are found in foods. But the reality is, most people don't get enough of these crucial nutrients. That's why certain individual supplements can help.*

Even if you take a standard, over-the-counter multivitamin, such as Centrum or One A Day, you may benefit from the following supplements because most multis don't contain enough of these nutrients. *Exception:* If you use a high-potency multivitamin (it has megadoses of nutrients and is usually labeled "high potency"), you're most likely getting enough of the necessary nutrients and probably don't need to add the supplements below. But you may still need these additional supplements if you have any of the health conditions described in this article.

*Be sure to check with a nutrition-savvy health practitioner before taking any supplements. To find one near you, consult the American Holistic Medical Association, *HolisticMedicine.org*, or the American Association of Naturopathic Physicians, *Naturopathic.org*.

THREE KEY SUPPLEMENTS

Supplements everyone should consider...

• **B-complex.** The B vitamins—*thiamine, riboflavin, niacin* and several others—are a must for the body's production of energy. They also play a key role in the health of the brain and nervous system.

But when foods are refined—for example, when kernels of whole wheat are stripped of their outer covering of fibrous bran and inner core of wheat germ and turned into white flour, as commonly occurs in American manufacturing practices—B vitamins are lost.

Recently published scientific evidence: A study of 104 middle-aged and older adults showed that taking three B vitamins (folic acid, B-6 and B-12) lowered levels of the amino acid *homocysteine* in people with very high levels (such elevations are linked to heart disease) and improved several measurements of mental functioning, such as memory.

Typical dose of B vitamins: Look for a B-complex supplement that contains at least 20 milligrams (mg) of most of the B vitamins, including B-6, thiamine and niacin...and at least 50 micrograms (mcg) each of B-12 and *biotin.*

• **Magnesium.** Without this mineral, your body couldn't produce energy, build bones, regulate blood sugar or even move a muscle. But most Americans don't get enough of this mineral in their diets.

Magnesium is used by nutritionally oriented clinicians to treat many health problems, including insomnia, chronic muscle pain, headache, heart disease, diabetes, osteoporosis and hearing loss. Overall, magnesium is the most beneficial supplement I have seen in my patients.

Typical dose of magnesium: 200 mg, twice a day. A capsule or a chewable or liquid form is preferable to a tablet, because it is more easily absorbed. But all varieties of magnesium—such as *magnesium oxide, magnesium citrate* and *magnesium aspartate*—are equally effective for most conditions. If you develop diarrhea, reduce the dose until diarrhea eases.

• **Vitamin C.** This vitamin is an antioxidant—a nutrient that protects you from oxidation, a kind of inner rust that destroys cells. A low level of oxidation is normal, but it's increased by many factors—such as stress and chronic disease.

Recent finding: A review of 13 studies involving nearly 4,000 people with *colorectal adenoma* (a benign tumor that can turn into colon cancer) found that people with the highest levels of vitamin C were 22% less likely to develop colon cancer.

Typical dose of vitamin C: 100 mg to 500 mg daily, for general nutritional support. If you have a family history of colon cancer (for example, in a first-degree relative, such as a parent or sibling), consider taking 1,000 mg, three times daily.

"ADD-ON" SUPPLEMENTS YOU MAY NEED

Certain people may need additional supplements to protect or improve their health. *Two key "add-on" supplements...*

• **Fish oil.** A large body of scientific research shows that fish oil can help prevent and treat heart disease.

Typical dose: About 1 gram (g) every day for people who want to reduce heart disease risk...and 2 g to 6 g daily for people diagnosed with the condition. People who have coronary heart disease need 360 mg to 1,080 mg daily of *eicosapentaenoic acid* (EPA) and 240 mg to 720 mg of *docosahexaenoic acid* (DHA).

Talk to a health practitioner before taking fish oil—it may increase bleeding risk.

• **Vitamin D.** Vitamin D deficiency is common, and it can increase risk for bone loss (osteoporosis), falls in older people (frailty), the flu, autoimmune diseases (such as rheumatoid arthritis, lupus and multiple sclerosis) and even cancer.

New thinking: 400 international units (IU) daily was once thought to preserve bone and prevent falls, but studies now show that 800 IU daily is preferable. An even higher dose (up to 1,200 IU daily) may be needed, depending on age (older people may need more)...weight (the obese are at greater risk for deficiency)... and skin color (people with dark skin produce less vitamin D when exposed to the sun). Ask your doctor for advice on the best dose for you, and use vitamin D-3 (the type derived from sunlight and animal sources).

6 Secrets to Holistic Heart Care

Joel K. Kahn, MD, clinical professor of medicine at Wayne State University School of Medicine in Detroit and director of Cardiac Wellness at Michigan Healthcare Professionals. He is a founding member of the International Society of Integrative, Metabolic and Functional Cardiovascular Medicine and author of *The Whole Heart Solution. DrJoelKahn.com*

You don't smoke, your cholesterol levels look good and your blood pressure is under control. This means that you're off the hook when it comes to having a heart attack or developing heart disease, right? Maybe not.

Surprising statistic: About 20% of people with heart disease do not have any of the classic risk factors, such as those described above.

The missing link: While most conventional medical doctors prescribe medications and other treatments to help patients control the "big" risk factors for heart disease, holistic cardiologists also suggest small lifestyle changes that over time make a significant difference in heart disease risk.* *My secrets for preventing heart disease...*

SECRET #1: Stand up! You may not think of standing as a form of exercise. However, it's more effective than most people realize.

Think about what you're doing when you're not standing. Unless you are asleep, you're probably sitting. While sitting, your body's metabolism slows...your insulin becomes less effective...and you're likely to experience a gradual drop in HDL "good" cholesterol.

A study that tracked the long-term health of more than 123,000 Americans found that those who sat for six hours or more a day had an overall death rate that was higher—18% higher for men and 37% for women—than those who sat for less than three hours.

What's so great about standing? When you are on your feet, you move more. You pace...fidget...move your arms...and walk from room to room. This type of activity improves metabolism and can easily burn hundreds of extra calories a day. Standing also increases your insulin sensitivity to help prevent diabetes. So stand up and move around when talking on the phone, checking e-mail and watching television.

SECRET #2: Count your breaths. Slow, deep breathing is an effective way to help prevent high blood pressure—one of the leading causes of heart disease. For people who already have high blood pressure, doing this technique a few times a day has been shown to lower blood pressure by five to 10 points within five minutes. And the pressure may stay lower for up to 24 hours.

During a breathing exercise, you want to slow your breathing down from the usual 12 to 16 breaths a minute that most people take to about three breaths. I use the "4-7-8 sequence" whenever I feel stressed.

What to do: Inhale through your nose for four seconds...hold the breath in for seven seconds...then exhale through the mouth for eight seconds.

Also helpful: A *HeartMath* software package, which you can load on your computer or smartphone, includes breathing exercises to help lower your heart rate and levels of stress hormones. *Cost:* $129 and up, at *HeartMath.com*. You can also sign up for some free tools on this website.

SECRET #3: Practice "loving kindness." This is an easy form of meditation that reduces stress, thus allowing you to keep your heart rate and blood pressure at healthy levels.

Research has shown that people who meditate regularly are 48% less likely to have a heart attack or stroke than those who don't meditate. "Loving kindness" meditation is particularly effective at promoting relaxation—it lowers levels of the stress hormones *adrenaline* and *cortisol* while raising levels of the healing hormone *oxytocin*.

What to do: Sit quietly, with your eyes closed. For a few minutes, focus on just your breathing. Then imagine one person in your life whom you find exceptionally easy to love. Imagine this person in front of you. Fill your

*To find a holistic cardiologist, go to the website of the American Board of Integrative Holistic Medicine, *ABIHM.org*, and search the database of certified integrative physicians.

heart with a warm, loving feeling...think about how you both want to be happy and avoid suffering...and imagine that a feeling of peace travels from your heart to that person's heart in the form of white light. Dwell on the image for a few minutes. This meditation will also help you practice small acts of kindness in your daily life—for example, giving a hand to someone who needs help crossing the street.

SECRET #4: Don't neglect sex. Men who have sex at least two times a week have a 50% lower risk for a heart attack than those who abstain. Similar research hasn't been done on women, but it's likely that they get a comparable benefit.

Why does sex help keep your heart healthy? It probably has more to do with intimacy than the physical activity itself. Couples who continue to have sex tend to be the ones with more intimacy in their marriages. Happy people who bond with others have fewer heart attacks—and recover more quickly if they've had one—than those without close relationships.

SECRET #5: Be happy! People who are happy and who feel a sense of purpose and connection with others tend to have lower blood pressure and live longer than those who are isolated. Research shows that two keys to happiness are to help others be happy—for example, by being a volunteer—and to reach out to friends and neighbors. Actually, any shared activity, such as going to church or doing group hobbies, can increase survival among heart patients by about 50%.

SECRET #6: Try Waon (pronounced Wa-own) therapy. With this Japanese form of "warmth therapy," you sit in an infrared (dry) sauna for 15 minutes then retreat to a resting area for half an hour, where you wrap yourself in towels and drink plenty of water. Studies show that vascular function improves after such therapy due to the extra release of *nitric oxide*, the master molecule in blood vessels that helps them relax.

Some health clubs offer Waon treatments, but the dry saunas at many gyms should offer similar benefits. I do not recommend steam rooms—moist heat places extra demands on the heart and can be dangerous for some people.

5 Foods That Fight High Blood Pressure (You Might Not Even Need Medication)

Janet Bond Brill, PhD, RD, a nationally recognized nutrition, health and fitness expert who specializes in cardiovascular disease prevention. She has authored several books on the subject, including *Blood Pressure DOWN*, *Prevent a Second Heart Attack* and *Cholesterol DOWN*. *DrJanet.com*

Is your blood pressure on the high side? Your doctor might write a prescription when it creeps above 140/90—but you may be able to forgo medication. Lifestyle changes still are considered the best starting treatment for mild hypertension. These include not smoking, regular exercise and a healthy diet. *In addition to eating less salt, you want to include potent pressure-lowering foods, including...*

RAISINS

Raisins are basically dehydrated grapes, but they provide a much more concentrated dose of nutrients and fiber. They are high in potassium, with 220 milligrams (mg) in a small box (1.5 ounces). Potassium helps counteract the blood pressure–raising effects of salt. The more potassium we consume, the more sodium our bodies excrete. Researchers also speculate that the fiber and antioxidants in raisins change the biochemistry of blood vessels, making them more pliable—important for healthy blood pressure. Opt for dark raisins over light-colored ones because dark raisins have more catechins, a powerful type of antioxidant that can increase blood flow.

Researchers at Louisville Metabolic and Atherosclerosis Research Center compared people who snacked on raisins with those who ate other packaged snacks. Those in the raisin group had drops in *systolic pressure* (the top number) ranging from 4.8 points (after four weeks) to 10.2 points (after 12 weeks). Blood pressure barely budged in the no-raisin group. Some people worry about the sugar in raisins, but it is natural sugar (not added sugar) and will not adversely affect your health (though people with diabetes need to be cautious with portion sizes).

My advice: Aim to consume a few ounces of raisins every day. Prunes are an alternative.

BEETS

Beets, too, are high in potassium, with about 519 mg per cup. They're delicious, easy to cook (see the tasty recipe on the next page) and very effective for lowering blood pressure.

A study at The London Medical School found that people who drank about eight ounces of beet juice averaged a 10-point drop in blood pressure during the next 24 hours. The blood pressure–lowering effect was most pronounced at three to six hours past drinking but remained lower for the entire 24 hours. Eating whole beets might be even better because you will get extra fiber.

Along with fiber and potassium, beets also are high in *nitrate*. The nitrate is converted first to nitrite in the blood, then to nitric oxide. Nitric oxide is a gas that relaxes blood vessel walls and lowers blood pressure.

My advice: Eat beets several times a week. Look for beets that are dark red. They contain more protective phytochemicals than the gold or white beets. Cooked spinach and kale are alternatives.

DAIRY

In research involving nearly 45,000 people, researchers found that those who consumed low-fat "fluid" dairy foods, such as yogurt and low-fat milk, were 16% less likely to develop high blood pressure. Higher-fat forms of dairy, such as cheese and ice cream, had no blood pressure benefits. The study was published in *Journal of Human Hypertension*.

In another study, published in *The New England Journal of Medicine*, researchers found that people who included low-fat or fat-free dairy in a diet high in fruits and vegetables had double the blood pressure–lowering benefits of those who just ate the fruits and veggies.

Low-fat dairy is high in calcium, another blood pressure–lowering mineral that should be included in your diet. When you don't have enough calcium in your diet, a "calcium leak" occurs in your kidneys. This means that the kidneys excrete more calcium in the urine, disturbing the balance of mineral metabolism involved in blood pressure regulation.

My advice: Aim for at least one serving of low-fat or nonfat milk or yogurt every day. If you don't care for cow's milk or can't drink it, switch to fortified soy milk. It has just as much calcium and protein and also contains *phytoestrogens*, compounds that are good for the heart.

FLAXSEED

Flaxseed contains *alpha-linolenic acid* (ALA), an omega-3 fatty acid that helps prevent heart and vascular disease. Flaxseed also contains magnesium. A shortage of magnesium in our diet throws off the balance of sodium, potassium and calcium, which causes the blood vessels to constrict.

Flaxseed also is high in *flavonoids*, the same antioxidants that have boosted the popularity of dark chocolate, kale and red wine. Flavonoids are bioactive chemicals that reduce inflammation throughout the body, including in the arteries. Arterial inflammation is thought to be the "trigger" that leads to high blood pressure, blood clots and heart attacks.

In a large-scale observational study linking dietary magnesium intake with better heart health and longevity, nearly 59,000 healthy Japanese people were followed for 15 years. The scientists found that the people with the highest dietary intake of magnesium had a 50% reduced risk for death from heart disease (heart attack and stroke). According to the researchers, magnesium's heart-healthy benefit is linked to its ability to improve blood pressure, suppress irregular heartbeats and inhibit inflammation.

My advice: Add one or two tablespoons of ground flaxseed to breakfast cereals. You also can sprinkle flaxseed on yogurt or whip it into a breakfast smoothie. Or try chia seeds.

WALNUTS

Yale researchers found that people who ate two ounces of walnuts a day had improved blood flow and drops in blood pressure (a 3.5-point drop in systolic blood pressure and a 2.8-point drop in diastolic blood pressure). The mechanisms through which walnuts elicit a blood pressure–lowering response are thought

TASTY RECIPE...

Dr. Janet's Roasted Red Beets with Lemon Vinaigrette

Beets are a delicious side dish when roasted, peeled and topped with a lemony vinaigrette and fresh parsley. This recipe is from my book *Prevent a Second Heart Attack*.

6 medium-sized beets, washed and trimmed of greens and roots
2 Tablespoons extra-virgin olive oil
2 teaspoons fresh lemon juice
1 garlic clove, peeled and minced
1 teaspoon Dijon mustard
¼ teaspoon kosher salt
¼ teaspoon freshly ground black pepper
¼ cup chopped fresh flat-leaf Italian parsley

Preheat the oven to 400°F. Spray a baking dish with nonstick cooking spray. Place the beets in the dish, and cover tightly with foil. Bake the beets for about one hour or until they are tender when pierced with a fork or thin knife. Remove from the oven, and allow to cool to the touch.

Meanwhile, in a small bowl, whisk together the olive oil, lemon juice, garlic, mustard, salt and pepper for the dressing. When the beets are cool enough to handle, peel and slice the beets, arranging the slices on a platter. Drizzle with vinaigrette, and garnish with parsley. Serves six.

to involve their high content of monounsaturated fatty acids, omega-3 ALA, magnesium and fiber, and their low levels of sodium and saturated fatty acids.

Bonus: Despite the reputation of nuts as a "fat snack," the people who ate them didn't gain weight.

The magnesium in walnuts is particularly important. It limits the amount of calcium that enters muscle cells inside artery walls. Ingesting the right amount of calcium (not too much and not too little) on a daily basis is essential for optimal blood pressure regulation. Magnesium regulates calcium's movement across the membranes of the smooth muscle cells, deep within the artery walls.

If your body doesn't have enough magnesium, too much calcium will enter the smooth muscle cells, which causes the arterial muscles to tighten, putting a squeeze on the arteries and raising blood pressure. Magnesium works like the popular *calcium channel blockers*, drugs that block entry of calcium into arterial walls, lowering blood pressure.

My advice: Eat two ounces of walnuts every day. Or choose other nuts such as almonds and pecans.

Avoiding the Sun Can Be Deadly

In a recent finding, women who said that they did not sunbathe and avoided the sun in other ways were twice as likely to die over a 20-year period as women with the greatest sun exposure.

Possible reason: Sunlight is necessary for vitamin D production—and low vitamin D levels are associated with increased risk for death from cardiovascular disease and other causes.

Pelle G. Lindqvist, MD, PhD, associate professor of obstetrics and gynecology and director of education at Karolinska University Hospital, Stockholm, Sweden. He is lead author of a study published in *Journal of Internal Medicine.*

Eat Nuts, Live Longer

In a study of nearly 119,000 adults, those who ate one ounce of any kind of nuts each day were 20% less likely to die of any cause over a 30-year period than those who didn't eat nuts.

Reason: Nutrient-rich peanuts and tree nuts such as walnuts, cashews and pecans help ward off cancer, heart disease and respiratory conditions.

To boost your overall health: Eat a handful of raw or dry-roasted, unsalted nuts every day.

Ying Bao, MD, ScD, associate epidemiologist at Brigham and Women's Hospital, Boston.

The Vitamin That Lowers Stroke Risk

Daily intake of a vitamin-B supplement can lower the risk for stroke by as much as 7%. The extent of the reduction depends on each person's absorption rate, the folic acid or vitamin B-12 concentration in the blood, whether a person has kidney disease or high blood pressure and other factors.

Analysis of 14 clinical trials involving 54,913 participants by researchers at Zhengzhou University, Zhengzhou, China, published online in *Neurology.*

4 New (and Delicious) Cancer-Fighting Foods

Alice G. Bender, MS, RDN, associate director for nutrition programs at the American Institute for Cancer Research (AICR), a nonprofit organization that analyzes research and educates the public on the links between diet, physical exercise, weight loss and the prevention of cancer. *AICR.org*

Researchers are continually investigating foods that may help prevent cancer. But which ones have the strongest evidence?

The American Institute for Cancer Research (AICR), a nonprofit group that keeps tabs on cancer and diet research, recently identified the following foods as being among those having the strongest scientific evidence for fighting cancer...*

PUMPKIN

Under the hard rind, orange pumpkin flesh is rich in *carotenoids* such as *beta-carotene, alpha-carotene, lutein* and *zeaxanthin.* A high intake of foods containing carotenoids has been linked to a lower incidence of many cancers, including those of the esophagus, mouth and larynx. Scientists have recently uncovered another protective compound in pumpkins—*cucurmosin*, a protein that has been shown to slow the growth of pancreatic cancer cells.

Smart idea: Eat pumpkin (plain, canned pumpkin is a convenient option) as well as the seeds.

What to do: Have a handful of pumpkin seeds (store-bought are fine) daily as a snack. To prepare your own, rinse fresh seeds in water, air-dry, add a touch of oil and bake at 350°F for 10 to 20 minutes.

GRAPEFRUIT

Grapefruit is a rich source of dietary fiber and vitamin C. The pink and red varieties also contain carotenoids (such as beta-carotene and *lycopene*) that decrease the DNA damage that can lead to cancer.

Scientific evidence: Strong research shows that foods like grapefruit help reduce risk for colorectal cancer. Other evidence suggests that it reduces risk for such malignancies as those of the esophagus, mouth, lung and stomach.

Helpful: Put red or pink grapefruit slices in a green salad with avocado. The tart grapefruit and creamy avocado are delicious together—and the fat in the avocado boosts the absorption of lycopene.

Caution: Grapefruit contains *furanocoumarins*, compounds that block a liver enzyme that breaks down some medications. (More than 85 medications interact with grapefruit, including cholesterol-lowering statins.) If you're thinking about eating more grapefruit and currently take one or more medications, talk to your doctor first.

APPLES

An apple a day is good for you—but two may be even better!

Scientific evidence: In a study published in the *European Journal of Cancer Prevention*, people who ate an apple a day had a 35% lower risk for colorectal cancer—and those who ate two or more apples had a 50% lower risk.

Apples are protective because they contain several anticancer nutrients (many of them found in the peel), including fiber, vitamin C and *flavonoids* such as *quercetin* and *kaempferol*—plant compounds that have stopped the growth of cancer in cellular and animal

*The studies cited in this article are only a small portion of the research supporting these cancer-fighting foods. The AICR and its international panel of experts review a much larger spectrum of research.

EASY-TO-DO...

5-Minute Trick to Prolong Life

Taking a five-minute walk every hour counters the negative effects of sitting at the desk or on a couch for long hours. Extended sitting is bad for blood pressure and cholesterol and contributes to obesity. Researchers believe the increase in muscle activity aids blood flow, which improves arterial function and could even prolong life span.

Study by researchers at Indian University School of Public Health, Bloomington, published in *Medicine & Science in Sports & Exercise*.

studies. Research does not specify any particular type of apple as being more protective, so enjoy your favorite variety.

A quick and easy apple dessert: Core an apple, stuff it with raisins and cinnamon, top the stuffing with one tablespoon of apple cider or water, cover the apple with waxed paper and microwave for two minutes.

MUSHROOMS (USED IN A SURPRISING WAY)

When it comes to preventing cancer with diet, it's not only what you eat—it's also what you don't eat.

Scientific evidence: The evidence is convincing that eating too much red meat is linked to colorectal cancer. The AICR recommends eating no more than 18 ounces a week of cooked red meat (such as beef, pork and lamb).

A cancer-fighting meal extender: An easy, delicious way to lower your intake of red meat is to replace some of it in recipes with mushrooms. They're a perfect meat extender, with a savory, meaty taste and texture.

What to do: In a recipe that uses ground meat, replace one-third to one-half of the meat with chopped or diced mushrooms.

In a recent study, people who substituted one cup of white button mushrooms a day for one cup of lean ground beef consumed 123 fewer daily calories and lost an average of seven pounds after one year.

If you're heavier than you should be, losing weight means decreasing cancer risk—the AICR estimates that 122,000 yearly cases of cancer could be prevented if Americans weren't overweight or obese.

How to Beat the 3 Big Mistakes That Worsen Diabetes

Osama Hamdy, MD, PhD, medical director of the Joslin Diabetes Center's Obesity Clinical Program and an assistant professor of medicine at Harvard Medical School, both in Boston. He also is coauthor of *The Diabetes Breakthrough*.

Despite what you may have heard, type 2 diabetes doesn't have to be a lifelong condition. It can be controlled and even reversed in the early stages or stopped from progressing in the later stages—with none of the dire consequences of out-of-control blood sugar.

Sounds great, right? What person with diabetes wouldn't want to do everything possible to help prevent serious complications such as coronary heart disease, kidney disease, blindness or even amputation?

The problem is, even people who are following all the doctor's orders may still be sabotaging their efforts with seemingly minor missteps that can have big consequences. Among the most common mistakes that harm people with diabetes are oversights in the way they eat and exercise. *For example...*

MISTAKE #1: Skimping on protein. The majority of people with type 2 diabetes are overweight or obese. These individuals *know* that they need to lose weight but sometimes fail despite their best efforts.

Here's what often happens: We have had it drummed into our heads that the best way to lose weight is to go on a low-fat diet. However, these diets tend to be low in protein—and you need *more* protein, not less, if you have type 2 diabetes and are cutting calories to lose weight.

What's so special about protein? You need protein to maintain muscle mass. The average adult starts losing lean muscle mass every year after about age 40. If you have diabetes, you'll probably lose more muscle mass than someone without it. And the loss will be even greater if your diabetes is not well controlled.

Muscle is important because it burns more calories than other tissues in your body. Also, people with a higher and more active muscle mass find it easier to maintain healthy blood-glucose levels, since active muscle doesn't require insulin to clear high glucose from the blood.

My advice: Protein should provide 20% to 30% of total daily calories. If you're on an 1,800-calorie diet (a reasonable amount for an average man who wants to lose weight), that's about 90 grams (g) to 135 g of protein a day. If you're on a 1,200- to 1,500-calorie diet (a sensible amount for an average woman who is dieting), that's about 60 g to 113 g of protein a day.

Examples: Good protein sources include fish, skinless poultry, nonfat or low-fat dairy, legumes and nuts and seeds. A three-ounce chicken breast has about 30 g of protein...a three-ounce piece of haddock, 17 g...one-half cup of low-fat cottage cheese, 14 g...and one-quarter cup of whole almonds, 7 g of protein.

Note: If you have kidney problems, you may need to limit your protein intake. Check with your doctor.

MISTAKE #2: Not doing resistance training. It's widely known that aerobic exercise is good for weight loss and blood sugar control. What usually gets short shrift is *resistance training*, such as lifting weights and using stretch bands.

When you build muscle, you use more glucose, which helps reduce glucose levels in the blood. If you take insulin for your diabetes (see below), toned muscles will also make your body more sensitive to it.

An added benefit: People who do resistance training can often reduce their doses of insulin or other medications within a few months.

My advice: Do a combination of resistance, aerobic and flexibility exercises. Start with 20 minutes total, four days a week—splitting the time equally among the three types of exercise. Try to work up to 60 minutes total, six days a week. An exercise physiologist or personal trainer certified in resistance training can help choose the best workout for you.

BETTER WAYS...

Eat Yogurt to Protect Against Diabetes

Yogurt may protect against diabetes. People who ate at least four-and-a-half servings of low-fat yogurt weekly—one serving equals 4.4 ounces—had 28% lower risk for diabetes than people who did not eat yogurt. The calcium, magnesium and vitamin D in fortified, fermented dairy products such as yogurt may have a protective effect.

Nita Forouhi, PhD, group leader, nutritional epidemiology program, University of Cambridge, UK, and leader of a study of 4,255 people, published in *Diabetologia*.

MISTAKE #3: Ignoring hunger cues. Many individuals are so conditioned to eat at certain times that they virtually ignore their body's hunger signals. Learning how to read these cues can be one of the best ways to achieve (and maintain) a healthy body weight.

The key is to recognize that there are different *levels* of hunger. It's easy to overeat when you do not acknowledge the difference between feeling satisfied and stuffing yourself.

My advice: Imagine a five-point hunger scale—1 means you're feeling starved...2 is hungry...3 is comfortable...4 is full...and 5 is stuffed. Before you start eating, rate your hunger between 1 and 5. Halfway through the meal, rate it again.

Here's the secret: Stop eating when you rate your hunger somewhere between "comfortable" and "full." If you give your hunger a ranking of 4 and you *still* want to eat, get away from the table and do something else!

Note: It can take up to 20 minutes for the "satiety signal" to kick in, so eat slowly. If you eat too quickly, you may miss the signal and overeat.

After just a few weeks of eating this way, it usually becomes second nature.

IF YOU TAKE DIABETES MEDS...

Sometimes, diet and exercise aren't enough to tame out-of-control blood sugar. *Traps to avoid...*

• **Drug-induced weight gain.** Ironically, the drugs that are used to treat diabetes also can cause weight gain as a side effect. If you start taking insulin, you can expect to gain about 10 pounds within six months—with oral drugs, such as *glipizide* (Glucotrol), you'll probably gain from four to seven pounds.

My advice: Ask your doctor if you can switch to one of the newer, "weight-friendly" medications.

Examples: A form of insulin known as Levemir causes less weight gain than Lantus, Humulin N or Novolin N. Newer oral drugs called *DPP-4 inhibitors*, such as Januvia, Onglyza and Nesina, don't have weight gain as a side effect.

Important: The newer drugs are more expensive and may not be covered by insurance. But if they don't cause you to gain weight, you might get by with a lower dose—and reduced cost.

- **Erratic testing.** You should test your blood sugar levels at least four to six times a day, particularly when you're making lifestyle changes that could affect the frequency and doses of medication. Your doctor has probably advised you to test before and after exercise—and before meals.

My advice: Be sure to also test *after* meals. This will help determine the effects of different types and amounts of foods.

Does Glucosamine Really Work for Arthritis?

It depends on what kind of glucosamine you are taking. Only *glucosamine sulfate* has been shown to be effective in reducing osteoarthritis pain. Sulfate helps the body to produce cartilage. That is why researchers believe this form works better than *glucosamine hydrochloride* or *N-acetyl glucosamine*, neither of which has sulfate. Studies have shown that glucosamine sulfate reduces pain about as much as *acetaminophen* and the nonsteroidal anti-inflammatory drugs *ibuprofen* and *piroxicam*. But NSAIDs relieved arthritis pain in about two weeks, while glucosamine sulfate took up to 12 weeks.

If glucosamine sulfate works for you, keep taking it. The recommended dose is generally 1,500 milligrams (mg) a day.

David Borenstein, MD, clinical professor of medicine, The George Washington University Medical Center, Washington, DC. *DrBHealth.org*

Ginger Compress Offers Pain Relief

When placed on the lower backs of people with osteoarthritis for 30 minutes daily, a warm ginger compress reduced overall pain and fatigue by half after just one week. The ginger compress was a cotton cloth soaked in a hot ginger infusion (two teaspoons of ground ginger to one-half cup of very hot water), squeezed well so that it was just moist.

Theory: Topical ginger seems to warm and relax the musculoskeletal system, increasing mobility. The compress likely will work on pulled muscles and achy joints, too.

Study by researchers at Edith Cowan University, Perth, Western Australia, published in *Journal of Holistic Nursing.*

TAKE NOTE...

Good News! Beer May Cut Risk for Rheumatoid Arthritis

In a recent finding, women who drank two to four beers weekly had 31% less risk of developing *rheumatoid arthritis* (RA) than women who never drank beer. Moderate use of any form of alcohol is linked to 21% lower risk for the chronic condition. Alcohol consumption also may improve symptoms in people who already have the disease.

Possible reason: RA is an inflammatory disease—and alcohol has a known anti-inflammatory effect.

Bing Lu, MD, DrPH, assistant professor of medicine at Brigham and Women's Hospital and Harvard Medical School, both in Boston, and lead researcher for a study of 238,131 women, published in *Arthritis & Rheumatology*.

Vitamin D for Knee Pain

Low levels of vitamin D may cause knee pain to worsen—especially if you have osteoarthritis and/or are obese, according to a recent analysis.

Explanation: Vitamin D is needed for muscle strength and to fight inflammation and lessen pain sensitivity.

To help prevent knee pain: Ask your doctor to test your vitamin D level. If it's low (under 20 nanograms per milliliter or ng/mL), take a supplement and get more sun exposure.

Toni Glover, PhD, assistant professor of nursing, University of Florida, Gainesville.

End Your Back Pain for Good: A Surgeon Shares His Surprising Secret

Patrick A. Roth, MD, FACS, chairman of the department of neurosurgery and director of the neurosurgical residency training program at Hackensack University Medical Center in Hackensack, New Jersey. He is also the founder of the North Jersey Brain & Spine Center in Oradell, New Jersey, and author of *The End of Back Pain.*

You're lucky if you haven't suffered a backache recently. It's common…make that very common.

In any three-month period, 25% of adults will suffer at least one day of back pain. Over the course of a lifetime, about 85% of us will experience back pain at some point.

My story: As a spinal surgeon and a former back pain sufferer, I've examined this malady from all angles. What I have discovered is that contrary to our culture of "pop a pill" or "go under the knife," the best course of action starts with discovering your "hidden" core.

FINDING YOUR HIDDEN CORE

If I told you that you needed to strengthen your core, you might assume that means doing crunches to work on your abdominal muscles, or abs. While washboard abs are the most visible and easily trained part of your core, they are only part of a larger muscle group that makes up the core.

In fact, strengthening your abs without also working on your hidden core can make back pain worse. That's because unbalanced core muscles cause an unstable spine.

The muscles you don't see: Your core is a group of muscles that encircles your midsection—front, sides and back. And most of the muscles lie deep inside your body—hidden from view. Taken together, these muscles form an internal brace around your spine, holding it erect, protecting it from damage. In order to reduce or limit back pain, you need to strengthen all your core muscles equally.

THE HIDDEN CORE WORKOUT

The workout I've developed targets all the inner muscles that make up your body's natural support system. Don't worry—even if you're not in great shape, you can start by doing the exercises at your own pace. However, do each of the exercises below so that you'll strengthen all the muscles equally to keep your spine in balance.

Here's the drill: Perform the exercises three times a week…and focus on maintaining proper form. Even if your back is aching, do the exercises if you can—they often give some immediate relief and help prevent future flare-ups.

Give it time: It may take three to four weeks before you notice significant pain reduction.

Important: These exercises can be safely done by most people, but check with your doctor first. See your doctor right away if you have back pain and severe leg pain (a sign of *sciatica*) or you have a history of cancer (back pain could be a sign that cancer has spread).

EXERCISE 1: Front plank. This exercise focuses on the muscles at the front of the core—the *rectus abdominis* (the abs) and the *transverse abdominis*—and the *obliques*, which are on the sides of the core.

What to do: Start by lying on

your stomach on a carpet or mat. Place your hands on the floor at about the level of your ears, with your elbows bent and close to your sides.

Slowly lift your body off the floor using just your forearms and rising up on your toes. Your elbows and hands should remain on the floor. Keep your back straight by contracting your front abdominal muscles. (If you cannot lift your body as described, try supporting your lower body from your knees rather than your toes.)

Breathe normally...and hold the position for 10 seconds. As you are able, increase the amount of time you hold the position. A minute is a good goal for most people.

EXERCISE 2: Side plank. This strengthens the sides of your core—the internal and external obliques.

What to do: Start by lying on the floor on your right side, with your feet together. Prop yourself up on your right elbow, with your right hand and forearm flat on the ground and your forearm perpendicular to your body. Put your left hand on your left hip. Contract your abdominal muscles, and lift your hips off of the floor until your back is straight.

Breathe normally, and hold the raised position for 10 seconds. As you are able, increase the amount of time you hold the position to 60 seconds. Repeat on your left side.

EXERCISE 3: Birddog. This exercise strengthens the back muscles that support your spine, including the *multifidus* muscles and the *erector spinae* muscles.

What to do: Start on your hands and knees, with your wrists below your shoulders (hands facing forward) and your knees below your hips. Stabilize your spine by tightening your abdominal muscles.

Simultaneously extend your right arm straight forward and your left leg straight back until both are parallel to the ground. Remember to keep your back and neck straight, without sagging or arching.

Hold this position for two seconds, then return to the starting position. Repeat, using the other arm and leg. Do the cycle five times. As you are able, increase the amount of time you hold the position each time for up to 10 seconds.

START RUNNING

If you have back pain, you've likely been advised to do only low-impact aerobic exercises and avoid running. I disagree. After years of examining runners, I noticed that their disks (and spines) tend to be healthier than those of nonrunners. Unexpected, right? But it makes sense.

All weight-bearing exercises stimulate bone cells so that the bones themselves become stronger. Similarly, disks also improve with high-impact exercise—the cells that make up the gel of a disk proliferate, retaining more water and becoming "fuller," which cushions the bones of the spine, reducing pain.

If you want to try running (and it doesn't cause you knee or hip pain), start slowly. Walk for one mile—and three times during that walk, run for 20 to 30 seconds. Thereafter, double the number of times you run until you're running more than walking. Try to work up to at least 30 minutes, three times a week.

Fun Way to Reduce Kidney Stone Risk

Exercise reduces risk for kidney stones.

Recent finding: Active postmenopausal women were 16% to 31% less likely than sedentary women to develop kidney stones over an eight-year period. Maximum effects were found at the equivalent of three hours a week of moderate-paced walking, one hour of moderate-paced jogging or four hours of light gardening.

Study of 84,225 women led by researchers at University of Washington School of Medicine, Seattle, published in *Journal of the American Society of Nephrology.*

Eating Fish Helps Hearing

In a recent finding, women who consumed at least two servings of fish a week had a 20% lower risk for hearing loss.

Reason: Blood-supply problems to the ears can cause hearing loss, and a higher intake of fish—rich in omega-3 fatty acids—may help to maintain blood flow.

Other ways to protect hearing: Exercise regularly, manage your weight, and avoid excessively loud noises—or wear protection if you can't.

Sharon E. Curhan, MD, an instructor in medicine and a clinical researcher in epidemiology at Brigham and Women's Hospital, Boston, and leader of a study of 65,215 women, published in *American Journal of Clinical Nutrition.*

The Drink That Staves Off Tinnitus

Coffee is linked to lower risk for tinnitus.

Recent finding: Women who consumed less than 150 milligrams (mg) of caffeine a day—the amount in about one eight-ounce cup of coffee—were 15% more likely to develop *tinnitus* (ringing in the ears) during an 18-year period than women who consumed 450 mg to 599 mg of caffeine a day.

Gary C. Curhan, MD, ScD, professor of medicine at Harvard Medical School and a physician at Brigham and Women's Hospital, both in Boston. He led a study of more than 65,000 women, published in *The American Journal of Medicine.*

Alzheimer's Symptoms Reversed! Breakthrough Research Shows It's Possible

Dale Bredesen, MD, the Augustus Rose Professor of Neurology and director of the Mary S. Easton Center for Alzheimer's Disease Research, the Alzheimer's Disease Program and Neurodegenerative Disease Research in the David Geffen School of Medicine, UCLA. He is founding president of the Buck Institute for Research on Aging in Novato, California. Dr. Bredesen has authored or coauthored more than 200 scientific papers that have appeared in *Journal of Alzheimer's Disease* and other medical journals.

Can Alzheimer's symptoms be reversed? A breakthrough treatment suggests that they can. In a study recently published in the journal *Aging,* Dale Bredesen, MD, director of the Alzheimer's Disease Program at UCLA's David Geffen School of Medicine, presented a new all-natural, multicomponent treatment program that reversed memory loss in four people with Alzheimer's and in five people with either subjective cognitive impairment or mild cognitive impairment (the stages of memory loss that typically precede Alzheimer's).

Here, Dr. Bredesen explains that his program is based on a new theory about why people get Alzheimer's. This theory was developed over two decades of cellular and animal research at the Buck Institute for Research on Aging and UCLA...

NEW THINKING

The current, widely accepted theory of Alzheimer's says that the protein *beta-amyloid* forms plaques outside neurons in the brain... somehow triggering the production of abnormal *tau tangles* inside neurons...thereby interfering with *synapses,* the information-laden connections between neurons that create memory and other mental activity.

New thinking: Normal mental function depends on a balance between *synaptoblastic* (synapse-making) and *synaptoclastic* (synapse-destroying) activity. If there is more synaptoclastic activity, memory loss may ensue. If there is chronic synaptoclastic activity, our research suggests that Alzheimer's occurs.

My colleagues and I have identified 36 unique synapse-affecting factors (including beta-amyloid). Addressing only one or two of these factors—with a drug, for example—will not reverse Alzheimer's. But addressing many factors—10, 20 or more—can effectively reverse the symptoms.

Here are several key factors in what we call the MEND (Metabolic Enhancement for Neuro-Degeneration) program—factors anyone can use to prevent, slow, stop or potentially even reverse memory loss...

RESTORING MEMORY

Synapse-making and synapse-destroying factors function in a "loop" that develops momentum, like a snowball rolling downhill. In the synapse-destroying momentum of Alzheimer's, you gradually lose memories, ultimately even basic ones such as the faces of loved ones. But because the synapse-making factors in the MEND program are so effective, they can reverse the momentum of Alzheimer's. The more of them that you incorporate into your daily life, the more momentum there is to protect and restore memory.

- **Optimize diet.** Eliminate simple carbohydrates such as anything made from white flour and/or refined sugar. Do not eat processed foods with either "trans fats" or "partially hydrogenated vegetable oil" on the label. If you're sensitive to gluten, minimize your consumption of gluten-containing foods, such as wheat and rye (there are simple tests to determine whether you are indeed gluten-sensitive). Emphasize fruits and vegetables. Eat nonfarmed fish for neuron-protecting omega-3 fatty acids.

Why it works: This dietary approach reduces inflammation and high levels of insulin (the hormone that regulates blood sugar), both of which are synapse-destroying.

Important: Dietary changes have more impact than any other factor in preventing or reversing memory loss.

Helpful: Four books that have diets consistent with MEND are *Eat to Live* by Joel Furhman, MD...*The Blood Sugar Solution* by Mark Hyman, MD...*The Spectrum* by Dean Ornish, MD...and *Grain Brain* by David Perlmutter, MD.

- **Have a nightly "fast."** Don't eat three hours before bedtime. Ideally, 12 hours should pass between the last time you eat at night and when you eat breakfast.

Example: Dinner ending at 8:00 pm and breakfast starting at 8:00 am.

Why it works: This eating pattern enhances *autophagy* (the body's ability to "clean up" dysfunctional cells, such as beta-amyloid) and *ketosis* (the generation of ketones, molecules that can help protect neurons). It also reduces insulin.

- **Reduce stress.** Pick a relaxing, enjoyable activity—walking in the woods, yoga, meditation, playing the piano, etc.—and do it once a day or every other day for at least 20 to 30 minutes.

Why it works: Stress destroys neurons in the *hippocampus*, the part of the brain that helps create short- and long-term memory. Stress also boosts *cortisol*, a synapse-damaging hormone. And stress increases *corticotropin-releasing factor* (CRF), a hormone linked to Alzheimer's.

- **Optimize sleep.** Sleep seven to eight hours every night.

Why it works: Anatomical changes during sleep flush the brain of toxic, synapse-damaging compounds. If you have trouble sleeping, we have found that 0.5 milligrams (mg) of *melatonin* at bedtime is the best dose for restorative sleep.

- **Exercise regularly.** I recommend 30 to 60 minutes per day, four to six days per week. Combining aerobic exercise (such as brisk walking) with weight-training is ideal.

Why it works: Among its many benefits, exercise produces *brain-derived neurotrophic factor* (BDNF), a powerfully synaptoblastic compound.

- **Stimulate your brain.** Brain-training exercises and games stimulate and improve your ability to remember, pay attention, process information quickly and creatively navigate daily life.

Why it works: Just as using muscle builds muscle, using synapses builds synapses. (Scientists call this ability of the brain to change and grow *plasticity*.)

Helpful: Brain HQ (*BrainHQ.com*) and Lumosity (*Lumosity.com*) are good, science-based online programs for stimulating your brain.

• **Take folate, vitamin B-6 and vitamin B-12.** These three nutrients can reduce blood levels of the amino acid *homocysteine*, which is linked to an increase in tau, increased age-related shrinkage of the hippocampus and double the risk for Alzheimer's disease.

However: To work, these supplements must undergo a biochemical process called *methylation*—and many older people don't "methylate" well, rendering the supplements nearly useless. To avoid the problem, take a form of the supplements that already is methylated (or activated)—folate as *L-methylfolate*, B-6 as *pyridoxal-5-phosphate* and B-12 as *methylcobalamin*.

• **Take other targeted supplements.** Along with the three B vitamins, there are many other supplements that target synaptoblastic and synaptoclastic factors. Check with your doctor about the right dosages. The supplements include vitamin D-3 (low levels double the risk for Alzheimer's)...vitamin K-2...vitamin E (as mixed tocopherols and tocotrienols)...the minerals selenium, magnesium and zinc (zinc, for example, lowers copper, which is linked to Alzheimer's)...DHA and EPA (anti-inflammatory omega-3 fatty acids)...coenzyme Q10, N-acetylcysteine, alpha-lipoic acid (they nourish *mitochondria*, energy-generating structures within cells)...and probiotics (they improve the *microbiome*, helping to strengthen the lining of the gut, reducing body-wide inflammation).

Also, certain herbs can be helpful. These include curcumin (1 gram [g] per day), ashwagandha (500 mg once or twice per day) and bacopa monnieri (200 mg to 300 mg per day). These have multiple effects, such as reducing inflammation and amyloid-beta peptide and enhancing neurotransmission.

TAKE NOTE...

Good News for Grandmas!

Postmenopausal women who took care of their grandchildren one day a week had better memory and faster cognitive speed (important for warding off dementia) than those who didn't.

Possible explanation: Active grandparenting includes positive interactions, ongoing learning and mental stimulation—all of which reduce risk for dementia.

Be careful, though...women who cared for grandchildren five or more days a week had significantly lower cognitive scores, possibly because they felt exhausted.

Cassandra Szoeke, MD, PhD, associate professor of medicine, The University of Melbourne, Australia.

A Spice That Reverses Brain Damage

When mice consumed cinnamon, it was converted into *sodium benzoate*, a compound that may improve motor functions and reverse brain damage caused by Parkinson's disease.

Journal of Neuroimmune Pharmacology.

Are You "Almost Depressed"? How to Get Out from Under That Dark Cloud...

Jefferson Prince, MD, an instructor in psychiatry at Harvard Medical School, Boston, and director of child psychiatry at MassGeneral Hospital for Children in Salem, Massachusetts. He is coauthor of *Almost Depressed: Is My (or My Loved One's) Unhappiness a Problem?*

Most people know if they're suffering from deep depression. But what's that vaguely uncomfortable, empty feeling you may have had lately? You're not

SELF-TEST...

Almost Depressed? Find Out Below...

Do any of the following statements apply to you?

- I get more frustrated than usual over little things.
- Instead of having fun with friends, I avoid them.
- I haven't been sleeping well lately.
- Nothing tastes very good.
- I would like to "stop the world" and take a break from everything.
- Nothing seems very funny (or interesting or exciting) these days.
- I get irritated more easily than I used to.
- I'm less interested in sex.
- I just want to be left alone.
- I have trouble concentrating on books or TV.
- I feel tired for no reason.

If you recognize yourself in two or more of these statements, you're likely almost depressed.

miserable, but it's as if the vitality has been sucked out of your life.

Though it often goes undiagnosed, so-called "almost depression" may have snuck up on you. It can prevent you from enjoying your leisure activities and leave you feeling unsatisfied with your family life, friendships and work.

Don't pooh-pooh it: You may be tempted to ignore these often subtle, though persistent, feelings of discontent. But don't. Almost depression can throw you into a downward spiral that deepens into serious depression—a condition that may increase your risk for chronic physical ailments such as heart disease and dementia.

The good news is that almost depression responds well to some surprising, life-affirming strategies that don't necessarily involve the conventional treatments (such as medication and/or therapy) that are usually prescribed for depression.

What you need to know now about almost depression...

LOOKING FOR CLUES

If you have almost depression, life may generally seem bland and gray. You haven't stopped eating, but nothing tastes very good. You still laugh at jokes...but just to be polite. These are red flags that the brain circuits responsible for processing your feelings of pleasure (the brain's "reward system") may have shifted into low gear—this is widely considered to be an underlying cause of almost depression.

Often, close friends and family members can see changes first. If you think you may be almost depressed, ask someone you trust for his/her candid opinion. For more signs of almost depression, see box at left.

GETTING BACK ON TRACK

If you are like most people, you can pull yourself out of almost depression—the trick is to take steps to rev up your brain's sluggish reward system. *The best ways to do that...**

- **Get up and at 'em.** Idleness due to illness or an emotional setback is a common trigger of almost depression. Fortunately, scientists are now finding more and more evidence that exercise improves mood, possibly by altering brain chemistry. In several studies, regular workouts were as effective as antidepressants. But of course, the longer you are inactive, the harder it is to get going—and a trip to the gym may sound impossible.

Best approach: Start by adding just a bit more activity to your day...the 10-minute walk you take is far better than the strenuous workout you avoid. Tomorrow, you may want to take a longer walk or do some gardening. Put yourself in motion...add a bit more activity week by week...and see what happens. It will be good!

- **Put more meaning in your life.** Do you often wonder, *What's all this for?* Almost depression can be a sign that you lack a sense of

*If you suspect that you are almost depressed, and there's no improvement after trying the strategies in this article, see your doctor for advice. Many physical conditions (such as diabetes, lung disease and cancer) can cause depressive symptoms, as can some blood pressure and cholesterol drugs, antibiotics and other medications. If none of these apply to your situation, your doctor may refer you to a mental-health professional, such as a psychiatrist or psychologist.

purpose for your life. Take a good look at your values. For some people, family comes first, and for others, it's career, spiritual growth or health. The key is, any of these can give you a sense of purpose.

Best approach: Identify your two or three top values. And be honest with yourself. You may think "helping others" should be your ultimate concern, but if, say, financial security actually takes priority, there's nothing wrong with making that your goal.

Then start including activities to promote these two or three values every day. Also look for small actions that promote your values. To "improve the lives of others," you don't have to volunteer at a soup kitchen—a smile or doing a favor for a stranger counts, too. Give yourself credit for these moments.

• **Let your creativity run wild.** When you scratch beneath the surface, most people with almost depression have bottled-up emotions. Expressing these dark feelings through a creative outlet is liberating—and healing. Don't worry about being talented...just allow yourself to tap into your creative side.

To express yourself: Set aside 20 minutes to write on a computer or by hand about something that's bothering you. Don't edit your feelings—no one will see this but you. In fact, you don't ever need to look at your writing again...the benefit is in the process, not the product.

The next day, write down a story about your life. It's human nature to see life as a narrative with heroes, villains and victims. Being almost depressed puts you in a story that isn't going so well. So go ahead and rewrite your personal narrative. Create a story where the main character has problems like yours but works things out—perhaps through personal change or new insights. The character you invent may teach you some useful strategies—and you will emerge happier.

If you're more of a visual person, you can draw or paint images that will help unleash trapped emotions. Whatever approach you choose, allow your creativity to flourish.

Gardening Is Good for Your Health!

Time to clean up the yard? Plant some flowers? Why? Outdoor chores are good for your mental and physical health. In a recent study, clinically depressed adults who spent six hours a week gardening reported a significant decline in depression and improved attention span after 12 weeks. Outdoor exercise, which is believed to reduce stress hormones, also improves sleep quality and burns calories.

Marianne Thorsen Gonzalez, PhD, researcher, Diakonhjemmet University College, Oslo, Norway.

Natural Cures for Anger

Jamison Starbuck, ND, a naturopathic physician in family practice and a guest lecturer at the University of Montana, both in Missoula. She is also a past president of the American Association of Naturopathic Physicians and a contributing editor to *The Alternative Advisor: The Complete Guide to Natural Therapies and Alternative Treatments.*

Explosive and out-of-control anger is not only harmful to relationships at home, work and/or school, it is also hard on the *health* of the angry person. Heart rate, blood pressure and the digestive system can all be affected. To curb anger, conventional doctors use both psychotherapy and prescription medications (such as antidepressants and tranquilizers). These two treatments can help. But among the many patients I've treated for anger problems, lifestyle changes and natural medicine offer longer-lasting results. It's normal and healthy to feel and appropriately express anger, but when it becomes excessive, problems can develop.

If you are struggling with anger, here's my advice...*

• **Watch your diet.** A good first step is to reduce known dietary nuisances such as caffeine, alcohol and high-sugar foods—all of

*If you have a chronic medical condition or take medication, talk to your physician before trying any supplements.

which affect the brain and can interfere with your ability to cope with anger.

• **Review your hormone health.** Women can experience significantly worse anger when they are premenstrual or going through menopause. In men, anger often kicks up during middle age when their testosterone levels are waning. For both males and females, anger is common during puberty. If you suspect that your anger may be tied to your hormone health, ask your doctor about testing your *testosterone*, *estrogen* and *progesterone* levels. Both men and women have all three of these hormones, and for optimal emotional health, all three should be correctly balanced.

• **Check for allergens.** All kinds of allergies can wreak havoc with one's emotional stability. Whether you're allergic to inhalants (such as pollen, pet dander or dust) or to foods (such as dairy, wheat or eggs), these allergens can cause big problems. Sometimes, the only symptom of an allergy is emotional distress, irritability and/or volatile anger.

If you have frequent anger: Keep a diary of explosive events and the foods you ate and possible allergens in your environment during the 12-hour period prior to your angry feelings. Look for patterns. If you suspect a link, speak to your doctor about allergy testing.

• **Get more B vitamins.** Anger is often linked to fatigue and low blood sugar. Vitamins B-5 (*pantothenic acid*) and B-6 (*pyridoxine*), in particular, can help with both conditions. To ensure that your B vitamin levels are balanced, look for a B-complex supplement that includes B-5 and B-6.

• **Try botanical medicines.** Gentler than pharmaceuticals, herbal remedies can calm emotions without dulling the brain.

My favorite anger-fighting herbs: Passionflower and skullcap. Pick a product (tincture, capsule or tea) containing either one or both of these herbs. Start with a low dose. Take it for several days to see whether your anger is improving. If it's not, slowly increase the dose, but do not exceed the manufacturer's recommended dose. Use during high-stress periods or any time that anger is a problem.

Hypnosis Heals: 6 Medical Problems It's Been Proven to Help

Marc I. Oster, PsyD, a psychologist and professor of clinical psychology at the Illinois School of Professional Psychology at Argosy University in Schaumburg, Illinois. He is a fellow and past president of the American Society of Clinical Hypnosis. *MarcOster.Homestead.com*

Don't confuse medical hypnosis with the flamboyant stage shows. Hypnosis-enhanced therapy is a legitimate treatment for various medical problems—and unlike many treatments, it is noninvasive and totally safe. *What hypnosis really helps...*

IRRITABLE BOWEL SYNDROME (IBS)

IBS is a mysterious, often debilitating condition that causes cramps and intermittent episodes of diarrhea, pain and constipation. Medications to treat it aren't very effective.

Several well-designed studies of hypnotherapy for IBS have shown that IBS patients who were treated with hypnosis had "substantial, long-term improvement" of gastrointestinal symptoms, along with less anxiety and depression. It's possible that hypnosis alters how the central nervous system responds to intestinal signals. It also diverts people's attention from their intestinal sensations and causes them to perceive less discomfort.

PAIN RELIEF

Hypnosis doesn't necessarily reduce pain, but it does alter how people react to it. Studies have shown, for example, that hypnotized dental patients have a higher pain threshold. They also have less anxiety, which reduces sensitivity to pain. One study, which looked at patients with burn injuries, used virtual-reality technology to induce hypnosis. Patients wore a fiber-optic helmet that immersed them in a make-believe environment. As they descended into a snowy, three-dimensional canyon, an audiotape with a clinician's voice prepared them for what they would experience during the treatment of the burn.

Result: They had a decrease in both pain and anxiety—and their need for potent painkillers was reduced by half.

HELP QUITTING SMOKING

About 65% to 70% of smokers who are treated with medical hypnosis quit successfully, according to research. That's much better than the quit rate from going cold turkey (about 20%) or using stop-smoking drugs including nicotine therapy (35% to 40%).

Hypnosis isn't a miracle cure for smoking or other addictions. Anyone who takes the time to schedule appointments with a therapist already is highly motivated. The success rate would be lower for those who remain on the fence about quitting. That said, hypnosis still is more effective than standard treatments.

BETTER CANCER CARE

The radiation therapy that's used to treat some cancers often causes fatigue as a side effect. Researchers from Mount Sinai Hospital in New York City found that cancer patients who underwent hypnosis during a common kind of counseling called cognitive-behavioral therapy experienced less fatigue than participants in a control group. The study, published in *Journal of Clinical Oncology*, showed that after six months, the average patient treated with hypnosis had less fatigue than 95% of those who weren't hypnotized.

LESS SURGICAL PAIN

Another study of cancer patients found that those who had a single, 15-minute hypnosis session prior to their surgery required less sedation and experienced less nausea, pain and fatigue than those in a nonhypnosis group.

Mount Sinai researchers analyzed 20 studies on hypnosis and surgery, and they found that in 89% of cases, hypnotized surgical patients had less pain, used less pain medication and recovered faster.

CHRONIC FATIGUE

A six-month study at Beth Israel Deaconess Medical Center, Boston, showed that 73% of participants who had chronic fatigue syndrome reported increased energy, more restful periods of sleep and better concentration at work. On average, only 23% improve with other types of therapy.

HOW YOU CAN TRY HYPNOSIS

Because of its long association with parlor tricks, hypnosis still is a subject of confusion.

A few facts: You don't go into a trance during hypnosis...you are more in control of yourself than usual, not less...and you won't do anything that you don't want to do.

A specially trained therapist will use guided imagery to focus and direct your imagination. It is the same technique sometimes used during meditation. *Example:* While you relax, the therapist will encourage you to breathe slowly and deeply...to imagine a soothing scene (such as walking in the woods)...and to keep your mind focused on just that one thing. This is known as the induction phase. Your brain activity slows, but you still are focused and alert.

At this point, medical hypnosis diverges from traditional meditation. While you are in a relaxed state, the therapist will guide your thinking toward particular issues. Suppose that you have arthritis and that your arm always hurts. The therapist might describe a scene in which you're walking to a lake...submerging yourself in icy water...and feeling your arm go pleasantly numb. The positive effects can last for minutes to hours to forever.

Research has shown that people who are mentally and physically relaxed are more receptive to taking in new ideas and feeling in new ways.

To find a hypnotist who can help you, look for a licensed health-care professional who offers hypnosis as only one part of his/her practice. Someone who only does hypnosis may not have the understanding of health-care issues to properly diagnose and treat you. The websites for the American Society of Clinical Hypnosis (*ASCH.net*) and the Society for Clinical & Experimental Hypnosis (*SCEH.us*) can help you find an expert in your area.

Expect to complete between four and 10 sessions. Depending on where you live, you might pay about $150 for a session with a psychologist.* You will pay less if you see a social worker, nurse or mental-health counselor.

Most insurance companies do not cover hypnosis per se, but they may cover therapy that includes hypnosis. Medicare covers "hypnotherapy" for certain conditions.

*Price subject to change.

Private & Personal

Big Feet, Big **** and Other Myths About Sex

Despite our sexually saturated society, Americans can be shockingly naïve about what's true and what is not about sex—and some myths just won't die.

Here, the most common myths and the truth...

MEN THINK ABOUT SEX ALL THE TIME

It has been widely reported—and often repeated in social media—that men think about sex every seven seconds. That would mean that men are having sexual thoughts about every time they take a breath. Impossible!

But men do think about sex more often than women do. In one study, 54% of the men surveyed said that they had sexual thoughts every day or several times a day. Among women, 19% thought about sex with the same frequency.

MEN DOING THE LAUNDRY TURNS WOMEN ON

True or false: A man who really wants sex should simply roll up his sleeves and do a load of laundry. His wife will tear his clothes off.

Answer: True *and* false. Women report higher levels of marital satisfaction when husbands help out around the house. And marital satisfaction is correlated with sexual desire in some studies, so perhaps housework will lead to satisfaction and satisfaction will lead to more desire.

But the laundry itself may be incidental—or, paradoxically, even detrimental. Data from the National Survey of Families and Households showed that couples actually had less sex when men did more of the "core" house-

---

Aaron E. Carroll, MD, MS, a professor of pediatrics at Indiana University School of Medicine, director of the Center for Health Policy and Professionalism Research and director of the Center for Pediatric and Adolescent Comparative Effectiveness Research. He is author, with Rachel C. Vreeman, MD, of *Don't Put That in There! And 69 Other Sex Myths Debunked.*

work (laundry, dishes, cleaning house, etc.), compared with couples in which the men did more traditional "man-typed" tasks, such as car repairs and yard work.

BIG FEET, BIG ****

No one wants to stare (or get caught staring) at the area beneath a man's belt. Is sneaking a peek at his feet a less embarrassing way to check his endowment?

It's not a reliable measure. In one survey (often referred to as "The Definitive Penis Size Survey"), 3,100 men reported information about the size of their penises and their other characteristics. It found no connection between erect penis size and shoe size.

By all means, check out a man's feet—but only if you're curious about his taste in shoes.

CHOCOLATE IS AN APHRODISIAC

Throughout history, people have believed that certain foods—such as chocolate, oysters and asparagus—are aphrodisiacs that increase sexual desire and performance.

There might be a kernel of truth to it. Chocolate, for example, contains compounds that dilate blood vessels and can potentially help a man get erections. Other compounds in chocolate stimulate the release of neurotransmitters that improve mood. People who feel good are more likely to want to have sex.

But there's nothing in chocolate, oysters or other foods that will stimulate desire in people. On the other hand, if you like those foods, there's no reason not to eat them.

WOMEN ARE TURNED OFF BY SWEATY, STINKY MEN

It seems like common sense that women would be turned off by sweaty, stinky men. Not so!

A group of scientists at University of California, Berkeley, conducted a study of how certain components of male sweat affected women. They found that women who smelled a component of male sweat called *androstadienone* had improved mood and reported more sexual arousal. They also saw their blood pressure increase, their heart rates go up and their breathing become more rapid.

SEX IS GREAT FOR WEIGHT LOSS

If you have frequent, vigorous sex that lasts as long as a run on the treadmill, you'll probably lose a bit of weight. Otherwise, forget about it.

You will burn calories during sex—anywhere from 85 to 150 calories in 30 minutes. But who has sex for a half-hour? The average duration of a sexual encounter is about five minutes—and the biggest increase in metabolism occurs for only about 15 seconds during orgasm. At that rate, you would have to have a lot of sex to lose weight.

SEX OFTEN CAUSES HEART ATTACKS

As discussed above, sex isn't nearly as strenuous as people think. The physical exertion that most people put in when having sex is similar to walking up two flights of stairs. If you're generally healthy, your risk of having a heart attack during sex is about one in a million. (The chance of being hit by lightning in a given year is one in 700,000.)

What if you already have heart disease? You still shouldn't worry. If you are able to pass a basic stress test, your risk of having a heart attack during sex increases to only 10 in a million.

Exceptions: Anyone who has recently had a heart attack or stroke or other cardiovascular event should talk to his/her doctor about the types of activities that he should or shouldn't do. Sex is unlikely to be on the "don't" list.

TAKE NOTE...

How to Tell If It's Love or Lust

Your eyes can reveal if you want love or lust. People who are interested in making a meaningful connection tend to make eye contact. People who are interested only in sex tend to focus on the body.

Study by researchers at University of Chicago and University of Geneva, Switzerland, published in *Psychological Science*.

5 Things That Can Ruin a Man's Sex Life

Steven Lamm, MD, a practicing internist, faculty member at New York University School of Medicine and director of men's health for NYU Langone Medical Center, both in New York City. He is author of several books, including *The Hardness Factor: How to Achieve Your Best Health and Sexual Fitness at Any Age. DrStevenLamm.com*

An erection is a manly miracle—a complex, coordinated effort of brain, blood vessels, nerves, muscles and hormones that increases blood flow to the penis sixfold. But because so much has to go right for a man to have an erection, there's also a lot that can go wrong.

The problem is called *erectile dysfunction* (ED)—the inability to get or sustain an erection hard enough to have enjoyable and satisfying sex. And it's a very common problem. Nearly one in five men have ED, including 44% of men ages 60 to 69 and 70% of men 70 and older.

A prescription ED drug such as *sildenafil* (Viagra), *vardenafil* (Levitra) or *tadalafil* (Cialis) can help. But this pharmaceutical solution isn't necessarily the best solution, because ED drugs don't address the underlying causes of ED—some of which can kill you.

What most men don't realize: An erection is the best barometer of a man's overall health—particularly the health of his circulatory system. The easier it is to achieve erections, the healthier the man. By identifying and correcting the factors that might be undermining erections, a man not only can restore his sex life—he might save his life.

Here, five factors that can ruin a man's sex life and what to do about them...

HEART DISEASE

An artery leads directly to the penis and subdivides into three more arteries, supplying the robust flow of blood on which an erection depends. If those arteries are narrowed or blocked, it's likely that there's a problem with all your arteries—including the arteries supplying blood to your heart.

Troubling recent finding: A decade-long study published in *Journal of Sexual Medicine* shows that men over age 50 with ED are 2.5 times more likely to develop heart disease, and men under age 50 are 58% more likely. And a study of men with ED who were already diagnosed with heart disease shows that they are twice as likely to have a heart attack and 90% more likely to die of heart disease, compared with men who have heart disease but not ED.

What to do: Adopt a Mediterranean diet, emphasizing vegetables, fruits, whole grains, beans, fish and healthy fats (in olive oil, avocado and nuts). It's a diet proven to prevent and treat heart disease—and several studies from Italy show that a Mediterranean diet also can prevent and cure ED.

Other conditions that increase the risk for ED: Type 2 diabetes, obesity, gout and sleep apnea—and studies show that these conditions also are helped with a Mediterranean diet.

Important: If you have ED, make an appointment with your doctor, tell him/her about your problem and ask for a complete workup to check for cardiovascular disease.

ALCOHOL

Alcohol is a central nervous system depressant, and despite what many people think, it dampens sexual arousal—and that's particularly true for older men.

What to do: Limit yourself to no more than one to two drinks per day. (A drink is one 12-ounce beer, a four-ounce glass of wine, 1.5 ounces of 80-proof spirits or one ounce of 100-proof spirits.)

What not to do: Washing down fried foods with beer (or any alcohol) is a double whammy. Eating fried food immediately spikes the level of blood fats such as triglycerides, impeding blood flow to the penis for several hours.

MEDICATIONS

ED can be a side effect of taking one or more prescription medicines. The most common offenders are drugs to treat high blood pressure, heart ailments, depression and allergies.

Telltale sign: You start a new medication, and you suddenly notice that you're having erectile difficulties.

What to do: Talk to your doctor about using a different medication to treat your health problem. For example, one class of antidepressants (*selective serotonin reuptake inhibitors*, or SSRIs) often leads to libido and ejaculation problems contributing to ED, but the antidepressant *bupropion* (Wellbutrin) rarely does.

LACK OF EXERCISE

Regular exercise lowers your heart rate and blood pressure and helps clear life-threatening plaque from arteries—all of which translates into preventing or reversing ED.

Important finding: A recent study in *Journal of Sexual Medicine* found that men who have risk factors for heart disease were 50% more likely to suffer from ED if they did not exercise regularly. Another study shows that exercise can improve ED even in men who are already taking a drug for ED.

What to do: Walk! It is a proven way to prevent and treat ED. When researchers from Duke University studied men with an average age of 62, they found that those who walked briskly for 30 minutes, four days a week, were 66% less likely to have ED.

STRESS

Too much stress can undermine erections by slowing the production of hormones (including *testosterone*, the master male hormone) and by impeding blood flow to the penis.

What to do: The best way to reduce stress is to spend at least 20 to 30 minutes a day doing something you personally enjoy—whether it's watching your favorite comedian on Netflix, participating in a hobby such as woodworking or going for a walk with your dog.

TAKE NOTE...

A Dangerous Position

The most dangerous sexual position for men is the woman on the top. Nearly half of all penile injuries caused by sex occurred in this position.

Possible reason: The woman has more control when on top, the man has her entire weight on his penis, and the man is least able to stop the sex if he is feeling pain.

Study of 42 patients with penile fractures led by researchers at University of Campinas, Brazil, published in *Advances in Urology*.

Nice Side Effect of Statins

Statins can boost sexual performance in men with *erectile dysfunction* (ED) who are taking the drugs to reduce cholesterol. Erectile function scores were 24% better in men taking statin medications than in men not using them. Statins may improve erectile function by helping blood vessels dilate properly and boosting blood flow to the penis.

Analysis of 11 clinical trials involving a total of 647 people by researchers at Robert Wood Johnson Medical School, Rutgers University, New Brunswick, New Jersey, published in *Journal of Sexual Medicine*.

More Pleasure for Women...

Testosterone is known as the "male" hormone—but women's bodies produce some, too. A testosterone deficiency in women may lead to lack of interest in sex. Prescription testosterone cream, which is compounded by a pharmacist and applied to the clitoris in small amounts—0.05 milligrams (mg) to 1 mg—daily, can help improve sensation, desire and arousal. It also increases the size of the clitoris (which may be diminished in postmenopausal women), making it more accessible. The treatment may take a month or more to work.

Barbara Bartlik, MD, a sex therapist in private practice and assistant professor, Weill Cornell Medical College, New York City.

How Orgasms Improve Communication

After orgasm, people are more likely to share important information with their partners.

Possible explanation: Orgasm raises the body's production of the hormone *oxytocin*, which is linked to social bonding and increased trust. This may make people feel safe about disclosing information.

But: Alcohol, which is widely thought to cause people to tell more of their secrets, does the opposite—immediately after sex, people who have been drinking may say things they had not planned to disclose, but what they reveal is less important and less positive. Alcohol, combined with failing to have an orgasm, produces even more negativity.

Study of 253 people, ages 18 to 45, by researchers at University of Connecticut, Storrs, published in *Communication Monographs*.

Medication May Blunt Love

Sexual dysfunction is a well-known side effect of long-term antidepressant use, but a recent study shows that these drugs may actually stifle feelings of love and attachment toward partners, especially among men. The effect was stronger for men taking *selective serotonin reuptake inhibitors* (SSRIs), such as *paroxetine* (Paxil) and *escitalopram* (Lexapro), than for those taking tricyclic antidepressants, such as *clomipramine* (Anafranil).

Donatella Marazziti, MD, professor of psychiatry at University of Pisa, Italy.

Alcohol Lowers Sperm Count

The more alcohol younger men drink, the lower their sperm count. Men who consumed 40 or more drinks a week had sperm concentrations 33% lower than men who consumed five drinks a week.

Study of more than 1,200 men, ages 18 to 28, led by researchers at University of Southern Denmark in Odense, published in *BMJ Open*.

BETTER WAYS...

Note to Wannabe Fathers...

Get your cell phone out of your pants pocket!

Recent finding: Cell phone radiation from a pants pocket may damage sperm and could interfere with fertility.

Environmental International.

Powerful PMS Prevention

Green veggies can halt PMS. Three servings per day of cooked green cruciferous vegetables such as kale, broccoli and brussels sprouts cut risk of developing premenstrual syndrome (PMS) by up to 40%, according to a 10-year study of nearly 3,000 women.

Why: Green cruciferous vegetables are high in iron, which is necessary to produce mood-elevating neurotransmitters in the brain.

Patricia Chocano-Bedoya, PhD, visiting scientist at Harvard School of Public Health, Boston.

Hot Flash Drug Does Double Duty

A new drug for menopausal hot flashes may also prevent osteoporosis.

Recent finding: Women taking the drug Duavee had 74% fewer moderate-to-severe hot flashes, compared with just 47% in women taking a placebo. It also significantly increased bone mineral density in the hip and spine.

The drug is not recommended for use by women who have a history of blood clots, bleeding disorders, liver problems or breast or uterine cancer.

Michelle Warren, MD, founder and medical director of the Center for Menopause, Hormonal Disorders & Women's Health, Columbia University Medical Center, New York City.

Better Hot Flash Defense

Hot flashes? Don't sweat it. That's the conclusion of research involving about 200 menopausal women.

Study details: Women who have the highest levels of "self-compassion"—that is, the ability to go easy on one's self in difficult or embarrassing situations—find hot flashes and night sweats to be less disruptive than do women who are self-critical.

If you suffer from hot flashes: Try gently telling yourself that this will pass, or make a physical gesture such as placing your hand over your heart.

Lydia Brown, MA, doctoral researcher, The University of Melbourne, Australia.

It's Not Too Late for Estrogen Therapy

A woman who went through menopause nine years ago at age 45 recently asked me if she was past the "window" for estrogen therapy.

My answer to her: You haven't missed the "window" for starting estrogen, especially since you had an early menopause and you're only 54 years old now—that's young! It is generally considered safest to begin estrogen therapy within 10 years after menopause, but this is not a rigid rule.

Some women may decide years after menopause that they would like to begin estrogen (to curb hot flashes or night sweats, for example), and this calls for personalized decision-making that weighs the benefits versus the risks for the individual patient. Estrogen has been found to raise risk for blood clots, stroke and breast and ovarian cancer (especially when taken with progestin). Some women who are not candidates for the pill form of estrogen may still be able to take a low-dose skin patch, gel or spray.

JoAnn E. Manson, MD, DrPH, professor of medicine and women's health, Harvard Medical School, Boston.

BREAKTHROUGH...

Cancer Milestone

A new breast cancer vaccine primes the immune system to attack *mammaglobin A*, a protein produced by cancer cells. About half of the breast cancer patients given the experimental vaccine showed no cancer progression after one year. More research is needed.

Clinical Cancer Research.

Don't Blame Bras

Bras do not raise risk for breast cancer. Some media reports have suggested that wearing a bra may inhibit lymph circulation and drainage, boosting breast cancer risk. *But:* A recent study found that there is no connection between wearing a bra and breast cancer risk.

Study of more than 1,000 women by researchers at Fred Hutchinson Research Center, Seattle, published in *Cancer Epidemiology, Biomarkers & Prevention.*

High Cholesterol Raises Risk for Breast Cancer

A recent British study found that women diagnosed with high cholesterol, defined by counts higher than 200 milligrams per deciliter (mg/dL), were 64% more likely to develop breast cancer than women without high cholesterol. Researchers reviewed the medical records of 664,159 female patients between 2000 and 2013. The researchers decided to do the study after a mouse study in 2013 linked aggressive breast cancer to a chemical created by the body's processing of cholesterol. Additional research is needed to confirm the findings. In the meantime, there is strong evidence that exercising regularly and maintaining a healthy weight can help lower the risk of developing breast cancer after menopause. The British study also suggests that taking statins (prescription drugs to reduce high cholesterol) could help prevent breast cancer, but a clinical trial of the use of statins for breast cancer would need to be conducted before statins could be prescribed for that.

Rahul Potluri, MD, honorary clinical lecturer in cardiology, Aston Medical School, Aston University, Birmingham, England. He is lead author of the ACALM study presented at the Frontiers in CardioVascular Biology 2014 Conference in Barcelona.

Why You Should Ask About Your Breast Tissue

Mary Pronovost, MD, a breast surgeon at Bridgeport Hospital in Connecticut.

About 40% of women have dense breasts, but 95% of them don't know it. Why does this matter? Studies have shown that women with dense breasts are more likely to develop breast cancer. Small tumors that are readily apparent on mammograms of "normal" breasts are harder to spot in dense breast tissue. You can't see or feel breast density...it shows up only on mammograms.

Recent development: In 24 states, the law now requires women to be told when they receive their mammograms whether they have dense breast tissue. (Legislation is pending elsewhere.) The laws also require doctors to inform women that tumors may be invisible on mammograms...and that additional tests should be considered. Does this added information really help? *Pros and cons...*

It's true that ultrasound or an MRI can detect tumors that mammography misses, but research has not shown that finding these cancers saves more lives. For many women, the cancers are not life-threatening.

Many women also experience tremendous anxiety when they learn from these other tests that a tumor might be present. They're more likely to undergo costly biopsies, many of which will prove to be unnecessary. Of course, some of the tumors will be serious enough to require treatment.

Best advice for now: After your next mammogram, ask about breast tissue, particularly if you live in a nondisclosure state—and ask your doctor if he/she advises further tests.

Keep Getting That Mammogram!

Don't let a recent study on mammograms stop you from getting screened. According to the Canadian study, mammograms do not cut mortality risk and they cause many women to receive unnecessary treatment.

But: Eight large studies show that the survival rates for women who had yearly mammograms were 20% higher than for those who had less frequent screening.

Bottom line: Women should continue to follow current guidelines—which recommend annual mammograms starting at age 40 for most women.

Margarita Zuley, MD, associate professor of radiology and medical director of breast imaging at University of Pittsburgh/Magee-Womens Hospital.

Breast Cancer Treatment with Fewer Side Effects

In a recent study, women with the most common form of noninvasive breast cancer who rubbed a *tamoxifen* gel into their breast tissue daily for six to 10 weeks had similar antitumor effects as those who took oral tamoxifen daily.

Possible reason: The drug was present in equal amounts in the breast tissue of both groups.

Bonus: Blood levels in the gel group were much lower than in those taking oral tamoxifen, which could result in fewer side effects, such as blood clots.

Seema A. Khan, MD, professor of surgery, Northwestern University Feinberg School of Medicine, Chicago.

Breast Cancer Drug May Cause Heart Issues

The breast cancer drug Herceptin may cause heart problems, but these problems typically reverse once treatment is over. Herceptin caused a reduction in the heart's pumping force in 5% of patients who took the drug for one year. Congestive cardiac failure occurred in less than 1% of patients.

Bottom line: Women should have a cardiac assessment before starting Herceptin and cardiac monitoring while taking it.

Brian Leyland-Jones, MBBS, PhD, vice president of molecular and experimental medicine, Avera Cancer Institute, Sioux Falls, South Dakota.

Better Radiation for Breast Cancer

Many breast cancer patients get radiation for longer than they need. Three to five weeks of post-lumpectomy radiation is now recommended for women over age 50 who have not had chemotherapy or lymph node involvement.

However: About two-thirds of women in this group are receiving the less intense conventional treatment, which lasts five to seven weeks. The two schedules involve about the same total amount of radiation, have similar side effects and are equally effective—but the shorter treatment is more convenient for patients and less expensive (*average difference*: $2,894).

Justin Bekelman, MD, assistant professor of radiation oncology at Perelman School of Medicine, University of Pennsylvania, Philadelphia, and lead author of a study of 15,643 lumpectomy patients, published in *JAMA*.

Before You Get Fibroids Removed...

The procedure for removal of fibroids can spread cancer. Many women have noncancerous fibroid growths in the walls of their uteruses. These fibroids are sometimes removed using *power morcellation*—a surgical procedure in which a rotating blade grinds up the fibroids. The fragments then are extracted through a small incision.

Problem: If a patient has an undiagnosed uterine cancer, the procedure may disperse malignant cells into the abdomen.

Linda Bradley, MD, vice-chair of obstetrics and gynecology at Cleveland Clinic, Ohio. She also is director of the clinic's Center for Menstrual Disorders, Fibroids & Hysteroscopic Services.

HRT Raises Ovarian Cancer Risk 40%

Ovarian cancer risk rises by 40% when receiving *hormone replacement therapy* (HRT)—even in women who take it for less than five years. HRT is used to relieve menopausal symptoms.

Best: Consult your physician about alternative treatments. And, women who choose HRT should use it for as short a time and at as low a dose as possible. The risk slowly declines after treatment is stopped.

Sir Richard Peto, FRS, professor of medical statistics and epidemiology at University of Oxford, England, and coauthor of an analysis published in *The Lancet*.

BREAKTHROUGH...

New Ovarian Cancer Drug Shows Promise

A new ovarian cancer drug shrinks tumors for eight months, on average. Lynparza (*olaparib*) is for women who have received at least three rounds of chemotherapy for advanced ovarian cancer associated with abnormal inherited BRCA genes. Trials are ongoing.

Edward J. Pavlik, PhD, director of the ovarian screening research program, Markey Cancer Center, Lexington, Kentucky.

Irregular Periods Can Double Ovarian Cancer Risk

Women with irregular periods may have double the risk for ovarian cancer, compared with women who have regular monthly periods.

Best: If you have irregular periods or if you have a condition called *polycystic ovarian syndrome*, ask your doctor if you should be screened for ovarian cancer.

Study of more than 14,000 women led by Barbara A. Cohn, PhD, MPH, director of Child Health and Development Studies at the Public Health Institute in Oakland, California, presented at the annual meeting of the American Association for Cancer Research, San Diego.

Cervical Cancer Much More Common Than Previously Thought

Earlier estimates of cervical cancer included women who had had hysterectomies. When they were excluded from the statistics, the actual rate of cervical cancer rose to 18.6 cases per 100,000 women.

Self-defense: The US Preventive Services Task Force recommends that women ages 21 to 65 have a Pap smear every three years...and women ages 30 to 65 be tested for HPV every five years.

Anne F. Rositch, PhD, MSPH, assistant professor, epidemiology, Johns Hopkins Bloomberg School of Public Health, Baltimore.

No More UTIs! The Best Ways to Avoid These Common and Troublesome Infections

Tomas L. Griebling, MD, MPH, the John P. Wolf 33° Masonic Distinguished Professor of Urology at The University of Kansas (KU) School of Medicine in Kansas City. He is a professor and vice-chair in the department of urology and faculty associate in The Landon Center on Aging. He has published more than 200 articles in peer-reviewed medical journals.

Anyone who has ever had a urinary tract infection (UTI) knows that it can be extremely unpleasant. The first clue may be that your urine is smelly and/or looks cloudy. You could also suffer burning or pain during urination, have blood in your urine and a fever or chills. To make matters worse, many people suffer repeated UTIs, and some doctors don't do much more than prescribe an antibiotic each time.

Good news: Studies now show that there are some surprisingly simple steps you can take to help guard against UTIs—whether you have suffered them repeatedly or never even had one.

WOMEN AND MEN GET UTIs

Even though UTIs are commonly considered a "women's problem," men develop them, too.

What men need to know: About 12% of men will suffer a UTI at some point in their lives, but men over age 50 are at increased risk. Common causes include *prostatitis*, a bacterial infection of the prostate gland that can also enter the urinary tract...and the use of urinary catheters in medical procedures.

What women need to know: More than 50% of women will experience a UTI at some point in their lives, and one-third of them will suffer recurring infections. Women are more prone to infection around the time of sexual activity due to the spread of *E. coli* bacteria to the vagina. In postmenopausal women, lower levels of estrogen decrease the amount of *Lactobacillus*, a "good" bacteria that grows in the vagina and serves as a natural defense against UTIs.

Symptoms are sometimes puzzling: Diagnosis of a UTI can be difficult in older men and women because they often don't suffer the classic symptoms but instead have atypical symptoms such as lethargy, confusion, nausea, shortness of breath and/or loss of appetite. If you suspect a UTI, ask that your doctor perform a urine culture.

STOP A UTI BEFORE IT STARTS

When a woman or man suffers from recurring UTIs (three or more infections in a one-year period), these steps will help break the cycle...

- **Go to the bathroom often.** Many people hold their urine longer than they should. This is a bad idea because the bladder may distend, making it more difficult to empty the bladder and preventing bacteria from being flushed out. To protect yourself, try to urinate roughly every four waking hours.

Important: People who are rushed when they are going to the bathroom may not fully empty their bladders. Take your time when urinating.

Helpful: When you think you are finished, give yourself another moment to see if there's any urine remaining before leaving the toilet.

- **Drink a lot of water.** You probably know that drinking water is a good way to help flush bacteria from the urinary tract. However, few people drink enough—you need to consume eight to 10 eight-ounce glasses of water each day. Water is best because it's pure and has no calories. Caffeine, soda and alcohol can aggravate the bladder.

Other preventives include...

- **Yogurt.** A 2012 study suggested that lactobacilli, found in probiotic supplements and yogurt, may be an acceptable alternative to antibiotics for the prevention of UTIs in women (with recurring infections, medication may be used for this purpose). The additional lactobacilli are believed to displace E. coli and stimulate the immune system to fight back against the infectious bacteria.

My advice: Consume a cup of yogurt each day—it should be low in sugar (avoid any yogurt that lists sugar as the first or second ingredient) and make sure it contains live cultures. Or take two probiotic capsules each day that have *Lactobacillus rhamnosus GR-1* and *Lactobacillus reuteri RC-14*—the probiotic strains used in the study mentioned earlier. Probiotic supplements with these strains include Pro-Flora Women's Probiotic from Integrative Therapeutics, *IntegrativePro.com*...and Ultra Flora Women's from Metagenics, *Metagenics.com*.

- **Cranberry juice or cranberry supplements.** Research has been mixed, but several studies have shown that drinking at least one to two cups of cranberry juice daily may help prevent UTIs. Just be sure to drink real cranberry juice—not cranberry juice cocktail, which has lots of sugar, is diluted with other juices and provides minimal amounts of the actual berry that contains protective compounds known as *proanthocyanidins*.

You may want to try a cranberry supplement if you have diabetes (even real cranberry juice contains carbohydrates) or if you don't like cranberry juice. Do not exceed label instructions on dosage—research suggests that high doses may increase the risk for kidney stones.

- **Estrogen creams.** For postmenopausal women, a small amount of estrogen cream applied inside the vagina several times per week has been shown to significantly reduce the risk for recurrent UTIs. The cream thickens the walls of the urinary tract, making it more difficult for bacteria to penetrate.

Important: Most women who take estrogen in pill or patch form can safely add an estrogen cream—the amount absorbed into the bloodstream is negligible. Women with a history of uterine cancer or certain breast cancers may not be suitable candidates for any form of estrogen therapy. Ask your doctor.

WHEN YOU NEED AN ANTIBIOTIC

If the steps above do not prevent recurring UTIs, you may need a long-term course (six months or longer) of a low-dose antibiotic. To minimize the development of bacterial resistance, it's wise to start with a milder antibiotic, such as *sulfamethoxazole* and *trimethoprim* (Bactrim), if possible. However, more powerful antibiotics, such as *ciprofloxacin* (Cipro), may be needed to help prevent or treat stubborn infections.

Important: Many women self-diagnose a UTI, call up their doctors and receive a prescription for an antibiotic when in fact they may have a condition, such as *vaginitis*, that mimics UTI symptoms. Urinalysis and/or a urinary culture is necessary to get an accurate diagnosis.

Natural Help for UTIs

D-*Mannose* is a natural sugar that inhibits the growth of certain *E. coli* bacteria in the laboratory. E. coli is the main source of urinary tract infections (UTIs). Though there is no clear evidence that D-Mannose supplements actually fight infections in the human body, there are anecdotal reports that it works. A person suffering from a UTI could try it for 24 hours. If there is no relief, he/she should immediately contact a doctor. If medical care is delayed, an infection may spread to the kidneys or have other serious consequences.

Also, there is some evidence that adding vitamin C, cranberry extract and fish oil to your daily diet can help prevent and/or treat UTIs. Consult a doctor before trying.

Andrew L. Rubman, ND, founder and medical director, Southbury Clinic for Traditional Medicines, Southbury, Connecticut. *SouthburyClinic.com*

If You Have Pelvic Organ Prolapse...

The most common surgeries to correct pelvic organ prolapse are equally effective and safe. Pelvic organ prolapse is a weakening of the pelvic organs, most often seen in older women and those who have given birth several times. The procedures—*sacrospinous ligament fixation* and *uterosacral ligament suspension*—involve stitching the top of the vagina to ligaments inside the pelvic cavity to stop the pain and incontinence associated with the condition.

Recent finding: Both surgeries had about a 60% surgical success rate.

Study of 374 women with pelvic organ prolapse led by researchers at Women's Health Institute, Cleveland Clinic, published in *The Journal of the American Medical Association.*

Prostate Cancer Linked to High Triglycerides

For every 10 points a man's triglyceride level rises above a baseline of 150 milligrams per deciliter (mg/dL) after prostate removal, his risk for cancer recurrence increases by about 3%, according to a 15-year study.

Possible reason: High lipid levels may fuel tumor growth.

If you've had prostate surgery: Ask your doctor about statins, diet, exercise and other therapies to keep your triglycerides down.

Stephen J. Freedland, MD, director, Center for Integrated Research in Cancer and Lifestyle at Cedars-Sinai Medical Center, Los Angeles.

High Cholesterol Caution for Prostate Cancer Survivors

Cholesterol is now linked to prostate cancer recurrence.

Recent finding: Patients with high blood levels of triglyceride fats—above 150 milligrams per deciliter (mg/dL)—had a 35% increased risk for recurrence following prostate cancer surgery. Elevated total cholesterol—above 200 mg/dL—also was associated with increased risk (9% for every 10-mg/dL rise).

But: Higher levels of HDL ("good") cholesterol were linked to reduced risk (39% decrease for each 10-mg/dL improvement) in men with low HDL.

Cholesterol and triglyceride levels can be improved through lifestyle changes and/or statin drugs.

Emma Allott, PhD, a former researcher at Duke University School of Medicine, Durham, North Carolina, and lead author of a study in *Cancer Epidemiology, Biomarkers & Prevention.*

Vasectomy Alert

Men who have had a vasectomy have a 10% higher risk for prostate cancer and a 19% higher chance of the lethal form of the disease. The link is strongest in men who had a vasectomy at a younger age. But the overall absolute increase in risk for lethal prostate cancer remains small.

Self-defense: Exercise regularly...maintain a healthy weight...and eat healthful foods, such as tomato-based products.

Lorelei Mucci, ScD, MPH, associate professor of epidemiology and leader of Cancer Epidemiology Track, Harvard School of Public Health, Boston. She led an analysis of data published in *Journal of Clinical Oncology.*

Inflammation Danger for Men

Inflammation contributes to prostate cancer, especially the aggressive form. Men with chronic inflammation in benign prostate tissue had almost twice the risk of developing prostate cancer as did men without inflammation.

To reduce inflammation: Get regular exercise...maintain a healthy weight and diet...and don't smoke.

Elizabeth A. Platz, ScD, MPH, professor and Martin D. Abeloff, MD Scholar in Cancer Prevention and deputy chair of the department of epidemiology, The Johns Hopkins Bloomberg School of Public Health, Baltimore. She is coauthor of a study published in *Cancer Epidemiology, Biomarkers & Prevention.*

New Prostate Cancer Test

The *Prostate Health Index* (PHI)—a new blood test—is three times more accurate than the *prostate-specific antigen* (PSA) test. Because the protein that is measured by the PSA test can be elevated due to prostate cancer (or prostate inflammation or enlargement) this test often leads to unnecessary biopsies.

Now: The PHI test, which analyzes three different protein markers, was found to be more accurate and reduced the need for unnecessary biopsies by 31%.

William J. Catalona, MD, director, Clinical Prostate Cancer Program, Robert H. Lurie Comprehensive Cancer Center of Northwestern University, Chicago.

Better Biopsies for Prostate Cancer

MRI-guided biopsy finds prostate cancer in places where traditional biopsies miss. The MRI biopsies also increase detection of high-grade cancer requiring treatment while reducing the diagnosis of a low-grade one unlikely to cause harm. Three US centers are experienced in MRI-targeted biopsies—Smilow Comprehensive Prostate Cancer Center at NYU Langone Medical Center, New York City...National Institutes of Health in Bethesda, Maryland...and UCLA Medical Center in Los Angeles. Or check local academic medical centers—some recently have started programs.

Samir Taneja, MD, director of the division of urologic oncology at NYU Langone Medical Center, New York City.

Why Watchful Waiting May Not Be the Best Course

Men under age 65 with localized prostate cancer should consider *radical prostatectomy* rather than "watchful waiting."

A recent finding: Among Swedish men whose cancers were found through *digital rectal exams* (DREs) before age 65, 18% treated with surgery had died from the cancer after an average of 13 years...compared with 34% who had died in the watchful-waiting group.

Jennifer R. Rider, ScD, MPH, assistant professor of medicine, Channing Division of Network Medicine, Brigham and Women's Hospital and Harvard Medical School, both in Boston. She is coauthor of a study published in *The New England Journal of Medicine.*

More Targeted Prostate Cancer Treatment

Men whose prostate tumors contain an abnormal protein called *AR-V7* are less likely to respond to two widely used prostate cancer drugs, *enzalutamide* (Xtandi) and *abiraterone* (Zytiga), a recent study has found.

Possible explanation: AR-V7 lacks a molecule that is targeted by these drugs.

If you have metastatic prostate cancer: Ask your doctor about a blood test for AR-V7. If you test positive, ask your doctor to recommend other chemotherapy or immunotherapy drugs or radiotherapy.

Emmanuel Antonarakis, MD, assistant professor of oncology, Johns Hopkins Sidney Kimmel Comprehensive Cancer Center, Baltimore.

New Treatment for Enlarged Prostate

Prostate artery embolization (PAE) could become a treatment of choice in the US after large clinical trials are completed. It is a minimally invasive method of closing off the blood supply to an enlarged, noncancerous prostate—a condition called *benign prostatic hyperplasia* (BPH), which affects more than half of men by age 60. PAE shrinks the prostate without surgery and without the complications seen with surgery, such as urinary incontinence and sexual dysfunction.

Man Hon, MD, vice-chairman of clinical radiology and chief, interventional radiology, Winthrop-University Hospital, Mineola, New York, and associate professor of clinical radiology, SUNY at Stony Brook School of Medicine.

Why Men Should Do Kegels, Too

Kegel exercises are not just for women. Pelvic floor exercise can help treat incontinence and sexual dysfunction in men as well. Pelvic muscles, like all muscles, weaken with age. To strengthen them, men should tighten the muscles used to cut off the flow of urine midstream. Hold the contraction for a few seconds, then release. Repeat the exercise 10 to 15 times for each set.

Andrew L. Siegel, MD, urologist, Bergen Urological Associates, Hackensack, New Jersey, and author of a paper about Kegel exercises for men, recently published in *Urology.*

EASY-TO-DO...

Stop Getting Up at Night!

Men who exercised just one hour a week had a 13% reduction in the need to get up twice or more during the night to urinate, according to a recent study of men with *benign prostatic hyperplasia* (BPH). More exercise provided even greater benefit.

Why: Exercise helps curb inflammation (a factor in BPH).

Kate Wolin, ScD, associate professor of surgery, Loyola University Chicago Stritch School of Medicine.

The Real Truth About Testosterone: Don't Get Swept Away by the Advertising Claims

Peter J. Burrows, MD, a practicing urologist in Tucson and a clinical assistant professor of urology at The University of Arizona College of Medicine, also in Tucson, and an adjunct assistant professor in the department of urology at the University of Southern California Keck School of Medicine in Los Angeles. He is a member of the American Society of Andrology and the American Urological Association.

For many men, it's the holy grail: A treatment that promises to beef up their muscles...rev up their sex drive...improve their stamina and concentration...and perhaps even help prevent a heart attack.

So it's no surprise that prescriptions for testosterone shots, gels and patches have nearly quadrupled over the last decade. About 3% of American men over age 40 now use testosterone therapy.

But is it safe? The answer to this crucial question depends on many factors that aren't clearly spelled out in the slick advertising—and, in some cases, even by the doctors who prescribe testosterone therapy.

What every man needs to know about testosterone therapy...

HOW THE RESEARCH STACKS UP

Testosterone is manufactured by the body and plays a key role in a man's health. It helps maintain his bone density...builds his muscles...allows him to produce sperm...and fuels his libido.

A man's testosterone levels start to decline, however, after age 30—usually by about 1% a year. This is not an illness—it's a fact of aging. If a man's testosterone drops farther than normal, though, it can cause fatigue, reduced sex drive, an increase in fat and a decrease in muscle. Some research suggests that low testosterone may also increase a man's odds of having a heart attack, diabetes and other serious health problems.

No wonder so many men are turning to testosterone therapy, which drug companies are now marketing in successful "low T" ads. The problem is, however, that many doctors are growing increasingly concerned that men whose testosterone levels are simply declining are loading up on the hormone, perhaps to the detriment of their health. Adding to those worries is recent research raising new questions about the safety of testosterone therapy.

A troubling recent finding: In research published in *The Journal of the American Medical Association*, men using testosterone had nearly a one-third increase in the rate of heart attacks and stroke.

Of course, this research doesn't prove that testosterone increases cardiovascular risks. In fact, other studies have shown the opposite—that men with higher testosterone may have fewer heart attacks. So what's going on? It's possible that the underlying low testosterone, rather than the treatment, was the cause of the increased heart attack risk. It is also possible that men who start testosterone feel so much better that they overextend themselves and get more exercise—and sex—than their hearts can handle.

For now, there is no clear explanation for the mixed research findings—that's why it's so important to use caution when considering testosterone therapy.

WHO CAN BENEFIT?

Even with these new safety questions, it's widely agreed that men who meet the clinical criteria for low testosterone need hormone replacement—the benefits outweigh the risks. But what about men whose testosterone levels are waning but do not meet that criteria? That's where it gets more complicated.

Researchers still argue over what testosterone level is "normal." When they test men of different ages, they find levels ranging from the low-300s to as high as 1,000 (expressed in nanograms per deciliter—ng/dL—of blood). The cutoff points between "healthy" and "deficient" are somewhat arbitrary. They're based on averages, not optimal levels.

For now, testosterone replacement is FDA-approved only for men with a clinical deficiency—currently defined as testosterone levels below 300 ng/dL. This condition (*hypogonadism*) is usually caused by problems in the testicles or the pituitary gland—both play a role in regulating a man's testosterone levels.

PLAY IT SAFE

For a reasoned approach to testosterone therapy, here's my advice...

• **Do not automatically blame testosterone.** The drop in testosterone in older men isn't caused only by their age. It can be due to chronic diseases, such as high blood pressure and kidney disease. Painkillers can cause it, too. (About three-quarters of men who take long-acting *opioids*, such as extended-release *oxycodone*, develop very low levels of testosterone.) Stress is also a factor.

Bottom line: Consider using testosterone only after other health problems have been addressed—and corrected.

Obesity and a sedentary lifestyle are common causes of low testosterone. Overweight men who exercise and lose weight can increase testosterone naturally by up to 25%—in some cases preventing the need for hormone replacement.

• **Take the test.** If your doctor has ruled out any physical ailment that may be causing symptoms, get your testosterone level tested (both total and free levels). Low testosterone is easily diagnosed with a blood test. Have the test early in the day, when testosterone levels tend to be highest. If your level is low, ask your doctor to repeat the test on another day, since levels can vary.

• **Get your heart checked out.** If your testosterone level is low, don't start replacement therapy without getting your heart checked out with a stress test, complete blood count (CBC) and tests for cholesterol and high blood pressure. Any cardiac condition that shows up on these tests must be resolved before beginning testosterone therapy.

Even though the research is not yet definitive, there are enough studies linking testosterone use to heart attack and other cardiovascular problems—especially in men with risk factors for heart disease, including smoking and obesity—that it's not worth taking a chance on this.

• **Use the right dose.** Since a man's optimal testosterone level is still not clearly defined, I advise a conservative approach. When choosing a dose, I try to get patients' blood levels within the upper one-fourth of the range generally recommended by endocrinologists—say, about 750 ng/dL—but no higher.

Different forms of supplemental testosterone are equally effective. Injections are the cheapest, but they must be repeated every 10 to 14 days. Most men learn how to administer the shots themselves.

Patches are another option, although some men don't like them, since they can trigger a rash. Testosterone gels and creams are the easiest to use, but they are expensive—and the medication can transfer to other people through skin-to-skin contact. They're usually applied to the shoulders or upper arms.

• **Go for checkups.** For anyone on testosterone therapy, it's crucial to get regular checkups. I advise men to get their testosterone levels checked at three months, then every six months. After that, if they're doing well, they can come in once a year for testing of lipid levels and liver function (testosterone can affect both). I also order tests every six months to monitor a man's red blood cell (RBC) counts—testosterone increases RBC levels, which can boost his risk for blood clots.

Other tests you'll need: A *prostate specific antigen* (PSA) test to check for prostate cancer every six months. Testosterone replacement doesn't cause prostate cancer, but it can cause tumors that are already present to grow more rapidly. Men with untreated prostate cancer should not take testosterone. However, testosterone can be given to those who have been successfully treated for prostate cancer. Studies show it does not trigger cancer recurrence.

In general, men who have low testosterone will feel better within a month after starting testosterone therapy. Optimal testosterone levels should help with weight loss and can boost natural production of the hormone—so many men find that they no longer need treatment.

BETTER WAYS...

The Best Laxatives

People who regularly used fiber-based laxatives had a 56% lower colorectal cancer risk than people who didn't use laxatives, according to a recent study. But regular users of *nonfiber* laxatives have a 49% higher risk. Fiber-based laxatives, which boost the water content and bulk of stool, include Citrucel, Fiberall and Fibercon. Nonfiber or stimulant laxatives, which force the colon to contract, include Correctol, Ex-lax and Dulcolax.

Jessica S. Citronberg, MPH, a predoctoral fellow at Fred Hutchinson Cancer Research Center, Seattle, and leader of a study, recently published in *The American Journal of Gastroenterology*.

Stop Sitting So Much to Reduce Colon Cancer Risk

Prolonged sitting increases risk for colon cancer. Men who were sedentary for more than 11 hours a day were 45% more likely to have a recurrence of *colorectal adenomas*—benign lumps associated with increased colon cancer risk—than men who were sedentary for fewer than seven hours.

Analysis of two studies of 1,730 people by researchers at Columbia University Mailman School of Public Health, New York City, presented at a meeting of the American Association for Cancer Research.

New Colon Cancer Test Approved by FDA

The FDA has approved *Cologuard*, a noninvasive screening test for colorectal cancer for adults over age 50. The new test screens stool samples for red blood cells and DNA mutations that may indicate the presence of cancer or precancerous growths. In a recent study of more than 10,000 adults, Cologuard detected more cancers and more advanced adenomas than the fecal occult blood test that is widely used in annual physicals. Routine colonoscopies are still recommended.

N. Jewel Samadder, MD, assistant professor of gastroenterology and hepatology, University of Utah School of Medicine, Salt Lake City.

Less Frequent Colonoscopy?

Colonoscopy patients with only one polyp removed may need less frequent follow-up. A recent Norwegian study suggested that a follow-up colonoscopy at 10 years may be enough in some cases when a polyp is small and low risk. When more or higher-risk polyps are removed, the follow-up should be in three to five years.

Randall W. Burt, MD, a gastroenterologist at Huntsman Cancer Institute, Salt Lake City.

The Danger *After* a Colonoscopy

Karen Larson, editor of *Bottom Line/Personal*, 281 Tresser Blvd., Stamford, Connecticut 06901. *BottomLinePersonal.com*.

What's the best part of a colonoscopy? When it's over, of course. But for someone I know, the end of a colonoscopy was just the start of a medical misadventure—she fainted two days after the procedure and wound up in the emergency room due to dehydration.

That's not uncommon, says Leo Galland, MD, founder and director of the Foundation for Integrated Medicine in New York City. The incident points to a troubling gap in colonoscopy communication—patients are told how to prepare for this procedure but often not what they should do afterward. *Dr. Galland's advice...*

- **Drink eight to 16 ounces of fruit juice right after the procedure.** Ask if the health facility will have juice. If not, bring your own.

Any beverage will help with dehydration, but fruit juice also wards off *hypoglycemia*—low blood sugar. Drink another 48 ounces of fluid during the day and 64 ounces the day after.

- **Eat a light snack as soon as you feel able.** Bring a sandwich or an energy bar with you to the health facility, too. Avoid foods with high fat content—fats are difficult to digest.
- **Take a probiotic supplement.** Take one just before your first meal following the procedure and twice a day for the next 10 days at the start of a meal. Consuming probiotics can reduce bowel irritation and promote good overall digestive health. Try a few different ones well before your colonoscopy to find one that seems to aid your digestion.

Poor Sleep Linked to Ulcerative Colitis

People who get less than six hours or more than nine hours of sleep a day are more likely to develop *ulcerative colitis*, which produces chronic inflammation in the intestines. A related finding is that six months of poor-quality sleep is associated with a doubling in the risk for flare-ups of Crohn's disease, another inflammatory condition. Multiple studies have shown that short and long sleep durations are associated with higher overall mortality, cardiovascular disease and cancer.

Self-defense: Get seven to eight hours of restful sleep every night.

Ashwin Ananthakrishnan, MD, gastroenterologist at Massachusetts General Hospital in Boston, and leader of a study published in *Clinical Gastroenterology and Hepatology*.

New Crohn's/Colitis Drug

The FDA recently approved the intravenous drug *vedolizumab* (Entyvio) for *ulcerative colitis* and *Crohn's disease* patients who have not responded to standard medications. In clinical trials of 2,700 patients with either of these inflammatory bowel conditions, about 50% of symptoms eased for at least a year. When given at least every eight weeks, Entyvio blocks certain inflammatory cells from entering areas in the gastrointestinal tract. Side effects may include headache, joint pain and liver damage.

Stephen Hanauer, MD, medical director, Digestive Health Center, Northwestern University Feinberg School of Medicine, Chicago.

Valuable Clue to Addictive Behavior

Addictive behavior may be linked to poor hormone development in childhood. The hormone *oxytocin* is important in bonding and social interaction. An exposure to drugs, stress, trauma or infection before age three may impair the development of oxytocin, and that may make some people more likely to abuse alcohol or drugs.

Study by researchers at School of Medical Sciences, University of Adelaide, Australia, published in *Pharmacology Biochemistry & Behavior*.

INTERESTING FINDING...

Most Alcoholics Don't Get the Meds They Need

Fewer than 9% of alcoholics get medication that could help them stop drinking. In a recent 12-week study, alcohol-dependent patients taking the anticonvulsant drug *gabapentin* were four times more likely to stop drinking altogether than those taking a placebo. The medication helps people to better cope with alcoholic cravings by improving sleep and mood.

Barbara J. Mason, PhD, codirector of Pearson Center for Alcoholism and Addiction Research, Scripps Research Institute, La Jolla, California. She led a clinical trial of gabapentin, published in *JAMA Internal Medicine*.

Not All Heavy Drinkers Are Alcoholics

Many people who drink too much at one time or over the course of a week are considered to be drinking excessively but are not physically or mentally addicted to alcohol, which defines "alcoholism." Twenty-nine percent of the US population meets the definition for excessive drinking—five or more drinks in one sitting or 15 or more during a week for men...four or more drinks at one time or eight or more during a week for women. But 90% of them are not addicted to alcohol.

Survey of 138,100 adults by researchers at the Centers for Disease Control and Prevention, Atlanta, reported in *The New York Times.*

Helpful App for Alcoholics

A new smartphone app helps recovering alcoholics stay sober. Study participants who used the *Addiction-Comprehensive Health Enhancement Support System* (A-CHESS) were 65% more likely to abstain from alcohol in the year following their release from a treatment facility than people who did not use the app. A-CHESS issues daily support messages and asks questions that help counselors assess the person's sobriety. It also tracks users' locations and issues warnings when users are near familiar bars or liquor stores. Other apps are available, but A-CHESS is the first to undergo a large-scale clinical trial.

Study of about 350 people by researchers at University of Wisconsin, Madison, published in *JAMA Psychiatry.*

Deadly Perfectionism

Perfectionism is a bigger risk for suicide than previously thought. Perfectionists tend to feel hopeless and hide their pain from others. Researchers note that doctors, attorneys and architects, in particular, are at increased risk for perfectionism-related suicide because their occupations emphasize precision.

Conclusion: Perfectionism is a suicide risk factor and requires intervention.

If you're troubled by your own perfectionism: Consider seeing a therapist.

Gordon Flett, PhD, professor of psychology, York University, Toronto, Ontario, Canada.

7

Money Manager

10 Things *Not* to Do with Your Money

If you want to get better at something—such as your job or playing an instrument or a sport—you need to work hard and put in the time. But in my three decades of covering the financial world as a reporter and author, I've learned that if you want to make your money grow faster, sometimes the best financial strategy is to *do less*, not more. This certainly doesn't work for everyone all the time, and I readily concede that it makes me sound like a curmudgeon, but it's worth considering before you do something that you might later regret.

Here are 10 money-related things that I'm glad I *don't* do...

1. Don't carry life insurance. When my children were younger, I had some term-life insurance, which is the cheapest way to get short-term coverage. Once I had amassed enough savings so that my family would be OK financially if I went under the next bus, I ditched the policy, saving lots of money in annual premiums.

2. Don't use a financial adviser. I am comfortable managing my own money, partly because I'm knowledgeable and partly because I know that I won't panic when the market next declines.

If you don't fall into that camp, consider a fee-only financial planner rather than one who gets a commission every time you invest in something. You might search for an adviser through *GarrettPlanningNetwork.com* and/or the National Association of Personal Financial Advisors (*NAPFA.org*).

Jonathan Clements, writer of a weekly column for *The Wall Street Journal* and author of *Jonathan Clements Money Guide 2015*. Previously, he was director of financial education for Citigroup at the bank's US wealth-management business. See more at *JonathanClements.com*

3. Don't buy individual stocks. It's risky to bet heavily on any one stock, and I don't fool myself into thinking that I can create a collection of stocks that will outperform the overall market or the best mutual fund managers. That's why all my stock market money is in mutual funds. I haven't owned any individual stocks in 15 years except for a small amount of shares in various companies that I worked for—and I sold those stocks as soon as I was able to.

4. Don't own municipal bonds. Based on my tax bracket, buying tax-free municipal bonds in my taxable account potentially makes sense. But I follow a different strategy that should deliver greater after-tax wealth. I keep taxable bonds—which yield more than munis—in my tax-sheltered retirement account. That way, I don't have to pay income taxes on the interest I earn each year. Meanwhile, I use my taxable account to buy and hold stock index funds. (See below for the tax advantages of that strategy.)

5. Don't invest in actively managed mutual funds. There's a mountain of evidence that most professional money managers fail to beat the market, once you factor in their investment costs. For instance, in 2014, just 13% of large-company stock funds outpaced the Standard & Poor's 500 stock index, according to the investment research firm Morningstar, Inc. That won't be true every year, but it's true often enough that I stick with passively managed index funds, which allow me to capture the market's performance while incurring low annual expenses.

Also, index funds generate modest annual tax bills because they don't have a big turnover in their holdings each year, as many actively managed funds do, so they're slow to realize taxable capital gains. And when they do, the gains will be taxed mostly at the lower rate that applies to long-term capital gains. Unless you're in the top federal income tax bracket, your long-term capital gains and qualified dividends are likely to be taxed at 0% for the lowest bracket or 15% for other brackets.

6. Don't pay attention to market pundits. Most of these folks simply do not know where stocks are headed or what will happen to interest rates—and yet they tell wonderfully convincing stories that can prompt investors to make big, unnecessary changes in their portfolios.

7. Don't act on investment opinions offered by friends and family. Don't get me wrong—I listen to what friends and family say, but mostly to find out what investments other folks are excited about. Those are the investments that I'm often tempted to avoid or cut back on in my own portfolio because the enthusiasm of others often is a sign that the investments are overvalued.

8. Don't budget. I have never created a detailed written budget or tracked my daily spending. I know I'm being sensible with my spending, so why bother?

How to determine whether you're spending sensibly enough to avoid creating a budget: If you're in the workforce, do you save 12% or more of your pretax income toward retirement? If you're retired, do you limit your annual portfolio withdrawals to 4% of your nest egg's beginning-of-year value? If you answered "yes," you're probably being prudent with your spending, so you, too, don't need to budget.

9. Don't carry any debt. I avoid borrowing money—even mortgage debt. I took out a 30-year mortgage in 1992, when I bought my first home, and paid it off within a decade. I know that many people cannot afford to do this. And I readily concede that the mortgage-interest tax deduction is a great tax break. But even with the tax savings, I found that my mortgage was costing me more than I could earn on high-quality bonds, so my "bond buying" strategy was to make extra principal payments on my mortgage in order to escape the mortgage and its interest costs more quickly.

10. Don't own a vacation home. You can think of a house as similar to a stock—there's the price appreciation and the dividend.

In the case of a home, the price appreciation typically is modest and is more than offset by all the costs you incur, including property taxes, homeowner's insurance and maintenance expenses.

In contrast, the dividend on a house or an apartment can be huge. I'm referring to the rent you receive if you're a landlord.

What if you buy a vacation property for your own use? Instead of rent checks, you collect so-called *imputed* rent—the pleasure you get from using the place. That can be a great thing—but it won't put cash in your pocket.

The implication: Buying a second home for your own use may be a good way to spend your money if you like to vacation in the same place year after year. But don't expect that vacation home to make you wealthier. I'd rather have the freedom to go wherever I want on vacation, so I have avoided the hefty cost of owning a second home.

Is Your Spouse Financially Unfaithful? 7 Warning Signs...

Deborah Price, both CEO and founder of The Money Coaching Institute, which offers financial coaching to individuals, couples and businesses in Novato, California. She previously spent 20 years as a financial adviser with Merrill Lynch, MassMutual and AIG. She is author of *The Heart of Money: A Couple's Guide to Creating True Financial Intimacy. MoneyCoachingInstitute.com*

There is a one-in-three chance that your spouse is cheating on you—*financially.* A recent study reported that 35% of married people and others who have merged their financial lives with a partner admit that they have deceived those partners about important money matters.

These spouses conceal major purchases, debts and investment losses...lie about the feasibility of plans for retirement...or even transfer money into secret accounts. They are getting away with it, too—victims often don't realize anything is amiss until they are in a deep financial hole. And financial devastation isn't the only consequence—financial infidelity also rips couples apart, undermining marital trust and often leading to divorce.

Here's how to spot the warning signs that your spouse might be financially unfaithful... how to understand why financial infidelity happens...how to reduce the odds that financial infidelity will occur in your own marriage...and how to overcome it if it has already occurred.

WARNING SIGNS

Seven clues that your spouse might be cheating on you financially...

1. Your money questions are met with evasive or defensive responses. Your partner responds to money-related questions with a vague "Don't worry, I have it under control"...change of subject...stall tactics such as "I'll have to check on that"...or with anger or defensiveness out of proportion to the innocent question being asked.

2. You propose holding regular household financial meetings—and your partner balks. Your request to simply update each other financially is refused even when you stress how important this is to you and promise that the meetings won't take much time.

3. Your financial statements disappear. You can't find recent bank, credit card, investment and/or loan statements in your filing cabinet or incoming mail—and your spouse can't or won't produce them.

4. There are unexpected cash withdrawals or outgoing transfers on account statements. When you query your partner about these in a casual—not suspicious—tone, you see signs of nervousness or defensiveness.

5. Your spouse encourages you to sign financial documents that you haven't had a chance to review—and then resists answering questions about them. When you try to read these papers or ask questions, you are told that there isn't time or you wouldn't understand them.

Example: A husband asked his wife to sign a stack of papers that he said would transfer management of the couple's savings from one investment company to another. He didn't mention that the documents also included a postnuptial agreement that signed away the wife's rights to most of the couple's assets.

6. Your partner always seems to have lots of new stuff. When asked about this, he/she always says that he got a great deal...or that the seemingly new item actually is something he has had for years.

7. Bank account and/or credit card statements show frequent shopping trips. A spouse who shops several times a week might have trouble controlling spending...or might think many smaller purchases are more likely to escape your notice than a few large ones.

Example: A wife convinced herself that it was OK to make purchases of less than $100 without informing her husband—then made so many moderate-sized purchases that she spent more than $10,000 a year.

THE HIDDEN CAUSE

The vast majority of financially unfaithful spouses are not intentionally misleading their partners—they are acting out the bad money lessons that they learned as children. The way we think about money is largely hardwired into our brains by the time we reach age 12, mainly in response to how we saw our parents deal with money. When we get married, our ingrained money patterns can come into conflict with our spouses' money patterns, triggering emotional trip wires that can lead to behavioral malfunctions.

Example: A woman grew up in a family in which money was spent freely and gifts were given to show love. Her husband, on the other hand, grew up in a family where tight budgets created tension. When they got married, the wife's free spending triggered fear in her husband, and he responded by becoming angry and controlling with money. The wife took his unwillingness to spend on her as a sign of insufficient love. As a result, she secretly spent even more money on herself to get even.

HOW TO PREVENT IT

Six ways to reduce the odds that financial infidelity will happen to you—or to catch it before it does major damage...

- **Come to a clear understanding with your spouse about spending limits.** Leave no doubt about how much each partner can spend without consulting the other.
- **Spot-check financial statements.** Scan for any large withdrawals, loans, transfers out of the accounts or changes in value that you don't understand, then calmly—not suspiciously—ask your partner about these.
- **React with compassion to your spouse's money missteps.** Reacting with anger, frustration or fear only increases the odds that your spouse will hide future missteps.
- **Note the date and details when your spouse tells you a purchase was on sale for a surprisingly low price.** If you have doubts, consider checking that date on your credit card or bank account statement to confirm that the purchase wasn't pricier than claimed.
- **Read your most recent tax return.** In most families, one spouse does the taxes and/or interacts with the tax preparer, while the other simply signs the completed tax forms. That tax return could tell you how much your spouse really earns, which investment firms you have accounts with and what investments were sold during the prior year.
- **If your spouse is willing, the two of you could see a therapist trained to handle money-related behavioral issues.** These therapists can help couples understand the underlying psychological causes of financial infidelity. This understanding can transform the anger that a victim-spouse is feeling into sympathy and greatly increase the odds that the behavior can be changed and the marriage saved. To find an appropriate therapist in your area, go to *FinancialTherapyAssociation.org*, then select "Search by State" from the "FTA Network" menu. Or to find a "money coach," who serves a similar purpose, go to my site, *MoneyCoachingInstitute.com.*

THREE MONEY PERSONALITIES

Here is a look at how three of the common money personalities that I have identified—all eight are described on my website—can lead well-meaning married people into financial infidelity...

- **Warriors** see it as their role to take care of their families, financially and otherwise. It can be wonderful to be married to someone like that—but when things go wrong financially, warriors tend to become defensive and feel that they have let their partners down.
- **Victims** believe that their financial misdeeds are justified because they have been wronged.

Example of a couple I counseled: A successful man who tightly controlled the family finances gave his wife a budget of $5,000 a month to spend as she liked. She instead spent four times that much. This woman felt she had been financially mistreated earlier in her life and overspent to get revenge on those who mistreated her—even though the husband believed he was treating her very fairly.

- **Innocent types** tend to be happy to hand off responsibility for financial matters to their spouses, leaving themselves free to focus on artistic or spiritual interests. These types often take their first close look at their finances when they approach retirement. Some are shocked to discover that their partners have been lying to them about finances for decades. The lying spouse committed the financial infidelity, but the "innocent" spouse enabled it.

Example: A successful woman with a creative mentality stood by passively while her serial entrepreneur husband invested the family's money in a series of businesses—all of which failed. Only in her 50s did she realize that he was hiding huge financial problems.

BETTER WAYS...

Sneaky Bank Fees and What to Do About Them

Fees for early account closures can be charged for closing recently opened accounts—find out how long an account must stay open to avoid the fee. A returned-mail fee may be charged if you move and do not file a change-of-address form with the post office, so mail from the bank is returned—always file a change-of-address form when moving. Minimum-balance fees are charged when an account falls below a specified level—find out the level and stay above it.

Payment to prevent overdrafts: Bank of America promises not to charge overdraft fees for account holders who pay $4.95 a month.* It is better to opt out of this and manage your account carefully—saving almost $60 a year. Reordered overdraft fees occur when banks post account transactions by size, not the order in which they arrive—so a single overdraft can become multiple ones if a big transaction causes several smaller ones to bounce. If this happens, ask your bank to reverse the fees.

DailyFinance.com

*Price subject to change.

Totally Free Checking Is Still Available!

Capital One 360 has no monthly fees or minimum-balance requirements—and it pays interest of 0.2% to 0.9%, depending on your balance.* Ally Bank Interest Checking also is totally free, paying interest of 0.1% on balances less than $15,000 and 0.6% on larger ones.

For Fidelity Investments customers, the Fidelity Cash Management Account offers no monthly fee or minimum balance. Schwab Bank High Yield Investor Checking Account has similar features for Schwab customers and pays 0.06%.

Other banks, investment firms and credit unions may have similar offers. Features and interest rates can change anytime—shop around.

Kiplinger's Personal Finance. Kiplinger.com

*Rates and offers subject to change.

Better Checking Accounts

The monthly maintenance on checking accounts averages $12.69...and only 28% of checking accounts are free. Online banks charge less—58% of their checking accounts have no monthly maintenance fees, and the average minimum to open an online account is just $98.40 (versus $400.45 for a regular bank checking account).

Online banks that have no maintenance fee and pay interest on checking accounts: Ally Bank (0.6% interest on balances of at least $15,000*)...Mutual of Omaha Bank (0.5% interest on balances of $1,500 to $250,000 and no fee on balances of at least $100).

Richard Barrington, CFA, senior financial analyst at *MoneyRates.com.*

*Rates and offers subject to change.

Banks Don't Have to Cash Old Checks

Banks may cash old checks at their discretion. A bank does not have to accept a check that is more than six months old, but some will if they know the customer. Banks even may choose to cash an old check that is preprinted with a notice that it expires after 60 or 90 days—but again, it is up to the bank. Banks are most likely to accept checks that are just a few days past the six-month or printed limit. Before trying to deposit an old check, consider where it came from and whether the issuer is likely to have put a stop-payment order on it—that could cause the check to be returned if the bank accepts it, and you could be charged a returned-check fee of up to $30. If you find an old personal check, consider contacting the person or business that wrote it and asking if it still is all right to cash it.

Bankrate.com

The Best Credit Cards: Top Choices for Cash Back...Travel Rewards...More

Odysseas Papadimitriou, founder and CEO of Evolution Finance, based in Washington, DC, and parent company of *CardHub.com*, an online marketplace for comparing credit cards, prepaid cards and gift cards.

Choosing the best credit card can be tricky. It depends on which features and rewards are most useful for you...how easy it is to qualify for those rewards...and what fees and interest rates apply. So we asked card expert Odysseas Papadimitriou to sort through all the available cards and pick the ones that are the best now. There's a card that makes it easy to get 2% back on all purchases. Another card offers 6% back at supermarkets. And one can deliver 9% back on gas. If you carry a balance on your credit card accounts, there are cards with variable interest rates as low as 8.25%...and cards with introductory rates of 0% valid for more than a year.

The best credit cards now (with no annual fee unless otherwise indicated)...*

CASH-BACK CARDS

• **Best for straightforward cash back**—Citi Double Cash Visa/MasterCard offers 2% back on all purchases, without any spending caps. You do not need to keep track of rotating rewards categories or other confusing rules. There is one unusual twist. Just half of the card's 2% reward is earned when you make a purchase. The other half is triggered when you make payments, whether you pay in full or over time. Your unredeemed rewards balance expires if you don't earn new rewards for 12 months. Rewards can be redeemed in the form of checks, statement credits or gift cards each time the $25 threshold is met.

Annual percentage rate (APR): 10.99% to 22.99%. *Citi.com*

Alternative: Fidelity Investment Rewards American Express also offers 2% cash back on all purchases—but those rewards are automatically deposited into a Fidelity account, which might make this rewards program less convenient for some consumers.

APR: 13.99%. *Fidelity.com/cash-management/american-express-cards*

• **Best cash-back card for groceries**—American Express Blue Cash Preferred offers 6% cash back on up to $6,000 in supermarket purchases each year. The card charges a $75 annual fee, but that is more than offset in the first year by a $150 bonus you receive for spending at least $1,000 on the card in the first three months. A 6% discount on $6,000 in annual grocery purchases equals a $360 savings—$240 more than a 2% cash-back card would get you. Blue Cash Preferred also provides 3% cash back on gas and on purchases at specified department stores and 1% back on all other purchases, including supermarket

*Rates as of August 7, 2015. The details of credit card offers change frequently without warning. Interest rates change based on changes in an index, and your rate may depend, in part, on your creditworthiness. Eligibility for a card may depend on your credit score.

purchases, in excess of $6,000 a year. Rewards can be redeemed as a statement credit whenever you reach the $25 threshold.

APR: 12.99% to 21.99% after a 15-month 0% introductory period. *AmericanExpress.com*

• **Best cash-back card if you would like to choose shopping categories**—U.S. Bank Cash Plus Visa offers 5% back on up to $2,000 in purchases per quarter in two spending categories that you choose each quarter. The categories recently included electronics stores, department stores and cell phone service. In addition, you get 2% back at gas stations, restaurants or grocery stores—you choose one of these categories each quarter—plus 1% on all other purchases. This card is appropriate only if you are willing to select rewards categories every quarter. Rewards can be redeemed as a statement credit or a deposit to a U.S. Bank account. You can apply at U.S. Bank branches located in 25 midwestern and western states or by invitation through the mail.

APR: 12.99% to 23.99%. *CashPlus.USBank.com*

• **Best cash-back card for small businesses**—Capital One Spark Cash for Business Visa provides a straightforward 2% cash back on all purchases without any spending caps. You can earn an additional $500 bonus by making at least $4,500 in purchases with the card in the first three months. Rewards checks are sent automatically each year, or you can request them anytime. The card charges a $59 annual fee, but it's waived in the first year.

APR: 16.9%. *CapitalOne.com/business-credit-cards*

• **Best student cash-back card**—Journey Student Rewards Visa by Capital One offers 1.25% cash back on all purchases without any caps—1% when the purchase is made plus an additional 0.25% when the credit card bill is paid on time (even if the student doesn't pay off the balance in full). That's an excellent rewards program for a student credit card—most students have very limited credit histories and will not qualify for the more appealing rewards cards listed above. The card also has no annual fee.

APR: 19.8%. *CapitalOneJourney.com*

TRAVEL AND GAS CARDS

• **Best travel card**—Capital One Venture Visa provides two "miles" per dollar spent for any kind of purchase, and each mile is worth one cent toward travel purchases such as airline tickets, hotel rooms, car rentals and more. It's the equivalent of earning 2% cash back that you can spend only on travel. You also can get a 40,000-mile bonus by spending $3,000 on the card in the first three months—that equals an extra $400 worth of free travel. Unlike with many travel-rewards programs, miles do not expire...are not subject to blackout periods or seat restrictions...and can be redeemed with any airline, hotel or car-rental company or with certain other travel-related businesses. There is a $59 annual fee, which is waived in the first year. A reasonable strategy with this card is to use it for a year, earning the 40,000-mile bonus and avoiding the annual fee, and then switch to a different card.

APR: 12.9% to 22.9%. *CapitalOneVenture.com*

• **Best gas card for all gas stations**—PenFed Platinum Cash Rewards Plus Visa offers 5% cash back for gas purchases that are paid at the pump. Cash rewards are not capped, and the rewards you earn are automatically applied to your account each month. There are two catches, however. First, you must be a member of the Pentagon Federal Credit Union to be eligible though anyone can become a member by making a onetime contribution of as little as $14 to one of two nonprofits that support American military personnel and their families (see PenFed's website for details). And second, you must have a PenFed checking account, money-market account, loan or another qualifying financial product to be eligible for the card.

APR: 9.99% to 17.99%. *PenFed.org*

• **Best single-brand gas card**—Marathon Visa offers 25 cents back per gallon of gas purchased at Marathon stations if you spend at least $1,000 on the card during a month, equal to 9% cash back with gas prices at $2.75. You get 15 cents back per gallon (equal to 5.5%) if you spend between $500 and $999 on the card during the month...or five cents (1.8%) if your spending is less than $500. You'll receive a Marathon Prepaid Card automatically whenever your rewards balance reaches $25. Non-Marathon purchases do not earn any rewards.

APR: 16.99% to 24.99%. *Comenity.net/marathon*

Runner up: Chevron and Texaco Visa offers 20 cents back per gallon of gas bought at those stations during months you spend more than $1,000 in monthly qualifying purchases and 10 cents per gallon during months you spend between $300 and $1,000. Cash-back point balances expire if no fuel purchase is made for six months. Total rewards are capped at $300 per calendar year.

APR: 26.99%. *ChevronTexacoCards.com*

CARDS WITH LOW INTEREST RATES

- **Best card for low ongoing interest rates**—First Command Bank Platinum Visa offers a low 8.25% rate that applies to purchases, cash advances and balance transfers. Other credit cards may advertise lower initial rates, but those "teaser" rates soon expire. *FirstCommandBank.com/Platinum-Visa.htm*

- **Best card for low initial rates**—Citi Diamond Preferred MasterCard offers a 0% interest rate on new purchases for the first 21 months—that is the longest 0% introductory rate currently available. After that, it charges a variable rate of 11.99% to 21.99%. *Citi.com*

- **Best card for balance transfers**—Chase Slate Visa has no balance-transfer fee and offers a 0% interest rate on balance transfers (as well as new purchases) for the first 15 months. After that, the interest rates climb to between 12.99% and 22.99% variable, depending on your creditworthiness. *CreditCards.Chase.com*

TAKE NOTE...

Simple Way to Boost Your Credit Limit

To boost your credit limit, transfer a portion of one credit card's spending limit to another card from the same issuer. Most issuers allow this, and it makes large purchases easier.

Example: If you have Chase Freedom and Chase Slate cards each with $2,000 limits, ask to transfer $1,000 from one to the other—giving you a $1,000 Freedom limit and a $3,000 Slate limit.

You also can open another credit card with an issuer you already use for the express purpose of transferring some of one card's limit to the other card.

Caution: Opening a new card temporarily lowers your credit score—and if you close the new account soon after transferring the spending limit, that will reduce your score even further.

Money.USNews.com

Store Cards Can Hurt Your Credit Score

John Ulzheimer, president, *CreditSesame.com*, based in Mountain View, California, which offers free credit scores and reports to consumers. He previously worked for Equifax Credit Information Services and Fair Isaac Corp., which designed the FICO credit-scoring system. *JohnUlzheimer.com*

Do not sign up for store cards lightly. These cards can reduce your credit score in several different ways—and those credit score reductions can really add up if you sign up for many store cards. *Here's why...*

- **Store cards tend to have very low credit limits, often less than $1,000.** Make a large purchase with one of these cards, and you will use up most of its credit limit. Credit-scoring systems penalize consumers who use a high percentage of their available credit, either overall or with specific cards.

Exception: "Co-branded" store cards featuring the logo of a general card issuer such as Visa, MasterCard or American Express often have higher credit limits.

- **Regularly signing up for store cards reduces the average age of your credit accounts.** Credit-scoring systems favor borrowers who have managed their accounts responsibly for many years. If you sign up for a

EASY-TO-DO...

Get Late-Payment Fees Cancelled!

Nearly nine out of 10 consumers who asked their credit card issuers for a waiver got one, according to a recent survey. And about two-thirds who asked for an interest rate reduction were successful. When asking for a lower rate, point out any lower-rate offers that you have gotten from other credit card issuers. For a suggested script of what to say when asking for a lower rate, go to *Bit.ly/1vupvri.*

Matt Schulz, a senior industry analyst at *CreditCards.com*, which sponsored a survey of 983 cardholders that was conducted by Princeton Survey Research Associates International.

few store cards each year, the average age of your accounts will remain short even if you have had other cards for decades.

- **Simply applying for store cards costs you credit score points.** Each credit card application you submit costs you points off your credit score for the next 12 months. A few points might not seem like much, but it can quickly add up if you apply for store cards frequently or if your credit scores are already marginal.

Little-Known Credit Card Fees

There are plenty of little-known credit card fees beyond the late-payment fee. Archive-statement fees may be charged if you need hard copies of old records. Duplicate-statement fees, also called copy request or copying fees, can be charged for an extra printout of a monthly bill. Costs may be as high as $10 per statement. Returned-payment, expedited-payment and stop-payment fees of $15 to $25 may be charged under some circumstances—added to fees that banks may charge. Over-credit-limit fees of up to $35 may be charged for consumers who opt in to overdraft protection and buy beyond their credit limit. Foreign-currency-conversion fees may be charged for purchases made in other currencies. Card-replacement fees may be charged if you lose a card. Reward-redemption fees may be charged for using points or miles to book a trip.

Not all card issuers charge all types of fees, and amounts charged vary widely.

Greg McBride, CFA, chief financial analyst for *Bankrate.com*, a personal finance website based in North Palm Beach, Florida.

New Rules Could Boost Your Credit Score

John Ulzheimer, president, *CreditSesame.com*, based in Mountain View, California, which offers free credit scores and reports to consumers. He previously worked for Equifax Credit Information Services and Fair Isaac Corp., which designed the FICO credit-scoring system. *JohnUlzheimer.com*

The major credit-reporting agencies have agreed to make changes in policy that could boost your credit scores. *What you can expect now...*

- **More help with errors.** Up to now, if you complained to a credit-reporting agency about an inaccurate entry on your credit report, the agency simply passed your complaint along to the creditor...then refused to adjust or remove the problematic entry if the creditor would not admit that there was a mistake. Under the new rules, if you provide documentation but a creditor does not back off its contention, the credit bureaus must assign an agent to review the documentation and could then change the entry despite the creditor's resistance.

- **More time to resolve medical bills.** Under the old rules, your credit report could show a collection—a debt that has been referred to a debt-collection agency—simply because the health insurance company was slow to pay a claim. Collections could lower your credit score by 100 points under certain circumstances.

Under the new rules, medical collections cannot be reported to the credit bureaus any sooner than 180 days after the date that the debt becomes delinquent, giving the insurance claim and payment process time to run its course.

• **No more credit score penalties for unpaid tickets and fines.** Currently an unpaid parking ticket or overdue library book fine can end up as a "collection account." Under the new rules, credit reports will not be allowed to include charges if you did not enter into a contract or sign an agreement to pay them.

TAKE NOTE...

Credit Scores: Myths and Realities

Myth—checking your own credit hurts your credit score.

Reality—you can check your own score as often as you like, but inquiries from third parties, such as when you apply for a loan or a new credit card, can lower your credit score.

Myth—if you work with a credit-counseling agency, it will be reported to credit bureaus.

Reality—seeking advice is not reported, but taking actions that are recommended by a counselor, such as making partial payments or agreeing with a creditor to settle a debt for less than the full amount, can affect your credit score.

Myth—earning less money means that you have a lower credit score.

Reality—income has no correlation with scores.

Myth—a low credit score may stop you from getting a job.

Reality—employers may look at a credit report (generally looking for red flags indicating irresponsible behavior) but not at the score. It is illegal to use credit scores to screen potential employees.

GoBankingRates.com

How to Get an Absolutely, Totally Free Credit Score

John Ulzheimer, president, *CreditSesame.com*, based in Mountain View, California, which offers free credit scores and reports to consumers. He previously worked for Equifax Credit Information Services and Fair Isaac Corp., which designed the FICO credit-scoring system. *JohnUlzheimer.com*

We no longer have to pay to learn the credit scores that play a major role in our financial lives. Certain credit cards and websites now offer truly free access to these crucial numbers that banks and other lenders, credit card issuers, insurers, landlords, cell phone providers, utility firms and others may use to evaluate our creditworthiness. We also can get free credit reports—the raw data that the scores are based on—but only from one website. Unfortunately, amid an onslaught of catchy tunes and commercials promising free credit information, it's not always easy to sort out the really free and useful offers from the ones with costly tricks.

Why credit scores matter: They can have a big effect on matters ranging from the interest rates we pay on loans and the kinds of credit cards we get to decisions on how much insurance costs us.

Offers of free credit scores are nothing new, of course, but in the past, the offers were never as attractive as claimed. Some were not really free—they required consumers to sign up for pricey monthly credit-monitoring services. Other offers were not really very useful—the credit scores they provided were very different from the scores that lending institutions use. There still are plenty of bogus offers today amid the really free and useful ones.

SCORES FROM CREDIT CARDS

Several credit card issuers now offer free FICO credit scores to some or all of their cardholders. Your FICO score, which uses a scale of 300 to 850, is the best one to check, because it's the one that is most widely used by lending institutions and others that evaluate your creditworthiness.

• **Barclaycard** allows holders of some of its types of cards to access their FICO credit scores for free through their online accounts.* For example, free scores are provided with the Barclaycard Arrival, Arrival Plus, Carnival, Frontier, Rewards and Ring MasterCards. The company has indicated that additional cards will be added to this program. *BarclaycardUS.com*

• **Discover** automatically provides cardholders with FICO scores for free on each monthly statement. *Discover.com*

• **First National Bank of Omaha** gives cardholders access to their FICO credit scores for free through their online accounts. *First National.com*

Warning: Capital One also offers free credit scores to cardholders. But unlike the issuers above, the scores are not FICO scores. In fact, the scores aren't anything that any lender is likely to access. Even Capital One itself doesn't use these scores when it evaluates card applicants. Scores obtained through this program should be considered a vague guide of one's creditworthiness, nothing more.

SCORES FROM WEBSITES

The four websites below provide truly free access to credit scores with no hidden charges and no need to enter a credit card number. You will, however, have to enter personal data including your e-mail address, Social Security number, mailing address and birth date. These websites are likely to use the information you provide—as well as your credit score—to target you with ads from lenders and others.

The scores that these sites provide are not FICO scores, but rather "VantageScores." VantageScores are accessed by thousands of real lenders—though nowhere near as many as those that access FICO scores. These scores usually are within 10 to 15 points of the comparable FICO score, so they are a very good gauge of how lenders view consumers.

What's more, by using several of the websites below, you can access VantageScores derived from the credit reports of all three major credit-reporting bureaus—Equifax, Experian and TransUnion. Each of these credit-reporting agencies maintains its own file on you, and erroneous information might find its way into your file with one but not the others.

*Offers subject to change.

• **Credit.com** offers free credit scores based on Experian credit files up to once a month. Click "GetStarted—It's Free!"

• **CreditKarma.com** provides free scores based on TransUnion credit files as often as you like (scores are updated weekly). Click "Get Started Now."

• **CreditSesame.com** provides free scores based on Experian credit files up to once a month. Click "Get Your Credit Score & More."

• **Quizzle.com** offers free scores based on credit files at Equifax up to once every six months. Click "Get Started—It's Free."

Best strategy: Use these websites to obtain free credit scores from each of the credit-reporting agencies at least a few times a year, and perhaps even more often. If you see one or more of these scores suddenly dip, that's a good time to request a free credit report from *AnnualCreditReport.com* for any credit-reporting agency where it has dropped (see below).

For example, if you learn from *Quizzle.com* that your VantageScore based on your Equifax credit report suddenly dropped by 50 points, obtain your Equifax credit report as described below and look for erroneous information that could be dragging down the score.

Warning: Take extreme care to spell each website's address correctly. If you mistype it even slightly, you could end up on a "squatter" site that a scammer has designed to look like a legitimate site. Rather than provide a free credit score, this squatter site might try to sell you credit-related services or, worse, ask for your Social Security number and other personal data so that the scammer can steal your identity.

FREE CREDIT REPORTS

The four websites listed above don't just offer free credit scores—they also say that they offer free credit reports.

Unfortunately, the credit reports that these sites provide really are just general summaries, not the detailed tallies of credit accounts and loan payments that consumers need to determine whether inaccurate information is unfairly dragging down their credit scores.

There remains only one place to obtain an actual credit report for free—*AnnualCreditReport.com.* By federal law, each of us is entitled to receive one free credit report from each of the three credit-reporting agencies every 12 months through this site.

Helpful: In some states—Colorado, Georgia, Maine, Maryland, Massachusetts, New Jersey and Vermont—consumers can obtain free credit reports more than once a year from each of the credit-reporting agencies.

50 SHADES OF FICO

In spite of a common misconception, you do not have just one FICO credit score—you have about 50. Which FICO score a lender sees when it evaluates a consumer depends on which generation of FICO software it uses... what type of lender it is (a different formula is used for mortgage lenders than for credit card issuers, for example)...and which credit-reporting agency's file it accesses.

Also, among the three major credit-reporting bureaus, it's fairly common for there to be differences among what they have in a consumer's credit files.

Still, knowing any one of your FICO scores usually provides a fairly accurate, although not perfect, estimate of what a lender will see when it checks your score. Though there are lots of variations of FICO scores, typically all of an individual's scores tend to be bunched within a range of 15 to 20 points or so.

There is one important exception to this, however. The differences between your credit scores could be much larger if there are major differences hidden in the files maintained on you by the three credit bureaus—perhaps one has mixed your credit history together with the credit history of someone who shares your name, for example. That's why it's important to monitor your credit reports from all three of the credit-reporting agencies for mistakes.

BETTER WAYS...

Handy Credit Card App

Turn credit cards on and off with your phone. Use a new mobile app called *Card Control* to activate a card when you are about to make a purchase—and deactivate it immediately afterward to prevent fraudulent use. You also can set cards to work at certain merchants but not at others. The app is offered through the financial institution that offers your card—check to see if yours makes it available.

Consumer Reports Money Adviser. ConsumerReports.org

Beware of These "Chip" Credit Cards

Odysseas Papadimitriou, founder and CEO of Evolution Finance, based in Washington, DC, and parent company of *CardHub.com*, an online marketplace for comparing credit cards, prepaid cards and gift cards.

Despite a run of credit card data breaches, major card issuers are choosing not to offer the most secure version of new credit cards in the US, opting instead for a version that is more convenient for consumers to use. The issuers, including American Express, Bank of America, Citigroup and JPMorgan Chase, are now adopting so-called "chip-and-signature" technology for hundreds of millions of new cards rather than "chip-and-PIN" technology.

A chip-and-signature card includes an embedded computer chip that generates a unique transaction code, making it difficult for a hacker to access card information when a cardholder dips the card into a chip-enabled terminal. But it doesn't require consumers to input a PIN, as the more secure chip-and-PIN technology does.

Reason: Issuers fear consumers would find it inconvenient to remember and input PINs.

However, if a chip-and-signature card is lost or stolen, it can easily be used for fraudulent transactions because the thief does not need a PIN code and few retailers actually check the signature when a card is used.

Chip-and-PIN technology has become the standard in Europe, Australia and Canada.

BEWARE...

Dollar Bills Are Covered in Bacteria!

Researchers examined dollar bills from a New York City bank and found 3,000 types of bacteria, including the superbug *methicillin-resistant Staphylococcus aureus* (MRSA).

Study by researchers at New York University Center for Genomics and Systems Biology, New York City.

Just a few issuers are choosing the chip-and-PIN cards for US consumers. These include Target Corp., which fell victim to a major data breach at the end of 2013...Diner's Club...and the United Nations Federal Credit Union.

New-Home Buyers: Negotiate for Incentives

Slower sales have forced builders in many parts of the US, especially in Las Vegas, Phoenix, Riverside-San Bernadino, California, and Washington, DC, to offer perks to complete deals on excess inventory.

What you can negotiate for: Upgraded appliances and kitchen cabinets...wood flooring...and having your mortgage closing costs covered.

Rick Palacios, Jr., vice president, director of research at John Burns Real Estate Consulting, Irvine, California. *RealEstateConsulting.com*

How Couples Can Survive Home-Buying Stress

Buying a new home is stressful for most couples. *What helps...*

Set priorities and make choices throughout the home-buying process as equal partners... not as a series of decisions made by one person and grudgingly accepted by the other. If one person is not onboard about decisions, he/she has no sense of ownership. Then if things go wrong, the person who was reluctant blames the person who made the decisions. Treat a home purchase like a business deal—focus on successful negotiations in which each person compromises. Each person should make a list of things that matter in order of importance to him/her—for example, a home office, a level yard, a two-car garage.

Justin Newmark, psychologist and copresident of the Psychoanalytic Couple & Family Institute of New England, Needham, Massachusetts, quoted in *The Boston Globe*.

Buying a Condo? What You Need to Do...

Before you buy an association-governed home or condominium, get a copy of the group's most recent reserve study to check its financial soundness. Also, ask how many members are beyond 60 days delinquent on fees—that percentage affects the association's cash flow. An estimated 70% of association-governed communities are underfunded. That leaves residents liable for large special assessments for emergency repairs (those who can't pay the assessments could face property liens or possible foreclosure). Ask your financial adviser for details.

Roundup of experts on the fiscal health of homeowner associations, reported in *Kiplinger's Personal Finance*.

Tips on Buying a Vacation Home

Don't buy vacation property while you are on vacation. It may be tempting to imagine a future with no hotels and no packing and unpacking—and the ability to get away to your own place whenever you wish. But many people find that they do not visit the property as often as they expected to...get bored going to the same place for all vacations...underestimate the cost of furnishing a second home...do not think about the repairs and maintenance that the property will need...and forget that there is no room service—you have to shop and do all your own cooking and cleaning.

Self-defense: Be realistic about how often you will use the property...add 20% to whatever costs you expect...and determine whether the property will fit your future lifestyle, not just your current needs.

Ric Edelman, chairman and CEO, Edelman Financial Services, Fairfax, Virginia.

Home Inspection Smarts

The following issues often get overlooked in a home inspection...

Partially blocked or damaged sewer lines can be difficult to detect...a cracked heat exchanger can be serious but might not be included in the average inspection—have an HVAC contractor check out any furnace more than 10 years old...electrical problems may be traceable only by an electrician...and structural problems may be spotted by an inspector, but their extent may be clear only to a structural engineer.

Self-defense: Hire a certified inspector who has long experience in your specific neighborhood—he/she tends to know what problems are common in the area. If the inspector recommends hiring specialists to check things out further, do so.

Roundup of experts on home inspection, reported at *FoxBusiness.com.*

Where Renting Is Better Than Buying

Renting now is better than buying a home in the most expensive cities in the US. For example, in and near San Francisco, Los Angeles and New York City, the relationship between home prices, rents and incomes points to a possible new housing bubble—making renting a better choice financially. In Boston, Miami and Washington, DC, home prices have risen enough that renting also is a better deal for many people, although those cities show less evidence of a housing bubble.

But: There are many markets where home prices remain 30% to 40% below 2006 levels—even more if inflation is taken into account. Those include Phoenix, Las Vegas and Orlando, Florida—where buying still is better than renting.

The New York Times. NYTimes.com

Beware the New Adjustable-Rate Mortgages

Greg McBride, CFA, chief financial analyst for *Bankrate.com,* a personal finance website based in North Palm Beach, Florida.

Home buyers, watch out! Financial institutions are now rolling out a new generation of hybrid adjustable-rate mortgages (ARMs) with very attractive initial rates. ARMs permit home buyers to increase their buying power and keep monthly payments more affordable—but they were a major culprit leading to hundreds of thousands of foreclosures in the 2008 housing meltdown. The new ARMs recently carried rates as low as 3.23% for the first several years,* compared with a nationwide average of 3.95% for a 30-year fixed-rate mortgage.

*Rates as of August 7, 2015.

TAKE NOTE...

Best Free Mortgage Calculators

For biweekly payments, which let you pay off your mortgage early: Malvern National Bank (*MNBBank.com/calculators*) lets you enter the mortgage amount, term and interest rate to figure out what your biweekly payments will be.

Mortgage qualification: Homefinder's calculator (*Homefinder.org/mortgage_qualifier.shtml*) helps you figure out how much house you can afford by entering the purchase price, down payment, property tax, insurance and other factors.

For adjustable-rate mortgages (ARMs): Malvern's calculator helps you figure out the cost of an ARM and compare it with the cost of a fixed-rate loan (*MNBBank.com/calculators*).

15-year vs. 30-year mortgage: Crown Financial Ministries (*Crown.org*, click "Calculators" under "Find Help") gives the difference in payments and interest between the two options.

Refinancing: Zillow's calculator (*Zillow.com*, then click "Refinance Calculator" under "Mortgages") shows how refinancing will affect payments, monthly savings and savings over the life of the loan.

GoBankingRates.com

Lenders say that the new features reduce the risk that borrowers will get into trouble when the fixed-rate period of the ARM ends. These features include initial interest rates that remain fixed for longer than the typical five-year period, giving borrowers more time to refinance or sell the home before the rate adjusts upward.

Example: Pentagon Federal Credit Union recently offered an ARM with an interest rate of 3.228% for the first 15 years of the 30-year loan. The rate adjusts once after the 15 years. The new ARMs typically are capped at a maximum of five to six percentage points above the initial rate—in the case of the Pentagon Federal Credit Union ARM, the rate could rise by six points to 9.228%.

If you are considering an ARM...

- **Look at the maximum rate allowed over the life of the loan** and how much the rate can rise each time it resets. Get help examining your mortgage terms and running the numbers from a nonprofit HUD-approved housing counselor (*HUD.gov* and put "Housing Counselor" and your state in the search box).

- **Avoid using an ARM as an excuse to buy an expensive house** that you couldn't afford with a fixed-rate mortgage. Even with an extended low-rate period, there's too much risk that you will be caught flat-footed and potentially have to give up the house later when the loan resets.

What to do: Ask yourself whether you could handle higher mortgage payments if you weren't able to refinance or sell your home before your payments adjusted upward.

Home-Equity Lines of Credit: The New Rules

Keith Gumbinger, vice president of HSH Associates, which publishes mortgage and consumer loan information, Riverdale, New Jersey. *HSH.com*

Home-equity lines of credit, which became scarce as banks pulled back and consumers grew wary during the housing market bust, are becoming widely available and popular again. But the new generation of these credit lines—known as HELOCs—carry restrictive features meant to lower the risk that the banks are taking. HELOCs are variable-rate loans that home owners can draw on as needed using their homes as collateral. Recent interest rates on HELOCs have been averaging below 5%.* The banks are pitching HELOCs to home owners as financing to pay for college, consolidate credit card debt, make home improvements and provide a source of money for emergencies.

Features to watch out for...

- **Loan-to-value (LTV) ratio.** The amount of money you can borrow with a HELOC now is limited to an amount that typically is based on an 80% LTV ratio. To calculate that, take 80% of your home's appraised value, then deduct the outstanding mortgage amount. So even if you have equity in your home, you may not be able to borrow very much via a HELOC.

*Rates as of August 7, 2015.

Example: If your home is appraised at $300,000 with a $230,000 mortgage balance, the most you qualify for is just $10,000.

• **Required credit score of 720 or above.** Home owners with lower scores may qualify for an LTV ratio of just 65%.

• **Curtailment clause.** Banks maintain the right to cut off your access to the HELOC just when you might need it most—if you get in financial difficulty, such as falling behind on your mortgage or suffering a large medical bill.

Important: If you have an existing HELOC with an interest rate that is higher than today's going rates and your home has gone up in value, there is a good chance that you can refinance or modify the terms. Most HELOCs still are owned by their original lenders, which means there may be great flexibility in working with home owners, compared with those loans that have been sold off to giant banks.

Surprise Jump in Your Mortgage Bill

Greg McBride, CFA, chief financial analyst for *Bankrate.com,* a personal finance website based in North Palm Beach, Florida.

Mailings from mortgage providers have included a surprise lately. Monthly payments have shot up. That is because taxes on property have been rising at the fastest rate since the US housing market crash...and insurance premiums in some parts of the US have jumped in the wake of a string of natural disasters.

That means mortgage providers are upping escrow amounts sharply for accounts on which they handle tax and insurance payments. And the bite is even worse if a mortgage provider, over the past year or so, underestimated how much those costs would rise—because the monthly escrow payment will shoot up even more sharply to make up for that underestimate. Alternatively, the provider might give you the option of making up the difference all at once in a lump sum.

Ways to avoid escrow shock: Notify your loan servicer if your taxes and/or homeowner's insurance increases, and request that your monthly payments reflect the change immediately. Shop for less expensive insurance. Or if your property taxes rise, contact your local assessor's office. While you can't contest property tax rates, you may be able to lower the assessed value of your home by filing an appeal.

New Ways to Get More When You Sell Your Home

Stan Humphries, chief economist at Zillow, the real estate information service based in Seattle, which has a database of more than 110 million US homes. He is coauthor of *Zillow Talk: The New Rules of Real Estate. Zillow.com*

The housing market is finally getting back to normal. This year, sales of existing homes are likely to match or top long-term historical averages for the first time since the early 2000s. But real estate economist Stan Humphries says that some of the conventional wisdom about buying and selling a home has changed drastically. That's partly because people have become much more wary about the future of real estate prices in the wake of the 2007–2009 housing-price meltdown...and partly because of the growing role of technology, especially the Internet, in real estate shopping. Humphries has analyzed millions of home listings, as well as data gathered from millions of monthly visitors to the Zillow real estate website. He has developed insights that can earn you thousands of dollars more on the sale of your home.

Conventional wisdom says that as a seller, you should overprice your home by 5% to 10% to leave yourself some wiggle room in negotiations...renovate your kitchen to add the most value to your house...and list early in the year to catch the spring and early-summer home-buying rush.

But here's what national and local housing data say are the rules that work better now...

RULE 1: Price a home as close as possible to fair market value. About half of all sellers still price their homes too high and have to make cuts to attract potential buyers. Zillow studied more than a million homes listed for sale and tracked price changes until they sold. Homes that required a 10% price cut spent an average of 220 days on the market and sold for 2% less than their estimated value. That's because buyers bargain more aggressively when a listing sits on the market a long time. Homes that were correctly priced to begin with needed no price cut to sell, spent an average of 107 days on the market and, best of all, sold for 2% more than their estimated value.

Best way to determine fair market value: Have a real estate agent prepare a market analysis of the recent selling prices of comparable homes in your area to help establish fair market value.

RULE 2: Make sure the last non-zero digit in your original asking price is a nine. This is the same kind of psychological pricing that works in retail stores, and it leads to faster, more lucrative sales for homes at every price level.

For example, the average US home that was listed initially for $449,000 wound up selling for about $4,000 more than a home listed at $450,000. What's more, comparable homes priced $1,000 lower than their counterparts sold four days faster on average.

Why it works: Consumers are conditioned to see prices ending in nine as signifying an attractive discount. That kind of pricing attracts more attention to your home's listing, which often translates into higher offers.

RULE 3: Make modest upgrades to your home that restore the basic functioning of the house. Modest upgrades have a much bigger relative impact on your home's value than renovations that add fashionable but frivolous luxuries. For example, upgrading a bathroom from poor to decent shape completely changes the livability of the property and appeals to just about everyone. But taking a fully functional bathroom and adding high-end elements, such as fancy jet-massage showerheads or dramatic tiling, actually may turn off many prospective buyers. Based on Zillow's analysis, a $3,000, midrange bathroom remodel—with such steps as replacing the toilet...updating lighting fixtures...adding a double sink...and painting or putting up wallpaper—resulted in a $1.71 increase in home value for every $1 spent on renovation. But plunking down $12,000 for a complete bathroom overhaul, including replacing the floor and moving plumbing, resulted in only an 87-cent increase in value per dollar spent.

Note: In contrast to conventional wisdom, kitchen renovations have a lower return than many other home-improvement investments, with a cost recovery of just 50 cents per $1 spent regardless of the scope of the remodeling work.

Reason: Prospective buyers are very particular about what constitutes a dream kitchen. They won't be excited about a kitchen renovation if it doesn't happen to match their needs and tastes.

RULE 4: List your home for sale in late March or later. Many home sellers choose to list early in the year, starting in late January or in February. They do this in order to have plenty of time to catch the spring and early-summer home-buying rush. But Zillow's data indicate that listing very early in the year has become so popular that you're better off waiting until after the first few weeks of March or even the second week in April in some markets, such as Boston. The average US home put on the market in late March 2015, for example, sold for over 2% more than the average home listed earlier in the year.

Reason: Your house doesn't get lost in a sea of new listings. That leads to more attention and potentially more offers.

RULE 5: Write long, carefully worded listings. Although the Internet allows home sellers to upload videos and lots of photographs of their homes, the data show that homes with written descriptions longer than the median length of about 50-to-70 words routinely sell for more than their asking prices, while those with shorter written descriptions do not. Prospective buyers want details, and those extra words give them additional information that makes a home worth seeing in person.

Note: After a listing reaches 250 words, additional length did not seem to help the sale price.

What to write: Avoid words in your listing that connote "small," "nothing special" or "needs work." These words include *cute...charming... potential...quaint...requires TLC...*and *unique.* Such words turn off buyers and can reduce the selling price by as much as 2% to 7% of the asking price.

On the positive side, lower-priced residences described in listings as *luxurious* beat their original asking prices by 8%, on average...and using *impeccable* bested their original asking prices by 6%. In more expensive homes, listings with the word *captivating* boosted the sale price by 6.5%, on average, and the word *gentle* (typically referring to the property description such as *gentle rolling hills*) was worth an additional 2.3%, on average. Words such as *remodeled* pushed up the selling prices of homes in every price range by an average of 1.7% to 2.9% and *landscaped* by 1.5% to 4.2%.

HOW TO BUY A HOME THAT SOARS IN VALUE

People choose to buy particular homes for a variety of reasons that have little to do with money. But if one of your primary goals in choosing a home is price appreciation, the data are clear—look at properties in up-and-coming neighborhoods.

If you can get to one of these neighborhoods within the first five years of it becoming hot, you have a chance of snatching a property at a much lower price point than in areas that are already well-regarded.

How you can spot these soon-to-be popular neighborhoods...

• **Use the Halo Effect.** Look for less developed areas adjacent to premier neighborhoods that already have taken off and have ample restaurants, cafés, parks and nightlife.

• **Look for a Starbucks.** Believe it or not, having a location of the popular coffee shop within a quarter mile of a house has proved to be one of the strongest, most reliable indicators of neighborhood gentrification and rapidly appreciating home prices. Between 1997 and 2014, US homes appreciated 65%, on average. But properties near a Starbucks appreciated 96%, on average, and they recovered much more quickly from the housing bust.

Reason: Starbucks has an army of analysts and geographic information specialists dedicated to finding the next hot neighborhood, assessing everything from traffic patterns to the kinds of new businesses opening in the area. In addition, the iconic coffee shop is seen as a proxy for gentrification by other potential upscale businesses.

Home-Repair Projects That Pay Off

The average project recoups 66% of its cost when the home is sold—up 5.5 percentage points over last year. And some projects return much more. Replacing an entry door with a steel door recoups almost 97% of its cost...a minor kitchen remodel, 83%...window replacement (wood), 79%...basement remodel, 78%...major kitchen remodel, 74%...bathroom remodel, 73%...replacement of roofing or of a backup power generator, 68%.

Remodeling Magazine, "2014 Cost vs. Value Report," for midrange projects, reported at *CNBC.com*.

What to Do When Relisting a Home for Sale

First, find out from a number of brokers and agents why they think the home didn't sell the first time, and correct problems that are frequently mentioned. Then make low-cost improvements that can freshen your home's appearance, and declutter to give the home an open, clean appearance—store, sell or give away unneeded furniture, kitchen appliances, even bathroom soaps and shampoo bottles. Also air out your home—you may not notice its odor, but all homes have one and potential buyers may notice.

Consider hiring a different agent from the one who handled the original listing. Review the original marketing strategy with the new agent, and find ways to do things differently. Do not necessarily reduce the asking price—unless market factors make that a good idea.

Roundup of experts in real estate sales, reported at *Bankrate.com.*

MONEYWISE...

Great Cities That Are Affordable, Too!

The best city to live in and save money is Portland, Oregon. It has relatively low rents, average unemployment and no sales tax.

The rest of the top 10: Anchorage, Alaska... Lincoln, Nebraska...Boise, Idaho...Madison, Wisconsin...Omaha...Wichita, Kansas...Fort Wayne, Indiana...Arlington, Texas...Corpus Christi, Texas.

Worst city for saving money: San Francisco, the most expensive city in the US, which has high housing costs and rents and some of the highest sales taxes and gas prices in the country.

Other worst cities for saving money: Los Angeles...Irvine, California...New York City...Oakland, California...San Jose, California...Long Beach, California...Fremont, California...Stockton, California...Santa Ana, California.

GoBankingRates.com survey of the best and worst cities for saving money based on sales tax, median home/condo value, median monthly rent, median income, unemployment rates and gas prices.

Why You Don't Want the House in a Divorce: And Other Assets You May Want to Forgo

Diane Pearson, CFP, CDFA, personal chief financial officer at Legend Financial Advisors, Inc., Pittsburgh. She has been included in *Worth* magazine's annual list of the country's top 250 wealth advisers four times. As a certified divorce financial analyst, she has helped hundreds of divorced people value their marital assets. *Legend-Financial.com*

Be very careful how you divide up the possessions if you split up with your spouse. Accepting certain assets in a divorce settlement could leave you with a smaller slice of the total pie than you deserve. You can't necessarily depend on your divorce attorney to warn you about all these potential potholes, either—most divorce attorneys are experts on family law, not asset values. And your financial adviser may not understand divorce law.

Six types of assets that you may not want in a divorce settlement...

- **The family home.** Some people desperately want to keep their homes in a divorce. This may be where they raised their kids. It's where they know their neighbors. It's where they expected to grow old. It's only natural to want to maintain these emotional connections as a marriage crumbles—but taking the home in a divorce settlement usually is a big financial mistake.

Homes typically are worth hundreds of thousands of dollars. To keep this asset in a divorce, you probably would have to agree to let your partner keep the lion's share of the family's retirement savings and/or other investments. But while that investment portfolio is likely to increase significantly in value over the years and produce much needed retirement income, a home is more likely to stagnate in value and perhaps even be a financial sinkhole.

Do not be fooled by the recent real estate recovery—homes simply are not good investments. From 1890 through 2012, on average, home prices gained absolutely nothing in value after adjusting for inflation. Owning a home actually costs money—lots of it. In addition to mortgage payments, home owners must pay thousands of dollars each year in property taxes and insurance, maintenance and utility bills.

Most divorced people are much better served by agreeing to sell the family home during the divorce process. Buy or rent a smaller home, possibly an affordable condo or apartment, instead. (Or let your partner keep the house if he/she likes, while you get the lion's share of the savings.)

• **Tax-deferred retirement accounts.** When is $100,000 in savings not worth $100,000? When there's a big tax bill due. Unlike most other types of savings, the assets held in tax-deferred accounts such as traditional IRAs or 401(k)s are taxed as income when the money is withdrawn. That means perhaps one-fifth to one-third or more of the savings might wind up in the government's pockets, not yours, depending on your federal and state income tax brackets.

Tax-deferred retirement savings may be illiquid, as well—you might face a 10% penalty if you withdraw any money from these accounts prior to age 59½.

In a divorce settlement, do not agree to take more than half of the tax-deferred assets, which eventually will be taxable, if that means your soon-to-be ex gets more than half of the Roth IRA savings, which typically won't be taxed, or more than half of the non-tax-advantaged savings.

Exception: You get more assets to make up for the future tax bite.

• **Investments that have gained a lot in value.** Which would you rather receive from your divorce settlement—$100,000 worth of a stock that has increased steadily in value since you purchased it...or $100,000 worth of a stock that has lost money for your portfolio? Intuitively it might seem wise to take the stock that has done well, because it's more likely than the laggard to continue to increase in value. But that's the wrong choice, and doing that could leave you saddled with a big tax bill.

When you sell an investment that you have owned for more than one year, any increase in its value from its cost basis—what it cost you—is taxed at your long-term capital gains tax rate, which currently is 15% for most taxpayers. (Taxpayers in the 39.6% income tax bracket pay a steeper 20% rate when the new net investment income tax is included. Profits from the sale of assets held less than one year are taxed at a taxpayer's income tax rate.) On the other hand, selling an investment that has lost money can decrease your income tax bill.

Don't agree to take your portfolio's winning stocks in the divorce settlement while your former spouse takes the losers unless you receive a larger share of the total assets to make up for your future tax bill. *A few exceptions...*

• Cost basis doesn't matter if an investment is held in a tax-advantaged retirement account. Whether or not they have gained value, investments held in tax-deferred accounts are taxed as ordinary income when withdrawn, while those held in Roth accounts typically are not taxed at all upon withdrawal.

• Low cost basis isn't a problem if you intend to leave the asset to your heirs. In fact, it can be an advantage to the family, because assets such as stocks that aren't held in tax-advantaged accounts generally receive a "step up in basis" upon your death. That means the capital gains up to that point are not taxed when the assets are later sold by your heirs.

• You don't have to pay long-term capital gains taxes if you are in the 15% income tax bracket or below. As of 2015, single filers with taxable income of up to $37,450 qualify for this tax bracket. These rules could change in future years.

• **Art, antiques and collectibles.** An appraiser typically is hired or a guidebook consulted during the divorce process to determine the value of any art, antiques and collectibles. Trouble is, the values these appraisers and guidebooks assign to these possessions often are much too high. The quoted amount is often what you would have to spend to buy a similar item in a shop, rather than the amount you would receive if you sold the one you have. Because of steep retail markups, these figures can be different.

Art, antiques and collectibles can be costly to insure. And if they eventually are sold for more than they initially cost, you might face a long-term capital gains tax of 28%.

If you don't want to give up your art, antiques or collectibles in a divorce, at least confirm that the appraiser or guidebook used will provide the amount your items would bring if you sold them, not their replacement or insurance value.

• **A small business** (unless you know as much as or more than your spouse about the business and its finances). Be very wary if your spouse suggests that you take the business in a divorce settlement if that spouse handles the finances. He/she might have good reason to believe that the company is worth less than its appraised value.

Example: Maybe your spouse knows that a key client is about to defect to a competitor.

• **Relatively new annuities.** Cashing out an annuity too soon (generally within five to 12 years of the date when it was purchased) could trigger a surrender fee of as much as 8% to 10%. Many annuities also have steep annual fees that can cut into their long-term value.

New College Savings Twist: Opportunity or Danger?

Paul Curley, CFA, director of college-savings research at Strategic Insight, a financial research firm, Boston. *SIOnline.com*

Some college-savings 529 plans now are offering investments that go well beyond mainstream stocks and bonds. This is both an opportunity and a danger for parents, grandparents and other investors.

The new options for account holders, which include funds that invest in commodities, floating-rate loans, foreign government bonds and real estate investment trusts (REITs), are meant to allow account holders to increase diversification and thereby reduce overall portfolio volatility and perhaps boost returns. Over the past few years, such new investment options have been added to plans in at least nine states—Colorado, Illinois, Iowa, Missouri, New Mexico, New York, North Dakota, North Carolina and Wisconsin—with more states expected to follow. *What to do...*

• **Review your current 529 plan's investment offerings at the plan's website or by phone.** If you have selected an "age-based" investment portfolio that automatically adjusts your asset mix to become less risky as your student approaches college age, the new alternative funds may already be incorporated. If you have invested in funds of your choosing, you may want to add some exposure to the new alternative funds.

• **Consider moving some money into your plan's principal-protected fund or money-market fund** if there are no alternative funds available and you want to reduce volatility.

• **Be aware that the new options can be risky, too.** For instance, floating-rate funds, whose interest rates can "float" up and down according to market rates, invest in corporate loans that may be below investment-grade, which may provide higher yields but may end up with a company defaulting on the debt.

Hidden Traps in Employer Tuition Programs

Mark Kantrowitz, senior vice president of *Edvisors.com*, a group of websites related to college finances, and founder of the college financial-aid site *FinAid.org* and the college scholarship site *FastWeb.com*. He is author of *Secrets to Winning a Scholarship*.

The coffee chain Starbucks drew a lot of attention when it announced that it would cover the cost of undergraduate college tuition for its employees. While the benefit is welcomed by many employees, the tuition-assistance program actually will cover the full cost of attending only the online program of Arizona State University (ASU) and only during junior and senior years. In freshman and sophomore years, Starbucks employees are eligible only for discounts from ASU that will lower the cost of attending its well-regarded online program by about 22%. (Starbucks employees who earn college credits at other institutions might be able to transfer into ASU's online program as juniors or seniors.) In other words, this tuition-assistance program, like many others, is not everything it may seem to be. *Other potential pitfalls with such programs...*

• **A portion of the tuition assistance could be considered taxable income by the IRS.** Employer-provided tuition aid generally is tax-free up to only $5,250 per year. Assistance above this level usually is taxed as income.

• **Tuition-assistance programs often reimburse employees after the fact** rather than pay tuition bills up front. Starbucks reimburses its eligible employees only after they have earned 21 credits, roughly seven courses.

• **Employer tuition-assistance programs can reduce students' eligibility** for need-based financial aid because they have to work while they go to school.

• **College-tuition programs often bind employees to their current employer.** Employers who offer these programs might require participating employees to continue to work for the company, perhaps for one year after graduation for each year of education.

Private College Loans with Better Rates Than Popular Federal Loan

Rates on newly issued federal Plus Loans, which parents of undergraduates often use, are 6.84% in 2015. If you have a credit score of 780 or higher, consider private lenders including Citizens Financial Group (*recent college loan rate*: 6.29%*), Discover Financial Services (5.99%) and Sallie Mae (5.74%).

Important: Repayment terms on private loans typically lack the flexibility and deferment options of federal loans.

Mark Kantrowitz, senior vice president of *Edvisors.com*, a group of websites related to college finances, and author of *Secrets to Winning a Scholarship.*

*Rates subject to change.

Smarter Donations

Check pockets, drawers, boxes and bags before donating clothing or furniture. Accidental donations of cash and jewelry occur frequently. *Example*: $40,000 in cash was accidentally left in the pockets of clothing donated to a Goodwill store in Monroe, Michigan. The cash was returned.

USA Today. USAToday.com

Insurance Insights

Get Your Health Insurer to Pay Up: A Former Claims Examiner Tells All

Every time that you make a claim under your health insurance policy, there is the substantial possibility that your insurer will decide to reject it.

When claims are rejected, policyholders must either pay out of pocket for medical bills—some of which can be massive—or spend an inordinate amount of time battling a corporate bureaucracy about complex insurance issues that they do not fully understand.

The more you know about how the system works and what you can do to make it work better for you, the more success you likely will have.

Here's how to reduce the odds that your health insurance claims will be rejected—and what to do when a claim is rejected.

BEFORE OBTAINING TREATMENT

When you require out-of-the-ordinary nonemergency medical care, especially from any provider that you haven't used before...

Get the go-ahead for the procedure from your insurer. This may seem obvious, but people often forget. It is worth doing whenever you need medical care that is more complex than the standard doctor's visit—even if the same procedure has been covered in the past. Ask to have this "preauthorization" sent to you in writing.

Obtaining preauthorization prevents the insurer from later denying your claim on the

---

Adria Gross, CEO of MedWise Billing, Inc., Monroe, New York, a medical-billing advocacy company that assists health insurance customers in disputes with their insurers. She previously worked as a claims examiner with Blue Cross/Blue Shield and American International Group. *MedWiseBilling.com* grounds that the procedure or the test was not medically necessary.

Insurers have begun to demand preauthorization more and more in recent years, and they are denying claims when it is not obtained. If your insurer will not preauthorize a procedure, do not assume this rejection is final. Ask your doctor to submit a letter to the insurer explaining why the procedure is required in your case.

If preauthorization is again denied, ask your doctor to try again, this time describing your health situation and the necessity of the procedure in greater detail. Insurers often back down when patients and doctors persist.

IF A CLAIM IS REJECTED

Investigate why the claim was rejected before paying a medical bill out of pocket. There might be a way to get your insurer to pay it after all. *Possible problems and solutions...*

PROBLEM: The health-care provider entered a billing code incorrectly. Every medical procedure has a five-digit "Current Procedural Terminology" (CPT) code. Every medical diagnosis has a specific code number, too.

If your health-care provider enters a procedure or diagnostic code incorrectly—which happens with surprising frequency—your insurer isn't likely to waste time trying to figure out what's wrong. It will just reject the claim.

What to do: If you believe that a code-entry error might be responsible for the claim rejection, present your concerns to the health-care provider's billing department and ask it to resubmit the bill to your insurer with the correct codes.

PROBLEM: The provider of health care billed under the wrong insurance policy. This is particularly likely if your insurance recently has changed...or if this is the first time that you have received treatment from the health-care provider.

What to do: When an insurer rejects your claim, confirm that the policy number and group number on the paperwork corresponds with your current policy.

PROBLEM: The insurer continues billing you after you've met your deductible and/or out-of-pocket maximum. If your insurer fails to properly track the medical procedures that you have had and/or the payments you've made during a year, you might be asked to pay more than you should.

What to do: Keep a file each year of your medical bills...health insurance Explanation of Benefits (EOB) statements...and a tally of the amounts you pay out of pocket.

When you believe that you have reached your annual deductible and/or out-of-pocket maximum, make sure that the insurer doesn't keep requiring you to pay more. If it does, ask the insurer to review its records and to explain why its tally doesn't match yours. Keep in mind that the insurer may not count the full amounts charged by out-of-network providers.

PROBLEM: It isn't clear why the insurer won't pay a claim. Insurance company claim rejections can be very difficult to understand.

What to do: Call up the insurer's customer service department, and ask for a plain-English explanation of why your claim was rejected. If you don't understand or agree with what you're told, ask to speak with a supervisor. If the first person you speak with doesn't provide clarity, call back repeatedly and speak with a different representative and supervisor. Take notes documenting the time and date of each call, the person you spoke with and what you were told.

OUTSIDE HELP

If speaking with the insurer proves to be fruitless, your options include...

- **Tell the insurer that you plan to contact local legislators and the local media.** If necessary, go to the legislators and the media and explain why you believe the insurer is being especially unfair and how this might affect other consumers, too. This often works well.
- **If you have group coverage, call your employer's human resources representative...**your union...or the organization through which you obtained insurance. Ask for help negotiating with the insurer.
- **If you're age 65 or older, contact your state, county or local Department of Aging to request assistance.** (Enter "Department

Aging" and your state, county or municipality into a search engine to find this agency—its name might be slightly different in your state.) These agencies often provide helpful advice and, in some cases, even may call the insurer, the medical provider and/or state insurance regulators.

- **Ask your state's Department of Insurance for guidance.** (Enter "Department Insurance" and the name of your state into a search engine. In some states, insurance issues are handled by the Department of Financial Regulation.) Often the regulators are very aggressive and helpful in getting insurers that are licensed by the state to pay—sometimes with interest.

- **Hire a claims-assistance professional.** Locate a claims-assistance professional through the website of the National Association of Healthcare Advocacy Consultants (*NAHAC.com*)...or the Alliance of Claims Assistance Professionals (*Claims.org*). You should expect to pay $75 to $175 an hour* for these services or, with some pros, up to 35% of the amount you save in medical costs.

A case may take as little as an hour to resolve if one phone call does the trick...or many hours in complex cases.

The professionals understand state insurance laws and policy details, and insurers are less likely to think that they can push the pros around.

NEGOTIATE OUT-OF-NETWORK BILLS

If you obtain medical treatment in a nonemergency situation from a health-care provider that is not in your insurance policy's network, you might be left with especially large out-of-pocket expenses.

Before receiving such services, go to *CMS.gov*, the website of the Center for Medicare and Medicaid Services, and use the Physician Fee Schedule Search tool to find the appropriate Medicare fee schedule for the procedure code in your area. (Ask your doctor for the procedure's five-digit CPT code.) Insurance companies often base their definitions of "usual, customary and reasonable" charges on Medicare fees.

*Rates subject to change.

Next, call the out-of-network provider's billing representative, and ask for its rate for the services.

If the rate is above the Medicare rate in your area, cite that rate and ask whether the provider can match it. Often, the medical provider will accept that going rate or whichever rate your insurer is willing to pay.

If not, contact the billing departments of other health-care providers in the area that can provide the services.

Also, contact your insurer to see whether it will increase the payment to get closer to what the provider is billing. Sometimes this works. But don't expect to receive 100% reimbursement for out-of-network costs under most insurance plans.

If You Have Employer-Provided Health Insurance...

Paul Fronstin, PhD, director of the health research and education program at the Employee Benefit Research Institute, a nonprofit, nonpartisan research organization, Washington, DC. He also is associate editor of the journal *Benefits Quarterly* and an appointee to the Maryland Health Care Commission. *EBRI.org*

Keep your eyes open during your employer's health insurance open-enrollment period this year. Widespread and substantial changes in employee health insurance plans—some of them hidden in the small print and easy to miss—could boost your costs or curtail your coverage.

Reason: Employers are trying to control ever-rising health insurance costs and cope with new rules under the Affordable Care Act, also known as Obamacare.

For instance, even though the "Cadillac tax" on employer-provided health plans that spend more than $10,200 per employee on coverage ($27,500 for families) doesn't take effect until 2018, employers already are searching for ways to avoid paying the penalty. They are doing so by lowering the costs of plans to below the tax threshold. That may mean reducing benefits and/or passing along additional costs to employees. Many employers are phasing in these changes over the next few years rather than making massive downgrades to the quality of this insurance all at once in 2018.

Here's what to look for when you choose health coverage now...

SPOUSAL SURCHARGE AND PER-CHILD PRICING

In 2013, the shipping company UPS took considerable flak when it announced that it would no longer offer health-care coverage to the spouses of its nonunionized employees if those spouses could obtain health insurance through their own employers. Rules like that are becoming more commonplace.

Some employers plan to reduce or eliminate subsidies for spouses and dependents of employees or have done so already, while others intend to eliminate coverage for spouses who could obtain insurance through their own employers or impose surcharges on coverage for spouses.

Also, more employers are expected to follow Obamacare's lead and charge extra for each child added to insurance coverage—a system known as "unit pricing"—rather than charge a single flat "family" rate regardless of the number of children covered. (Obamacare charges extra for each child added to individual health coverage up to three children.)

What to do: Spousal surcharges and unit pricing make it more important for two-income families to carefully sort through the options offered by both of their employers before either spouse makes benefits choices. An increasing percentage of two-income couples will discover that they're better off obtaining coverage separately through each spouse's employer than together as a family.

If one spouse's employer charges extra per child, that might be a money saver for a small family...while big families are more likely to save if they insure their children through the employer that still charges a flat family rate.

HIGH-DEDUCTIBLE PLANS

Some large employers intend to offer "consumer-directed health plans" (CDHPs), which feature high deductibles as the only option.

This presents two challenges for employees who face high-deductible plans for the first time. The first is the potential for steep out-of-pocket costs—at least $1,300 (at least $2,600 for families) out of pocket before insurance covers any part of medical expenses (with the exception of certain basic preventive services, which must be fully covered under Obamacare). Even after this steep deductible is reached, you still must pay hefty co-insurance—typically 10% to 35% of the cost of care—until you reach an out-of-pocket maximum that could be as much as $6,450 ($12,900 for families). Your employer might make a contribution to a *health savings account* (HSA) to help you with these out-of-pocket costs, but that contribution is unlikely to come close to covering your potential extra expenses.

The second challenge of high-deductible plans is that the HSAs that often accompany employer-provided high-deductible plans can be an added source of confusion for employees already struggling to understand complicated health insurance policies.

What to do: Despite the drawbacks described above, high-deductible plans generally have significantly lower monthly premiums than other health insurance, so they often are a good fit for people who tend to have limited medical expenses. If your health-care needs are substantial, however, investigate whether you could obtain more substantial coverage at affordable prices elsewhere, such as through a spouse's employer. It even might be worth paying a spousal surcharge. If you do end up in a high-deductible plan, it pays to take an active role in controlling your health expenses. If your doctor prescribes a drug, ask if there's an effective generic option, and compare prices at several pharmacies. If your doctor prescribes a test, call several labs in your provider network to see which charges the lowest price.

Take the time needed to understand how HSAs work if one is included with your high-deductible plan.

CARROTS AND STICKS

An increasing number of employers are expected to include "Value-Based Insurance Design" (V-BID) and/or "wellness" programs in health insurance coverage. These programs

GOOD TO KNOW...

Telemedicine May Be Covered by Your Insurance Plan

Telemedicine now is covered by some insurers in 20 states and the District of Columbia. Laws are being developed in 13 other states that will require coverage of some types of telemedicine. Patients connect with doctors, most likely not their own, via phone or the Internet and pay deductibles.

Telemedicine providers: *eHealthInsurance.com/telemedicine...AmeriDoc.com.*

Roundup of experts in telemedicine, reported at *MarketWatch.com*.

use carrots and sticks to encourage plan members to use health care in a more cost-effective manner.

A wellness program might charge individuals who meet particular health-care goals and requirements reduced premiums, copayments and/or deductibles than those who don't meet these goals. A V-BID program might decrease or eliminate out-of-pocket expenses for drugs and other treatments related to the care of a chronic condition such as diabetes, asthma or high blood pressure to encourage employees to manage potentially costly conditions responsibly and avoid hospitalization.

On the other hand, a V-BID program might impose additional out-of-pocket expenses on someone who goes to the emergency room in what is clearly a nonemergency situation, such as a standard case of the flu. The penalty usually is relatively small, however—perhaps an additional co-pay of around $50.

What to do: Try to meet your employer's health requirements. If you (or your spouse or dependent) have a potentially costly chronic health issue, ask whether any of the health insurance options available to you feature incentives for responsible management of this condition. Also, carefully read the section of a health insurance policy that explains your coverage for emergency room visits to see if there are financial penalties for using the emergency room in nonemergencies.

HIGH-END DRUGS

High-end "specialty" drugs such as the arthritis medication Humira and cancer drug Gleevec can cost four figures per month. If you (or your spouse or a dependent who is covered by your health insurance) takes such a drug regularly, do not sign up for any coverage until you read the section of the policy that covers pharmaceuticals. More and more plans are upping the amount that must be paid out of pocket for the costliest drugs and/or adding new requirements for the drugs to be covered at all.

What to do: Scan the plan's formulary—its list of covered drugs—or contact the insurer to find out how much you will have to pay out of pocket to obtain any pricey drugs you require. If you do not currently take expensive prescription drugs, still check to see how well top-tier drugs are covered in general. Take particular note of whether you will be charged co-insurance or, instead, a co-payment with these drugs. A co-pay could be substantial, but at least it's a fixed amount. Co-insurance is a percentage of the cost of the drug, which could be extremely expensive with specialty drugs.

Also, look for new rules related to the coverage of specialty drugs. Some insurers are adding new requirements that this priciest tier will be covered only if the insurer has provided preauthorization and/or the drugs are purchased through a designated seller, possibly a mail-order pharmacy.

4 Costly Medicare Traps to Avoid

Robert Carlson, CPA, JD, managing member of Carlson Wealth Advisors, LLC, and chairman of the board of trustees of the Fairfax County (Virginia) Employees' Retirement System. He is editor and publisher of *Retirement Watch*, a monthly newsletter. *RetirementWatch.com*

If you fail to fully grasp certain Medicare rules, you could end up paying unnecessarily high premiums for the rest of your life. That may be true if you have not enrolled in Medicare yet or even if you already have enrolled. And in some cases, you could even face a gap in coverage and have to pay big medical bills out of pocket.

Four common and costly Medicare misconceptions and mistakes—and how to protect yourself whether you are a current or future enrollee...

• **Thinking that your Social Security retirement age is the same as your Medicare-enrollment age.** Over the years, the age at which people become eligible for "full" retirement benefits has increased. If you were born between 1943 and 1954, for example, your full retirement age is 66, not 65. Trouble is, many people think this full retirement age also applies to Medicare.

Not only is the Medicare-eligibility age still 65 for everyone who qualifies to receive benefits, but failure to sign up during your initial eligibility period can lead to higher Medicare premiums for the rest of your life. (Your initial eligibility to enroll lasts for seven months—the month of your 65th birthday plus the three months immediately before and after.)

How much could a sign-up delay cost you? With Medicare Part B (that's medical insurance), for each full 12-month period that you are late in signing up, a 10% penalty is tacked on to your premiums (basic premiums are $104.90 per month in 2015) for as long as you keep getting Part B. With Part D drug coverage, the penalty is 1% of the "national base beneficiary premium" ($33.15 per month in 2015) multiplied by the number of full uncovered months you were eligible but failed to sign up. The penalty applies if you are not enrolled for 63 days or more in a row when you don't have *creditable* prescription drug coverage. (Creditable coverage means that your plan's coverage is comparable to Part D plans.)

All of that could add up to perhaps $3,000 to $5,000 in penalties over the course of your retirement if you are one year late signing up...or climb to more than $10,000 if you are several years late.

Exception: If you are covered by a group plan offered by your employer or your spouse's employer when you reach age 65, you *might* be able to delay signing up for Medicare without incurring penalties (see below).

• **Thinking that it doesn't matter which option you choose to pay for Part B.** Medicare enrollees can have their Part B premiums automatically deducted from their Social Security benefits or they can pay for them separately. What most people don't realize is that paying with Social Security deductions could save money.

By law, if you have your Part B premiums deducted from your Social Security benefits, any future increase in those premiums cannot result in a "net reduction" in Social Security benefits. In other words, if the government increases the price of Part B, your premiums cannot increase by more than the amount that Social Security's cost-of-living adjustments increase your benefits. If you pay for Part B separately (not from Social Security), you have no such protection against premium increases.

Exception: If you sign up for Medicare before you begin claiming your Social Security benefits, you will *have* to pay separately for Medicare at that time. Switch to paying via Social Security deductions as soon as you start your Social Security benefits.

• **Thinking that you don't need to sign up for Medicare as long as you're covered by an employer.** People who are covered by group health insurance plans when they turn 65—either through their employers or their spouse's employers—often assume that they do not yet need to sign up for Medicare. But this is correct only if the employer has 20 or more employees. If your health coverage is provided by a small employer—one with fewer than 20 employees—this coverage automatically becomes "secondary" to Medicare when you turn 65. That means it will cover only the portion of your medical bills that would not be covered by Medicare if you had signed up for Medicare. If you haven't signed up for Medicare, you will have to pay most of your medical bills out of pocket.

If you are not 100% certain whether your employer has 20 or more employees, ask the employer's benefits department and its health insurance provider for clarification. Asking both of them decreases the odds that you will receive inaccurate information. If you receive conflicting responses and your initial Medicare-enrollment period is nearing its end, sign up for Part B and the cheapest Part D plan available to you until you can clarify the situation.

Warning: Do not just do a head count to determine whether your employer has 20 or more employees—some people who seem to be employees might actually be independent contractors. Sign up for Medicare Part B and Part D immediately if you are 65 or older and the employer providing your group coverage shrinks in size from 20 or more employees to fewer than 20 employees.

Several vital related points...

- Sign up for Medicare Part A (hospital coverage) during your initial enrollment period even if you are covered by a large group health plan. There is no downside to signing up—Part A typically does not charge any premiums.

- If you are covered by an employer's group plan when you first become eligible for Medicare and remain covered with no coverage gaps longer than eight months, you should qualify for an eight-month "special enrollment period." This may be useful if your circumstances change. During this period, you will be able to sign up for Medicare without penalties even if your initial enrollment period has long since passed. Go to *Medicare.gov* for more information.

- COBRA and retiree health plans do not protect you from Medicare late-enrollment penalties because they are based on former employment, not current employment. (With COBRA coverage, a person pays to remain on a former employer's health plan, generally for up to 18 months.) If you are obtaining health coverage through a retiree plan or COBRA, sign up for Medicare during your initial enrollment period (within eight months after leaving your employer) to avoid future penalties and coverage gaps.

- If you are covered by a large group health plan at or after age 65, confirm with both this employer's benefits department and the insurer providing its health plan that the drug coverage component of the group plan qualifies as "creditable coverage" under Medicare rules. If not, sign up for a Part D drug-coverage plan during your initial enrollment period to avoid future penalties. High-deductible health plans are particularly likely to have drug coverage that does not qualify as creditable.

- **Not realizing that a high income you earned a few years ago could unnecessarily increase your Medicare premiums this year.** The Medicare system imposes higher Part B and Part D premiums on people who have modified adjusted gross incomes above $85,000 ($170,000 for married couples filing jointly). But the income figure used in this calculation actually is your income from two years earlier—your 2013 income affects your 2015 Medicare premiums, for example. If this two-year look-back takes you to a time when you and/or your spouse still were working, you could easily be charged higher Medicare premiums even though your retirement income is below the threshold.

If this happens to you, carefully read the paperwork that comes with your Medicare premium notice. It will explain how to file an appeal of your rates based on the change in your financial circumstances.

How to Stop Getting Double-Billed by Your Doctor!

Charles B. Inlander, a consumer advocate and health-care consultant based in Fogelsville, Pennsylvania. He was founding president of the nonprofit People's Medical Society, a consumer advocacy organization credited with key improvements in the quality of US health care, and is author or coauthor of more than 20 consumer-health books.

Here's a cautionary tale for those of you who aren't paying close attention to your doctor bills—four times this past year, I was double-billed for the co-payments I am required to pay at each doctor visit. I always pay cash for those payments, and I request a receipt. But in each of those instances, I later received bills for the amount I already had paid.

I am not the only one having this double-billing problem. Health-care industry reports suggest that double-billing is growing as more consumers have insurance plans that require point-of-service co-payments and/or have high deductibles (the amount you pay before your insurance kicks in).

To help you keep track of what you owe—or do not owe—I have devised a simple system that allows you to monitor your medical bills for errors...

• **Get it on paper.** The first—and most important—step is to create an annual log or list of your medical visits. I keep mine in separate file folders for each month of the year.

Here's what I do: On a single sheet of paper, I list the date of my visit...the doctor or medical service I received...and any payment I made at the time of visit. I attach to that single sheet any receipts that I received for payments I made. If I have multiple medical visits in any given month, they are put into the appropriate monthly file. You can also maintain a log of your visits on a computer, but keep a file folder for the actual receipts.

Insider tip: Always get a receipt for any amount (even if it's small) you personally pay in cash or by credit card or check at the time of your visit. This will prove that you have already paid if an issue arises later. Keep your receipts for 18 months, since providers usually have up to one year to submit claims.

• **Check your EOB.** In most cases, anywhere from a few weeks to many months after your medical visit, you will receive an "Explanation of Benefits" (EOB) from your insurance company or Medicare explaining what the insurer was charged, what the insurer paid the provider and how much you're responsible for. Look carefully at what each EOB says you owe. It may very well be the co-payment that you've already paid. You may also owe the provider for your part of any deductible you have not already met in that calendar year. Attach the EOB to your log sheet for that visit. When and if you receive a bill from the provider for that service, check it against the EOB and your earlier receipts.

Insider tip: Never pay any portion of your deductible to a provider until your claim has been submitted and your EOB received. If you are on Medicare, it is illegal for the provider to require payment before that time. Most private insurers have the same rules. By waiting, you allow the insurer to make sure the amount billed is correct. There's also a chance that by the time the bill is submitted, you will have met the deductible through payments to other providers.

• **Get help—fast!** Despite all your recordkeeping, you may still have a problem with a provider who thinks that you owe him/her money. Don't wait around hoping the problem will go away. Doctors and hospitals are turning "overdue" bills over to collection agencies after two or three months. Immediately call your insurance carrier or Medicare/Medicaid, and ask for help. Your insurer will usually be able to get the issue cleared up quickly.

Doctors and Hospitals Are Adding Sneaky Fees

Charles B. Inlander, a consumer advocate and health-care consultant based in Fogelsville, Pennsylvania. He is author or coauthor of more than 20 consumer-health books.

Many doctors and hospitals are adding on sneaky fees for services that used to be included with routine visits and treatments. And the fees typically are not covered by insurance.

Example #1: A patient who went to see a mental health therapist was billed an additional $100 "facility" fee for the room in which the visit took place.

Example #2: A woman who walked into an emergency room after a bicycle accident was charged a "trauma activation" fee of $2,457 for the hospital to alert trauma personnel, including a surgeon, none of whose services were ever used.

If you are covered by Medicare, the medical provider is required by law to clearly inform you in advance about any service that may not be covered and to estimate what the cost to you will be. However, private insurers are under no such obligation if patients don't ask for this information.

Self-defense...

• **Speak to your doctor and the person in charge of billing before you are treated.** *Ask:* "Is everything you are going to do for me covered by my insurance? If not, you need to tell me in advance." If they disclose an unexpected fee, check ahead of time whether your insurer will agree to cover it as part of the general treatment. If not, tell your doctor, "I'm not able to afford to pay anything beyond my co-pay and deductibles," and ask to have the fee removed or reduced. Many doctors will comply.

• **Refuse to pay a bill if there's a fee that was not disclosed even though you asked.** File a report with the state insurance department requesting that it launch a fraud investigation. Many insurance providers would rather dismiss a miscellaneous charge than endure an investigation.

TAKE NOTE...

Mental Health Care Is Now More Affordable

Insurance plans that are bought on state insurance exchanges must include mental health care as one of the 10 mandated benefits under the Affordable Care Act. Large employers' health plans that include mental health coverage must treat it like other medical care in terms of prior authorizations, number of annual visits and other factors. Companies' employee-assistance programs (EAPs) often provide five or six sessions of no-cost counseling—and about three-quarters of companies offer EAPs. But finding a therapist on your own still can be challenging and costly. Because of low reimbursement rates and billing issues, only 55% of psychiatrists accept private insurance, compared with 89% of doctors in all other medical specialties. Coverage under Medicare also has improved. Medicare beneficiaries pay 20% of mental health care costs as of 2015, down from 50% in earlier years.

Money.com

Hospital-Bill Sucker Punch

Elisabeth Ryden Benjamin, vice president of health initiatives at Community Service Society, a nonprofit advocacy group, New York City.

The latest health-care trap—what starts out as an in-network hospital visit fully covered by insurance turns into a surprise out-of-network bill for hundreds or even tens of thousands of dollars. That's what many patients are discovering after they undergo treatment and/or surgery, especially in emergency situations.

The reason: Doctors and hospitals belonging to your insurer's network may use out-of-network specialists, consultants, assistants and other hospital employees without you knowing it. The insurer then covers only a small portion—or none—of the out-of-network provider's fee, and you are billed for the rest.

Example: One ER patient got a bill for $937. Insurance paid just $151.02. The patient owed $785.98.

Patients typically don't realize they are authorizing this when they sign hospital consent forms. Unlike in-network providers who agree to discounted rates negotiated with the insurer, out-of-network providers charge their full fees, which may be 20 to 40 times higher.

There is some legal protection. Medicare doesn't allow providers who accept Medicare payments to bill patients beyond what Medicare covers. And 13 states have a variety of restrictions on whether and how much patients can be charged for medical services such as anesthesia that often are provided by out-of-network providers.

To protect yourself...

• **Know which hospitals are in your network in case of an emergency.** Then ask what percentage of ER doctors and other personnel there are out of network. If most are out of network, consider choosing a different hospital.

• **If you're having a planned procedure, ask your doctor well in advance who else might be involved in your case,** and insist that everyone be in-network unless there is an overriding need for someone out of network to take part. Seek to work out terms in advance with out-of-network providers.

If you do face out-of-network fees...

• **Your insurer may be willing to cover more of the cost and/or convince the provider to lower the bill.** You also can file an appeal with the insurer.

• **Ask your state attorney general to intercede on your behalf.**

The 7 Worst Long-Term-Care Insurance Mistakes

Bunni Dybnis, director of professional services for LivHome, an at-home senior-care company with 16 locations across the US. She is a certified care manager, a member of the Older Adults Task Force for the city of Santa Monica, California, and a Fellow in The Leadership Academy of the National Association of Professional Geriatric Care Managers. *LivHome.com*

People who consider buying long-term-care insurance to cover future nursing home or in-home care costs often focus on a single key issue—is it worth the high price? But even if long-term-care coverage is worth the cost for you, there are many additional crucial questions that you must ask about this costly and complex product before buying—otherwise you might wind up paying for a policy that does not cover your long-term-care needs as well as you expect. Seemingly small details buried in a policy's fine print could have a massive impact on how well the insurance provides for your care decades later. Consumers often overlook or don't understand these details, leading to painful mistakes.

The challenge has become even more difficult in recent years. Leading long-term-care insurers, including MetLife and Unum, have stopped selling this kind of coverage...premiums have been rising, sometimes dramatically, for both new and existing policies...and new products that combine long-term-care insurance with life insurance offer a potentially appealing option—and a new source of confusion.

Seven potentially costly consumer mistakes and how to avoid them...

MISTAKE: Buying a policy that you won't be able to afford in retirement. A typical long-term-care insurance policy might cost a 55-year-old man around $2,000 a year. But the greatest challenge isn't fitting those premiums into your budget when you obtain the policy, typically in your 50s or early 60s (or even later than this, with higher premiums)—the problem is fitting them into your retirement budget down the road. Compounding the problem, insurers often increase the premiums of existing policies, sometimes by as much as 40% to 60%. Many people end up dropping no-longer-affordable policies just as they approach an age when they are increasingly likely to require care.

What to do: Speak with a fee-only financial planner about fitting the premiums into your projected retirement budget—not just your current budget—before buying coverage.

In addition, consider purchasing a hybrid life insurance/long-term-care insurance policy. With these, you pay up front for a life insurance policy rather than pay annual premiums that likely would stretch into your retirement. If you require long-term care, the policy provides benefits like a long-term-care policy does—and if you die without ever requiring long-term care, your heirs receive a death benefit, as they would with a conventional life insurance policy. These do require a hefty up-front investment, however—the average buyer plunks down around $130,000.

Helpful: If you already have a policy that has become prohibitively expensive during retirement, do not drop the coverage without first investigating options for limiting the policy's premiums by reducing benefits.

Important: Individuals who have less than $100,000 saved for their retirement typically are better off skipping long-term-care insurance and relying on Medicaid to pay for any future nursing home stays. Those with more than $500,000 saved that could be spent on long-term care may be better off paying out of pocket.

MISTAKE: Buying a policy that overly restricts your care options. Some policies cover only certain types of care—in-home care but not nursing home care, for example. Other policies cover all types of care but not equally—the maximum daily benefits for in-home care might be 50% of the per-day maximum for nursing home care, for example.

What to do: As far as you can afford, choose a policy that provides strong benefits for all types of care, including nursing home care, assisted-living care and home care.

MISTAKE: Misunderstanding waiting periods. Modern policies have various types of "elimination periods"—a specified number of days (often 90) that the policyholder must pay for long-term care out of pocket before benefits kick in. "Calendar day" elimination periods simply count 90 days from when care begins... while "service day" elimination periods count only days when care actually is provided.

Example: If you receive in-home care every other day, a 90-day service-day elimination period actually will last 180 days.

What to do: If you compare two similarly priced policies, the one with the calendar-day elimination period is a better buy than the one with the service-day elimination period, all else being equal.

MISTAKE: Ignoring limits on the type of care provider you can hire. Some policies will pay for in-home care only if you hire a state-certified care provider and/or work through an agency licensed by the state. That could prevent you from hiring someone you know and trust, such as a family member or a caregiver recommended by a trusted friend. And it could cause major headaches if your state does not license home-care agencies at all.

What to do: Favor policies that are not restrictive about who can supply in-home care.

MISTAKE: Ignoring important inflation-protection details. To be effective for you, a policy must protect against climbing long-term-care costs. Without an annual cost-of-living adjustment (COLA) of at least 3%—preferably 5%—the policy is unlikely to cover anything close to the full cost of your care 20 or 30 years down the road. Unfortunately, even consumers who understand the importance of inflation protection often fail to notice crucial nuances in how this inflation protection is worded in their contracts.

Some contracts use compound COLAs...others use simple COLAs (explained below).

Some policies offer COLAs but do not include them for the basic price. Policyholders must pay an additional fee—potentially a very substantial one—to get the inflation protection that they thought was included in their policy when they signed the contract.

What to do: Although for some people low cost is most important, generally favor policies that do not charge extra for inflation protection...and that use compound COLAs, which add up much faster than simple COLAs. For example, a policy with a $200 daily benefit and a 5% simple COLA will pay a maximum of $450 per day 25 years later...while a similar policy with a 5% compound COLA will pay a maximum of $677.27 a day—a difference of nearly $83,000 per year in potential benefits.

MISTAKE: Overlooking subtle differences in benefit caps. A policy that caps benefits at $200 per day is not similar to one that caps them at $6,000 per month, even though $6,000 divided by 30 days equals $200. A monthly cap of a given amount provides far more flexibility, and potentially far more reimbursement, than a daily cap. If, for example, you require in-home care costing $400 every other day, a policy with a $6,000 monthly benefit cap would pay more or less the whole thing—15 of those $400 visits per month would equal $6,000. But a policy with a $200 daily cap would pay only half of each $400 visit for a total of just $3,000 in monthly coverage.

What to do: Favor policies that have monthly benefit caps over policies that have daily ones, all else being equal. Carefully read the section of the policy describing benefit limits—in addition to the overall benefit cap, some policies have caps covering specific types of services.

MISTAKE: Not understanding how disabled you must be to receive benefits. Policies generally provide benefits only when the policyholder requires assistance with a specified number of "activities of daily living."

TAKE NOTE...

Some Life Insurers Are Rewarding Healthier Living

They are offering 10% or higher premium reductions or rewards from retailers to policyholders who have annual health screenings, lose weight, get annual flu shots, take online health courses and/or do regular physical activity. Offerings, requirements and prices vary and change often. Shop around using comparison-pricing sites such as *Term4Sale.com*, *FindMyInsurance.com* and *IntelliQuote.com*, and also check with direct sellers such as *TIAA-CREF.org* and *USAA.com* to make sure that the premium rates being offered are competitive.

The Wall Street Journal. WSJ.com

These include bathing, dressing, eating, toileting and transferring (such as from a bed to a wheelchair).

What to do: Lean toward a policy that provides benefits when you require assistance with two activities. It can be significantly more difficult to receive benefits when this figure is higher—many people require assistance with dressing and bathing long before they require assistance with a third activity.

Also: Favor long-term-care insurance that specifically includes dementia coverage even when the policyholder does not yet meet the policy's activity triggers.

Say *No* to This Type of Life Insurance

James H. Hunt, CFA, a life insurance specialist at Consumer Federation of America, a consumer advocacy group, Washington, DC. He is a life insurance actuary and a former insurance commissioner of the state of Vermont. *ConsumerFed.org*

A type of life insurance policy called *indexed universal life* (IUL) has soared in popularity, thanks in part to the long bull market in stocks. But the policy may be more of a good deal for insurance companies than for their customers.

How it works: The policy includes a traditional death benefit and, in addition, a portion of your monthly premiums is invested in a tax-deferred investment account that typically tracks the Standard & Poor's 500 stock index. In years when the index falls, your insurer uses financial derivatives to protect you from losses.

The catch? Your insurer caps the annual gains on your account and can lower the cap...does not credit your account for dividend payments as a mutual fund would...and charges steep sales commissions, fees and other expenses. And because the money to cover expenses is drawn directly from your investment account, the expenses can eat up much of your long-term returns, especially during weak periods for the stock market.

Better: Buy much cheaper "term" life insurance, which pays a death benefit for a specified period (for example, 20 years if the goal is to protect your children until they are adults). Invest the cash you save on premiums in retirement accounts such as IRAs and 401(k)s. Alternatively, if you want "permanent" insurance, which does not set a defined period of coverage, and have already maxed out your annual retirement contributions, consider a "variable" universal life policy offered by low-cost insurers such as TIAA-CREF or Ameritas Direct. Their policies are sold free of agents' commissions and give investors the flexibility to invest in equities.

Are You Lying to Your Auto Insurer?

Dan Toups, managing editor of *CarInsurance.com*, an online auto insurance marketplace and information website.

More than 34% of all drivers regularly lie to their auto insurance providers, according to a recent survey by *CarInsurance.com*. Some dishonest drivers claim to drive far fewer miles each year than they really do...others supply an address in a neighborhood that has low insurance rates when they really live in a high-rate area or falsify some other information in hopes of securing lower premiums.

These drivers are taking a bigger risk than they likely imagine. According to the survey, 43% of people who gave dishonest information to an auto insurance provider were later caught in their lies by the insurer. For one-third of the people who lied, the result was a denied claim. Having an insurance company refuse to pay a claim can be financially devastating—potentially hundreds of thousands of dollars if the claim involves an accident that caused major injury or property damage.

When the lie was uncovered before a major claim was made, the result often was higher premiums or even canceled coverage—and in around 8% of cases, the dishonest driver was sued for fraud by the insurer.

Helpful: Review the information you initially provided to your insurer to make sure that it still is accurate each time you renew your auto insurance policy. Failing to update facts upon renewal could be viewed as dishonesty by the insurer even if the information was correct when the policy originally was written.

How Auto Insurers Punish Good Drivers

J. Robert Hunter, director of insurance for the Consumer Federation of America, Washington, DC. He is a former Texas insurance commissioner. *ConsumerFed.org*

Just because you haven't had any accidents or gotten any traffic tickets doesn't mean that you won't be hit with a big auto insurance rate increase. About half of the major auto insurers in the US have started raising rates by as much as 20% for trouble-free customers, even though their risk profiles have not increased. The insurers judge that those customers are unlikely to balk at the higher price. The process is called "price optimization."

How it works: The insurer uses personal consumer data and statistical models to estimate how much of a price increase a policyholder might tolerate and how likely it is that the customer would respond to an increase by looking for lower-price coverage. About one-quarter of consumers never shop around for auto insurance and just accept an increase in premiums.

Although state regulators typically require auto insurers to file rate schedules that charge customers who have the same coverage and risk levels the same rates, companies have many ways of getting around those restrictions, and using price optimization is one way to increase their profits. *What to do...*

- **Avoid complimenting your insurer's customer service agents.** This may sound far-fetched, but one of the criteria used to identify customers who will accept higher premiums is whether you've written to upper management, spoken with a representative commending the company or praised the company on well-known social-networking sites.

Other potential negatives: You never call the company with complaints, and you buy

MONEYWISE...

If You Have a Teen Driver...

Save money when insuring a teen driver by increasing your deductible at the same time that you raise your coverage levels. Higher coverage is important, because if a teen has an accident, the injured party's lawyer likely will come after the teen's parents' assets. But simply adding coverage can raise premiums significantly—you can minimize the cost increase by raising your deductible, which means you pay more out-of-pocket in case of a claim. Always add a teen to your policy as soon as he/she gets a license or learner's permit—otherwise he may not be covered. Talk with your insurance agent about how to keep premium hikes as low as possible and about any discounts you may be entitled to.

Roundup of experts on car insurance, reported at *Money.MSN.com*.

your insurance through an agent rather than online.

• **Comparison shop and find the same insurance coverage for less.** If you find a lower price, use that as leverage to convince your insurer to pull back on a price increase, especially if you threaten to switch.

Minor Traffic Tickets Have Big Hidden Costs

Laura Adams, senior analyst at *insuranceQuotes.com*, an insurance rates comparison website.

Most people know that serious violations such as drunk driving can cause insurance premiums to rise. But relatively minor moving violations—such as driving a few miles per hour over the speed limit, failing to use a turn signal or driving alone in a car pool lane—increase auto insurance costs by 18% to 21%, on average, for three to five years.

The typical driver pays around $800 a year for auto insurance, so a 20% increase for three years equals nearly $500 in additional costs—much more than the $100 to $250 the ticket itself tends to cost. (Some insurers advertise that they do not penalize policyholders for getting one minor traffic ticket—but policies that include this feature often cost more than those that don't, offsetting any savings.)

Major moving violations can increase insurance rates even further—an average of 93% for driving under the influence (DUI)...82% for reckless driving...30% for driving 31+ miles per hour (mph) above the speed limit...or 28% for driving 16 to 30 mph over the limit, for example.

To avoid insurance increases...

• **Take a driving class.** In many states, you can wipe tickets (or "points") off your driving record by completing a defensive-driving class. Call your state's DMV or visit its website to find out if this is an option and for a list of qualifying classes.

GOOD TO KNOW...

File Just One Claim and Your Premium May Jump

Filing even one insurance claim makes a home owner's premiums jump by an average of 9%. The biggest increases tend to be in Wyoming, averaging 32%, followed by Connecticut (21%), Arizona (20%), New Mexico (19%) and California (18%). Always ask your insurance agent or insurance firm how much your premium might rise if you file a claim and consider whether filing is worth the extra cost.

Laura Adams, senior analyst at *insuranceQuotes.com*, which conducted a survey of the effects of filing a claim on premiums for six large insurers in 50 states.

• **Hire an attorney.** An attorney might charge $200 to $400* to contest a traffic ticket—but that could be money well spent if the ticket would significantly increase your insurance rates. You can find an attorney who specializes in contesting traffic tickets for a flat fee through your state's bar association (go to *AmericanBar.org*) or your local *Yellow Pages*.

Alternative: Consider contesting the ticket on your own if it isn't worth paying an attorney. Your ticket is likely to be dismissed if the officer who gave it to you fails to appear in court, which is not uncommon. Contesting the ticket might trigger additional administrative court fees or surcharges, however.

• **Shop around.** The insurer that offered you the best rate when you had a clean driving record might no longer offer the best deal now that you have a ticket.

*Rates subject to change.

Auto Insurance for a Leased Car

Because a leased car still is owned by your leasing company, you might be required to purchase additional insurance coverage that can inflate the cost of your annual premiums by as much as 30% above regular new-car insurance, depending on the level of coverage you typically buy for cars that you own.

Expect to pay more for mandatory collision and comprehensive coverage, plus higher liability coverage than the legal minimums for most states, including at least $100,000 coverage for the other driver's medical expenses in an accident and $50,000 for damage to the other vehicle. Also, most leases prevent you from choosing a deductible of more than $500.

What to do: Factor these higher insurance costs into your lease-or-buy decision.

Philip Reed, senior consumer advice editor in Los Angeles at *Edmunds.com*, which provides new- and used-car information and reviews.

Is Lending a Car Covered by Your Policy?

Occasional lending of a car to a friend or neighbor usually is covered by your insurance. Regular lending to a friend or roommate or lending to an extended-stay houseguest also might be covered—but you may have to list that person as an additional driver. Letting your teenager drive requires informing your insurer and paying higher rates. Renting to strangers through a car-sharing app typically is not covered under your policy, but the rental service may provide some insurance at low cost.

ConsumerReports.org

Little-Known Home Insurance Discounts

Three out of 10 home insurance companies offer early-shopper discounts, which reward you when you get a price quote from a new insurer and switch companies before your old policy expires. However, loyalty to the same insurer rewards customers who stay with the company long-term.

New or renovated homes often get lower insurance rates. And stronger roofs get discounts for being less likely to be destroyed in a major storm.

Seniors may be eligible for discounts based on their age. And memberships in professional associations or groups, even a fraternity or sorority, will sometimes provide a discount. Not smoking—and not having any smokers in the house—may produce a discount as well.

These rate reductions are in addition to better-known ones for having security systems and smoke alarms in your home. Discounts vary by company and location and change frequently—shop around or ask your insurance agent.

Roundup of experts on home insurance, reported at *CBSNews.com.*

Insurance Coverage You May Not Know You Have

Little-known insurance coverage that you may already have...

Volcanic eruptions are covered in standard homeowners policies. Auto policies typically cover vehicle damage from earthquakes and floods, and most comprehensive policies cover rodent damage to a car's electrical system. Homeowners and comprehensive auto policies cover damage caused by riots and terrorism—but not war. Most homeowners policies protect college students' belongings when they are away from home. Dog bites generally are covered by homeowners policies up to specified limits—an umbrella policy is helpful to offset the risk of a costly court verdict. Homeowners and auto policies also cover lawyers and other legal costs in case of home- or car-related claims—but here, too, an umbrella policy may be needed to protect against a big judgment.

Roundup of insurance experts, reported at *Chicago Tribune.com.*

How Domestic Partners Can Get Insurance

Unmarried domestic partners can get insurance more easily now if they follow companies' rules carefully. For home insurance, put both names on the policy to get joint coverage—or if one partner owns the house, get an endorsement for additional occupants. For auto insurance, ask if marriage discounts are available for domestic partners. If you have more than one vehicle, list each other as secondary drivers. For renters, request a shared policy.

Greg McBride, CFA, chief financial analyst for *Bankrate.com*, a personal finance website based in North Palm Beach, Florida.

Best Insurer for Consumer Satisfaction

In a recent survey, USAA ranked highest in customer satisfaction.

The rest of the top 10, in order of consumer preference: State Farm, Geico, The Hartford, Progressive, Allstate, AAA, Nationwide, Travelers, Liberty Mutual.

The ratings reflect to what degree consumers believed that the insurance company was successful in resolving issues, whether the company was easy to work with and how consumers felt about working with the company. Ratings exclude health insurance.

Survey of 10,000 US consumers by Temkin Group, reported at *Credit.com.*

9

Tax Tune-Up

How to Fight Back When the IRS Says You Owe More Taxes

You paid your taxes—but now the IRS claims that you owe them more. Every year, the IRS sends out millions of notices requesting additional payments from taxpayers who made math errors on their returns…neglected to report certain income…claimed tax credits or deductions that they were not entitled to…or made other mistakes.

But what if your tax return was right and it's the IRS that's wrong?

Taxpayers who receive notices from the IRS tend to just pay what they're told they owe. But most IRS notices are generated by computers—computers that sometimes misinterpret data. And even if a notice was sent by an actual IRS agent, that agent might have misinterpreted the tax code.

Taxpayers truly can take on the IRS. In fact, in June 2014 the IRS adopted a "Taxpayer Bill of Rights," a list of 10 rights—including "The Right to Challenge the IRS's Position and Be Heard."

Here, a five-step plan to fight an IRS notice that you believe to be wrong…

STEP 1: Look for instructions in the notice itself about what to do if you disagree. Believe it or not, following these instructions often is all it takes to get a matter cleared up in your favor, particularly when the matter is fairly clear-cut—the IRS thinks you earned more from your employer than you actually did, and you have the W-2 to prove it, for example. But you should follow the instructions *exactly*.

Typically, you can check a box on the notice stating that you disagree…add a short note explaining why you disagree…attach copies

Scott M. Estill, JD, a former trial attorney for the IRS who currently is of counsel to Estill & Long, LLC, a Denver tax law firm. He is author of *Tax This! An Insider's Guide to Standing Up to the IRS. EstillandLong.com* of any supporting documents...then return this section of the notice to the IRS mailing address listed. Send these materials—and any other letters to the IRS—by the deadline via certified mail with return receipt requested.

A short, to-the-point explanation will be more effective here than a long one.

Example: "My total income from ABC Corp was $50,000, not $100,000, and was fully reported on my tax return. Enclosed is a copy of my W-2."

Be sure to keep copies of all your correspondence with the IRS.

STEP 2: Decide whether it's worth hiring a tax professional to assist you. The key factor here is how much money is at stake. If the IRS is asking for a few thousand dollars or less, you're probably better off not hiring an enrolled agent, CPA or tax attorney.

There's a good chance that you would have to pay that tax pro several thousand dollars to challenge an IRS notice—potentially more with a tax attorney—even if the case appears straightforward. It is not worth spending that much money unless there is a significantly larger amount at risk.

STEP 3: Request supervisor involvement. If you receive a notice that rejects your challenge and it mentions a specific IRS employee, call this agent and very politely ask to speak to his/her supervisor—there is probably no point in discussing it any further with the IRS employee mentioned by name, because he is the one who already rejected your written explanation. Don't tell this named IRS employee that you want to talk to his boss because you think his decision was wrong—that would only build antagonism. Instead, frame the situation as a disagreement between honest, well-meaning people, both of whom want the same thing—an "agreed case" where the taxpayer and the IRS see eye to eye about the situation. IRS agents are evaluated in part by their success in obtaining agreed cases, so this is to the agent's benefit, too.

Example: You might say, "Listen, obviously we both think we're right. Can we take this to your supervisor? Maybe we can get an agreed case so that we can keep this out of the appeals process."

The IRS is particularly anxious to make cases go away when the dollar amounts involved are very small—less than $1,000 or so.

When you speak to the supervisor, present your case more or less as you did to the original agent. But if that original agent provided a specific reason why he disagreed with your position, you will also need to specifically explain why the agent was incorrect. (If the notice you receive stating that the IRS still believes you owe additional money does not mention a specific IRS agent's name, send a certified letter to the address listed requesting that someone at the supervisory level reconsider your case.)

If the IRS doesn't back down after your discussion with a supervisor...

STEP 4: Take your case to the Office of Appeals. The Office of Appeals is an independent unit within the IRS. It will give your case a fresh and fair hearing.

By this point in the process, you might feel that you are presenting the same facts again and again, beating your head against a wall of bureaucracy. Well, that's how you fight the IRS—you keep presenting your case to as many different IRS employees as possible until you find one who agrees with you.

The notices you received from the IRS should include instructions on how to take your case to the Office of Appeals. Otherwise, go to the IRS website (*IRS.gov/appeals*) for more information about filing this appeal.

STEP 5: Take your case to the US Tax Court as a last resort. If $50,000 or less is in dispute, you can opt to represent yourself in a "small tax case" procedure. This is similar to small-claims court—there is no jury, and your inexperience with courtroom procedures will not be held against you. You just tell your side of the story one more time, present your evidence and answer the judge's questions. The only real downside to a small tax case is that the decision of the US Tax Court cannot be appealed.

There's little reason not to go to Tax Court if you're representing yourself and you believe you're right. (If you hire representation, your costs could climb well into four figures, sometimes higher.) All you have to lose is a few hours of your time, travel costs to the closest city where Tax Court is held, a $60 filing fee and potentially some interest charges. But at this point, your matter might not even get to court—an IRS attorney might offer to settle for less than the full amount that the IRS claims you owe before your case is heard.

The notices you receive from the IRS should explain how to bring your case before the Tax Court. Or you can download the necessary form from *USTaxCourt.gov* (click on "Forms," then "Petition").

BEWARE...

Biggest Tax Scams Now

Be on the look out for some of these prevalent tax scams...

Phone scams involving aggressive, threatening calls from criminals claiming to be IRS agents...phishing scams using phony e-mails or fake websites to try to steal personal information...identity theft by criminals who file returns using other people's Social Security numbers... and return-preparer fraud, in which preparers misrepresent refunds or use their knowledge of personal information to steal identities.

If you are suspicious about any issues involving taxes, contact the IRS.

Internal Revenue Service. *IRS.gov*

The IRS May Be After You—Who's Getting Audited

Scott M. Estill, JD, a former trial attorney for the IRS who currently is of counsel to Estill & Long, LLC, a Denver tax law firm. He is author of *Tax This! An Insider's Guide to Standing Up to the IRS. EstillandLong.com*

IRS audit rates are trending downward, but that doesn't mean you should feel safe—approximately 1 million Americans still will be audited this year. In fact, audit risks actually are rising for some. The IRS is paying increasingly close attention to taxpayers who report income in excess of $200,000...who own small businesses or rental properties...and/or who are in professions related to real estate.

If you are audited, the accuracy of the information in your tax return won't be the only factor that affects how costly and frightening the experience becomes. Things you do or say during the audit process could influence the outcome as well. You probably can guess that it's wise to respond to audit notices by the deadline and to be polite to IRS agents. But some other savvy audit strategies are less obvious to taxpayers—and even to some tax pros.

Five insider audit tips from Scott M. Estill, JD, who has both worked for the IRS and represented hundreds of taxpayers in audits...

- **Ask the IRS to provide a written list of the paperwork you should bring to the audit.** IRS agents are required to provide this list upon request. Bring only the specifically requested paperwork to the audit. Bringing additional documents could expand the scope of the audit.

Example: An IRS agent requests that you bring receipts for your small business related to 2012 advertising expenses. During the audit, an unrelated deduction on your return catches his/her eye and he asks for documentation of this as well. If you have not brought with you the additional information that he wants, he might choose to drop that line of inquiry—preventing the audit from expanding into that area.

If an agent does ask for something you didn't bring to a meeting, explain to the agent that you didn't bring the documents he is requesting because he didn't ask you to bring them. In theory, the agent could ask you to bring this additional information to a second meeting, but in practice, this is unlikely. Recent IRS staffing cuts have left agents stretched very thin. If an agent doesn't find major problems with the information you provide during your initial meeting, he probably won't bother scheduling a second one.

• **Answer questions, and then shut your mouth.** Most taxpayers are nervous when they meet with the IRS, and nervous people tend to talk more than they should. IRS agents are trained to exploit this by asking questions, then remaining silent after the reply in hopes that a long, uncomfortable silence will trick taxpayers into adding details that work against their own interests.

• **Take a time-out if you realize that you are in over your head.** Can't decide whether to pay a tax professional to help with your audit or go it alone? What most taxpayers don't realize is that they don't necessarily have to make this decision before their audit. By law, taxpayers have the right to request a postponement at any time during the audit process for the purpose of seeking a tax pro's help. Taxpayers who request this postponement typically are given at least a few weeks to find a professional.

• **Fact-check IRS agents.** You are not the only person who doesn't completely understand all the ins and outs of the tax code—the IRS agent handling your audit may not either. It is surprisingly common for IRS agents to make tax code mistakes during audits. It's gotten much worse in recent years—because of budget cuts, IRS agents receive a lot less training than they once did. Unfortunately, taxpayers and even tax professionals often assume that IRS agents always know what they are talking about.

What to do: Before your audit, read all the IRS documents that you can find related to the section of your tax return that is being audited, particularly if you intend to represent yourself in the audit. If the agent says something that you suspect might be incorrect during the audit—claiming that the type of evidence you supplied to defend a deduction was not sufficient, for example—ask the agent to put this in writing, then request an opportunity to further research this point or to consult with a tax professional about it.

Even if the agent won't delay his decision, you always have the right to appeal—and if tax law truly has been misinterpreted, you have an excellent chance of winning this appeal. For more information, log on to *IRS.gov* and search for IRS Publication 5, *Your Appeal Rights and How to Prepare a Protest If You Don't Agree.*

• **If there is more than one agent present for your audit, ask each agent about his/her role.** Usually a single agent handles an audit. The presence of two or more could suggest that the IRS thinks that there are major issues with your return—why else would it devote so much manpower to you? It might make sense to call an immediate halt to the tax audit so that you can hire a tax professional if you haven't already done so.

The good news is that the IRS agents present are legally required to disclose their roles to you upon request.

If you are told that one (or more) of the agents is from the IRS Fraud Division, immediately halt the audit so that you can hire a tax attorney. Do this even if you already have a tax preparer assisting you. The Fraud Division's presence suggests that the IRS is considering bringing criminal charges against you. CPAs and enrolled agents (the highest credential that the IRS awards) cannot offer you the "attorney-client privilege" that tax attorneys can. If your case were to go to trial—a possibility if the Fraud Division is involved—CPAs and enrolled agents could be subpoenaed and forced to disclose everything you told them.

If you are told that an extra agent in the room is there simply for training purposes, proceed with the audit. Training is the one multiple-agent situation that does not mean the IRS is paying special attention to your case.

INTERESTING FINDING...

Tax Preparers Almost Always Make Errors

Seventeen of 19 unregulated tax preparers randomly tested by the Government Accountability Office (GAO) made mistakes in a recent study.

Best: Check the tax return for common errors, such as omitting non–W-2 income and claiming an ineligible child for the Earned Income Tax Credit.

GAO undercover study reported in *USA Today.*

IRS AUDITS CAN COMPLICATE YOUR STATE TAXES

If an IRS audit determines that you owe additional federal income tax, there is a very good chance that you owe additional state income tax as well (assuming that you live in a state that has an income tax). Eventually your state is likely to mail you a notice informing you of the additional tax owed—but it could take months or even years for your state to get around to doing this. This delay is not good for you—because by then, interest charges might have significantly inflated your bill.

Generally, the best option is to minimize interest charges by filing an amended state return and paying any additional taxes as soon as possible following an IRS audit.

Warning: Some audited taxpayers might be tempted to not file an amended state return in hopes that their state will never figure out that they owe this additional money. But the IRS shares the results of its audits with the states, and while it is possible that you might slip between the cracks and never hear from your state, this is uncommon—in my experience, approximately 80% to 90% of taxpayers in this situation eventually do get bills from their states.

A Taxpayer Victory (and a Defeat)

Barbara Weltman, Esq., Vero Beach, Florida, author of *J.K. Lasser's 1001 Deductions & Tax Breaks* and publisher of *Big Ideas for Small Business*, a free monthly e-letter. *BarbaraWeltman.com*

Tax rules are not always clear-cut. Two recent rulings, including one victory for taxpayers and one defeat, help clarify the rules and provide lessons that could help you save money on taxes and/or avoid a fight with the IRS...

- **Be careful how you pay your employees, especially your children.** When Patricia Diane Ross asked her three children to handle chores such as filing, shredding and stuffing envelopes at her employment agency in Washington, DC, she figured that she could take a tax deduction for their wages as a business expense because she considered them to be employees. She prepared time sheets and W-2 forms for the children, ages 15, 11 and eight, but she never took any income tax withholding from their pay or issued them any paychecks. Instead, Ross used their salaries to pay for their pizza, tutoring and other things that she said they "directed" her to spend the money on. She deducted these disbursements as wages on tax returns for her business and cited several IRS publications as backup.

IRS Position: The payments were not wages that she could deduct because what she gave the children were the kinds of things that all parents might normally provide—food and tutoring—rather than wages tied to work.

Tax Court Ruling: The deduction is not allowed because there was a lack of correlation between the dates and amounts of the payments and the hours supposedly worked by the children.

Example: When the Tax Court divided the disbursements on behalf of the oldest child by the hours worked, in one month he was effectively paid $3.40 per hour while in another month he received $25 per hour.

Also, the arrangement in which the children helped the mother in exchange for eating out and receiving tutoring seemed to be more in the nature of parental training and discipline than of services rendered for an employer by an employee. Ross had to pay a penalty and back taxes.

Lesson: While there's no bar to employing one's own minor children for nonhazardous work (within limits on hours), if you want to be able to deduct what you pay them as an expense of your business, it's vital to keep a careful record of the time of work and work performed...issue paychecks for this work and withhold income taxes...and set the wages at a rate properly reflecting the work performed.

Patricia Diane Ross, Tax Court Summary Opinion 2014-68

- **There can be slight leeway on personal use of a home office.** Lauren Miller was the New York City account director for a public relations firm based in Los Angeles. Because Miller was the only employee in New York, the company didn't provide her with office space and asked her to use part of her 700-square-foot studio apartment as an office that included her desk, two shelving units, a bookcase and a sofa. Her apartment's address and phone number were listed as the company's New York space on its website even though it did not reimburse her for this space.

She claimed a sizable home office tax deduction as an unreimbursed employee business expense.

IRS Position: The IRS denied her write-off, claiming that she violated the law's requirement that a home office be used exclusively—meaning 100%—for business purposes. She admitted that she used portions of the office space for nonbusiness purposes.

Tax Court Ruling: Miller was eligible for the deduction because her personal use of the space was minimal and "wholly attributable to the practicalities of living in a studio apartment of such modest dimensions."

Lesson: Although you need to clearly limit personal use of a home office in order to qualify for a tax deduction, minor unavoidable use of the space for personal use might not disqualify you.

Lauren Elizabeth Miller, Tax Court Summary Opinion 2014-74

Is There Trouble in Your Will? Don't Let Your Heirs Lose Out

Herbert E. Nass, Esq., founding partner of Herbert E. Nass & Associates, a New York City law firm specializing in wills, estates, probate and trusts. He is author of *The 101 Biggest Estate Planning Mistakes* and *Wills of the Rich & Famous. NassLaw.net*

Taxpayers have entered a new era in estate planning. Now that the federal estate tax is not triggered until assets top $5.43 million (or even higher, inflation-adjusted levels in future years), the vast majority of Americans no longer need to structure their estates to avoid the tax.

But estate planning is not just about avoiding taxes. It also is about distributing assets according to one's wishes and taking care of surviving family members—and in these areas, people continue to make critical errors.

Below, top estate-planning attorney Herbert Nass explains what kinds of mistakes are common now...

- **Listing specific tangible assets in the will rather than in a side letter.** If you spell out in your will which of your heirs should receive which of your possessions, you will have to amend the will whenever a major asset is sold or acquired...whenever you or your heirs change your minds about who should get what...and possibly whenever the values of certain assets change.

That antique armoire that was appropriate for your daughter when she lived in a big house down the road might no longer make sense for her after she moves to a condo 1,000 miles away.

Better: Write in your will that your executor should distribute your tangible assets according to your wishes, then provide a side letter to that executor laying out these wishes. You can easily update this letter later if necessary without paying an attorney to amend your will. But choose an executor you trust—he/she is not legally bound to follow the instructions in this letter.

- **Bequeathing real estate without taking into account the mortgages.** If you leave real estate to an heir in your will, that heir likely will be responsible for paying off any mortgages or loans against the property. The debts of the deceased typically are paid by the estate, which usually is responsible for making mortgage payments during the probate process. However, secured debts such as mortgages generally pass to the person who inherits the property. This wrinkle can have unintended consequences.

Example: A widow with two children leaves her house to the daughter, who has been living with her, and a second piece of property to her son. The widow intended for these bequests to be of comparable value... which they would have been except that she took out a home-equity loan against the house after the will was drafted, leaving her daughter with $50,000 of debt.

Better: If you do not wish to leave mortgage debt to your heirs, you could include a bequest in your will stating that your heirs should receive cash (or liquid investments) equal to any mortgage debt remaining against the property they receive.

• **Bequeathing real estate without taking into account the tenants.** Renting out an entire property that you own—or even renting out just a room in your home—brings income to you now, but it also could leave your heirs with a major headache after you pass away.

Your heirs might not have the time, temperament or home-maintenance skills to act as landlords themselves. Serving as a landlord is especially inconvenient for heirs who live far away. And the lease agreements and/or local housing laws might make it expensive or impossible for your heirs to remove the tenants from the property in a timely manner.

Selling the property with the tenant in place isn't a great solution either. Most buyers don't want to be landlords, so the property's selling price is likely to be substantially reduced—if the property sells at all.

Heirs who inherit tenants sometimes end up paying those tenants tens of thousands of dollars to leave, and that can significantly reduce the value of the inheritance.

Better: If you have tenants, include language in their lease agreement that allows your heirs to terminate their leases and requires tenants to vacate within some reasonable period of time—perhaps 90 days—in the event of your death.

Exception: Having tenants in place can be a good thing if the property is an apartment building that potential buyers will want to rent out anyway.

• **Accidentally disinheriting descendants not yet born when the will is drafted.** It's not uncommon for wills to list by name children or grandchildren who will inherit. Trouble is, if additional children or grandchildren are born after the will has been drafted—and you don't update the will to include these children—the fact that they are not listed might mean that they don't inherit a share of your estate. It even could lead to an expensive and acrimonious legal battle among your heirs.

Better: Rather than list your descendants by name, your will could state that the assets should be divided among your descendants *per stirpes.* That stipulation means the assets will be divided equally among them, but if any of your children dies before you, that heir's share will be divided equally among his children.

One reason people like to list heirs by name is to avoid the possibility that someone will come forward claiming to be a child born out of wedlock in hopes of receiving a portion of the estate.

If this is a concern, you could specify that your assets should be "divided equally among children being from the marriage of [You] and [Your spouse]. I intentionally make no provision for any nonmarital children."

• **Owning a bank safe-deposit box if you hope to avoid probate.** People with relatively simple estates sometimes can avoid the costs and delays of the probate process through joint ownership of assets...by designating beneficiaries on accounts...and/or by titling assets to a revocable living trust.

Unfortunately, people who do this sometimes neglect to account for their bank safe-deposit boxes. These boxes are sealed upon the death of their owners and usually cannot be opened without passing through an often lengthy, court-controlled probate process.

Despite the common misconception, creating a power of attorney that gives a spouse or heir the right to access a safe-deposit box will not solve the problem—your power of attorney ends upon your death.

Example: A New Yorker thought that he had spared his family the hassles of the probate process. But probate was required because he put some gold coins in a bank safe-deposit box, costing his family several thousand dollars.

Better: List your spouse or a trusted heir as co-owner of your safe-deposit box. A co-owner is allowed access to the box even after his fellow co-owner's death. Or name a revocable living trust as the owner of the box, with you as trustee and your spouse or heir as successor trustee.

BEWARE STATE ESTATE TAXES, TOO

Just because you are safe from the federal estate tax doesn't necessarily mean that you are not vulnerable to costly state tax rules. Fourteen states and the District of Columbia still have estate-tax exemptions far below today's federal exemption levels—in some cases, it's less than $1 million.

Examples: In New Jersey, the exemption is just $675,000...in Rhode Island, just $1.5 million.

And in some cases, it can be very complicated figuring out what that tax would be. In one of the most complex situations, on April 1, 2015, New York's state estate-tax exemption climbed to $3.125 million. It's scheduled to continue to climb in the coming years. But there's a trap hidden in this apparent good news. If you exceed the exemption amount by more than 5%, it isn't just the amount above the exemption level that will face state estate-tax rates as high as 16%—your entire estate could be taxed.

Example: If your estate is worth $3.17 million, all $3.17 million is taxable in New York State.

Other states including Rhode Island and Connecticut have had similar estate-tax "cliffs" in the recent past, though they no longer do, and additional states could, in theory, enact them in the future. But even without a cliff, a state estate tax can take a big bite out of an estate. *Three ways you can reduce the size of your estate...*

- **Leave additional assets to a spouse.** Money left to a spouse is not included in the taxable amount.
- **Give away assets while still alive.** You can give gifts of up to $14,000 per recipient per year without tax ramifications. Recipients don't have to be related to you. And you can give to people of any age.
- **Make donations to charitable organizations in your will.**

A Will Is Not Enough: Financial Power of Attorney Essentials

Martin M. Shenkman, CPA, JD, an estate- and tax-planning attorney with the law firm Martin M. Shenkman, PC, which has offices in New York City and Paramus, New Jersey. He is coauthor of *Powers of Attorney: A Key Estate Planning Document. LawEasy.com*

Many people spend lots of time carefully crafting their wills so that their assets will be distributed appropriately when they die.

But they often pay too little attention, or no attention at all, to a document that could be vitally important while they are still alive.

And then something terrible happens to them—they become incapacitated...chaos ensues...and their assets are squandered.

Fortunately, there's a document—a *financial power of attorney*—that can stop such a sad scenario from ever occurring. It would dictate how your assets are to be handled if you become unable to manage your own affairs.

If well-written, it can help safeguard your assets while you are still alive and in need of the assets but unable to make sensible decisions. It can play as vital a role as the health-care power of attorney, which dictates who would make health-care choices for you.

Without a financial power of attorney in place, there might not be anyone poised to take over your financial affairs if you become unable to do so yourself, particularly if you are not married. (And if you are married, your spouse will not have control over assets held in your name unless your power of attorney puts your spouse in charge.)

Eventually your family might petition a court to appoint a guardian to look after your financial affairs. But the process of appointing this guardian can be lengthy and expensive, possibly costing tens of thousands of dollars, and the court might select someone you do not want.

Generally, a court-appointed guardian receives some compensation for his/her time. And the court proceedings are part of the public record, which means that private details about your health or mental status could become widely known.

Another trap: People who do have financial powers of attorney often don't realize that the documents are poorly written—so they won't provide the intended safeguards.

Here's how to make sure the financial power of attorney that you create or that you already have created avoids major problems...

PROBLEM: Your power of attorney does not take effect until it is needed. In many states, you have the option to create a "springing" power of attorney that goes into effect only if and when you become incapacitated. That sounds like a great idea—why grant anyone power over your finances sooner than is absolutely necessary?

Trouble is, a springing power of attorney can lead to delays and headaches for your financial agent—the person you designate to take charge of your finances. That's because strict health privacy laws make it difficult for your doctor to be able to sign a document stating that you have become incapacitated.

What to do: Consider having an "immediate" power of attorney, which goes into effect as soon as you sign it, rather than one that goes into effect when you are officially declared to be "disabled" or "incapacitated."

Important: Monitor your financial accounts after your power of attorney takes effect to make sure that your agent does not take advantage of his access to them. If you cannot monitor your own accounts closely, or fear that you might not be able to in the future, ask a CPA or trusted friend or family member to monitor your accounts.

PROBLEM: You empower your financial agent to make gifts. Many financial powers of attorney include a "gift provision" that lets your designated agent make gifts from your savings on your behalf. Unfortunately, this creates a greater risk that your agent could steal your assets by making excessive gifts to himself or to his friends and family.

In years past, it made sense for many people to include a gift provision despite the risk. That's because by allowing the agent to make gifts to your family members on your behalf, you could reduce the size of your estate before you pass away, lowering your estate tax bill. But the amount that is excluded from federal estate tax has been increased to $5.43 million or more, depending on the year of death. That means the vast majority of people would never have to pay federal estate tax (although they might be subject to a state estate tax).

What to do: Make sure that your power of attorney does not grant your agent unlimited power to make gifts. If your estate is large enough that federal estate tax is a concern, tell an estate-planning attorney that you would like to discuss safer options to reduce that tax, such as authorizing your agent to make gifts only to recipients of your choosing and only up to the amounts that help reduce estate taxes.

PROBLEM: You choose your agent based on age. It is vital for your agent to have—in order of importance—unimpeachable integrity...solid common sense...and at least a modest amount of financial knowledge. But what tends to happen is that people simply name their oldest adult son or daughter regardless of whether that person is the most qualified. That's probably because the oldest child acted most responsibly when your kids were still kids.

What to do: Name whichever family member best meets the three requirements of the position listed above—even at the risk of offending your oldest child or other family members. If none of your close family members fits the bill, consider naming a close friend. You should also designate a successor agent, especially if your primary agent is as old as you or older. You can change your agent any time you wish, as long as you are not yet incapacitated.

PROBLEM: You do not give your agent any instructions. Think about how challenging it can be to manage your own financial affairs. Now imagine what your agent will face if he has to keep your financial house in order without any help from you. He might have to guess your financial goals and priorities. He might have to dig through your files just to figure out which financial institutions you work with.

What to do: Sit down with your agent, and explain what, specifically, you would like him

PLANNING PAYS...

Your Children Need Their Own Estate Plans

Young adult children need their own estate plans and advanced health-care directives. Once a child reaches the age of majority—18 or 21, depending on the state—parents cannot make medical decisions or get information on their child's condition. In an emergency, such as a serious accident, parents must ask a court to appoint them as legal guardians under a judge's supervision. Also, young adult children may have bank or investment accounts and custodial holdings such as UGMA and UTMA accounts that transfer to them at the age of majority. Adult children should draw up durable powers of attorney for financial decisions and directives for health-care decision-making. Parents or grandparents can be named agents. And beneficiaries should be chosen for brokerage or retirement accounts.

Kyle Krull, estate-planning lawyer, Overland Park, Kansas, quoted in *Kiplinger's Retirement Report. Kiplinger.com*

to do if you are incapacitated. It's best not to include these specific instructions in the power-of-attorney document itself, because you then would have to go to a lawyer to have the document amended each time something about your finances related to your instructions changes.

Also create a list of your financial accounts, recurring bills, passwords and log-in information, and let your agent know where he can find this. Or use a bill-paying and financial-management software program such as *Quicken*, then provide your agent with the passwords needed to access your computer and this program. This not only gives your agent a listing of your accounts and bills, it also allows him to go back to prior months to see how you handled your financial affairs in the past, providing a template for how you would want them handled in the future.

WHAT IF THERE'S NO ONE YOU TRUST

People need to designate a financial agent even if there is no relative or close friend they trust enough to take charge of their finances. Surprisingly, some choose a person who has chronic money problems or a history of unethical behavior. This can be a big mistake.

What to do: If you know no one who is suitable (and willing) to serve as your financial agent under a financial power-of-attorney document, tell your estate-planning attorney that you would like to discuss setting up a *revocable living trust* as your *primary* financial document. With this sort of trust, you can name a financial institution as trustee, so a financial pro—not someone who lacks financial expertise and/or is not trustworthy—will take charge of your finances if needed.

Yes, it's true that this could increase your costs, but it might be worth it to ensure that your finances will be in good hands. A bank might charge 1% per year of the value of your assets to manage those assets and serve as trustee. A financial power of attorney still could be used for relatively minor financial matters, such as paying small bills.

Income Taxes Are Still Due After Death

The executor of an estate is responsible for filing taxes after a death, and they must be filed by the April 15 deadline required of living taxpayers. If the deceased person is due a refund, the executor must use Form 1310, *Statement of a Person Claiming Refund Due to a Deceased Taxpayer,* to claim it. Income must be reported from the beginning of the year to the date of death. Income after the date of death is reported by the estate. Investments and pensions typically are taxed to the person who inherits them. Deductions may include medical bills incurred prior to death and paid within one year of death.

The spouse of a deceased taxpayer with a dependent child can file as a qualifying widow/widower for up to two years. This allows the surviving spouse to benefit from filing jointly.

GoBankingRates.com

10

Investment Insider

The Biggest Mistakes Investors Are Making *Now*

Many of the investor clients who visit Peter Mallouk's offices in a Kansas City suburb have just one big request—do not let me make a fatal financial mistake. That is especially true lately, as investors worry about where the stock market is headed. Mallouk, who was named by *Barron's* as the top independent financial adviser in the US for two straight years, tells investors that he cannot predict where today's market is headed, but he can make sure that they never make a terrible investment decision again.

Here, Mallouk talks about the biggest mistakes investors are making today as they maneuver through challenges ranging from low interest rates to global terrorism and regional conflicts. Some of the following mistakes may sound familiar to you—but amid today's challenges, they are trapping even sophisticated investors...

DON'T LET TODAY'S CONDITIONS RATTLE YOU

I began my career 15 years ago as an estate attorney working with stockbrokers, financial planners and their clients. What astonished me was how many people—including investors *and* advisers—let themselves make certain mistakes even when they probably knew better. That's happening again today.

Human beings have powerful biases—to do what other individuals are doing...to panic and run from danger...and to always want more no matter how much they have. To be

Peter Mallouk, JD, CFP, president and chief investment officer of Creative Planning Private Wealth Management, a financial advisory firm for high net-worth clients with more than $12 billion in assets under management, Leawood, Kansas. He is author of *The 5 Mistakes Every Investor Makes and How to Avoid Them. ThinkingBeyond.com* a successful investor and protect yourself, you need to be aware of these impulses as you experience them and create practical steps to override them.

Four of today's big mistakes…

MISTAKE #1: Dumping stocks when you think the market has peaked.

What can happen: Some of my clients clamor to exit stocks when they think the market has peaked. The problem with market timing is that you don't need to be right just once. You need to be right twice—when you get out and then again when it's time to get back in. To beat the long-term returns of the broad market, studies show that you actually need to make the right call 70% to 90% of the time, depending on market conditions.

What to do instead: Don't try to time the market. You likely will see many more bear markets and corrections in your lifetime. You may be able to sidestep some of them, but trying to do that is highly likely to do great damage to your portfolio in the long run.

MISTAKE #2: Buying or selling investments based on today's relentless onslaught of news and opinions.

What can happen: Many investors overreact to articles, to "experts" on TV and even to tweets—all supposedly explaining what's going on in the world and how it might affect investments.

For example, I have a client who watched the market drop because of Russian president Vladimir Putin's moves against Ukraine, and he was convinced that another Cold War was about to unfold. He wanted to sell stocks and buy US Treasuries.

Another client saw the market spike in reaction to comments from the latest Federal Reserve meeting about raising short-term interest rates—and she wanted to sell US Treasuries and buy stocks, exactly the opposite!

What to do instead: Do not make big investment changes based on daily events in the world. You cannot predict how those events will affect your portfolio. The only news that should cause you to alter your long-term investment plans is a big event in your own life—you retire, you want to change careers, etc.

MISTAKE #3: Rebalancing your portfolio based on the calendar.

What can happen: Investors have been "brainwashed" to follow the conventional wisdom that they should trim or add stocks and bonds on a set timetable, such as every year or quarter, to get their portfolios back in line with their long-term asset-allocation plans. However, rebalancing on a set schedule often creates unnecessary transaction fees and/or generates unneccesary tax bills…and if you sell winners too early, you might dampen your long-term returns.

What to do instead: Use "opportunistic rebalancing." When any stock or bond fund in my portfolio drops by at least 5%, I buy

MONEYWISE…

Pick Your Portfolio

Here are four portfolios from Peter Mallouk, JD, CFP, with the best allocations to achieve common goals…

***Goal:* Beat historical market gains averaging 9% to 10%.** Very aggressive investors who want to outperform the S&P 500 over a 10- or 20-year period require big allocations to volatile stock categories. *Allocations:* 25% US small-caps…25% foreign stocks…25% emerging-market stocks…25% US large-caps.

***Goal:* 7% annual returns.** This is very achievable for moderately aggressive investors. *Allocations:* 60% stocks (25% US large-caps…20% foreign stocks…15% US small-caps) and 40% bonds (25% US bonds…15% foreign bonds).

***Goal:* 5% annual returns with low volatility.** Keep enough assets in bonds to take monthly or annual distributions without being forced to sell stocks in down markets. *Allocations:* 40% stocks (20% US large-caps…10% US small-caps…10% foreign stocks) and 60% bonds (40% US bonds…20% foreign bonds).

***Goal:* I just want to grow my portfolio modestly with the least volatility.** If you already have a big enough nest egg, you can draw down 3% of your assets each year without ever touching principal. *Allocations:* 10% stocks (all in US large-caps) and 90% bonds (70% US bonds…20% foreign bonds).

enough additional shares to return it to its intended allocation level.

To make these purchases, I use cash from new contributions or from income the portfolio produces. For winning funds, I wait to take profits for a minimum of one year (to avoid short-term capital gains taxes) and continue to hold them until the fund has risen 5% above its intended allocation in the portfolio before I trim the investment.

MISTAKE #4: Choosing a mix of mutual funds that is not tied to your long-term goals.

What can happen: Many investors think that they can beat the S&P 500 index by selecting a few big winners among stocks and/or mutual funds. But extensive studies have shown that the mix of asset classes that you choose is what's responsible for about 88% of your returns.

What to do instead: Don't try to win the mutual fund lottery by banking on a few supposedly extraordinary funds. Instead, decide what your goals and risk tolerance are and choose an asset mix—and a mix of funds—based on that. For examples of smart fund portfolios based on various goals, see the box on the previous page.

What's Ahead for Stocks? A Legendary Financial Adviser Answers the Tough Questions

Burton Malkiel, PhD, the Chemical Bank Chairman's Professor of Economics, Emeritus, at Princeton University, Princeton, New Jersey. Dr. Malkiel is also author of the classic finance book *A Random Walk Down Wall Street*, which has sold more than 1.5 million copies, as well as chief investment officer at Wealthfront, an investment advisory firm overseeing more than $2.3 billion in assets. He is a former member of the White House Council of Economic Advisers.

The stock market's dizzying heights and occasional swoons have many investors wondering whether it's too dangerous now to stick with stocks. For some expert answers, we decided to interview legendary investment strategist Burton Malkiel, PhD, author of the classic *A Random Walk Down Wall Street,* and chief investment officer at Wealthfront, a firm overseeing more than $2.3 billion in assets, for his views on today's market—and what investors should do.

Our questions and his responses...

• Is it smart to add new money to stocks after a big drop in the market?

Or should we take profits and avoid the market for a while? Thinking you can time when to get in and out of the stock market can be particularly stressful. You might buy stocks right after a pullback only to watch the market continue to fall. Conversely, you might sit on the sidelines only to watch the stock market keep rising steadily. The fact is, no one can consistently time the market, but there are not many other places to achieve a reasonable return.

• Can we still expect stocks to produce good returns for the long term?

This is what should concern investors the most.

The US and the rest of the developed world are likely to experience anemic economic growth for a long time. We'll be lucky to reach and maintain 3% annual growth in gross domestic product (GDP). When I factor that into various prediction models for the US stock market, the news is not great. I would expect average annual S&P 500 returns in the mid single digits—not the low double digits that many people are used to—for the next decade or more.

• Are there better opportunities than investing in the S&P 500?

Yes there are more attractive opportunities, but they are not in the US. Even conservative investors and retirees need to consider adding some emerging-market stocks to their portfolios. These stocks, which have become substantially undervalued during the long US bull market, can provide annual returns averaging above 10% over the next decade or longer. Emerging markets now make up half the world's economic activity. They are volatile, of course, but as part of a diversified portfolio, the risk will be manageable.

You can get low-cost exposure to emerging markets through exchange-traded funds such as the iShares MSCI Emerging Markets ETF (EEM) and the Vanguard FTSE Emerging Markets ETF (VWO).

More aggressive investors might consider some excellent closed-end funds, which are selling for much less than the value of their underlying holdings. These include Aberdeen Latin America Equity (LAQ)...Morgan Stanley Emerging Markets (MSF)...and Templeton Dragon (TDF).

•Do we need to prepare our portfolios for higher inflation?

Inflation has been very low in recent years, and I don't expect it to break out anytime soon.

However, now is a good time to start building exposure to real estate investment trusts (REITs), which invest in commercial real estate such as apartment buildings and shopping malls.

REITs can provide both dividend income and some degree of protection against inflation as rents tend to increase when prices increase. And they are relatively attractive now, having lagged the stock market over the past several years. Consider ETFs such as iShares US Real Estate ETF (IYR) and the Vanguard REIT ETF (VNQ).

•When will interest rates rise?

A combination of tepid economic growth in developed nations and a lack of significant inflation means that many central banks around the world are likely to keep interest rates lower than historical averages for many years to come.

Just because the US Federal Reserve has indicated that it will start hiking short-term interest rates soon does not mean that yields on low-risk investments, such as savings accounts, CDs and US Treasuries, will rise enough for you to live on the income they produce in the foreseeable future.

In the past, I have recommended that investors could meet their fixed-income needs by investing their long-term bond money in a total bond market index fund. But these types of funds, which hold US government bonds and high-quality corporate bonds, recently provided meager yields in the 2% range.* And if I am wrong about interest rates and they do suddenly spike, bond prices will plummet and these funds could easily lose 5% to 15% of their value.

•Should we adjust our investment portfolios for the likelihood that interest rates will rise sharply?

Think about dividing your long-term bond money among three different classes of assets. *These three classes entail varying levels of risk, but they can provide higher yields, better total returns and less pain if US interest rates rise...*

•Municipal bonds. These tax-exempt bonds, normally attractive only for investors who are in high tax brackets, today represent unusually good value versus US Treasuries even for people not in high tax brackets.

The bankruptcy of Detroit and debt problems of Puerto Rico have chilled the US muni bond market. The result is that high-quality munis with very little default risk often sell with yields equal to or higher than those of comparable Treasury securities. The iShares National AMT-Free Muni Bond ETF (MUB) recently had the same yield as many taxable intermediate-term US Treasury funds.

•High-quality dividend stocks. You will be better served owning blue-chip, dividend-paying US stocks now than holding bonds in the same companies.

For example, AT&T's stock recently yielded 5.5%, which is higher than the yield on that company's 10-year bonds. And if inflation accelerates, rising prices on goods and services will help boost the company's earnings, making the stock's outlook and risk level compared with bonds even more attractive.

•Emerging-market bonds. These particular investments can work for the aggressive end of your bond portfolio. Many developing nations actually are in much better fiscal shape than the US, with less debt and balanced budgets. But because their economies are less established and less trusted by investors, especially in times of global crisis, they must offer much higher yields

*Yields as of August 7, 2015.

TAKE NOTE...

Best Investment Portfolios by Age

Here are portfolio allocations recommended by Burton Malkiel, PhD, for investors of various ages who seek a balance of good performance and stability...

20s to early 30s: 75% stocks (one-half in the US, one-quarter in other developed nations, one-quarter in emerging markets)...20% income-oriented (one-third each of muni bonds, emerging-market bonds and dividend stocks)...and 5% cash.

Late 30s to 50: 65% stocks (one-half in the US, one-quarter in other developed nations, one-quarter in emerging markets)...20% income-oriented (one-third each of muni bonds, emerging-market bonds and dividend stocks)...10% REITs...and 5% cash.

50s to late 60s: 55% stocks (one-half of that in the US, one-quarter in other developed nations, one-quarter in emerging markets)...27.5% bonds (one-third each of muni bonds, emerging-market bonds and dividend stocks)...12.5% REITs...and 5% cash.

Late 60s and older: 40% stocks (one-half of that in the US, one-quarter in other developed nations, one-quarter in emerging markets) ...35% income-oriented (one-third each of muni bonds, emerging-market bonds and dividend stocks)...15% REITs...and 10% cash.

on their government bonds in order to attract investors.

A broadly diversified emerging-market bond fund such as Vanguard Emerging Markets Government Bond ETF (VWOB) is an easy way to do this—it was recently yielding 4.6%.

Afraid of Stocks? How to Safely Ease into the Market or Increase Your Stake

Janet M. Brown, president of FundX Investment Group, San Francisco, and managing editor of *NoLoad FundX*, which is ranked by *The Hulbert Financial Digest* as one of the best-performing fund investment newsletters over the past 25 years. For more information, go to *FundX.com*

Have you waited a bit too long to pour a little—or a lot—of your money into the stock market? Surely you have been tempted as you continue to get extremely low yields on cash in bank accounts, CDs and bonds. Or perhaps you are still haunted by past market crashes.

If you are somewhat nervous about investing more, or perhaps even any, of your money in the stock market, here is a very simple strategy that I like to use with my clients. It gets you off the sidelines (or lets you increase a small stake) but also guards against the risk of large losses so that you can sleep soundly at night.

First, decide on the total amount you want to invest in stocks. Perhaps you have a total of just $50,000 and it's all in savings and bonds and you have never invested anything in the stock market. Or maybe you have $250,000, or even a few million, but pulled out a large amount of money when times started to get a bit scary.

For most investors, the basic process to decide how much to invest is the same. *Divide your available cash reserves into three different categories...*

- **Emergency cash.** This amount should typically equal three to six months' worth of your bills and living expenses. It should be held in safe, immediately accessible accounts such as money-market or savings accounts even if it means getting little or no yield. You need this money to remain liquid in case you lose your job or suffer some unexpected costs, such as a major car repair or a medical crisis.

• **Savings you may need in the next five years.** That includes money intended, for example, to pay for a child's college education, go on a special vacation or make anticipated home repairs. Consider keeping this money in low-risk, fixed-income investments that offer better yields than bank accounts—such as CDs and short-term bonds—especially if you don't need immediate access.

• **Savings you don't need to touch for at least five years.** This is the money that you can invest in the stock market. Historically, five years is the length of a typical stock market cycle encompassing both a bull and a bear market. Of course, you don't have to put all of this long-term savings in stocks...but you should not put in more than this.

DECIDE HOW MUCH TO INVEST

Your horizon for needing cash is just one factor in deciding how much to invest. *Other factors to consider...*

• **What kind of return on your investments do you need to meet your long-term financial goals?** Over the past century, stocks with dividends reinvested have returned about 10% annually, on average, compared with about 5% for bonds, but stocks have entailed much more risk along the way. If you don't have to achieve a high return to meet your particular needs, you may not have to invest much, if any, in stocks.

• **How much risk can you tolerate, especially during market drops?** Long-term investors need to be able to maintain the money that they allocate to stocks through both bull and bear markets. If you have invested before, you may already have a long-term asset-allocation plan dividing your portfolio between stocks and bonds.

If not, you can evaluate your risk tolerance and determine how much of your cash to allocate to stocks with the help of free tools at *Individual.ML.com* (click "Start" under "Risk Tolerance Evaluator") and/or at *Personal.Vanguard.com* (search for "Investor Questionnaire").

HOW TO INVEST

Once you decide how much money you want to invest, move into the market based on this strategy...

• **Immediately invest 30% to 50%** (depending on how comfortable you are with market ups and downs) of the total amount of cash you plan to put into stocks. This makes sense because the lion's share of the stock market's long-term gains are made in a few big "up" days. Over the past 20 years, if you missed the five days of biggest gains, your annualized returns dropped from 9.2% to 7%. If you missed the 10 biggest days, they dropped to 5.5%...and the 20 biggest days, 3%.

However, investing all your cash intended for stocks at once is just too unnerving for most people, so holding back 50% to 70% limits the pain in the event that there is a sudden market pullback.

• **Add the rest gradually.** Divide the remaining cash that you want to put into the stock market into 10 equal portions. Invest one of these portions at the end of each calendar month. So if you start with $30,000 and invest $10,000 immediately, you are left with $20,000, or 10 portions of $2,000 each, to invest over the next 10 months.

If you are especially jittery, spreading out your investments rather than diving in all at once also might help you avoid panicking and pulling out your money at the wrong time if the market drops sharply. Very risk-averse investors may want to ease in even more slowly, putting in a 10% portion every other month, which would get you fully invested in 20 months.

INTERESTING FINDING...

About Half of Americans Are Not Investing in Stocks

Fifty-three percent report they don't have the money, 21% say they don't know enough about stocks, 9% say they don't trust stockbrokers or advisers, and 7% say the market is too risky.

Bankrate.com, based on a telephone survey by Princeton Survey Research Associates International.

TAKE NOTE...

Brokerage Firms Are Offering Cash Rewards

Cash rewards up to $2,500* are being offered by more than a dozen brokerage firms to clients who move investments or cash over to them.

Examples: Fidelity, Schwab and E*Trade offer rewards ranging from $100 for shifting $50,000 or more...to $2,500 for bringing $1 million or more.

The rules vary on how long the money must be kept at the brokerage firm, although typically the minimum is one year. The cash reward may be taxable unless it is in a tax-deferred retirement account, such as an IRA. Some firms offer bonuses in the form of free stock trades or frequent-flier miles.

CBSNews.com/MoneyWatch

*Rates subject to change.

Important: Discipline is the key to easing into the market. The least profitable strategy over time is to follow your emotions, leaping into the market when stock prices shoot up or hoarding cash as soon as the market pulls back.

- **Invest an extra 5% of your cash each time the market pulls back by 5%.** This is smart no matter how gradually you decide to invest because it allows you to incrementally add to positions at lower prices and actually use market declines to your advantage. Historically, markets have averaged approximately three 5% pullbacks a year.

Example: Say the market drops 5% in a particular month. Instead of investing a 10% portion, invest a 15% portion.

- **Establish a system for how you divvy up cash among specific stocks and/or funds.** This will vary among investors. For example, I spread new money evenly among the top three funds in my model portfolio based on having the best average performance over the past one, three, six and 12 months.

But there are many other valid approaches to choosing your stock investments. For instance, if you already have a portfolio that you like, you could simply add equal portions to all your stocks and funds. Or for investors who focus on buying bargain-priced stocks, you could add to holdings that lost the most (or gained the least) over the past year.

Finally, if all this still feels too scary or a bit uncomfortable, consider using the above basic methods...but invest in a balanced mutual fund instead of stocks or stock funds. Balanced funds temper the ups and downs of the market by allocating a portion of the portfolio to bonds.

Better Yields for the Conservative Investor

Patrick O'Shaughnessy, CFA, principal, O'Shaughnessy Asset Management, Stamford, Connecticut, and author of *Millennial Money: How Young Investors Can Build a Fortune. OSAM.com*

Many cautious investors who are seeking stable companies that offer decent income and good value look at dividend yields. But there's a better yield measure to help you judge whether an income-producing stock is a good value. Check on "shareholder yield," which is the sum of the dividend yield and the percent of outstanding shares in its own stock that a company has bought back over the past year.

Example: A company that has bought back 3% of its shares and has an annual dividend yielding 2% has a 5% shareholder yield.

Why include the buyback percentage? Large buybacks indicate that senior management thinks the stock is a bargain, and the buybacks often push up the stock price. (Whether the stock is a bargain also depends on what multiple the stock price is of sales, earnings and cash flow.)

Stocks that have relatively high shareholder yields have outperformed broad market indexes in the periods from January 1, 1927, through November 30, 2013...and from January 1, 2000, through November 30, 2013.

My favorite undervalued stocks with some of the highest recent shareholder yields in the S&P 500...

LyondellBasell Industries NV (LYB) makes chemicals for products ranging from antifreeze to cosmetics (*recent shareholder yield*: 17.5%*). Northrop Grumman (NOC) specializes in military aviation and missile defense systems (9.7%). Seagate Technology (STX) makes data-storage products including hard drives (15.0%). Travelers Companies (TRV) offers insurance (11.8%). If you prefer the diversification of a fund, the Cambria Shareholder Yield ETF (SYLD) invests in about 100 stocks with high shareholder yields.

*Yields as of August 7, 2015.

These Stocks Beat Up and Down Markets

Douglas Gerlach, editor in chief of the *Investor Advisory Service* newsletter, Madison Heights, Michigan. Gerlach is also president of ICLUBcentral, which makes stock-analysis software for investment clubs, and author of six books including *The Armchair Millionaire. InvestorAdvisoryService.com*

Some investors have stock portfolios that soar during bull markets but plunge during bear markets. Other investors have portfolios that hold up relatively well when the going gets rough, but they're pretty lackluster when the stock market is zooming upward.

But what if you could beat the market no matter which direction it was headed? That is what investment-newsletter editor Douglas Gerlach has done. He and his team of analysts use a strategy that originally was devised for amateur investment clubs in the 1950s. It is simple enough for the average person to use, yet comprehensive enough to compete with professionals.

Combining the approaches of several legendary investors, including Warren Buffett and John Templeton, the strategy was refined for decades by hundreds of clubs across the country and hundreds of thousands of investors.

Since 1996, the newsletter's model portfolio has gained an average of 13% annually, compared with 8.5% for the Wilshire 5000 stock index. It was recently named to *The Hulbert Financial Digest*'s Honor Roll of newsletters that have consistently beaten market averages in both up and down markets year after year.

Below, Douglas Gerlach shares his investment secrets...

FOCUS ON THE BUSINESS

We do not worry much about the overall movements of the stock market or economic forecasts. And we don't seek out sexy, high-profile stocks such as Tesla or Twitter. Those companies may have vast potential, but their fates are very uncertain and the stocks are very volatile.

Instead, we focus our time and energy on identifying high-quality companies to invest in. Once we add a stock to the model portfolio, we keep it there as long as the company continues to perform up to the standards that we consider important. If a business consistently makes money and grows over time, the share price tends to rise more in bull markets than the overall stock market and fall less than the market in bear markets.

The top three fundamental characteristics of great businesses...

• **Consistent earnings growth.** Stock prices bounce around for lots of reasons, but over the long term, earnings growth is the single most important factor justifying rising stock prices. In choosing stocks, we want to see average annual earnings growth of at least 15% over the past five to 10 years for small-sized companies...at least 10% for mid-sized companies...and at least 7% for large companies.

• **Stable profit margins.** A company with stable margins (the percentage of revenue that is realized as profit) that are greater than those of its competitors has a better chance of performing well in economic downturns or when industry-related problems strike.

• **Long-term competitive advantages.** It's important to make sure that the company has attributes that will help it keep growing in the future and do better than its competitors. For example, the business may have patented technologies, strong brand loyalty from customers or new markets overseas.

Important: We stay fully invested through bull and bear markets because market timing has such a low success rate. This can be challenging because my growth-oriented strategy does not include many shares of defensive, slow-growth companies such as utilities or consumer staples. Consequently, our portfolio is likely to endure losses in bear markets and market corrections, but the losses tend to be less severe than those of the broad market, and the rebound is more pronounced than that of the broad market. For example, in 2008, when the S&P 500 stock index dropped 37%, the newsletter's portfolio fell just 28%. And over the next five years, it returned 23% annually, on average, compared with 18% for the S&P 500.

PAY A REASONABLE PRICE

We avoid "cheap" stocks—those that have a price-to-earnings ratio (P/E) that is considerably below the stock's average P/E over the past five years.

Reason: A cheap stock typically signifies that something has gone very wrong with the business and/or that investors have lost confidence in it. Besides, it's tricky to judge whether management has the talent and insights to turn around such a troubled company.

Instead, we prefer companies that are doing well but that have experienced a dip in the stock price because of a temporary business setback or a broad market drop in which worried investors dump holdings indiscriminately. Typically, we like to see a stock's P/E slightly below, or equal to, its five-year average.

FOUR STOCKS TO CONSIDER

Shares of each of these high-quality businesses have matched or beaten the S&P 500 over recent years but also have held up better in bear markets. Moving forward, each of these companies has a good chance of experiencing strong revenue growth that can drive the stock's price up by as much as 15% annually over the next several years.

- **Catamaran Corp. (CTRX)** is a leading pharmacy benefits manager (PBM) in the US. It handled the processing for, and negotiated discount prices on, more than 350 million prescription drug claims in 2013 for organizations including managed-care firms and health-care plan administrators. The claims that the PBM industry oversees are expected to nearly double by 2020 because of the government expansion of health-care benefits and the rising cost of specialty drugs. *Recent share price:* $61.47.*

- **IPG Photonics Corp. (IPGP)** pioneered the manufacturing of fiber-optic lasers for industrial cutting, drilling and welding in products ranging from Gillette razors to Volkswagens. Compared with conventional lasers, fiber-optic lasers offer more precision but are far more expensive. IPG's manufacturing costs have dropped markedly in recent years, and the company is just beginning to penetrate industries such as aerospace manufacturing, telecommunications and medicine. The company owns hundreds of patents on fiber-optic laser design, giving it a major advantage over competitors. *Recent share price:* $94.15.

- **Realty Income Corp. (O)** is, in my opinion, the best-managed real estate investment trust (REIT) in the US, with impressive occupancy rates and reliable cash flow. It has been able to increase its dividends for the past 19 years in a row. The company owns more than 4,200 properties in 49 states and Puerto Rico that are leased to businesses including FedEx, Walgreens and BJ's. Its shares recently yielded 4.8%, making it attractive for investors seeking income. *Recent share price:* $47.46.

- **ResMed (RMD)** develops and manufactures medical devices to treat sleep apnea and other respiratory problems. The business should see an enormous influx of new customers among baby boomers in the next few years because sleep-disorder breathing tends to worsen dramatically with age and weight gain. ResMed is the technological leader in this health-care niche, with the highest brand-name recognition among physicians. *Recent share price:* $54.88.

STOCKS LOOKING GOOD FOR THE FUTURE

The powerful bull market over the past six years left the stocks of many terrific businesses too expensive to buy. However, consider tracking the following stocks and buying them when they have big pullbacks...

*Prices as of August 7, 2015.

• **Aflac (AFL)** is best known for its TV ads featuring a duck quacking "Aflac," but many investors don't realize that it is one of the world's largest underwriters of supplemental health, life and cancer insurance, a highly profitable and fast-growing market sector. *Recent share price:* $64.04. Purchase at $50 per share or below.

• **Fastenal Company (FAST)** distributes maintenance supplies, including a selection of more than a million types of bolts, fasteners, screws and electrical tools, to industrial and construction customers. Fastenal Co. still has plenty of room for growth, with just a 2% share of the highly fragmented $140-billion-a-year market in maintenance supplies. *Recent share price:* $40.00. Purchase at $37 per share or below.

• **Fiserv (FISV)** is the leading provider of core-processing services, such as electronic fund transfers and loan processing, for thousands of US banks and credit unions. *Recent share price:* $87.51. Purchase at $44 per share or below.

• **O'Reilly Automotive (ORLY)** is the second-largest do-it-yourself auto-parts retailer in the US, with more than 4,000 stores. Its business will continue to grow rapidly as owners keep their cars longer. *Recent share price:* $244.46. Purchase at $120 per share or below.

---

6 Winning Stocks from the "Oracle of Tampa"

Harold J. Bowen III. Since 1998, he has been CEO and chief investment officer of Bowen, Hanes & Company, Inc., an investment advisory firm founded by his father, Harold J. Bowen, Jr. The Atlanta-based firm has more than $2.7 billion in assets under management and has managed the Tampa Firefighters and Police Officers Pension Fund since 1974. *BowenHanes.com*

Harold J. Bowen III is not ashamed to say that he follows the generally boring, plain-vanilla approach of legendary investors such as Warren Buffett. It's just that Bowen, known as Jay, does it better than nearly all other big investors—so well that, similar to Buffett's moniker of the Oracle of Omaha, Bowen often is referred to as the Oracle of Tampa because he has managed the $1.9 billion Tampa Firefighters and Police Officers Pension Fund since the late 1990s.

The fund has achieved phenomenal results—an annualized return of 12.2% since its inception in 1974. That has put it in the top 1% of all public pension plans with more than $1 billion in assets—outperforming such giants as the $288 billion California Public Employees' Retirement System (Calpers) and the Standard & Poor's 500 stock index.

Much of what Bowen does to keep the fund on a steady and profitable path can help small investors, too...

DON'T TAKE BIG RISKS

In overseeing the pension fund, I need to be very risk-averse but, at the same time, pursue long-term growth.

My approach...

• **Avoid tricky strategies.** The fund does not pursue more speculative strategies such as investing in hedge funds and private equity, shorting stocks (betting on price drops) or buying options and futures. Many institutional investors have turned to these types of sophisticated investment techniques to help boost returns, but they can backfire. Instead, I use an old-school, buy-and-hold mix of stocks and bonds. I invest in about 70 high-quality medium- and large-cap stocks and replace only about 10% of them each year. The companies all have strong businesses, growing their earnings year after year, and solid balance sheets. This may sound dull, but the steady, stable quality of these holdings allows me to stay, for the most part, fully invested in both bull and bear markets, so I don't have to engage in tricky market timing.

• **Maintain an allocation of about 65% stocks/35% bonds.** Stocks are meant to drive long-term capital gains in the portfolio. On the fixed-income side, high-quality corporate bonds (rated A or higher) along with Treasury securities are held to maturity, then the proceeds are reinvested in new bonds to provide stability and consistent yield.

• **Establish an extremely long-term horizon.** I think in terms of 20-year periods, which means that I rarely make moves based on short-term emotions. Because of this, I find it easy to ride out bumpy periods, and most important, I focus on finding the best businesses to own instead of trying to gauge what's going to happen to a stock in the next quarter or the next year. I have owned many stocks for decades.

HOW I PICK WINNING STOCKS

I always ask an initial question to help me narrow down the universe of potential stocks to choose from...

• **Is the company tapping into an emerging long-term economic and/or industrial trend?** I particularly like businesses that are benefiting from a trend in surprising ways that most investors overlook or aren't immediately aware of. For example, domestic gas and oil production is soaring, thanks to hydraulic fracturing, or fracking, from underground shale rock. This is great for companies that provide services to the energy industry such as railroad transport and high-tech drilling equipment.

Other trends I am capitalizing on: The global need for clean water...the rise of genetically modified agriculture, which allows farmers to vastly increase their crop productivity...the demand for greater energy efficiency in both industrial and consumer markets... and the burgeoning economic power of the developing world.

Once I have identified favorable long-term trends, I typically ask the following questions before I buy a stock or add to one that I already own...

• **Does the company have great management?** I look for executives who create ongoing competitive advantages in their companies to help fend off competitors and keep growing earnings. I also pay attention to a financial metric called "return on equity" (ROE), which tells me not just that the company can make money from the existing business but that it also efficiently employs profits to make more money for the shareholders. (A company's ROE should be well above the historical 13.6% average for S&P 500 companies.)

• **Does the company offer a rising dividend and buybacks of its shares?** Price appreciation in a stock is more exciting than dividend growth, but from December 1926 to December 2012, one-third of the S&P 500's monthly total returns have come from dividend income.

• **Is the stock currently out of favor with investors and attractively priced?** Buying high-quality companies whose stock is selling at a discount due to some temporary setback provides you with the potential for significant capital appreciation long term.

SOME OF MY FAVORITE STOCKS

These fit one or more of my criteria...

• **BHP Billiton Ltd. (BHP)** is the world's largest publicly traded mining conglomerate. BHP produces everything from oil and gas to nickel, copper and coal. Its stock price has floundered—recently it was about 63% below its five-year high—because commodities have been weak, global growth tepid and inflation low. But the company is extremely well-positioned to exploit improving economic growth and higher rates of inflation. *Recent share price:* $38.64.*

• **Canadian National Railway (CNI).** Railroads have proved to be a cheap and efficient way to transport commodities such as oil. No competitor can match Canadian National's tracks, which run from the East Coast to the West Coast and down through Chicago to the Gulf of Mexico. *Recent share price:* $62.14.

• **E I du Pont de Nemours & Company (DD)** still is seen as a chemical company, but it also is one of the world's largest providers of genetically modified seeds. Its agriculture business now makes up about one-third of the company's operating profit. *Recent share price:* $53.43.

• **Honeywell International (HON)** is capitalizing on the world's need for energy efficiency and safety with services ranging from nuclear waste remediation at Japan's

*Prices as of August 7, 2015.

Fukushima Daiichi nuclear power plant to smart home thermostats for consumers. The company has paid a stock dividend every year since 1887. *Recent share price:* $105.46.

• **Pentair Ltd. (PNR)** is a major player in the global market for water-filtration and pressure equipment, with users ranging from pool owners to the food-and-beverage industry to wastewater plants. *Recent share price:* $61.14.

• **3M (MMM).** The creator of Scotch Tape and Post-it Notes actually is a diversified industrial firm dedicated to technologies that shake up industries. Recent discoveries include a new kind of film coating designed to make colors brighter on flat-panel TVs and tablet computers...and new finishes that provide better protection for smartphones from scratches and dings. *Recent share price:* $148.89.

The 3 Best Stock Sectors Now... and the 3 Worst

Sam Subramanian, PhD, founder of AlphaProfit Investments, LLC, and editor in chief of the *AlphaProfit Sector Investors' Newsletter*, Sugar Land, Texas. *AlphaProfit.com*

Investors often focus on the ups and downs of the overall stock market or a few individual stocks. But there is a better way to gauge where the most attractive opportunities and the biggest dangers lie. It involves concentrating on sectors—the industry categories that help investors determine which companies are benefiting the most and the least from economic and other trends.

Over the past year through August 7, 2015, health-care stocks soared the most of the 10 major sectors, gaining 29.9%. But as investors start to grow nervous about the stock market, which sectors will hold up best?

Below, sector specialist Sam Subramanian, PhD, forecasts what lies ahead and what it could mean for investors...

SECTOR TRENDS

When large numbers of investors rotate into a sector, the sector typically outperforms the broad market for the next one to three years. That doesn't necessarily mean that investors should plunge heavily into a sector that looks hot. But interpreting the trends correctly can help investors seize opportunities and avoid dangers at a time like this. Your best chance of outperforming the stock market is to have a great deal of exposure to fast-growing, undervalued sectors.

I look at three main factors in evaluating sectors...

• **The sector must have attractive valuations from a historical perspective.** The sector should typically have a price-to-earnings ratio (P/E) that is at or below its five-year average.

• **It must have strong momentum relative to the Standard & Poor's 500 stock index.** I like to see a sector that is beginning to pick up momentum, outperforming the index's returns over the last three to six months.

• **It should have "favorable catalysts."** That means economic and business trends that clearly can benefit the sector.

FAVORITE SECTORS

The following sectors have strong growth prospects. You can gain exposure to these sectors through individual stocks or—my preference—sector funds, which make it easier to gauge and adjust your sector exposure over time. Exchange-traded funds (ETFs) offer a convenient, low-cost way to invest in specific sectors, but there also are attractive mutual funds focusing on sectors, including the Fidelity fund below. Conservative investors should consider limiting sector funds to no more than 10% of their overall portfolios because the funds can be volatile. *Here are some of my favorite sectors to invest in...*

AUTOS

The NASDAQ OMX Global Auto Index gained 17% annually over the past three years ending August 7, 2015 (versus 16.5% for the S&P 500) as the automobile market recovered from the impact of the global financial crisis. Lower unemployment, easier car financing and strong pent-up demand will continue to push up auto-industry profits for the next several years.

US auto sales likely will exceed 17 million for 2015, the highest since 2006, and even car sales in Western Europe have rallied from a six-year slump. *Funds...*

- **The First Trust NASDAQ Global Auto ETF (CARZ)** invests in about 40 stocks and focuses on global automotive manufacturers. *Performance:* 17.1%.*
- **Fidelity Select Automotive (FSAVX)** is an actively managed mutual fund that offers exposure to smaller areas of the auto industry, such as tire manufacturers and aftermarket parts suppliers. *Performance:* 22.4%.

HEALTH CARE

The S&P Health Care Select Sector Index has trounced the S&P 500 over the past three years, gaining an annualized 27.2%, and with a P/E of 23, it is just slightly overvalued on a historical basis. A good deal of that outperformance was fueled by biotech stocks. Other subsectors of health care, such as the stocks of medical-device companies, have lagged and are significant bargains. Overall, growth prospects for this sector even without biotech are exciting. Companies are just starting to benefit from implementation of the Affordable Care Act, and they are sitting on record-high levels of cash, which increase the possibility of stock buybacks and mergers. *Fund...*

- **The First Trust Health Care AlphaDEX Fund (FXH)** takes a value-oriented approach, weighting stocks not by market capitalization but by sales growth, cash flow and other measures. The 75-stock portfolio is dominated by health-care providers, medical-device makers and pharmaceuticals. *Performance:* 31.1%.

CLEAN TECHNOLOGY

This alternative energy sector focuses on renewable energy sources such as wind and solar power and companies that specialize in providing technology such as water-filtration systems and energy-efficient lighting. Many of these stocks struggled after the 2007–2009 recession. But governments are taking a new interest in clean energy production and saving energy. Also, so-called green energy has become more affordable. *Fund...*

- **PowerShares Cleantech ETF (PZD)** invests in about 60 stocks of green-technology firms. *Performance:* 13.0%.

THE WORST SECTORS

Currently, I am avoiding three sectors, all of which are sporting overall valuations that are excessive and are facing economic and/or industry headwinds. While share prices in these sectors may continue to rise a while longer due to investor excitement, investing in these sectors has become more risky. You should not make new purchases in these sectors, and you should consider cashing in on profits for at least a portion of any holdings you have in these sectors.

In July 2014, Federal Reserve Chair Janet Yellen, in a report to Congress, singled out two of these sectors—biotech and social media—explaining that their valuations were "substantially stretched."

*Performance figures are three-year average annualized returns through August 7, 2015.

MONEYWISE...

Does Your Brokerage Firm Have Insurance?

Uninsured investment advisers and firms may be unable or unwilling to pay if they are found at fault for steering clients to the wrong investments. Brokers and firms are not required to carry professional liability insurance, so even an award won in court or through arbitration may be unenforceable.

Troubling: Some $50 million of arbitration awards from 2012 remains unpaid. And the Securities Investors Protection Corporation doesn't cover losses from brokers' bad decisions.

Self-defense: Do not use firms that do not carry insurance—these typically are small firms... ask about insurance before investing, and get the information in writing...and avoid firms that focus on charging commissions (rather than a flat management fee)—they tend to have more claims because their brokers face pressure to put clients into high-commission products.

The Wall Street Journal. WSJ.com

• **Biotechnology.** Stocks in biotech have gained more than double the total return of the S&P 500 over the past three years. Criticism of biotechs has been mounting over the costs of specialty drugs. A treatment for hepatitis C at $1,000 per pill has sparked calls in Congress for reform of medication pricing.

• **Internet stocks focused on social media and networking.** This sector rose by 73% in 2013 and was essentially flat in 2014, even though many of the companies don't even have earnings or profits and still are trying to figure out how to capitalize on their vast user bases.

• **Utilities and other interest rate–sensitive sectors.** Utility stocks were bid up over the past few years by yield-hungry investors, leaving only specific segments of the industry, such as small regional utilities in areas with strong economies, still bargain priced. Valuations in the overall utilities sector were recently 20% above their historical long-term averages, and growth forecasts have slowed. Moreover, rising interest rates are likely to make these defensive holdings less attractive to investors because their dividends become less attractive as yields on bonds increase.

"Theme" Investing Opportunities: Portfolios for the Future

Hardeep Walia, CEO of Motif Investing, an online brokerage that offers theme-based portfolios for small investors in San Mateo, California. In addition to Motif's own portfolios, it has 35,000 homegrown theme portfolios created by individual investors that can be used by anyone who joins the site. Formerly, Walia was Microsoft's director of corporate development and strategy, overseeing its investments and acquisitions. *MotifInvesting.com*

Would you invest in a collection of stocks based on the theme "Fighting Fat"? Or how about "Cybersecurity"? Or the idea of "No Glass Ceilings," focused on companies with women CEOs?

Buying stocks based on these and other themes that tap into where consumers and the corporate world might be headed can lead to impressive profits.

A few asset-management companies are offering theme portfolios. For example, Invesco offers thematic exchange-traded funds, including clean energy and global agriculture... Global X offers an ETF focused on social media...Robo-Stox offers one focused on global robotics and automation...and AllianceBernstein has a Global Thematic Growth Fund that focuses on seven themes, including gene-based therapies and the evolution of the web.

But it is a four-year-old online brokerage called Motif Investing that is offering the greatest variety of theme portfolios—including the three mentioned at the top of this article and more than 100 others, ranging from "World of Sports" and "Child's Play" (child-focused products) to "Kings of K Street" (companies that spend the most on lobbyists, who tend to have offices on K Street in Washington, DC) and "High Spirits" (alcoholic beverages). Motif Investing also helps individual investors create their own thematic portfolios that others can invest in as well, including "Pay It Forward" (digital-payment services), "Everything Coca-Cola" (distributors of the beverage company's brands) and "Best Companies to Work For."

Motif Investing portfolios have attracted various notable investors, including former Securities & Exchange Commission chairman Arthur Levitt and ex-Bank of America brokerage boss Sallie Krawcheck. Both also are on Motif's board of directors.

To learn more about the thinking behind thematic investing, we spoke with Hardeep Walia, CEO of Motif Investing...

INVESTING IN IDEAS

At Motif, we identify themes—driven by economics, politics, technology, the environment, culture and/or demographics—that we believe will catch on in the next few years. We have come up with more than 150 of these themes (I call them "motifs") and created portfolios around them. Each motif typically holds between 15 and 30 stocks. Unlike many traditional ETFs, which give the biggest companies the greatest weight in a portfolio, we give the greatest weight to those that most strongly fit the theme.

Example: In our Shale Gas motif, companies that are heavily involved in the Marcellus shale region, which includes parts of Pennsylvania and West Virginia, are given the biggest weighting because of the huge potential for natural gas production there.

We seek the greatest opportunities not just in the US but in the world.

Example: We have a motif called China Internet. China already is the biggest Internet market in the world, with 600 million users, but less than half of households have Internet access. Over the past year through August 7, 2015, the portfolio fell 2%, compared with an 11% gain for the Standard & Poor's 500 stock index.

Thematic strategies are designed for an increasingly global and complex world, in which the best investment opportunities often span different sectors, industries, market capitalizations and countries at the same time.

For instance, take our motif called Robotic Revolution. With advancements in automation technology, companies across multiple industries are realizing that they can employ robots not just on a factory floor but in unexpected and groundbreaking ways to improve safety and production. And they are calling on companies of many different sizes to help. The 20-stock motif includes a small-cap (California military drone maker AeroVironment) and a large-cap (FMC Technologies, a Texas-based provider of remotely operated vehicles that are used for deep-water oil exploration). *The motif's one-year performance:* -0.3%.*

Thematic investing does have drawbacks. Although we have some low-volatility portfolios, various Motif Investing portfolios are likely to be much more volatile than a broad ETF or mutual fund or even industry sector fund. And although we have portfolios designed to do well in bear markets, many themes can fall way out of favor when the market is going through a bearish phase. Even powerful themes tend to develop in fits and starts.

*Figures as of August 7, 2015.

Example: We developed a portfolio of mining companies called Dr. Copper, based on the strong hunger for that metal in developing economies. But China's slowdown in economic growth has pushed the portfolio down by 40.4% over the past year.

Because of these risks, you may want to use thematic investing as a satellite strategy, putting a small portion of your overall assets into thematic stocks or funds in hopes of boosting overall long-term returns.

PICKING A THEME

Follow these guidelines for successful thematic investing...

- **Make sure the theme has massive scale and potential.**

Example: Corporations are just beginning to address the lucrative opportunities in innovative medical treatments for the chronically overweight. The latest FDA-approved weight-loss drug, Qysmia, is expected to reach $2 billion in annual sales by 2017. For the Fighting Fat motif, we picked 17 stocks, including Vivus (which makes Qysmia) and Novo Nordisk (which makes products to treat diabetes). *The motif's performance:* 11.4%.

- **See if the theme still is new enough that it is misunderstood or underappreciated by the market.** This allows you to pick up stocks with big potential while they still are cheap. While a theme doesn't need to be generating peak profits for companies, it should start to play out over the next five years.

Example: Hacking incidents have sent corporations rushing to ratchet up spending on computer security, creating a new global industry for security companies. You have never heard of many of the companies in the Cyber Security motif, including data-protection software and security providers such as Imperva and Proofpoint, but I believe you will. *The motif's performance:* 37.7%.

HOW TO USE THEMES

A theme really is just a filter, narrowing the universe of possible investments down to a manageable number of stocks that can be closely examined. After choosing a theme, identify those industries likely to reap benefits from the theme...then find the most dominant, or the "best-of-breed," companies within those industries.

Example: There now are 24 female CEOs of Fortune 500 companies, which is up from just two in 2000. Research shows that when more women hold senior or board positions, companies see boosts in profitability, return on equity and overall organizational effectiveness. We followed this No Glass Ceilings motif into some diverse and surprising areas, including defense (CEO Marillyn Hewson at Lockheed Martin)...banking (Beth Mooney at KeyCorp)...and chemicals (Ellen J. Kullman at DuPont). *The motif's performance:* 1.9%.

How to Invest in Health Care: Best Strategies Now

Todd Rosenbluth, senior director overseeing mutual funds for S&P Capital IQ, an equity research firm that provides investment research and analytical tools to more than 4,000 investment banks, private-equity firms and financial-services clients, New York City. *SPCapitalIQ.com*

One type of stock fund has outperformed all others over the past five years. And some analysts report it is well-positioned to continue its winning ways. The category? Health-care funds.

They gained an annualized 25% over the past five years, on average, and outperformed the Standard & Poor's 500 stock index by an average of 10 percentage points a year over that period. They gained 36% for the year ending August 7, 2015, compared with 11% for the S&P 500.

Health-care companies have long been a favorite of cautious investors looking for stable investments. When we get sick, we pay for essential drugs and medical services regardless of how the market or economy is doing.

In recent years, however, the industry has undergone dramatic changes, finding strong profits in new medicines and treatments, a trend that has transformed health-care companies into market leaders.

But how long can health-care stocks continue to zoom ahead, especially since overall health-care spending has risen quite slowly since the 2007–2009 recession began?

Below, we asked top mutual fund analyst Todd Rosenbluth what's ahead for health-care funds and which ones he likes now and for the future...

POWERFUL TRENDS TO WATCH

Health-care companies overall have stocks that are attractively priced despite years of strong gains. In early August 2015, the stocks were trading at prices about 24 times estimated 2015 earnings, on average, compared with a price-to-earnings ratio (P/E) of 19 for all the S&P 500 stocks overall.

Moreover, health-care spending only recently began to recover from the Great Recession. From 2009 to 2013, it grew less than 4% annually, well below its historical rate as Americans cut back in the face of stagnant wages and a weak economy. But in 2014, health-care spending grew an estimated 6%. And spending will continue to accelerate, thanks to several trends.

Scientific advances are producing breakthroughs in biotechnology, medicines and treatments. In the past four years, the Food and Drug Administration (FDA) approved a total of more than 130 new drugs, compared with 89 in the previous four years. A rapidly aging US population has an insatiable demand for those products and services. In addition, the Affordable Care Act has spurred millions of formerly uninsured Americans to sign up for coverage. And globally, a growing middle class in emerging markets is adding to demand.

Despite these developments, investors in health care need to be selective. Even picking the right health-care fund has become a challenge, with more than 60 health-care mutual funds and exchange-traded funds (ETFs) to choose from, ranging from narrowly focused ones that are some of the most volatile in the entire fund universe to broadly diversified funds that are more conservative than the S&P 500.

Because you may already have health-care exposure in your portfolio through individual stocks or diversified mutual funds, you should consider limiting your investment in a health-care fund to no more than 5% to 10% of your total stock allocation. That should be enough to give your overall returns a boost without taking on excessive risk.

The best health-care funds for various types of investors...

AGGRESSIVE INVESTORS

These funds focus on the fastest-growing or most undervalued health-care companies. The gut-wrenching volatility of these stocks requires a lot of patience, but they are likely to offer the highest returns in the industry over the next five years or longer...

• **Fidelity Select Biotechnology Portfolio (FBIOX)** focuses on some of the most exciting, and riskiest, stocks in the entire market—biotechs. Many biotech stocks are subject to wild price swings because their fates often depend completely on FDA approval of new drugs.

Fund manager Rajiv Kaul, whose performance ranks in the top 1% of the fund category over the past five years, takes a less aggressive approach than most fund managers in the category, reducing volatility somewhat. He holds about 200 stocks, investing three-quarters of the fund's assets in already profitable biotech firms that have many new drugs under development. The remaining assets are invested in speculative stocks of small companies with potential blockbuster treatments still in clinical trials. *Performance:* 42%.* *Fidelity.com*

• **iShares US Healthcare Providers ETF (IHF)** invests in about 50 top insurers, diagnostic companies and pharmacy-benefits managers. These stocks offer some of the best values in health care now. Their performance has lagged other parts of the sector because they are more closely tied to the growth of the overall US economy. With US economic growth likely to continue to strengthen, these stocks could play catch up and do well. *Performance:* 30.6%. *iShares.com*

*Performance figures are for three years through August 7, 2015.

MODERATELY AGGRESSIVE

These funds mix both aggressive and more stable stocks that span the entire health-care industry.

• **Fidelity Select Health Care Portfolio (FSPHX)** invests in what the managers believe to be very reasonably priced large-cap growth stocks. Fund manager Edward Yoon anchors the fund by investing one-third of assets in stable pharmaceutical companies such as Bristol-Myers Squibb and the generic-drug company Activis. Earnings growth rates among drug companies are finally bouncing back after a wave of patent expirations on high-profile drugs back in 2012 opened up their big sellers to competition. Yoon also has been reducing the fund's exposure to biotechs and increasing positions in companies that help cut costs in the health-care system. *Performance:* 36.4%. *Fidelity.com*

• **T. Rowe Price Health Sciences Fund (PRHSX)** follows a game plan similar to that of the Fidelity fund but devotes a bigger allocation to biotech stocks and keeps about 40% of the fund in small and mid-sized companies. *Performance:* 36.2%. *TRowePrice.com*

CONSERVATIVE INVESTORS

If you worry about the stock market becoming rocky, this fund provides some defense by limiting exposure to particularly volatile stocks, focusing on very large, cash-rich companies and looking for stocks at bargain prices.

• **Vanguard Health Care Fund (VGHCX)** is one of the largest and least expensive actively managed health-care funds, with an annual expense ratio of 0.34%. It's also one of the least volatile. Manager Jean Hynes has nearly half of the assets in global pharmaceutical giants such as AstraZeneca, Merck & Co. and Roche Holding, which derive an increasingly large amount of revenue from emerging markets. This is a good choice if you want to try to beat the S&P 500 consistently with limited risk. *Performance:* 30.6%. *Vanguard.com*

Internet Funds Are Back

Neena Mishra, CFA, ETF research director at Zacks Investment Research, Chicago. *Zacks.com*

Companies focused on the Internet have come a long way since the dot-com bubble burst in the early 2000s. Many are enormously profitable…or headed in that direction. And their stock prices generally are not absurdly high multiples of their earnings. But even now, Internet stocks are 40% more volatile than the Standard & Poor's 500 stock index, on average. That is because investors have high expectations for their growth potential, which keeps their valuations elevated but makes them vulnerable to sharp pullbacks on disappointing developments.

For investors who can stand the volatility, some Internet stocks can pay off big. Priceline has averaged a 49% annual return over the past decade*…and Netflix, 45%. This sector will continue to offer enticing investments as the Internet becomes even more deeply ingrained in how we shop, entertain ourselves and interact with others. *Investors can temper some of the volatility through three exchange-traded funds (ETFs) that spread the risk…*

• **First Trust Dow Jones Internet ETF (FDN)** invests in about 40 stocks of US-headquartered companies ranging from giants such as Amazon.com, Facebook and Google to small firms such as Cornerstone OnDemand, which provides management software. Over the past five years, the ETF had annualized returns of 22%, compared with 15.5% for the S&P 500.

• **PowerShares Nasdaq Internet ETF (PNQI)** invests in about 100 stocks including foreign Internet companies listed on US stock exchanges. It had annualized returns of 22.1% over the past five years.

• **Emerging Markets Internet & Ecommerce ETF (EMQQ),** which was launched in 2014, invests in about 40 stocks including the Chinese e-commerce giant Alibaba.

*Annualized returns as of August 7, 2015.

STOCK OPPORTUNITY…

Cybersecurity Companies

Data breaches at big companies benefit software companies that specialize in protecting data networks and intellectual property from computer hackers. The cybersecurity market is expected to grow 63% by 2019, to $155 billion annually.

Stocks likely to benefit: Barracuda Networks (CUDA)…FireEye (FEYE)…and Palo Alto Networks (PANW).

Frederick Ziegel, CFA, vice president and senior analyst specializing in security software and infrastructure for Topeka Capital Markets, New York City. *TopekaCapitalMarkets.com*

Want to Invest Abroad? Consider a Hedged ETF

Most exchange-traded funds (ETFs) hold stocks in the relatively weak currencies of the stocks' home countries, such as the euro. That hurts the ETF's performance when converted to the soaring US dollar. But a hedged ETF uses "forward contracts" to neutralize currency-exchange fluctuations.

Favorites: Deutsche X-trackers MSCI Europe Hedged Equity (DBEU)…iShares Currency Hedged MSCI EAFE (HEFA)…and Wisdom Tree Japan Hedged Equity (DXJ).

Neena Mishra, CFA, ETF research director at Zacks Investment Research, Chicago. *Zacks.com*

The Small-Cap Funds That Can Boost Your Returns

Todd Rosenbluth, senior director overseeing mutual funds for S&P Capital IQ, an equity research firm that provides investment research and analytical tools to more than 4,000 investment banks, private-equity firms and financial-services clients, New York City. *SPCapitalIQ.com*

Mutual funds that invest in the stocks of small companies can boost your long-term portfolio returns—but if you choose the wrong ones, they may cause you a lot of sleepless nights. Small-cap funds have outperformed large-cap funds on average over the past five-, 10- and 15-year periods ending August 7, 2015. However, they also have experienced much greater volatility, typically falling 25% more than large-cap funds in down markets. And in 2014, they took investors on a wild ride before finally eking out a gain of less than 4% for the year, compared with 11% for large-cap funds.

So how big a role should small-cap funds play today in your investment portfolio, and which funds will likely fare best if there are rough times ahead? *See below...*

WHAT TO EXPECT

The overall stock market is facing more volatility now than in recent years, as nervous investors worry that the Federal Reserve will finally start to raise short-term interest rates. But that doesn't mean you should avoid small-cap funds. I don't foresee deep or lasting pullbacks in the near future for small-cap stocks. In fact, small companies could do relatively well. That's because, unlike many large companies, most small companies get their revenue mainly from the US rather than exports, and the US economy, though hardly on fire, is doing very well compared with the economies of many other major countries. The US economy is expected to grow 3.4% in 2015, its fastest pace since 2005.

The key is to find steady small-cap funds that curb excessive volatility enough that you can stick with them through ups and downs.

What I look for...

- **Experienced managers** who use a reliable, disciplined stock-picking style that has worked in the past and can work in the future.
- **Low beta.** A fund's beta measures its volatility compared with that of the overall stock market. It captures the fund's sensitivity to market swings, typically against a benchmark like the Standard & Poor's 500 stock index. The higher a fund's beta, the more volatile it has been relative to the index. For example, if a small-cap fund has a beta of 1.25, that means whenever the S&P 500 moves up or down 10%, the fund is expected to swing 12.5%. You want funds with betas around 1 or less, indicative of similar or lower volatility compared with the S&P 500.
- **Top long-term returns.** Do not sacrifice performance for safety. A small-cap fund that takes few chances can have a very low beta... but mediocre returns. Focus on funds that have had returns that rank high among their peers and that have beaten the S&P 500 over the past several years.

MY FAVORITE SMALL-CAP FUNDS

Small companies—those that have a stock market value of $2.5 billion or less—make up about 10% of the overall stock market, so that's a good starting point for your own portfolio allocation. Aggressive investors may want to have greater exposure and conservative investors less.

The five no-load mutual funds below are all rated four or five stars by my research firm, S&P Capital IQ. The funds for moderately aggressive investors tend to be slightly more volatile than the S&P 500, but their superior returns can make them worth a bit more risk. The ones for conservative investors have about the same volatility as the S&P 500 or less, so over time you get better performance without taking on any additional risk...

MODERATELY AGGRESSIVE INVESTORS

- **Brown Advisory Small-Cap Fundamental Value Fund (BIAUX)** looks for companies that generate strong cash flow year after year and have little or no debt. Their stock prices are low either because they are misunderstood or overshadowed by sexier, faster-growing companies. In fact, the fund has a knack for selecting businesses that get taken over by larger companies at significant premiums to their share prices.

Recent top holdings: Convenience store distributor Core-Mark...Broadridge Financial Solutions, which provides back-office processing for banks and brokerage firms. *Performance*: 16.7%.*

- **Pax World Small Cap Fund (PXSCX)** proves that investing with a conscience can provide top returns even in the small-cap category. This socially responsible fund doesn't just

*Performance figures are for three years through August 7, 2015.

avoid "sin stocks," such as companies that provide alcohol or benefit from gambling. Manager Nathan Moser searches for companies that are highly profitable but also encourage diversity in the workplace and improve the quality of life in communities in which they operate. The fund reduces risk by trimming back each stock as soon as it reaches what Moser considers fair value...and investing the proceeds in a more undervalued security.

Recent top holdings: Capitol Federal Financial, a 120-year-old community bank that is one of the top lenders in the state of Kansas... Hologic, a manufacturer of diagnostic and surgical products for women's health care. *Performance*: 18.0%.

• **Wasatch Core Growth Fund (WGROX)** invests in about 60 companies that fund manager J.B. Taylor expects to deliver steady earnings growth of at least 15% a year despite the economy's ups and downs. Taylor likes to make the occasional bold pick if he thinks it will pay off, such as a biotech or cloud-computing company, but he mostly sticks with high-quality growth stocks and hangs on to winners even as they turn into medium-sized companies.

Recent top holdings: Copart Inc., which auctions vehicles over the Internet...discount airline Allegiant Air...and marketing-services company Cimpress. *Performance*: 17.3%.

CONSERVATIVE INVESTORS

• **Mairs & Power Small Cap Fund (MSCFX)** is a young fund, launched in 2011, with an intriguing pedigree. It uses the same buy-and-hold procedure as its low-volatility, multicap sibling, the Mairs & Power Growth Fund, which has beaten the S&P 500 over the past 20 years by an average of three percentage points annually. Over the past three-year period, the small-cap fund ranks in the top half of its category. It invests two-thirds of its assets in companies headquartered in the Midwest, so the fund managers, based in St. Paul, Minnesota, can easily visit and get to know top management. The fund leans toward well-run industrial and technology companies that have long-term competitive advantages in their industries.

Recent top holdings: Cray, which makes supercomputers for clients such as the Mayo Clinic and the US government...Gentherm, a manufacturer of heated seats for the automobile industry. *Performance*: 15.7%.

• **Value Line Small Cap Opportunities Fund (VLEOX)** has a well-diversified portfolio of 100 to 120 small-cap growth and value stocks based on the ranking system created by its venerable parent, the investment research firm Value Line. The system, which is designed to reduce volatility while boosting performance, considers only companies with a record of 10 years or more of consistent earnings and stock price growth.

Recent top holdings: Commercial cookware manufacturer Middleby Corp...LED lighting maker Acuity Brands...and Lennox International, a global supplier of climate-control products. *Performance*: 17.6%.

Balanced Funds for Cautious Investors

Janet M. Brown, president of FundX Investment Group, San Francisco, and managing editor of *NoLoad FundX. FundX.com*

Many investors never bother adjusting their portfolios to restore their desired balance of stocks versus bonds. But there is a type of mutual fund that does the rebalancing for you.

Balanced funds invest in both stocks and bonds—in many cases, around 60% large-cap stocks and 40% high-quality government and corporate bonds, although many balanced funds have leeway to stray from the standard mix. This formula provides a cushion of safety along with potential for strong gains and significant yields. You even might choose a balanced fund as your only fund.

Three attractive balanced funds...

• **Hennessy Equity and Income (HEIFX),** which outperformed 93% of funds in its category over the past five years, keeps about 60% of its portfolio in stocks, especially dividend-paying stocks. It puts the rest in bonds and cash and is willing to hold higher levels of cash than most other balanced funds do, recently about 6.5% of total assets. *10-year annualized return:* 7.4%.*

• **Fidelity Puritan (FPURX)** has outperformed 92% of funds in its category over the past five years by combining an aggressive stock strategy with a cautious bond strategy. It emphasizes blue chip growth stocks such as Apple. *10-year annualized return:* 7.2%.

• **Dodge & Cox Balanced (DODBX),** which can devote as much as 75% or as little as 25% of its portfolio to stocks, outperformed 97% of funds in its category over the past five years. It tends to be more volatile than the standard balanced fund and often invests in out-of-favor stocks, including Hewlett-Packard and Target. *10-year annualized return:* 6.5%.

*Annualized returns as of August 7, 2015.

Beyond Stocks and Bonds: The Alternative Investments You Need

Charles Zhang, CFP, managing partner at Zhang Financial, a financial advisory firm in Portage, Michigan. *Barron's* has ranked Zhang as one of the nation's Top 100 Financial Advisors nine times since the list's inception in 2004. *ZhangFinancial.com*

Jitters about the stock market and the bond market have many investors wondering whether it's time to include some other types of investments in their portfolios.

Leading financial adviser Charles Zhang says that some of these so-called "alternative investments" will do well because they are among the few bargains left in the investment world...and because inflation will start to rise, hurting the stock and bond markets. *Here, Zhang explains how to use alternative investments and which ones to choose...*

SOARING INFLATION AHEAD

If you're willing to move just a little outside the comfort zone of traditional holdings, then adding certain alternative investments is likely to stabilize your portfolio and improve overall performance. It's true that alternative investments carry their own risks. They can be volatile and hard to understand, and with inflation still low, they generally have been weak in recent years. But alternative investments have proved to be valuable diversifiers when mixed with other investments.

I am convinced that this kind of diversification will be vital over the next few years, especially for older and retired investors.

Reason: It's likely we will face the highest inflation in decades, a period of rising prices that will erode the buying power of your money. That's because powerful, global economic forces are aligning to start pushing up inflation. These forces include the end of cheap labor costs from emerging markets that have kept the price of consumer goods low for years...and the willingness among developed nations to pay off their massive debts by, in effect, printing new money rather than curbing spending.

Rising inflation typically is followed by higher interest rates, which hurt the value of most bonds that you already own and eventually stocks as well. But, certain types of alternative investments actually thrive on inflation.

In the next few years, I expect inflation to rise to 5% or higher. That's why I am investing in the alternatives described below. They all have very little correlation with, or move in the opposite direction of, the broad stock and bond markets, and each one provides different kinds of protection and opportunities.

Remember, the time to buy inflation insurance is when it's cheap, and in my view, these alternatives now are selling at bargain prices.

WHAT TO BUY

The particular investments that you choose are as important as the category. I generally use funds, but I avoid funds that use highly complex strategies, charge high fees and/or make it difficult to gauge the risk you're taking. These include "leveraged" funds that use borrowed money to invest...funds that short (bet against) specific investments...and hedge funds, which often charge high fees and lock up investors' money for extended periods of time.

Instead, I prefer low-cost exchange-traded funds (ETFs) that I can buy and sell as easily as stocks and that allow me to see exactly what I am investing in. For a typical investor, it might make sense to buy equal amounts of each of the following three funds plus Treasury Inflation-Protected Securities (TIPS), as described below, so that they constitute a total of 20% of your overall investment portfolio (5% in each category). *Some of my favorites...*

• **Vanguard REIT Index ETF (VNQ).** Over the past 15 years, shares of real estate funds have outperformed US stocks, returning 9.7% annualized versus 4.3% for the Standard & Poor's 500 stock index.* Their high dividends also make them attractive as income providers. Real estate investment trusts (REITs) can be particularly appealing in inflationary periods because rents and real estate values tend to climb with rising prices. This Vanguard ETF tracks the MSCI US REIT Index, which includes office, mall, health-care, apartment, industrial and hotel REITs. *Recent yield:* 3.9%. *Annual expense ratio:* 0.12%.

• **PowerShares DB Commodity Index Tracking ETF (DBC).** Commodities can be volatile, and their subpar short-term performance has left them extremely undervalued. Overall, they lost 32% in 2013 and have lost an average of 5% annually over the past five years as of August 7, 2015. But commodities are likely to be one of the best-performing investments in periods of fast-rising inflation because the prices of raw materials used to make consumer goods tend to soar. This fund uses futures contracts to track the prices of 14 different commodities, mostly oil and gas, agriculture and industrial metals. *Annual expense ratio:* 0.86%.

• **SPDR Gold Shares ETF (GLD).** After peaking above $1,900 per ounce, gold now trades for around $1,100 per ounce. Gold's longer-term performance is equally dismal. Since 1980, it has gained an average of 3.4% annually. But in a limited strategic role as portfolio insurance, owning gold still makes sense. Although gold prices don't increase directly with inflation, they do tend to move in the opposite direction of the US dollar's value on global currency markets—and if inflation in the US spikes, the value of the dollar typically depreciates against the other major currencies. *Annual expense ratio:* 0.4%.

TAKE NOTE...

Good *and* Bad Wines Can Be Good Investments

Wines from Haut-Brion, Lafite-Rothschild, Latour, Margaux and Mouton Rothschild outperformed government bonds from 1900 to 2012, although they underperformed equities. In the first few decades, great vintages rose in value quickly, but wines from mediocre and even bad vintages started to catch up after about 50 years.

Reason: A 100-year-old wine of any vintage is rarely drunk...the bottles look good on display... and both good and bad vintages are scarce after a century.

Study by three finance professors, published in *Social Science Research Network.*

A DIFFERENT KIND OF BOND INVESTMENT

Treasury Inflation-Protected Securities (TIPS) are bonds, but they are structured specifically to provide protection in the event of rising inflation. TIPS, issued by the US Treasury, pay interest twice annually based on a fixed rate. Unlike ordinary Treasuries, the principal value of TIPS adjusts up and down based on the Consumer Price Index (CPI). The payout you receive is based on the *adjusted* principal.

Example: You invest $10,000 at the beginning of the year in a new TIPS 10-year note with a 3% rate. If inflation is 1% during the first six months of that year, then by midyear the inflation-adjusted principal amount of the security will be $10,100 and you will receive the first semiannual interest payment of $151.50 ($10,100 times 3% divided by two).

While you are guaranteed to receive the return of your principal upon maturity, TIPS do carry some risk. For example, deflation (falling prices) could cause the value of your TIPS holdings to drop before maturity. So could a sharp drop in what investors think future inflation will be. You can purchase TIPS directly at *TreasuryDirect.gov.*

*Figures as of August 7, 2015.

11 Super Shopping

Secret Consumer Scores: They're Not Credit Scores, but They Can Cost You Big

They know what you buy. They know what you eat. They know whether you're healthy.

"They" are data-tracking and analysis companies, and they compile files full of highly personal information about you. These files are used to assign you "consumer scores"—different from your credit scores—that lenders, insurers, marketers, employers and other businesses use to size you up and decide whether they want to work with you at all and, if so, under what terms.

AnalyticsIQ, for example, which is one of the tracking companies, has a score called RiskIQ...and ScoreLogix offers the Job Security Score, which predicts the stability of your income.

Laws eventually might be passed guaranteeing consumers the right to see all of their scores and the data used to calculate them. *But until that happens, here are nine strategies you can use to increase your secret scores...*

SPENDING STRATEGIES

Your purchases play a major role in calculating many of your secret scores. Marketing companies use scores based on your spending habits to decide how to target you. Credit card issuers and other lenders use them to determine what terms to offer you. The things that you buy even could be used to gauge your health—with potentially significant effects. If

Note: Prices, rates and offers throughout this chapter and book are subject to change.

Pam Dixon, founder and executive director of the World Privacy Forum, a nonprofit public interest research and education group in San Diego. She is coauthor of the report "The Scoring of America: How Secret Consumer Scores Threaten Your Privacy and Your Future." *WorldPrivacyForum.org* the secret scorers decide that you're unhealthy, it might become more difficult to obtain affordable health, life or disability insurance...to land a job...or to secure appealing loan rates—lenders shy away from unhealthy people because they sometimes end up with big medical bills that they cannot pay.

For higher secret scores...

• **Don't pay with a credit card, debit card or check if you don't want a purchase to count against you.** The companies that compile the data used in secret scores can link a purchase to you only if you pay with one of those methods or if you use a customer loyalty card. *Times to pay with cash...*

• If you buy alcohol or tobacco or gamble at a casino or racetrack. Such purchases can have a very negative effect on consumer and health scores.

• If you buy books about health problems and/or addictions. Pay with cash even if it's a friend or relative who has the problem. But use credit or debit cards to buy books about exercise and fitness.

• **Buy clothes.** Believe it or not, this will boost the scores that gauge your health. People who care enough about their appearance to regularly buy new clothes also tend to care enough about their appearance to eat well and live a healthy lifestyle. If you don't often buy new clothes for yourself, boost your scores by buying clothing as gifts for others.

Exceptions: Don't overdo the clothes shopping. People who spend excessive amounts on clothes in relation to their incomes might be viewed as undisciplined, something that is considered a negative for both health and consumer scores. How much clothes shopping is too much varies from score to score, but if you suspect that you spend more on clothing than most people in your income bracket, use cash or gift cards to make some of your purchases.

Tip: Always use cash or gift cards when buying plus-size clothing. Plus-size clothing buyers are likely to be considered more unhealthy in determining health scores.

• **Make a purchase at an elite department store.** Each year, make at least one purchase from a high-end department store such as Neiman Marcus, Nordstrom or Saks Fifth Avenue. This will elevate you to "elite shopper" status with certain consumer scores, a potentially significant score increase.

• **Join a club.** Use a debit or credit card to pay for membership in a social club, such as a bridge club or theatergoers group, and/or to make ongoing purchases related to a safe hobby—gardening or golfing, for example. Club memberships and extended participation in safe hobbies tend to be viewed as signs of discipline and engagement. Disciplined, engaged people are considered more likely to pay their bills on time and take care of their health.

HEALTH STRATEGIES

To avoid damaging your scores by being viewed as unhealthy...

• **Pay for fitness activities.** That can include subscribing to a hiking magazine or a health-related newsletter...joining a gym...or even purchasing running shoes, hiking shoes, exercise apparel or sporting gear. Making a few purchases each year that suggest you're interested in fitness or an outdoor activity will have a very positive effect on secret scores that gauge your health.

• **Do not register with your real name or regular e-mail address on health-oriented websites or complete their surveys.** Health sites often sell the data they collect about their users to the companies that compile secret scores. Your scores are likely to suffer if you disclose a health problem on a health site's survey—or even just investigate a health problem.

Exception: It is OK to use health sites to research health conditions if you have not registered with your real name and/or regular e-mail address or filled out a survey that personally identifies you.

• **Fill prescriptions related to chronic health conditions well before your current supply of the medication runs out.** If you wait until the last minute to refill these prescriptions, it might be taken as a sign that you are not managing your condition responsibly and perhaps that you are not disciplined and/or health conscious.

• **Deny companies the right to access your Obamacare Individual Health Risk Score.** This score was calculated for you if you signed up for health insurance through an Affordable Care Act (ACA) marketplace. It does not affect your health insurance rates—it's used to compensate insurance companies that end up with especially unhealthy pools of policyholders. But if your low score becomes known outside the ACA system, it can have far-reaching implications for your employability, loan rates, insurance rates and more.

If someone asks for your permission to obtain your Obamacare score—or asks you to obtain your score and pass it along—don't do it. True, the company that is asking for this score might be less likely to work with you if you don't comply, but denying it access to your score reduces the odds that your low score will be distributed to other companies outside the ACA system. Point out that the scores are meant just for insurers.

NEIGHBORHOOD STRATEGY

Some secret scores judge you based on your neighbors. Evaluating people based on the neighborhoods they live in is nothing new—zip codes have long been used to help set insurance rates, for example. But such evaluations have historically been done based on a wide area. Now they might be done based on areas as small as a "census block," which could be just a few residences in a rural area. When you shop for a new home, lean toward a relatively small home on an upscale street rather than one of the nicest homes on a lesser street. Living in a more upscale area will improve your secret scores, and as a bonus, homes in nicer areas tend to be easier to resell.

EASY-TO-DO...

Trick to Spend Less

You know not to go to the grocery store hungry—you'll buy more. Well, walking into a mall hungry causes you to buy more nonfood items. In fact, hungry participants spent 64% more in a department store than participants who were not hungry. Eat before any type of shopping, even online shopping.

Study led by researchers at University of Minnesota, St. Paul, published in *PNAS*.

Don't Be a Victim of "Decision Fatigue"

Karen Larson, editor of *Bottom Line/Personal*, 281 Tresser Blvd., Stamford, Connecticut 06901. *BottomLine Personal.com*

Recently, I bought expensive eyeglasses that I don't like. I wanted a pair that would work with my prescription—I'm very nearsighted and also need progressives—and look good. I tried on many, many pairs. Finally I just picked one.

It turns out that my poor selection was due to "decision fatigue." Making multiple decisions saps our mental energy much more than we tend to realize, leaving us primed for poor choices. That's why car salespeople ask us to make so many decisions about our new vehicle's color and options before they recommend overpriced extras such as underbody rust protection and extended warranties, explains Roy F. Baumeister, PhD, a psychology professor at Florida State University, Tallahassee, and co-author of the best-seller *Willpower*.

Ways to fight decision fatigue...

• **Make big decisions first thing in the morning.** That's when our mental energy is highest. Soon after lunch is another good time. Make only one or two big decisions a day.

• **Have a snack.** Choose a candy bar if you need a rapid but brief rebound in decision-making ability...or a high-protein snack such as almonds for a longer-term but slower-starting boost.

• **Divide important decisions into several sessions.** For example, don't make all of your estate-planning decisions in one sitting.

• **Look for signs of decision fatigue,** such as making choices that avoid change...being less open to compromise...focusing on one factor, such as price...or making snap decisions instead of thinking things through.

What Stores Do to Encourage Buying

Some common tricks stores use to promote buying…

In display windows, mannequins appear to be looking to the left or right to make eye contact with shoppers walking by. Stores use floral or citrus scents, which encourage longer browsing…or vanilla or lavender to make shoppers feel relaxed. Fresh lemon and grassy scents are used in dressing rooms as distractions from the odors of previous customers. The music piped in is newer versions of what was popular with a store's target customers when they were 18, to encourage nostalgia and comfort. Product placement matters—a $20 item seems like a bargain if placed next to a $40 one. And red ink makes sale signs look more compelling.

Self-defense: Always bring a list. And shop alone—people shopping with others spend 7% to 17% more. Also, never make a major purchase without waiting, preferably overnight.

Kiplinger's Personal Finance. Kiplinger.com

Traps Retailers Set for Consumers

Satisfaction guaranteed may mean full refunds anytime, but it also can mean returns are allowed only for an exchange—and if the exchange is also unsatisfactory, you are out of luck. *Going out of business* may be phony—some stores go out of business, change their names and reopen. And going-out-of-business prices are not always lower than those at other stores or online. *Free* is a powerful word—but the regular price of an item must be high to allow the retailer to give something free with it. And items offered for free may come with other charges—for instance, high shipping costs.

Self-defense: Read store policies before making a purchase. Comparison shop at other stores and online—and if you like a retailer, ask if it will match a price you found elsewhere. If you do not know a retailer, search online for customer comments on it.

ConsumerReports.org

Companies with the Worst/Best Customer Service

In a survey of the quality of customer service at 150 of America's best-known companies in 15 industries, each of these firms earned a "poor" service rating—Citigroup, Wells Fargo, AT&T, AOL, Time Warner Cable, DirecTV, Dish Network, Sprint, Comcast and Bank of America.

Companies with the best customer service include: Amazon, Hilton Worldwide, Marriott International, Chick-fil-A, American Express, Trader Joe's, UPS, Sony, Hewlett-Packard and Apple.

To see the entire list, go to *247WallSt.com.*

Survey of 2,500 adults done by Zogby Analytics, a research survey group based in Lake Luzerne, New York, published on *247WallSt.com.*

Easy Tracking of Online Prices

Camelcamelcamel.com lets you set up price watches on *Amazon.com* products. It alerts you when prices change, and you can browse products with the biggest price drops.

Recent example: A Hoover vacuum dropped $56 over 30 days.

Also consider: *InvisibleHand*, a browser extension for Chrome, Firefox and Safari. When you land on a page selling a product, it automatically searches the web for the lowest price.

Money.com

Compare Online and In-Store Prices

I've started saving a lot of money by comparing online and in-store prices at the same store. Major retailers increasingly are offering different prices online than in their own stores. This seems to be particularly common at Walmart, Sears and Kmart. When I helped a friend replace his major kitchen appliances last summer, I found that he could save $550 by buying at *Sears.com*, compared with buying the same appliances in a Sears store. When I shopped for a barbecue grill at Kmart, I saved around $80 by buying in a store rather than at *Kmart.com*. The only way to know is to visit both the website and the store. If you have a smartphone, you can check the online price while in the store. If the online price is lower, some stores match it.

Edgar Dworsky, an attorney as well as founder of the consumer advocate websites *ConsumerWorld.org* and *MousePrint.org*. Formerly, he served as consumer education consultant for the Federal Trade Commission and was an assistant attorney general in Massachusetts.

TAKE NOTE...

Never Say This to Customer Service

Do not say to customer service that you will never use the company's products again—reps are trying to retain customers and have little reason to help you if you say you will no longer be one. And do not say that you are going to the media—only higher-ups, not ordinary reps, will care, and then only if you can show you have thoroughly researched the press and know where to go to have an impact. Don't threaten to call your lawyer when speaking to a customer service representative. If you are serious, there is no value to saying this—if not, you gain nothing and will probably just be disconnected.

Also: Do not threaten to get the rep fired or to bankrupt the company—those are empty claims.

AARP.org

A Helpful Price-Comparison Tool

The Walmart price-comparison tool gives refunds if you would have paid less elsewhere for selected items.

How it works: You log into the *Savings Catcher* at Walmart's website (*Walmart.com*), and then enter the receipt number—Savings Catcher searches print and online ads from major area retailers and gives you a gift card for the difference if it finds a lower price. The tool compares 80,000 food and household items—but not weighed items such as meat and produce and not clothes or electronics. And comparisons are with only brick-and-mortar stores, not online retailers. The competitor's lower price must have been advertised on the date of your purchase for you to get a refund.

The Washington Post. WashingtonPost.com

Retailers That Credit You If a Price Drops

Within 30 days: *Backcountry.com.*

Within 15 days: Best Buy.

Within 14 days: Anthropologie, Banana Republic, Express, Gap, Hollister, The Limited, Macy's, Old Navy, Sears.

Within 10 days: Meijer.

Within seven days: The Children's Place, Gymboree, J.Crew, Kmart, Target, Walmart.

Other stores may have their own policies. Rules vary—refunds may be given only if you originally paid full price for the item without a coupon and have the receipt to prove it. Seasonal items, storewide sales, promotional events and other special situations may be excluded. And policies may change at any time.

Helpful: Create a price alert at a website such as *TrackIf.com*—the site will send you an e-mail if an item you are tracking goes on sale.

Kiplinger.com

Cash-Back Websites

Cash-back websites give you back a portion of the money you spend online. Savings vary—check out multiple sites to decide which to use.

Examples: *ShopatHome.com* offers 5% to 10% back from more than 3,000 sellers. *Ebates.com* provides coupon codes, and users earn 5% to 10% cash back on some purchases. *FatWallet.com* sends e-mail alerts about deals and offers cash back from hundreds of stores. *Swagbucks.com* offers cash back for shopping and gives out its own virtual currency (that can be redeemed for gift cards) as rewards for searching, taking surveys and other activities. *MyPoints.com* offers points that can be redeemed for cash, gift cards and travel miles. *MrRebates.com* gives cash-back rebates of up to 30% and a $5 bonus after a user's first purchase. *Upromise.com* offers credits redeemable for cash or directed to a college savings plan or to pay down student loans.

GoBankingRates.com

Coupons Galore

To get online coupon codes, go to coupon sites such as *CouponSherpa.com, DealNews.com, Promocodes.com, RetailMeNot.com* and *Savings.com.* Also call customer service to ask whether any unpublished coupon codes are available, and visit retailers' websites—stores often display codes on their home pages.

Best times to get coupons: First of the month—retailers offer more coupons then, and most are good all month...early in the week—many stores release offers on Sunday...around major holidays—usually about two weeks in advance...August and October—those months have more coupons than average.

Another idea: Consider following retailers on Facebook or Twitter—followers sometimes get one-day sales and giveaways.

For free-shipping offers, try *FreeShipping.org.*

Money.MSN.com

The Easiest Money You'll Ever Save

Karen Larson, editor of *Bottom Line/Personal,* 281 Tresser Blvd., Stamford, Connecticut 06901. *BottomLinePersonal.com*

One short phone call saved me $1,200. My family of four was paying a hefty $248 per month for cellular service. Then I saw a TV ad for a much lower-cost family plan. Though it was for new customers and I was locked into a contract, I called my provider anyway. I asked to get that rate—and got it, without any hassle at all. The new plan saves me $100 a month—$1,200 a year.

Many people can easily—and dramatically—trim their cell phone bills these days, says Clark Howard, host of *The Clark Howard Show,* a syndicated radio program about saving money. Cellular rates are falling fast—so fast that anyone who obtains cellular service through a major provider who hasn't shopped around for a lower rate in the past year almost certainly can save a bundle by just calling his/her provider and asking if a lower rate is available.

Two more easy discounts...

- **Pay TV.** Call your cable- or satellite-TV provider and say that you would like to discontinue your service. Odds are very good that a customer-retention employee will offer you a discount of perhaps 15% to 20% to stay. (This often works with Internet service as well.)
- **Bricks-and-mortar retailers.** An increasing number of retailers, including Target and Best Buy, now match major Internet retailers' prices. If you have a smartphone, you don't even have to research lower prices in advance. Use a free smartphone shopping app such as *RedLaser* (*RedLaser.com*) to find a lower online price in seconds, then show your phone to a customer service rep.

DID YOU KNOW THAT...

Cable-TV Subscribers Watch Very Few of the Channels They Pay For

An average American television household only watches around 18 of the 189 channels it gets. Some consumer groups advocate "unbundling," in which consumers would pay for only the channels they watch—but cable companies say that would result in consumers paying about the same for fewer channels.

The Nielsen Company, which provides data about what people watch, New York City.

Beware of These Plumber Tricks

We all need a plumber at one time or another. *What to watch out for...*

Some unlicensed and uninsured plumbers offer lower prices—but then you have nowhere to turn if work is poor, and an inspector could make you tear out a job and redo it. A sight-unseen estimate is a danger sign of a less-than-reputable plumber—always get an in-person inspection and written quote. Beware of bait-and-switch tactics—get the make and model numbers of parts to be used, in writing, with your estimate. Do not use a plumber who asks for cash—this is dishonest tax evasion and could mean dishonesty in the work, too. Bills may be padded by sending extra plumbers—have the estimate state how many people the job requires. High charges for the first hour may be justified, but if your job takes less than an hour, have the plumber do small ones during the same time.

Roundup of experts on plumbing scams, reported at *MoneyTalksNews.com.*

Protect Yourself Against Shoddy Repairs

If a problem arises with an appliance, contact the manufacturer first—the issue may be a common one for which the manufacturer has developed a fix, possibly at no cost. If you do need someone to do the repair and do not have a relationship with an appropriate person or shop, ask the manufacturer to recommend a repair person in your area and ask people you know for recommendations. Also check out companies with the Better Business Bureau, and verify that the repair shop meets state licensing requirements.

Get a diagnosis and written cost estimate before repairs are done. If you do authorize repairs, ask for the old parts back if they are not too big or bulky and need not be returned to the manufacturer—this can encourage a repair person to be more thorough and reduces the likelihood of fraud.

When the job is done, pay with a credit card so that you can contact the card issuer in case of problems.

ConsumerReports.org

Solar Power Becoming More Affordable

The cost of residential solar panels has dropped by 7% a year since 2000. Several lenders now provide low-interest, no-money-down solar loans. And homes with owned, not leased, solar panels often sell for almost $25,000 more than comparable houses without solar panels.

Roundup of experts on solar power, reported at *Money.*

Simple Ways to Lower Air-Conditioning Costs

To lower the expense of air-conditioning...

- **Close curtains or shades during the day on windows that face south or west,** to block solar heat. *Savings:* 3% to 5%.

- **Leave inside doors and air-conditioning vents open,** so air can flow freely. Do not put furniture in front or on top of vents. *Savings:* Up to 20%.

• **Open windows on cool nights,** but only when the humidity is below 60%. *Savings:* Up to 3%.

Money. Money.CNN.com

The Showerhead That Saves You Money

Save $75 a year in wasted hot water by installing a *Ladybug Shower-Head Adapter,* available at *EvolveShowerheads.com* and at *Amazon.com* for about $30. The adapter slows water to a trickle as soon as it is warm, so if you tend to wait a long time before you get into the shower, you'll stop wasting hot water. Pull a chain to return water to full flow when you are ready to shower.

Consumer Reports Money Adviser. ConsumerReports.org

Renovating? The Latest Home Materials Look Good, Save Money

The latest home materials save money, look good and reduce maintenance...

Cellular PVC trim looks natural, can be cut and shaped like lumber, has a 25-year warranty and doesn't need painting. (Wood trim needs to be painted every five to seven years. Hiring a pro might cost you $1,500 or more.) *Fiber-cement siding* will not rot, warp or cup...it looks handcrafted...typically comes with a 30-year warranty...and needs no painting for 15 years—and then only every seven to 10 years. *Engineered quartz countertops*—chips of natural quartz mixed with high-tech resins and pigments—will last as long as your house, need only sponge cleaning, don't require sealing and will not stain from dark liquids or etch from acids. *Fiberglass entry doors* include insulating foam that is three times as energy efficient as wood.

Money.CNN.com

Cut the Cost of Renting a Moving Van

Planning a big move? *Here's how to save on the van...*

Rent early in the month and on a weekday—most people rent late in the month and on weekends, so companies tend to offer discounts at other times. Rent the smallest truck you need—bigger ones cost more, so use rental firms' online tools to estimate what size you need. *Recent example:* A six-by-12-foot trailer cost $166, versus $231 for a 14-foot truck. *Savings:* $65. Check moving companies' online message boards to find people moving to the same college or area so that you can share

MONEY SAVER...

No Need to Overpay for Good-Looking Glasses

With name-brand eyeglasses, you are paying for the name, but the glasses usually are made by the same firms that make less expensive ones.

Example: Luxottica produces Chanel, Prada and Versace glasses, which can cost $350 or more—and also ones for LensCrafters, Pearle Vision, Sears Optical and Target Optical, which can be less than $100.

Better: Instead of buying from an eye doctor or optometrist, shop discount stores. Costco gets especially high satisfaction ratings. Also look online at sites such as *SimplyEyeglasses.com* and *LensesRx.com.* Stores and websites sometimes have coupons and half-price deals that can cut costs. You may have to buy two pairs, which can be a good idea in case one pair gets lost or breaks.

ConsumerReports.org

a truck—check Craigslist, too. Before buying rental firms' insurance, check your existing policies and credit cards—you may already be covered. Finally, clean and refuel the van before returning it to avoid surcharges.

Roundup of experts on moving costs, reported at *Bankrate.com.*

Hardware Help

Free ship-to-store service at hardware-store websites saves money, especially on heavy items. To better compete, many smaller hardware/supply chains across the country now allow you to purchase thousands of items online and have them shipped at no cost to the store closest to you. These include *AceHardware.com*...*DoItBest.com*...and *TrueValue.com*.

Danny Lipford, a remodeling contractor and host of the nationally syndicated TV program *Today's Homeowner with Danny Lipford*. He is based in Mobile, Alabama. *TodaysHomeowner.com*

Unusual Items You Can Rent

Items you may not know you can rent...

Chickens: Businesses rent coops and egg-laying hens for set time periods—costs vary depending on the company and length of the rental. One company offered a $180 rental of two hens and a coop for four weeks. Expect about six eggs a week per chicken.

Lego sets: *Pley.com* charges $19.99 and up per month to deliver a set to your home—you can keep the set as long as you want, then exchange it for another.

Designer handbags: *BagBorroworSteal.com* rents costly purses by the month.

Caskets: Many funeral homes will rent a casket for viewing or services for $750 to $900—compared with $2,000 to $5,000 to buy one.

Kiplinger.com

Big Discounts on Some Fragrances

Fragrance refills are offered in some retail stores at up to 40% less than the cost of purchasing the same bottled fragrance. The refill trend is intended to bring customers to the stores so that they will buy more products—and to drive brand loyalty to refillable fragrances. Look up "fragrance fountain" to find a location or put the name of the perfume and the word "refill" in any search engine.

Karen Grant, analyst who tracks the beauty industry for the research firm NPD Group, quoted online at *MarketWatch.com.*

Beware Counterfeit Perfumes

Fraudulent perfumes may contain toxic ingredients—arsenic, carcinogenic chemicals such as DEHP and even urine.

Self-defense: Look carefully at the packaging, which usually differs slightly from authentic brands. And avoid products advertised as "limited editions" and sold at significantly lower prices than original brands. Also note the color—too pale, it probably has too much alcohol...too dark, too many toxic chemicals.

Report by Federal Bureau of Investigation, Washington, DC.

Better Flatware Buying

Look for flatware labeled "18/10" for durability. The numbers refer to the chromium and nickel content that helps the flatware maintain its shine and resist corrosion. Inexpensive flatware may be listed as 18/0—so it is likely to stain easily and lose its shine quickly.

Caution: Many vendors selling online do not disclose chromium and nickel amounts.

DailyFinance.com

Easy Sticky Tag Remover

To remove a tag from china or glass, put the item in a bowl, pot or the sink. Dribble about one-quarter cup of white vinegar onto the tag. Then pour just-boiled water on the spot, enough to cover the sticky area. Let cool. The tag should rub off easily.

Joan Wilen and Lydia Wilen, authors of *Bottom Line's Treasury of Home Remedies & Natural Cures* and the free e-letter at *HouseholdMagicDailyTips.com*.

CONSUMER SMARTS...

Little-Known Trick from Cereal Makers

Cereal-box characters are designed to make eye contact to build brand loyalty. Characters on cereals intended for adults, which usually are placed on upper store shelves, generally look straight ahead or slightly up to make eye contact with adults. Characters on child-oriented cereals look slightly downward to make eye contact with kids.

Study by researchers at Cornell Food and Brand Lab, Ithaca, New York, published in *Environment and Behavior.*

Companies Are Diluting Products to Boost Profits

Edgar Dworsky, an attorney as well as founder of the consumer advocate websites *ConsumerWorld.org* and *MousePrint.org*. Formerly, he served as a consumer education consultant for the Federal Trade Commission and was an assistant attorney general in Massachusetts.

Next time you shop for a whole chicken or boneless chicken breasts in a supermarket meat section, give the labels a quick read. Buried in the small print of some, you might find phrases like "enhanced with up to 15% chicken broth." The poultry company has pumped fluid into the chicken to increase its weight. Some of that chicken you're paying for actually is water.

Consumer-products manufacturers typically have three ways to boost profits on each unit sold. They can increase prices...reduce the amount of product included in the package but charge the same price...or dilute the product by replacing expensive ingredients with cheaper ones. That third option has been popular of late. *Examples...*

- **A new nonconcentrated version of Dawn dish detergent called Dawn Simply Clean** looks like well-known Dawn Ultra on store shelves but is more watery. A larger quantity must be used to get dishes clean.
- **Some varieties of Breyers "ice cream" are no longer officially ice cream.** Breyers has reduced its butterfat content by so much that by FDA rule, it must be called "light ice cream" or "frozen dairy dessert" instead. This is not a "diet" product. Breyers has another line that is labeled "½ the fat."
- **Procter & Gamble recently started selling certain varieties of Tide liquid detergent** in 92-ounce jugs, an 8% reduction from past 100-ounce jugs, even as prices climbed. On top of this, the new bottles wash 48 loads, compared with 60 loads for the old ones, a 20% drop that exceeds the 8% reduction in detergent quantity. This suggests that the detergent might have been diluted.

What to do: Pay close attention to labels and ingredients, particularly when a product you have purchased many times doesn't seem to be as effective or enjoyable as in the past. Or type this disappointing product's name into a search engine to see if other consumers are voicing similar complaints. Call or e-mail consumer-products companies to complain when you purchase a diluted product. They might send you coupons good for free products.

Free Apps That Help You Save on Groceries

Cellfire delivers deals and digital coupons on your smartphone. *Checkout 51* lets you get rebates by buying featured groceries—take a picture of your receipt, and the rebate is added to your account, from which you can request a check when the total reaches $20. *Ibotta* is similar but pays out at $10. *Coupon Sherpa* adds coupons daily and uses your phone's GPS to find deals at stores near your location. *Favado* compares prices among local stores and notifies you when favorite brands go on sale. *Grocery iQ* lets you build a shopping list from a searchable database and manage different lists for different stores. *mySupermarket* compares prices among retailers and sends price alerts. *SnipSnap* turns physical coupons into scannable bar codes and lets you know when you enter a store for which you have coupons.

All these apps are available for Apple and Android.

DailyFinance.com

Beware: Most Food Coupons Promote Processed Foods

In a recent analysis, 25% of online coupons were for snack foods such as chips, crackers and desserts…14% for frozen dinners and other prepared meals…and 12% for beverages (half of which were for sugary juices and drinks). Only 3% were for fruits and vegetables, and 4% for milk, eggs or yogurt.

Study of 1,056 online coupons from six grocery chains, published in *Preventing Chronic Disease.*

Automatic Billing: What Happens When Your Credit Card Expires

When you give a merchant your credit card number for automatic billing, that merchant can no longer charge you after your card expires or the card number changes. Your credit card issuer will not give your new information to a service provider even if you've agreed to be autobilled.

When a company with which you have an account submits a credit card charge, it must provide your name and billing address…credit card number…expiration date…and the security code that appears on the back of the card. If any of this data is incorrect, the charge will be rejected as an "invalid transaction."

Example: If a magazine automatically renews a magazine subscription every year using your credit card information, it won't be able to do so once the card expires.

John Ulzheimer, president, *CreditSesame.com*, based in Mountain View, California, which offers free credit scores and reports to consumers. *JohnUlzheimer.com*

If You're in the Market for a New Computer…

When looking to buy a new computer, consider a "refurbished" computer from the manufacturer's website. Despite the name, these usually are new machines that were returned after purchase, often for trivial reasons—and they have been inspected more closely than machines sold as new. They cost less and carry the same warranty.

David Pogue, founder of Yahoo Tech, quoted in *AARP Bulletin.*

Do You Really Need to Register a Newly Purchased Product?

Many companies include registration cards with new products to harvest personal information that they can sell to marketers. Having your sales receipt usually is enough if you need to make a claim on the warranty, but some companies do require the registration card.

Best: Review the warranty to determine whether the registration is required. If you must send it in, give as little information as possible (leave off demographic or lifestyle information), and consider the upside to registering—the company will have your contact information in the event of a product recall.

Privacy Rights Clearinghouse, a nonprofit consumer-education organization, San Diego, reported in *Consumer Reports.*

Outlet Shopping Online

Outlet malls can be many miles away, requiring time and gas to shop at them. But retailers are making outlet deals available online. Check out Banana Republic Factory Store (at *www.BananaRepublic.com/products/banana-republic-factory-store.jsp*)...J. Crew Factory (*Factory.JCrew.com*)...Nordstrom Rack (*NordstromRack.com*)...as well as Saks Off Fifth (*SaksOff5th.com*).

Consumer Reports Money Adviser. ConsumerReports.org

Better Online Shopping

Walmart and Target can be lower-price alternatives to *Amazon.com* when shopping online. Both had generally lower prices in the categories of clothing and shoes, electronics, housewares, health and cosmetics. Walmart's prices were 10% lower than Amazon's, and Target's were 5% lower, excluding shipping costs and taxes. As when buying at physical stores, it pays to shop around.

InternetRetailer.com reporting on a year-long price-comparison study by Wells Fargo Securities LLC and price-tracking firm 360pi.

Why You May Not Get What You Pay for at Amazon

The online retailer *Amazon.com* commingles products sold by third-party merchants with what appears to be the same product sold by Amazon. This speeds shipping—when you order something, an item with the correct bar code is sent, no matter which manufacturer or merchant supplied it to Amazon. But some merchants send Amazon counterfeit versions of products rather than branded products, which may result in Amazon sending you the counterfeit version.

If you suspect you've received a subpar product or a fake: Use Amazon's return system to send it back.

The Wall Street Journal. WSJ.com

Easy Way to Get Restaurant Reservations

Get hard-to-get last-minute restaurant reservations through apps such as *Resy* and *Table8*. These services offer a guaranteed table at exclusive restaurants in a limited number of cities. Fees for reservations vary widely by city and restaurant from free to $30 or more.

Or: Ask a restaurant if you can hold a table by prepaying for your meal or making a deposit toward your food. This may be worthwhile if you want to dine somewhere special.

Kiplinger's Personal Finance. Kiplinger.com

Free Wi-Fi While You Eat or Shop

National chains are offering customers free access to Wi-Fi. Most require you to accept their terms and conditions, but you won't need a password.

Restaurants offering free Wi-Fi include Applebee's...Arby's...Chick-Fil-A...Denny's...Dunkin' Donuts...Einstein Bros...Jimmy John's...Krispy Kreme...McDonald's...Quiznos...Starbucks...Taco Bell...Tim Hortons...and Wendy's.

Retailers include Apple Store...Best Buy...Lowe's...Macy's...Meijer...Nordstrom...Office Depot...Safeway...Sam's Club...Staples...Target...and Whole Foods.

For a longer list, go to *Bit.ly/1nlT1jO*.

LifeHacker.com

FUN FREEBIES...

Birthday Freebies Worth at Least $5

ACE Hardware gives ACE Rewards members a $5-off birthday coupon. DSW gives members of its rewards program a $5 gift certificate. Black Angus Steakhouse gives a free steak dinner—with the purchase of a second main course—on a person's first birthday after he/she joins its Prime Club. Red Lobster offers a free appetizer or dessert for rewards-club members. Starbucks gives a free drink or pastry to members of its rewards club. UNO Chicago Grill gives a free entrée to rewards-program members.

Many other establishments have offers of their own—ask at ones you like.

AllYou.com

Save $$$ on a Wedding and Still Wow Your Guests

Alan and Denise Fields, authors of the best-selling book *Bridal Bargains*. Dubbed the "Wedding Watchdogs," they started writing wedding guides 24 years ago after planning their own nuptials. They live in Boulder, Colorado. *WindsorPeak.com*

If you are planning a wedding, you want it to be wonderful—but is it possible to pull that off without spending a small fortune? In the US, the average wedding comes to about $26,000. Of course, wedding-related costs vary widely depending on where you're getting married and how many people you invite. But even if you're planning a big-city celebration with a guest list that numbers in the hundreds, there are many ways to save without sacrificing style. *Here, nine of the best...*

- **Don't say this word.** When you are gathering your initial price quotes for the site rental, catering and music, you are likely to save as much as 20% if you can manage to avoid using the word "wedding." Yes, it may sound like sacrilege to a couple wanting to shout it from the rooftops, but the truth is that many vendors mark up their prices for weddings. You could call it a family reunion (it is, right?) or simply a party. Of course, you will have to spill the beans sooner or later, but you will be in a better position to bargain if you have seen first the prices other folks would have to pay.

- **Time it right.** An off-season wedding can be a win-win for all involved. Your guests are grateful to have a party on the calendar in a less busy month such as March or early November, and you can save significantly (15% or more) on everything from food to photography, venue to flowers. The busiest—and thus priciest—wedding months are May, June, September and October...the December holiday season and Valentine's Day are quite popular, too. Other time tweaks that can cut costs include setting a date that's just a few months away (most weddings are booked a year in advance, so open dates a few months out often can be had at a deep discount) or, conversely, one that's more than a year in the future. Also, consider Friday evening instead of Saturday or Sunday.

Example: At one country club outside Boston that has a 500-seat-capacity ballroom, a peak-season Saturday reception costs $17,000, while a peak-season Friday night reception costs $11,000—a savings of $6,000.

- **Be creative about location.** You can save hundreds, perhaps thousands of dollars, with creative site-sleuthing. Think like a tourist—what's interesting about where you live? Natural settings (farms, fields, vineyards, beaches and parks) range from free to inexpensive, but you need to budget for bringing everything in—including a tent in case of rain. Local landmarks (municipal buildings, airports, train stations, museums and mansions) often can be had at reasonable rates. Aquariums and zoos also can be fun. Go online and add your search term to "wedding" (*Example:* "museum wedding" and your city). You likely will bring up an unexpectedly rich and varied list of options in your area.

Bonus: If you choose a property run by a nonprofit, you may be able to deduct the rental fee.

Helpful: Don't ignore your own church or synagogue's community room. With festive decorating and romantic lighting, even the plainest room can look beautiful—and guests love the convenience of a 30-second walk to the reception.

• **Go digital on invites.** You can make a modern and earth-friendly statement by going digital rather than sending out traditional engagement announcements, save-the-dates, shower invitations, wedding invitations and thank-you notes. Many websites offer options that are inexpensive, often free—try *PaperlessPost.com* and *Evite.com*.

Example: Save an average of $97 (plus postage) for digital save-the-dates versus paper. Even if you opt for paper invitations, set up a special e-mail account for responses such as *JoeandGloria@gmail.com*.

Tip: You can set up a website for your wedding (free at *TheKnot.com* and *WeddingWire.com*). This is a great way to make sure that guests get the details right (including where you're registered), and it's fun to share your story, photos and wedding pictures later on.

• **Save on blooms.** Wholesale price clubs such as Costco and Sam's Club sell roses and other wedding flowers at 60% less than retail prices. Order them in advance, pick them up the day before the wedding and arrange them in simple containers from Michaels, Target or The Home Depot. Also, picking in-season blooms offers significant savings.

Examples: Tulips cost about $1 a stem in April but $3 in November. If you're getting married in the summer, a nearby farmers' market may supply flowers and even arrange them at a fraction of retail florist prices.

Another centerpiece option: Potted plants from garden centers.

Example: Pink hydrangeas cost $15 at Lowe's. Add a container for about $20. That's a total of $35, a savings of $65 off the standard centerpiece price of $100 (or more). On a dozen centerpieces, that's a savings of $780.

• **Serve a signature drink.** Alcohol often is the highest wedding expense. The most common way couples pay for liquor is to have an open bar, for an average cost of about $52 per guest. Serving a festive "signature drink" such as a watermelon mojito or a prickly pear cactus margarita (search *TheKnot.com* and *MarthaStewartWeddings.com* for recipes and ideas) as well as an edited selection of beer and wine comes to about $30 a person. For 150 guests, that's a savings of $3,300.

As for the champagne toast, you can save money by purchasing sparkling wine instead of French Champagne. Champagne generally starts at $30 to $40 a bottle, whereas a quality Spanish Cava or Italian Prosecco can be had for about $12 a bottle. Also, have servers fill champagne glasses half to two-thirds full—many guests take only a sip for the toast. Servers can offer more bubbly to those guests who want it.

• **Trade the cake for cupcakes.** The average wedding cake costs about $500, and one in five couples spends more than that, upward of $1,000. And that doesn't include the cutting fee when you don't use an in-house baker. The cutting fee ranges from $2 to $5 per slice for cutting, serving and cleaning up afterward. Thus many couples have embraced the cupcake craze. You can offer a variety of flavors to please every taste—and cupcakes can be displayed on a tiered cake plate to mimic a tiered traditional cake.

Tip: Instead of wedding favors, invite your guests to help themselves from a candy bar that you have stocked with your childhood favorites. You can buy these in bulk from a wholesaler and display them in a variety of glass bowls. Crate and Barrel has a nice selection, and you can use these in your home later.

• **Choose a playlist.** Guests dance as happily to a well-chosen playlist piped over a great sound system as to a DJ (average cost—$940) or a live swing band ($3,000). When you invite your guests, ask them to send in song requests with the RSVP. If your venue doesn't have a sound system, you can likely find a local DJ

BETTER WAYS...

Alternative Wedding-Registry Ideas

Who says you have to register for place settings? *Here are some great alternatives...*

- **Register at a home-improvement store** or online at *Amazon Wish List* or *MyRegistry.com*. Each lets you include items from multiple Internet sites.
- **Register at *HoneyFund.com*** to get contributions to your honeymoon.
- **Ask for donations to a goal.**

Example: Helping you buy a home, at *HatchMyHouse.com*.

- **Register at a store you already frequent for items that you buy regularly,** such as pet food or cleaning products.

If you really do not want gifts from wedding guests, designate a favorite charity and say that guests who wish to contribute can donate in your name. *JustGive.org* makes it easy.

Money.MSN.com

willing to rent one to you at a reasonable day rate (a pair of speakers plus an amp rents for about $70). If live music is a priority for you, top-notch talent can be had for far less when you hire student musicians. Put "student musicians" and your city in a search engine to find singers and bands at reasonable rates.

- **Take candids.** Wedding photography is pricey (the average cost is $2,260 for a package that covers everything from the engagement portrait to the end-of-the-evening good-byes). Ways to save include asking a camera-savvy pal to cover some of the event (say, the bridal party dressing-room scenes) while hiring a pro for a few hours of shooting—perhaps the ceremony or up through the first dance at the reception. Ask guests to contribute candid shots after the event, and make your own slide show (easily done on your computer, including music and special effects). It's fun and far more intimate than having a professional videographer—and then there's the matter of the $1,000 or more you'll save!

Avoid Funeral Overcharges

Federal law requires funeral homes to provide three pricing lists—one for all goods and services...one for caskets...and one for grave liners or outer burial containers. Ask for all three lists. Funeral homes cannot require services that are optional by law, such as embalming, and cannot insist that caskets or other items be bought from them as a condition of providing memorial services. In addition, you cannot be charged extra for services if you buy a casket elsewhere.

AARP.org

How to Get Good Dental Care for Lots Less

Jim Miller, an advocate for older Americans who writes "Savvy Senior," a weekly information column syndicated in more than 400 newspapers nationwide. Based in Norman, Oklahoma, he also offers a free senior e-news service at *SavvySenior.org*.

Taking care of your teeth these days can take a big bite out of your budget. This is especially true for the 108 million Americans who don't have dental insurance and are stuck paying full out-of-pocket expenses every time they visit a dentist. But even many people who have dental coverage often end up paying a lot for what their insurance doesn't cover.

There are a number of strategies, resources and services that can help you reduce your dental bills or maybe even get care for free. Of course, the most obvious way to reduce costs is to simply ask for a discount—many dentists will readily shave off 10% for any uninsured customers. And if you're over age 55 or 60, it is wise to ask whether there is a senior discount program, which is quite common even though it's not usually advertised.

Here are more ways to save...

JOIN A DISCOUNT PLAN

There are various plans that provide members access to networks of dentists who have agreed to offer their services at discounted rates. You pay an annual membership fee—roughly $80 to $200 a year—in exchange for 10% to 60% discounts on cleanings, crowns, implants, root canals and other procedures from participating dentists. To locate a plan, go to *DentalPlans.com* (or call 888-632-5353), the biggest resource with more than 40 dental discount plans listed. You can search by zip code and get a breakdown of the discounts offered in your area.

Another discount option currently available only in the southern California area is Brighter. It provides free access to a network of dentists offering an average discount of 35% on services. Call 888-230-5305, or go to *Brighter.com.*

CONSIDER MEDICARE ADVANTAGE

If you are a Medicare beneficiary, you already may know that original Medicare (Part A and Part B) and Medigap supplemental policies do not cover most dental care—but there are some Medicare Advantage (Part C) plans that do. Many of these plans, which are sold through private insurance companies, cover routine dental care along with vision care, hearing care and prescription drugs, in addition to all of your hospital and medical insurance. To find Medicare Advantage plans in your area that offer dental care, call 800-633-4227 or go to *Medicare.gov/find-a-plan*.

You can switch from original Medicare to a Medicare Advantage plan each year during the open-enrollment period, which is between October 15 and December 7. Or, if you are about to enroll in Medicare for the first time, you may want to consider a Medicare Advantage plan that covers dental.

USE A DENTAL SCHOOL

To get dental care at a reduced price, find a college or university near you that has a dental school. Most of the 65 accredited dental schools in the US and Puerto Rico offer comprehensive care provided by dental students who are overseen by experienced, qualified teachers. You can expect to pay about half of what a traditional dentist would charge and still receive excellent, well-supervised care.

Or, if you want to get your teeth cleaned, you can check with local colleges that offer dental-hygiene programs. For training purposes, most of the 335 US programs provide supervised dental cleanings by their students for 50% to 75% less than you would pay at a dentist's office.

To locate dental schools or dental-hygiene programs in your area, visit *ADA.org/dental schools*.

DENTAL BENEFITS FOR VETERANS

The US Department of Veterans Affairs provides free dental care to certain veterans who have a service-connected dental condition or disability...and to former prisoners of war. To learn more about this benefit and the eligibility requirements, call 877-222-8387 or visit *VA.gov/dental*.

If you're not eligible for its free dental care, the VA also is now offering a national VA Dental Insurance Program that gives you the option to buy dental insurance through Delta Dental (*DeltaDentalVAdip.org*) and MetLife (*MetLife.com/vadip*) at a reduced cost. To be eligible, you must be a veteran enrolled in the VA health-care program or an individual enrolled in the VA's Civilian Health and Medical Program. To find out more about these last two programs, including eligibility, call 877-222-8387 or visit *VA.gov/dental*.

LOW-INCOME OPTIONS

If your income is low, there are various programs and services that provide dental care at a reduced rate or for free. *Here's where to look...*

Medicaid & CHIP benefits: All states provide dental-care services to children covered by Medicaid and the Children's Health Insurance Program (CHIP), but dental coverage for adults on Medicaid will vary by state. Go to *Medicaid.gov* for coverage/eligibility details.

State and local services: Some state and local programs as well as local clinics offer reduced-rate or free dental care to people with low incomes—generally below 200% of the federal poverty level. To find out what's available in your area, call your state dental director (see *ASTDD.org/state-programs* for contact information) or your state or local dental society (*EBusiness.ada.org/mystate.aspx*).

HRSA health centers: Supported by the US Health Resources and Services Administration, there are nearly 1,300 health centers that operate more than 9,200 locations around the US that provide discounted or free health and dental care based on financial need. To find a center near you that provides dental care, call 877-464-4772 or visit *FindaHealthCenter.HRSA.gov*.

Free health clinics: There are around 1,200 nonprofit, privately funded, volunteer-based free clinics across the country that provide a range of medical, dental and pharmacy services to economically disadvantaged people. Call 703-647-7427, or go to *NAFCClinics.org*.

Dental Lifeline Network: This national humanitarian organization provides free dental care to the elderly and disabled people who can't afford to pay. The program operates through a volunteer network of more than 15,000 dentists and 3,600 dental labs across the US. It also offers the Donated Orthodontic Services program in Illinois, Indiana, Kansas, New Jersey, North Carolina, Rhode Island, Tennessee and Virginia that enables low-income children to receive orthodontic treatment for a fee of $200. Call 888-471-6334, or go to *DentalLifeline.org*.

Remote Area Medical: This is a nonprofit, volunteer, charitable organization that provides free health, eye and dental care to people in need in certain areas of the US based on requests from local health departments and civic groups. The 2015 clinic schedule includes a total of 21 stops during the year in parts of Texas, Tennessee, California, Virginia, Illinois, Kentucky and Nevada. Call 865-579-1530, or go to *RAMUSA.org*.

Indian Health Service (IHS): This is an agency within the US Department of Health and Human Services that provides free dental care at more than 230 IHS dental clinics across the US to American Indians and Alaska Natives who are members of federally recognized Indian tribes. Visit *IHS.gov*.

Is the Cheaper Store-Brand Supplement Really as Good?

Edgar Dworsky, an attorney as well as founder of the consumer advocate websites *ConsumerWorld.org* and *MousePrint.org*. Formerly, he served as a consumer education consultant for the Federal Trade Commission and was an assistant attorney general in Massachusetts.

Store-brand vitamins and supplements can save you money, but they may not be as perfect a match to national brands as you often are led to believe.

Examples...

• **Walgreens One Daily Women's 50+ Multivitamin** (about $13) may seem like a good substitute for the Centrum Silver Women 50+ Multivitamin/Multimineral Supplement (about $16). But the Walgreens supplement contains only 23 specific vitamins, minerals and nutrients, while Centrum has 31, including boron and potassium, which are not in the Walgreens version, and higher daily doses of vitamins A, C and E.

Which is better? That may depend on an individual shopper's nutritional needs. But what's clear is that the Walgreens version isn't an exact substitute for the national brand.

• **CVS Advanced Eye Health softgel tablets** (about $17) say on the label that they're "comparable" to the AREDS 2 study formula softgels popularized by Bausch & Lomb PreserVision (about $35). The Bausch & Lomb product contains all six ingredients that were used in that study by the National Institutes of Health, which resulted in slower progression of age-related macular degeneration, a very serious eye condition that could lead to partial blindness. The CVS product contains only two of the six ingredients—lutein and zeaxanthin—while leaving out all of the study's proven vitamins and minerals (vitamin C, vitamin E, copper and zinc).

Bottom line: Compare the ingredients of supplements carefully.

Pay Less for Your Drugs!

Rebecca Shannonhouse, editor, *Bottom Line/Health*, 281 Tresser Blvd., Stamford, Connecticut 06901. *BottomLineHealth.com*

If you want to get me fired up, just tell me about someone who is suffering from an illness but can't afford medication to treat it. This happened not long ago when I learned about a dear friend who was struggling to pay $1,400 each time she needed a refill of her pricey medication for Crohn's disease. And she has insurance!

What I recommended—chances are it will work for you, too...

Print the drug-discount card that's listed on the front page of *NeedyMeds.org*, the website of a nonprofit group that serves as a resource for more than 7,000 programs that help people save on their prescription drugs and other health-care costs. Hand this card to your pharmacist when you fill your prescription. The average savings for covered drugs is about 50%. Other websites, such as *GoodRx.com*, also offer card discounts.

Even if you have insurance, using the card instead may offer a better discount, says Richard J. Sagall, MD, founder of NeedyMeds. "I just heard from an insured cardholder who said that the drug his daughter needed cost $1,200 with insurance but $550 with the discount card."

Other ways to save...

- **Browse NeedyMeds.org** for patient-assistance programs that offer free (or very low-cost) drugs. Don't assume you won't qualify. A family of four with an income of about $90,000 might be eligible.

- **Compare prices.** Pharmacies (even in the same zip code) charge wildly different prices. *Consumer Reports* found that a generic form of Plavix cost as little as $15 at Costco and a whopping $180 at CVS.

Here's wishing you big savings!

The "Do Not Call" Registry Doesn't Always Work...What Does...

Edgar Dworsky, an attorney as well as founder of the consumer advocate websites *ConsumerWorld.org* and *MousePrint.org*. Formerly, he served as a consumer education consultant for the Federal Trade Commission and was an assistant attorney general in Massachusetts.

Signing up for the federal government's Do Not Call Registry was supposed to protect us from unwanted telemarketing phone calls. But a lot of unwanted calls still sneak through, and it's only getting worse. Inexpensive international Internet-based calling allows telemarketers to evade US laws by contacting us from overseas. And certain callers, including pollsters, politicians and charities, are exempt from the National Do Not Call Registry restrictions.

You still should register your landline and cell phone numbers with the Do Not Call Registry (*DoNotCall.gov*) because it does reduce unwanted calls. *But here are four additional steps to further block these calls...*

1. Stop writing your phone numbers on forms and entering them into websites. Retailers, websites, charities and political organizations often ask for phone numbers, but that doesn't mean you have to provide them. Handing out phone numbers to such organizations increases the odds that the numbers will end up on additional call lists. An e-mail address should be sufficient when contact information is needed.

When a website won't let you proceed without entering a phone number, supply a fake one starting with "555" after the area code. (No real numbers start with 555.)

Exceptions: Do provide your real phone number(s) to doctors' offices, insurers, credit card providers and other organizations that might have a legitimate reason to contact you quickly.

2. Sign up for Nomorobo—if your telecom provider is eligible. This is a free service that recently won the top prize from the Federal Trade Commission for coming up with a technological solution to reduce the number of robocalls.

Incoming calls to your phone number are routed not just to your phone but also to Nomorobo's computers. These computers very quickly determine whether the call is from an automatic dialer—a tool used by many of the worst telemarketers to call several numbers quickly—and hang up on the caller after the first ring if it is.

Nomorobo does allow legitimate automated phone calls through, such as reminders about doctor and other appointments.

Unfortunately, you can use Nomorobo only if your phone provider and/or cellular provider offers a service called "simultaneous ring," which allows calls to one phone number to ring at a second number as well.

Most Internet- or cable-based telecom providers offer Nomorobo, but many cellular and traditional landline providers currently don't, although that could change if Nomorobo continues to gain popularity. At *Nomorobo.com*, click "Get Started Now" to determine whether you can sign up.

3. Block calls from troublesome phone numbers. Some telecom providers allow their customers to block incoming calls from specific numbers, perhaps by entering a code immediately after receiving a call from someone you don't want to hear from again. Contact your provider(s) to find out if such a feature is available to you.

Unfortunately, blocking individual phone numbers won't stop the most unethical telemarketers—they tend to use "spoofing" technology to make their calls appear to come from a different phone number each time.

Because of this limitation, it's usually worth blocking individual numbers only if your phone provider lets you do so for free.

Also: Some telemarketers block their own numbers so they don't appear on your caller ID at all. Some phone-service providers offer the option of blocking incoming calls from callers that have blocked numbers—ask your provider.

4. Ask legitimate organizations to "put me on your do-not-call list." Pollsters, politicians and companies that place unsolicited calls generally are required to maintain their own do-not-call lists. Ethical organizations comply with requests to be placed on these lists.

Exception: Prerecorded-message calls typically include instructions for opting out of future calls, usually by pressing a key on the phone's keypad. Do not follow these directions if the automated call is from an unknown or a potentially untrustworthy caller—doing so can lead to an increase in call frequency.

EASY-TO-DO...

If You Want to Sell Your Old Cell Phone...

To sell an old cell phone, shop online. *Gazelle.com* will pay for an old phone by check, PayPal or Amazon gift card. And *SellCell.com* compares prices from the top buyers so that you get the most cash for your old cell phone (a typical phone sale comes to nearly $100). You can also go to the website or physical location of a Best Buy, Target, Staples or Walmart to swap your phone for a gift card—but be aware that online quotes do not always match what you are offered in-store. Or try a machine called an ecoATM—there are more than 1,100 in 44 states. They analyze the device and give cash for it. Find locations at *EcoATM.com*.

Money.com

Online Selling Tips

Take these helpful precautions when selling online...

When using websites such as *Craigslist* or *eBay*, insist on being paid through PayPal or with a cashier's check for deals of more than $100. Do not include your address or phone number in posts that offer products for sale. If you're shipping an item, require a signature on delivery so that the recipient cannot claim it never arrived. Consider buying shipping insurance for additional protection. To protect against swap-out scams—in which someone orders an item identical to an already broken one, then returns the broken one and claims the shipment arrived damaged—take detailed photos of the item and any distinguishing marks it has. If you're concerned about safety, meet a buyer at a neutral, busy location, such as a supermarket parking lot that has video surveillance.

Roundup of experts on online selling and scams, reported at *Bankrate.com.*

Items That Usually Are Better Deals Online

The following items typically cost less on the web than in other places...

Electronics: The selection is wider than in stores, and prices usually are cheaper on everything from big-ticket items to smaller ones, such as HDMI cables and cell phone cases.

Small appliances: Websites offer a better selection of blenders, toasters and other kinds of small appliances.

Pet supplies: Scheduled food deliveries arranged online can save 15%.

Theme-park tickets: These may be discounted if you have certain credit cards or an AAA membership, and buying them online helps you avoid lines at the park entrance.

Baby supplies: Diapers, baby food and other items are cheaper online, and with a delivery program such as Amazon's Subscribe & Save, you get a 15% discount on the entire order if you choose five or more items.

ConsumerReports.org.

12

Retirement Rundown

9 Worst Retirement Regrets: Many You Still Can Fix

Enjoying retirement is near the top of most people's wish lists. But when I was researching my book on retirement, I heard again and again from retirees what they wished they had done differently before retiring—and many of these retirees had the same regrets.

By heeding the advice of the already-retired, you can avoid the common regrets and enjoy your retirement that much more…

• **Not retiring sooner (because maybe you can afford to do so).** Most of the retirees I spoke with were enjoying their retirement immensely, and when I asked about any regrets, they often said, "My only regret is that I should have retired sooner!" Many went on to explain that once they settled into retirement, they found that their spending and general cost of living dropped to a level where they realistically could have afforded to retire earlier. While undersaving for retirement is a scary and real possibility for many people, oversaving for retirement happens quite a bit, in part because, according to data from the Bureau of Labor Statistics, we naturally spend less and less as we age throughout our retirement years on nearly all types of consumer goods and services…with the notable exception of health care.

• **Not doing your homework.** Many retirees admitted that they took the time to learn how some of the most basic features of retirement worked only when they were on the cusp of retirement or even after they were fully retired. Many retirees confessed that they waited too long to learn the ins and outs of

---

Jeff Yeager, AARP's official "Savings Expert" as well as host of a weekly AARP web program on YouTube (*YouTube.com/CheapLifeChannel*). Located in Accokeek, Maryland, he is author of several popular books about frugal living, including *How to Retire the Cheapskate Way. UltimateCheapskate.com*

Social Security and Medicare…what benefits they were entitled to receive under their pensions and retirement accounts…and the fine points of things such as long-term-care insurance and reverse mortgages. Not doing this type of homework earlier cost one person I interviewed $6,000 a year in lost pension benefits that she could have started collecting years earlier, while she still was working. She told me, "I looked into it only when I was actually ready to stop working—a big mistake."

• **Not burying the hatchet sooner.** It's never too early to patch things up with family members or others with whom you have a strained relationship, but carrying that emotional baggage with you into retirement really can tarnish your later years. Not only will you have more time in retirement to sit around and brood about such unpleasant affairs (if that's how you choose to spend your time), but having close, supportive relationships with family and friends—a care network that you can depend on—can be a tremendous asset, particularly in retirement.

• **Not planning for all that leisure time.** If you are used to working full time and have few leisure-time interests, filling all that newfound time during retirement can be a real challenge. Retirees say that you should cultivate hobbies and other activities before you retire so that you're not overwhelmed by all of that additional free time. Also, if one spouse is used to being alone around the house and has been primarily responsible for managing the household, injecting a second person into that situation can create stress in a relationship, to the point where one woman told me, "I wanted to get a job when my husband retired because having him around all the time drove me crazy." Respecting each other's boundaries and need for alone time, and agreeing upon and sharing responsibilities for household management, before you retire make the transition easier.

• **Not downsizing earlier.** Downsizing your household and lifestyle—by doing such things as moving to a smaller home, getting rid of unwanted items and maybe selling off a second car—is a pretty common practice among retired folks. And once they've done it, many retirees say they wished they had done it years earlier, long before they retired. "It's so liberating being free of all that extraneous stuff," one retired man told me. "I just wish I'd done it when I was 50 instead of 70…well, actually, I wish I never would have bought most of that stuff in the first place." Of course, downsizing earlier also can allow you to build your retirement nest egg that much faster and allow you to retire with less debt—or better yet, with no debt.

• **Not kicking a bad habit earlier.** Having more time on your hands can prompt you to further indulge in any bad habits. Maybe the cocktail hour you have always enjoyed starts earlier in the day and lasts longer…or an occasional trip to the racetrack becomes a daily gambling obsession. Being relatively isolated at home and having more free time to indulge are among the chief reasons why substance abuse among elderly people is an expanding problem, according to a 2011 study by the Substance Abuse and Mental Health Services Administration.

• **Not drawing Social Security at the best time.** Many financial experts suggest holding off as long as possible, ideally until age 70, when you're entitled to the largest monthly benefit, nearly 75% more than if you start drawing at age 62 (the current minimum age).

While that may be a good strategy for many, when my wife recently turned 62, we did the math and found that since she wants to continue to work part time and we are in a position to invest rather than spend her Social Security checks, she should start drawing benefits immediately. In all likelihood, she will come out ahead in the long run, compared with waiting until she's 66 (currently the full retirement age for many people).

Here's a calculator to help you figure out the optimum age at which you should start to receive Social Security benefits—*SSA.gov/retire2/otherthings.htm.*

• **Not traveling earlier in retirement.** Many older retirees expressed regrets about not traveling or pursuing other activities that require more physical stamina at the front end of their retirement years. There is a tendency to postpone those activities when you are newly retired, both because you believe that your health will remain largely the same and you fear burning through too much of your retirement savings too soon. "Do what you can when you still can," one globe-trotting retiree told me, "because you never know how much longer you'll be able to do it."

• **Not taking better care of your health.** Mickey Mantle once said, "If I knew I was going to live this long, I'd have taken better care of myself." Entering retirement in ill health can have dire consequences in terms of both quality of life and finances. Maintaining optimum health throughout life and specifically "going into training" leading up to retirement, as one retiree put it, truly can make your retirement the best years of your life. But don't despair if your health is less than perfect when you hit retirement. A number of retirees said they were able to markedly improve their health once retired, when they had more time to devote to fitness.

High-Tech Ways to Age at Home

Majd Alwan, PhD, senior vice president of technology and executive director of the LeadingAge Center for Aging Services Technologies, a nonprofit for aging advocacy in Washington, DC. He is a former assistant professor and director of the Robotics and Eldercare Technologies Program at the University of Virginia Medical Automation Research Center. *LeadingAge.org/CAST*

Where do you plan to live during your retirement years—including your later years? If you are like most people, you want to stay right at home.

But that doesn't work for everyone. People with chronic illnesses and/or physical disabilities may end up moving into assisted-living facilities or nursing homes—and often sooner than they had hoped.

Now: High-tech devices can help you stay in your home much longer than before (even if you live alone) while also giving loved ones the assurance that you are safe.

To stay at home as long as possible, people have traditionally installed ramps, grab bars, brighter lighting and other such products to accommodate their changing needs. But that doesn't scratch the surface of what's available today.

Impressive high-tech devices to help you stay at home as you age...

"CHECKUPS" AT HOME

There's now an easy way to quickly alert your doctor of important changes in your health that may be occurring between office visits.

What's new: Remote patient monitoring. You can now use an at-home glucose monitor, weight scale, pulse oximeter (to measure oxygen in the blood) and other devices that store readings, which you can then easily share with your doctor—on a daily, weekly or monthly basis, depending on your condition and how well you're responding to treatments.

Example: A wireless glucose monitor, such as the iHealth Align ($16.95,* without test strips), available at *iHealthLabs.com*. It works with a smartphone to take glucose readings and automatically log and track measurements over time and send them to the doctor.

In development: Systems with wearable sensors that automatically take and transmit important readings. A steering wheel that measures blood glucose? Watch for that too in the next few years!

FALL MONITORS GO HIGH-TECH

We're all familiar with the older fall-monitor systems that require users to press a button on a pendant to initiate communication with a call center. Staffers then contact you (via an intercom-like device) to ask if you need help.

What's new: Devices that don't require the push of a button, so fall victims who are immobilized or unconscious also can be helped.

New-generation fall monitors are equipped with accelerometers that can tell when you've fallen. The units, worn around the neck, on the wrist or clipped to a belt, contact a call center or a designated caregiver. If you don't answer a follow-up call, emergency responders will be sent to your address.

*Prices subject to change.

Why the new technology is important: Fall victims who receive help within one hour of a fall are six times more likely to survive than those who wait longer.

Examples: Philips Lifeline HomeSafe with AutoAlert (automatic fall detection with push-button backup and 24-hour call center/emergency response) starts at $44.95/month. GoSafe is a wireless alternative that starts at $54.95/month, plus a onetime GoSafe mobile button purchase of $149. Both are available at *LifelineSys.com.*

Traditional-style fall monitor: Walgreens Ready Response Vi Alert System (390-foot range and 24-hour call center/emergency response) requires the fall victim to push a button. Available from *WalgreensReadyResponse.com* for $29.99/month.

ACTIVITY MONITORS

By tracking activity—and noting changes in routines—an off-site loved one or caregiver can tell when you've become more or less active or when you're spending more time in certain parts of the house. A sudden increase in bathroom visits, for example, could indicate a urinary tract infection that hasn't yet been diagnosed.

What's new: Sensors that track daily activity—for example, how often refrigerator doors are opened, when the stove is turned on and how often the bathroom is used.

Examples: GrandCare Activity Monitoring Package. A caregiver can log in to the system to view activity reports and/or set up "alert parameters" that will trigger a text if there's no movement at expected times. Available at *GrandCare.com*, $299.99, plus $49.99/month.

A less expensive option is Lively Activity Sensors for Living Independently. Small, disk-shaped sensors are attached to household objects such as the refrigerator and a pillbox. The sensors detect and send text/e-mail notifications when there's a movement, such as the opening of a refrigerator door. A package of six is available at *Amazon.com* for $39.95, plus $24.95/month.

HOW'S YOUR WALKING

A change in walking speed could indicate that someone has balance problems, muscle weakness or other issues that can interfere with daily living.

What's new: Wearable devices (available from your doctor or physical therapist) that monitor gait, balance and walking speed. The devices store information that can be electronically transmitted to a doctor or physical therapist.

If walking speed has declined, it could mean that an underlying health problem—such as congestive heart failure—isn't well-controlled by medication…or that you need physical therapy to increase muscle strength and stamina. Detecting such changes in gait in high-risk patients can allow treatment adjustments that help prevent falls and improve mobility—critical for staying (and thriving) at home.

Examples: StepWatch from Modus Health straps onto your ankle and has 27 different metrics to measure gait and speed. Available at *ModusHealth.com*. LEGSys from Biosensics includes portable, wireless sensors that analyze gait and generate easy-to-read reports. It's easy to put on with a Velcro strap. Available at *Biosensics.com/LEGSys-overview.*

It Takes a Virtual Village

Karen Larson, editor of *Bottom Line/Personal*, 281 Tresser Blvd., Stamford, Connecticut 06901. *BottomLinePersonal.com*

My mother-in-law, a widow, would have liked to "age in place" in her house in New Jersey, but she was feeling isolated and moved to a senior living facility.

Back in 1999, Susan McWhinney-Morse faced a similar dilemma. She loved her Boston town house but was worried that she'd have to struggle to obtain needed support.

Her solution: She helped launch a nonprofit group that would provide her—and other retirees in her area who wished to remain in their homes—with help and social activities. Today that nonprofit group, Beacon Hill Village, has nearly 400 members. What's more, it has inspired approximately 150 similar "virtual villages" around the country, with roughly 120 more in the planning stages.

These virtual villages do not typically provide actual day-to-day support to members, just guidance about where and how to obtain support. They vet local service providers—from plumbers to home health aids. (Some of these providers offer discounts to group members.) They connect members in need of assistance with fellow members or local volunteers who are willing to help. And they typically have someone on staff who can advise members about the ins and outs of senior services. Virtual villages also sponsor get-togethers and outings, says McWhinney-Morse, who still is in her town house as she enters her 80s. The membership fees typically are $300 to $500 a year,* though a few villages charge as much as $1,000.

The Village to Village Network website (*VTV Network.org*) can help you locate groups in your area. If there is no group nearby, click the "Start a Village" link on the site to learn more.

*Fees subject to change.

TAKE NOTE...

10 Worst States for Retirees

The 10 worst states for retirees, based on cost of living, crime statistics, tax rates, health care and weather are New York (which is the worst), followed by West Virginia, Alaska, Arkansas, Hawaii, Alabama, Louisiana, Oklahoma, Maryland and Kentucky.

The five best states are South Dakota, Colorado, Utah, North Dakota and Wyoming.

Bankrate.com

Retire Happily on $25,000 a Year (Hint: You'll Have to Move)

Dan Prescher, senior editor of *InternationalLiving.com* and Suzan Haskins, Latin America editor of *InternationalLiving.com.* The couple currently resides in Ecuador and has lived in seven different locations in Latin America—Quito and Cotacachi in Ecuador...Panama City, Panama...San Juan del Sur, Nicaragua...and Lake Chapala, San Miguel de Allende and Mérida in Mexico. They are coauthors of *The International Living Guide to Retiring Overseas on a Budget.*

Millions of folks are coming to the realization that they cannot afford the comfortable retirement they expected. The solution could lie south of the border.

Retirees can live very comfortably in Latin America for $25,000 a year or less—that's about half of what it would cost in some parts of the US. Property taxes are extremely low in Latin America. We pay property taxes of less than $55 a year for our 1,100-square-foot condo in Ecuador. Health care is inexpensive. Great meals cost just a few dollars. Homes can be very affordable. Some Latin American nations even offer special discounts to retirees.

Example: Panama's "pensionado" program offers retirees 50% off many entertainment-related costs and the closing costs of a home loan, among many other savings.

And despite what many Americans fear, you can live in Latin America without sacrificing safety or high-quality health care...and without feeling isolated or out of place. Residency permits tend to be easy to obtain, and US pensions and other US retirement income often are not taxed. (But US citizens are required to report income annually to the US government and pay US income taxes no matter where they live.) *Here's what you need to know...*

HEALTH CARE

Many parts of Latin America now have excellent—and affordable—health care. Urban and suburban areas popular with foreign retirees often have modern hospitals and doctors who speak English well and who were educated in well-regarded US or European universities. (The quality of health care may not be up to par in rural parts of Latin America, however.)

Paying for medical care in Latin America usually isn't a problem, either. Most countries in the region have a socialized health-care system that is open to foreign residents. If this public system does not meet your medical needs, there's often a high-quality private health-care system as well.

Prices in this private health-care system are likely to be much lower than in the US. Doctor and dentist appointments typically cost $20 to $40*...hospital procedures tend to cost one-quarter of what similar procedures cost in the US...health insurance for people of retirement age can cost as little as $50 a month—sometimes with no deductible. (Alternatively, many top hospitals in Costa Rica, Nicaragua, Panama and Uruguay have plans that provide steep discounts on hospital services for perhaps $25 to $75 per month.)

In some ways, medical care in Latin America is even better than in the US. Doctors tend to spend more time with their patients than they now do in the US...and some doctors make house calls and/or give patients their personal cell phone numbers.

Examples: Costa Rica has a very good national health-care system and an excellent private system. Areas of Mexico popular with expatriots, such as Lake Chapala and Puerto Vallarta, feature very strong private medical providers who are used to treating American retirees. Panama City has a Johns Hopkins–affiliated hospital that is as technologically advanced as an elite US hospital.

If a major medical issue arises and you are enrolled in Medicare, you also could return to the US and use Medicare to pay for treatment. However, Medicare does not cover medical treatment in foreign countries.

SAFETY

When Latin America is mentioned in American news reports, the story is often about political instability or violent crime. That is not typically the reality faced by American retirees. There are very legitimate safety and stability issues in Venezuela, El Salvador, Argentina and near the US/Mexican border, but most of Latin America is quite safe. Even countries such as Nicaragua and Colombia that are associated with war and drugs in Americans' minds now are safer and more stable than before.

Staying safe in Latin America is like staying safe in the US—stay out of the bad areas. The local expat community can warn you about places to avoid. In our 13 years living in seven different parts of Latin America, we've never felt unsafe, much less witnessed or experienced violent crime. The most serious crime we've encountered is pickpocketing on trolley cars.

ISOLATION

One of the major complaints of Americans who retire abroad used to be that they felt cut off from their families, friends and culture. The Internet has significantly reduced this problem. Today's expats can use the Internet-calling service *Skype* to make video calls back to the US for free. They can watch US television shows, movies and certain US sporting events over the Internet, too. And certain Latin American expat communities have become so large and well-established that they feel almost like US communities.

Examples: Large, well-established expat communities include Lake Chapala, Puerto Vallarta and San Miguel de Allende in Mexico... Boquete, Coronado and Panama City in Panama...and the Central Valley of Costa Rica.

In some parts of Latin America, many locals speak English, too, further easing any feelings of isolation. Still, you will enjoy living in Latin America more if you learn to speak Spanish.

If you live in or near a Latin American city that has a major airport in a country not too far from the US, flying back home for visits won't be much different from flying back to a northern state from, say, Florida or Arizona.

CLIMATE AND CULTURE

Americans tend to associate Latin America with warm winter weather and relaxing beachfront living. If that's what you're looking for, there are plenty of options.

Examples: Puerto Vallarta, Mexico...Coronado, Panama...Dominical, Costa Rica...Ambergris Caye and Placenia, Belize.

But if you consider steamy summer temperatures a turnoff, head to higher elevations. We live in the mountains of Ecuador and never need air-conditioning or heating.

Examples: For nice temperatures year-round, consider Costa Rica's Central Valley... the Sierra (or mountain) region of Ecuador,

*Prices subject to change.

including Quito and Cuenca...the Mexican highlands including San Miguel de Allende and Lake Chapala...Medellín, Colombia...and Boquete, Panama.

And if cosmopolitan city life is more your speed, there are plenty of culturally vibrant cities in Latin America.

Examples: Panama City, Panama...Mérida, Mexico...Quito, Ecuador...and San José, Costa Rica.

TO FIND YOUR RETIREMENT SPOT...

Visit online bulletin boards aimed at expats to learn more about potential Latin American retirement destinations. Just type the name of a Latin American city, region or country and the word "expat" into a search engine to find these.

Examples: Gringo Tree offers bulletin boards for Cuenca and Quito, two popular spots for expats in Ecuador (*Tribelr.com*). Facebook is another resource where you will find plenty of expat-related pages.

On these bulletin boards, you'll find expats chatting about what life really is like for Americans in these places. Post any questions that you have about retiring to the area. You even might strike up friendships with retirees who already are in the area—knowing someone in the area could make a future visit more enjoyable and informative.

Spend at least one month, preferably longer, visiting an area before deciding to retire there. Rent a home rather than stay in a hotel or tourist condo during this trial phase—the touristy parts of Latin America tend to be very different from the areas where people actually live. Latin America does not have many property-rental agencies, but some real estate agents rent out homes on behalf of clients. Request real estate agent recommendations on the area's expat bulletin boards. In addition to some sightseeing during this visit, try to do the everyday, ordinary things you actually would do if you lived there. For more information, go to our website, *InternationalLiving.com.*

Social Security Secrets: You May Be Entitled to More Than You're Getting

Laurence J. Kotlikoff, PhD, professor of economics at Boston University, a fellow of the American Academy of Arts and Sciences and a former senior economist with the President's Council of Economic Advisers. He is also president of Economic Security Planning, Inc., which develops financial-planning software, and coauthor of *Get What's Yours: The Secrets to Maxing Out Your Social Security. MaximizeMySocialSecurity.com*

Social Security might end up being your most valuable retirement asset...and the most difficult to understand. The system has more than 2,700 core rules and thousands more codicils. A single misstep could cost you as much as one-third of the money you might have received. *Here's a closer look at four Social Security guidelines that are poorly understood, even by financial planners...*

- **You might have more than one benefit available to you, but you can't claim more than one at a time.** *Examples of benefits in addition to your standard retirement benefit...*
  - If your spouse (or former spouse if you are divorced and your marriage lasted at least 10 years) is alive, you might qualify for a monthly spousal benefit equal to as much as 50% of your spouse's "full retirement benefit"—the amount your spouse would receive if he/she starts his/her benefits at his "full retirement age," which is 66 for people born between 1943 and 1954...between 66 and 67 for people born between 1955 and 1959...and 67 for people born in 1960 or later.
  - If your spouse or ex passes away, you might be entitled to a monthly survivor benefit of as much as 100% of the retirement benefit that he could have received if he were still alive.

Social Security rules make it difficult to understand that you can't get more than one of the benefits at the same time. The rules seem to indicate that you can receive your own retirement benefit plus the portion of another benefit that is in excess of your retirement benefit—but that's really just a confusing way of saying that the smaller of the two benefits is eliminated.

What to do: It sometimes is worth claiming first one benefit, then switching to a different one later on. Doing this delays the start of the second benefit, which could increase the size of the check that you receive each month from that benefit for the rest of your life.

There are many complex rules governing this. It is easy to make a mistake and apply for two benefits even though you intended to apply for just one. If this is the case, you might eliminate any upside to switching benefits later. *Below are three important benefit-switching guidelines...*

- It may not be wise to claim a spousal benefit before you reach your full retirement age. Doing so would cause you to be deemed to be filing for your own retirement benefit at this early age, too, forever reducing your monthly retirement benefit.
- If you are married, you cannot file for a spousal benefit until your spouse has filed for his own retirement benefit (though if you are divorced, you can).
- Although your monthly retirement benefit continues to increase in size for each month you delay starting it until age 70, spousal and survivor benefits stop increasing once you reach your "full" retirement age, so there is no advantage to delaying the start of these benefits any further.

• **Mishandling Medicare premiums could lead to a Social Security loss.** It's not uncommon for people to start Social Security benefits and then later suspend them. Suspending benefits, like delaying the start of benefits, can result in larger monthly benefits later.

Example: A woman applies for her retirement benefit at age 62. Four years later, her husband turns 70 and starts his own retirement benefit, so she suspends her retirement benefit and switches to a spousal benefit based on his earnings. That way, her own monthly retirement benefit checks will be larger when she restarts them at age 70.

Trouble is, many people have their Medicare Part B (doctor visits and treatment) premiums withdrawn directly from their Social Security benefits—and if these premiums are withdrawn from a suspended account, the account might not be considered fully suspended. When the benefits are later restarted, the recipient might be shocked to discover that her monthly checks are no larger than they were when the payments were supposedly suspended years earlier. The whole point of suspending benefits is to receive larger monthly checks later. If future checks are not larger, years of checks have been sacrificed for nothing.

What to do: Switch to paying Medicare premiums out of pocket if you suspend your Social Security benefits. If you currently are paying Medicare premiums out of a suspended Social Security account, contact the Social Security Administration immediately. If you have not yet reached age 70, you can request a lump-sum payment of what you could have earned while the account was suspended. Your future benefits will not be increased, however—your checks still will be the same size that they were before the account was suspended. This money likely is gone forever if you do not request the payment by your 70th birthday.

• **If you claim your benefit early, your spouse might pay the price.** Many people start their retirement benefits as soon as they become eligible at age 62. That can be a very costly decision—especially if you are a man who is both older and higher-earning than your wife. If your spouse outlives you, as is usually likely, her survivor benefit will be based on the monthly retirement benefit you are receiving (or entitled to) when you pass away. And the retirement benefit you are receiving will be larger the longer you wait, up to age 70.

Example: A 67-year-old man was diagnosed with cancer and told he had two years to live. His local Social Security Administration office suggested that he file for benefits immediately—better to receive two years of benefits than nothing at all. But that advice assumed the man's goal was maximizing his own benefits rather than the combined amount he and his wife would receive. The couple would have been better off if he continued to delay the start of his benefits until he turned 70 or died. If this man's monthly benefit was $2,000 at age 67, two years of benefits would net him

$48,000—but delaying benefits by two years would increase his wife's future monthly survivor benefits by 16%, putting an extra $3,840 in her pocket for every year that she survived him (actually a bit more, because Social Security benefits are inflation-adjusted). She would steadily earn back that forgone $48,000 over a period of 12.5 years, and after that all of the additional benefit amount would be a bonus.

• **Social Security's earnings penalty often is not much of a penalty at all.** You might have heard that the "earnings penalty" makes it foolish to continue to work while receiving Social Security benefits, whether it's standard retirement benefits or spousal or survivor benefits. After all, this penalty can claim $1 of your benefits for every $2 you earn above a very low income limit (currently $15,720). But this earnings penalty may not be as bad as it seems for two reasons. It applies only to people who have not yet reached their full retirement age...and benefits lost to the penalty are paid back later in the form of a higher monthly benefit starting at full retirement age (unless you are receiving benefits as a survivor because you are caring for a minor or disabled child).

Your monthly benefit will be adjusted by the amount that would fully compensate you for the withheld money if you live to a certain age. If you don't live to that age, you will come out behind...live longer, and you will come out ahead.

What to do: Most people should not let the earnings penalty stop them from earning more than $15,720. But if you have not yet reached your full retirement age and poor health or family history suggests a short life span, it is worth avoiding. And anyone who does incur the earnings penalty probably shouldn't switch from one type of benefit to another during retirement. Only the specific benefit that is subject to the penalty will be adjusted upward later.

Example: If you are receiving a survivor benefit when the earnings penalty is imposed, only this survivor benefit will be increased at your full retirement age to pay back the earnings penalty.

EASY-TO-DO...

Get Free Help on Social Security Benefits

Free online Social Security tools can help you determine the best time to take benefits...

• **SSAnalyze!** from Bedrock Capital Management is easy to use and lets you customize life expectancy, current value of future benefits and more. At *BedrockCapital.com*, click on "SSAnalyze."

• **The Social Security Benefits Calculator** from AARP shows how to claim the highest monthly—not lifetime—benefit and figures out how much of your monthly expenses Social Security will cover. At *AARP.org*, type "Social Security Calculator" in the search window.

• **The Social Security Planner from Financial Engines** figures the probability that a user and spouse will live to various ages, then picks their best lifetime-benefits strategy. At *FinancialEngines.com*, click on "For Individuals," then "Retirement Readiness."

The Wall Street Journal. WSJ.com

Take income taxes into account when you decide whether to continue earning income while receiving Social Security benefits, however. Your benefits could be taxable if you earn more than $25,000 a year ($32,000 for joint filers). Unlike money lost to the earnings penalty, money lost to income taxes is gone forever.

What Social Security Isn't Telling You About Your Future Benefits

William Meyer, founder and managing principal of Social Security Solutions, based in Leawood, Kansas, which offers personalized Social Security benefits optimization guidance. *SocialSecuritySolutions.com*

Official estimates of your future benefits from the Social Security Administration can be both helpful and misleading. The agency has resumed mailing out the future-benefits statements after having halted the practice in 2011 to save money. Now you can expect to receive one every five years if you're 25 to 60 years old...or every year after age 60 if you are not yet receiving benefits, unless you have signed up to view annually updated statements on the Social Security website.

Here's how your benefits estimate might mislead you...

• **It assumes that you will continue at your current income level until you begin receiving benefits.** This means that your future benefits may be overestimated if your income was exceptionally high during a recent calendar year or if you intend to retire years before you claim your benefits. Your statement will probably underestimate your future benefits if your income climbs significantly before you retire.

• **It ignores your spouse's (or ex's) income.** You could opt to claim a spousal benefit equal to 50% of your spouse's retirement benefit rather than your own, assuming that your marriage lasts at least 10 years. If your spouse or ex dies and you wait until your full retirement age, you could claim a survivor benefit equal to 100% of that spouse's benefit rather than your own benefit.

• **It doesn't mention that your benefits might be taxed.** As much as 85% of your Social Security benefits might be subject to income taxes, depending on your income. That means many people will pocket much less from the Social Security system than they expect.

Get Your Social Security Benefits Tax Form Here

The Social Security Administration (*Social Security.gov*) now provides an online replacement option to recipients who have lost the SSA-1099 tax form sent out annually by the agency. About 1.7 million people request replacements every year by mail or by going in person to a Social Security office. Those options still are available—or you can call 800-772-1213 to ask for a replacement. Obtaining one online is fastest.

USA Today. USAToday.com

Social Security Offers Widows/Widowers More Flexibility

Widows and widowers have more flexibility when collecting Social Security than spouses do. A widow or widower can begin benefits based on his/her own earnings and later switch to survivor benefits—or begin with survivor benefits, then switch to his own, even if the surviving spouse files before full retirement.

Dan Keady, director of financial planning, TIAA-CREF Financial Services, quoted at *Bankrate.com.*

Can You Collect Social Security If You Retire Abroad?

You can collect your Social Security no matter where you live. You even can have it directly deposited in your foreign bank account if the bank allows it. And more people are doing it. The Social Security Administration sent benefit checks to more than 346,000 retirees living outside the US in 2011, the latest year for which figures are available. That's up from about 307,000 in 2008.

Dan Prescher, senior editor of *InternationalLiving.com*, and coauthor of *The International Living Guide to Retiring Overseas on a Budget.*

Power Up Your IRA: With These Moneymaking Investments

T. Scott McCartan, CFA, CEO of the financial-services firm Millennium Trust Company, which is one of the country's largest independent custodians for self-directed IRAs, Oak Brook, Illinois. It holds more than $13.5 billion in assets in more than 340,000 client accounts. *MTrustCompany.com*

Although most investors don't realize it, you can turn your retirement account into something much more diverse than a collection of stocks and bonds. You can include unconventional investments ranging from condominium apartments to a franchise business to an alpaca farm. Or you can choose some slightly more familiar investments such as certain gold and silver coins or bullion...a vacation time-share...or lending someone money and charging him/her interest.

Sound fascinating and potentially lucrative? It is, on both counts. This type of "self-directed" IRA strategy can cushion your nest egg against setbacks for stocks and bonds in your conventional IRAs and improve your overall returns. But don't expect to hear much about self-directed options from major investment firms such as Fidelity or Merrill Lynch. They tend to offer mainstream, publicly traded investments such as stocks, bonds and mutual funds, as well as real estate investment trusts (REITs) and certificates of deposit (CDs).

To incorporate unusual investments in your retirement savings, you'll need to establish a self-directed IRA with an IRA custodian that specializes in privately traded assets. That isn't hard to do. But it's vital to understand that unconventional investments require more personal effort and expertise on your part than do run-of-the-mill investments. That is why only about 3% to 5% of the entire $6.5 trillion IRA market in the US is invested in these specialized IRAs.

Below, we spoke with IRA expert T. Scott McCartan, CFA, about how to decide whether a self-directed IRA is right for you and ways that it might help you diversify your nest egg...

DO-IT-YOURSELF

Over the next several years, traditional retirement investments face many challenges. Stocks are nearing the end of a long bull market, and rising interest rates will make bond prices volatile. Investors are rethinking how to smooth the future ups and downs of the markets and juice up returns.

One way is private investments. Opportunities in private investments are far less publicized and may offer greater potential returns than stocks or bonds. You also have more control because your ability to make a profit largely depends on your own skills and judgment.

Example: I had a client who, after spending years watching and studying his local real estate market, invested $150,000 of his IRA money in a condo near where he lived. He rented out the condo and has netted $1,000 a month after expenses, an 8% annual return. That money flows back into the IRA, and until he withdraws assets from the IRA, he doesn't have to pay taxes on the income—or on potential profit when he sells the condo in the future.

Do-it-yourself investing like this is inherently risky because the investments lack the built-in diversification and liquidity that you could get from, say, investing in shares of a REIT that owns thousands of condominiums. Also, determining valuations of assets that are not easily converted to cash can be complicated. For these reasons, most investors might want to consider dedicating no more than 15% of their overall retirement money to specialized IRAs. *Steps to get started...*

SET UP AN ACCOUNT

Funding a self-directed traditional IRA or self-directed Roth IRA is similar to funding a standard IRA. You can even roll over cash into a self-directed IRA free of penalty from your existing IRAs or from an existing 401(k) or 403(b) when you retire or change jobs. All the standard annual IRA contribution limits apply. However, you do need to open an account with a custodian qualified by the IRS to handle self-directed investments, typically a trust company. To find a reputable one, ask a financial adviser or visit the website of the Retirement Industry Trust Association

(*RITAUS.org*). Some custodians cater to multimillion-dollar retirement accounts and handle a variety of investments...others handle smaller sums and more specific investments.

The custodian of a self-directed IRA won't provide investment advice or sell you financial products. The custodian simply holds your assets, makes sure that appropriate tax documents are filed, fulfills your requests to buy and sell assets, and credits your account for any recurring income such as dividends or rent. If you are not satisfied with your custodian, you can transfer your self-directed IRA to a different one without incurring a tax penalty. You can even liquidate your investments and roll the money back into a regular IRA. However, custodians often charge an account-termination fee, as well as a transfer fee if you are transferring the investments without liquidating them. Both types of fees vary widely.

Expect to pay the custodian a fee of 0.3% of the assets in your account each year (that's $300 on every $100,000). Depending on the complexity of your self-directed IRA investments, you may also need to pay for the guidance of a tax or small-business attorney in addition to paying custodian fees.

DECIDE WHAT TO INVEST IN

Options in self-directed IRAs include the following three categories...

Real estate is, by far, the largest and most popular investment. Owning apartments and multifamily homes is a business in which many investors feel they have or can develop a reasonable expertise and edge. Some IRA investors team up with friends or partners to pool their money to buy larger commercial properties such as office buildings and storage facilities.

Promissory notes and loans represent one of the fastest-growing alternatives for self-directed IRA investors. With this type of investment, you use your IRA assets to lend money. In return, your IRA receives interest from the borrower each month until the borrower pays back the principal.

Example: *LendingClub.com*, which matches up investors with borrowers who need personal loans that range from $500 to tens of thousands of dollars, is popular with self-directed IRA investors, who may earn 5% to 10% interest or higher on loans. If a borrower fails to make payments, LendingClub will turn over the account to a collection agency, but there is a chance that you could lose your principal.

Private equity—owning a partnership interest in a private business or acting as a venture capitalist for a start-up company—requires extensive expertise and research, but it may provide the highest return over time.

AVOID THE PITFALLS OF SELF-DIRECTED IRAs

Self-directed IRAs have unique risks and specific guidelines that an investor must understand. *These include...*

• **Lack of government protections.** Due diligence is up to you. If you invest in a private deal and it turns out to be a fraud, you can file a lawsuit against the con artist, but unlike publicly traded stocks, private investments have little oversight or scrutiny from government regulators.

• **Lack of liquidity.** It's easy to bail out of a bad mutual fund. But if you invest in, say, commercial real estate, you may not have access to your money for years until the building is sold.

Caution: Tied-up assets can be tricky for older investors who reach age 70½ and have to start withdrawing required minimum distributions (RMDs) each year. Because your RMD is based on the aggregate of assets in all your IRAs and you do not have to withdraw a proportionate amount from each IRA, you will need to make sure that you have enough money to withdraw from more liquid IRAs to satisfy IRS requirements.

• **Prohibited investments.** Some are off-limits even in self-directed IRAs, including life insurance contracts and certain collectibles such as artwork, rugs, antiques, gems, stamps, certain rare coins and wine.

• **Self-dealing.** The IRS strictly prohibits owners of self-directed IRAs from using the accounts' assets for self-benefit or profit other than distributions. *Example*: If you invest in a vacation home in your IRA, you can rent it out or resell it, but you cannot stay in the home yourself—not even for a single night—or allow immediate family members to stay there, even if they pay you to do so.

This prohibition against "self-dealing" also applies to non–real estate investments. *Example:* You can't use your IRA money to invest in a business start-up owned by your son.

If you cross these legal lines, the IRS could disqualify the IRA's tax-deferred status and force you to pay income tax on the full value of the holdings, as well as a 10% penalty on that amount if you are under age 59½.

New Limit on IRA Rollovers

The Tax Code allows you to withdraw money from a traditional IRA without facing taxes or penalties as long as you redeposit the money within 60 days. That has provided a loophole for many people who use the money as a short-term loan. But as a result of a recent Tax Court ruling, starting January 1, 2015, you are limited to only one such rollover within 12 months no matter how many different IRAs you have (rather than one rollover for each IRA).

Ed Slott, CPA, president of Ed Slott and Co., a consulting firm specializing in IRAs, Rockville Centre, New York. He is author of *Ed Slott's Retirement Decisions Guide 2015. IRAHelp.com*

Inherited IRAs: What You Need to Know

Inherited IRAs are not protected from creditors in a bankruptcy case. The US Supreme Court recently ruled that creditors can go after assets in inherited IRAs because the accounts are not treated the same as regular IRAs, which are regarded as retirement assets.

Examples of differences: Unlike original owners, heirs cannot add money to the IRAs and can take money out of them anytime without penalty.

This decision is particularly important for spouses. A spouse who inherits has the option to roll the assets into his/her own IRA—subject to a 10% early-withdrawal penalty if he takes money from his own IRA before age 59½. If the spouse does not do the rollover, the account is considered an inherited IRA and is not protected in bankruptcy. This makes the rollover a better choice for many people—but every situation is different, so consult a knowledgeable financial adviser.

Forbes.com

BETTER WAYS...

Time to Rebalance Your 401(k)?

Older 401(k) investors rarely adjust their mix of investments. Among people age 55 and older, 34% say they have *never* made a change in how their retirement money is invested—compared with 59% of millennials saying that they had made such a change in the past year. A 401(k) investment is designed for the long term—but rebalancing, by selling some of the best-performing investments and buying more of those that have not performed well recently, leads to much higher returns than simply choosing investments and leaving them alone for decades. A buy-and-hold approach results in a portfolio more heavily weighted to stocks, which tend to outperform bonds—but it exposes retirement savings to stocks' greater risk. Ask your financial adviser for advice on how and when to rebalance your 401(k).

CBSNews.com

How to Handle IRAs and 401(k)s in a Divorce

IRA funds can be transferred after divorce from one spouse to the other without incurring penalties. After the divorce is final, a transfer is allowed and is not considered a taxable distribution. Transfers also can be made after a legal separation agreement is approved by a judge. Retirement plans run by an employer, such as pensions and 401(k) plans, can be transferred only using a court order called a Qualified Domestic Relations Order (QDRO). A QDRO can be part of a divorce decree—or if not, should be drawn up at the same time as the divorce settlement or immediately afterward.

Rules are complex and must be followed carefully—consult knowledgeable legal and financial advisers.

Ed Slott, CPA, president of Ed Slott and Co., a consulting firm specializing in IRAs, Rockville Centre, New York. He is author of *Ed Slott's Retirement Decisions Guide 2015. IRAHelp.com*

Buy a Home with a Reverse Mortgage

Jack M. Guttentag, known as the Mortgage Professor. He is professor of finance emeritus, Wharton School, University of Pennsylvania, Philadelphia. *MtgProfessor.com*

For years, people age 62 or older who have paid off their mortgages have been able to use reverse mortgages to convert equity in their homes back into cash. But thanks to a change in the rules, there's another way to use a reverse mortgage—to buy a home.

Benefit: You don't have to reach as deep into savings to buy a home. And, as with a regular reverse mortgage, principal or interest payments don't have to be made until the home is sold or you and perhaps your spouse pass away.

Before you decide to do this, consider the costs and risks to you and your heirs as well as the benefits. *What to know...*

• **A reverse mortgage can cover some, but not all, of the home's price.** The amount available to put toward the purchase typically is one-third to a little over one-half of the home's value, depending in part on how big a mortgage-insurance premium you are willing to pay.

Because no payments are being made, the balance due on a reverse-mortgage loan rises over time. Lenders limit the loan amount in relation to the property's value to protect themselves. You can use the free reverse-mortgage calculator at *MtgProfessor.com* to get an idea of rates, fees and other costs.

Example: A 70-year-old couple wants to buy a $300,000 home that they expect to live in for the next 10 years. They can get about $100,000 from a reverse mortgage by paying the minimum mortgage-insurance premium of 0.5% of the $300,000 price, which is $1,500. If instead they pay $7,500 in mortgage insurance (a 2.5% premium), they can raise that to about $164,000.

• **There are advantages to an adjustable-rate reverse mortgage.** Conventional wisdom says that adjustable-rate mortgages are risky now because interest rates might rise. But an adjustable-rate reverse mortgage provides an advantage over fixed—it allows a borrower to draw more money in the future by accessing an optional line of credit. In contrast, fixed-rate reverse mortgages require the borrower to draw all of the proceeds at the outset.

• **Your spouse's age matters.** The US Department of Housing and Urban Development requires borrowers to be 62 years old and considers a spouse younger than 62 to be "noncontracting" to the mortgage and, under rules adopted in 2014, able to stay in the house after your death. However, the allowed amount of borrowing is decreased to take into account the age of the noncontracting spouse.

• **You might leave nothing for your heirs.** If you want to transfer your full equity in a home to your heirs, do not take out a reverse mortgage. Since there are no required payments during the life of the loan, unless you make voluntary payments, the amount owed grows every year. And if property values in your area have not increased enough, the amount that will be owed to settle the mortgage may exceed the home's value at your death, leaving nothing for your heirs.

Typically, when the owners die, the house is sold, the balance of the reverse mortgage is repaid, and the excess is paid to the estate. If the proceeds from the sale are smaller than the debt, the loss is covered by a Federal Housing Administration reserve fund. If instead the heirs want to keep the home, the estate has up to one year to pay off the mortgage balance.

How to Save Big on Taxes in Retirement

Jonathan Clements, writer of a weekly column for *The Wall Street Journal* and author of *Jonathan Clements Money Guide 2015*. Previously, he was director of financial education for Citigroup at the bank's US wealth-management business. *JonathanClements.com*

Here's another reason to love retirement—the ability to save big money by managing your annual tax bill. Once retired, you decide when you get paid—and from which accounts to draw that money.

How can you turn this flexibility to full advantage? *Here are three strategies...*

LOW-INCOME YEARS

Conventional wisdom says retirees should tap their taxable accounts first, traditional retirement accounts next and Roth retirement accounts last. That way, you squeeze more tax-deferred growth out of your traditional retirement accounts, such as your 401(k) and IRA, and more tax-free growth out of your Roth 401(k) and Roth IRA.

But if you follow the conventional wisdom and pay for your initial retirement years by dipping into, say, savings accounts and certificates of deposit held in taxable accounts, you may find yourself paying little or no taxes—which in the long run is a terrible waste.

Better strategy: Take advantage of these low-income, low-tax-rate years to withdraw some money from a traditional IRA or 401(k). You even could convert part of your traditional IRA to a Roth IRA. The conversion would trigger a tax bill on the sum converted, but thereafter the money in the Roth would grow tax-free.

By shrinking the size of these traditional retirement accounts in your 60s, you may avoid big tax bills once you're in your 70s and you have to take required minimum distributions (RMDs) from your retirement accounts. Those RMDs will boost your taxable income and could, in turn, trigger taxes on up to 85% of your Social Security benefit!

Suppose you expect to be in the 25% federal income tax bracket once you start RMDs in your 70s. To reduce those big tax bills, you might want to generate enough taxable income in your 60s to get to the top of the 15% bracket. In 2015, that would mean generating at least $74,900 in total income if you're married filing jointly or $37,450 if you're single. Because income that high could lead to taxes on your Social Security benefit, consider delaying your Social Security benefits until as late as age 70. That can be a smart move anyway because your monthly check will be significantly larger as a result of the delay.

HIGH-DEDUCTION YEARS

Got a year with large itemized deductions, perhaps because of hefty medical expenses or large charitable contributions? Those deductions will reduce your taxable income, and you could find yourself in a lower tax bracket than normal. To get more value out of your tax deductions, consider making larger-than-usual withdrawals from your traditional IRA.

HIGH-COST YEARS

Suppose you need to buy a new car or replace your home's roof. To generate the necessary spending money, you might be tempted to take an extra-large withdrawal from your traditional IRA. But not only could that withdrawal get taxed at a high rate, the extra taxable income also might trigger taxes on your Social Security benefit.

What to do instead? Consider tapping your savings account or money-market fund held in a regular taxable account or, alternatively, making a tax-free withdrawal from your Roth IRA.

What Some States Are Doing to Attract Retirees

Some states are easing the estate tax burden to attract retirees or keep them from moving to lower-tax states. The Tennessee estate tax exemption rises to $5 million in 2015 from $2 million and will disappear in 2016. Maryland's increases to $1.5 million from $1 million. Minnesota's rises to $1.4 million from $1.2 million. And New York's goes up to $3.125 million from $2.062 million. Maryland and New York will continue to increase thresholds every year until they match the federal exemption in 2019 (which is $5.43 million for 2015 and is adjusted for inflation annually). Minnesota's exemption rises $200,000 a year until it reaches $2 million in 2018.

Kiplinger.com

Tax Breaks for Older People

The standard deduction for 2015 is $7,850 for a single taxpayer age 65 or older—compared with $6,300 for younger taxpayers. Taxpayers age 65 and older who itemize can deduct medical expenses that exceed 7.5% of adjusted gross income—the threshold for younger taxpayers is 10%. Those who become self-employed after leaving a job can deduct the premiums paid for Medicare Part B and Part D, the cost of Medigap policies or the cost of a Medicare Advantage plan. The working spouse of a retiree can contribute up to $6,500 a year to the retiree's IRA. There are limits and special circumstances affecting some of these tax breaks—consult your financial adviser.

Fidelity.com

Discounts for Seniors

Amtrak gives 15% off the lowest available fare for most trains for travelers age 62 and older.* Southwest Airlines provides fully refundable senior fares for fliers age 65 and older whose plans change—although these may not be the lowest fares offered. Verizon Wireless discounts cell phone service for people 65 and older. Walgreens and RiteAid have monthly senior-discount days (nonprescription items are discounted by 20% to 25%).

Roundup of experts on travel and other discounts for seniors, reported at *HuffingtonPost.com*.

*Rates and offers subject to change.

MONEYWISE...

Why Senior Discounts Aren't Always the Best Deals!

Discounts available to people of all ages or at specific websites can sometimes be better than senior discounts. *For instance...*

- **AARP members** get 5%-to-20% discounts at certain hotel chains.* *Examples*: One recent AARP discount at Holiday Inn Chicago-O'Hare Airport brought the one-night rate to $114.95. But a seven-day, advance-purchase rate for any traveler was $106.95—total savings of $8. And a booking through the *Last Minute Travel* app was $101 (a $14 savings over the AARP rate).
- **For car rentals,** deals through *Hotwire.com* may be 50% lower than Avis and Budget rates with AARP discounts.
- **Lower-than-senior-discount rates** also are available at daily-deal websites including *Groupon* and *LivingSocial*.

Kiplinger.com

*Rates and prices subject to change.

Free or Low-Cost College for Older Adults

Many state universities and colleges offer tuition waivers for residents who are age 60 or older and who meet specific requirements that vary by state and institution. Some schools make for-credit courses free. Others permit older adults to audit classes without a charge. Certain private colleges also allow community residents to audit some courses for free. Schools that do not offer free courses may make them available at low rates.

Examples: San Diego State University's College of Extended Studies offers courses for as little as $45* (*example of money saved on one course*: $314)...Case Western Reserve University charges $75 to $85 for some Lifelong Learning Program classes.

ConsumerReports.org

*Prices subject to change.

What You Know About Aging Is Wrong!

Marc E. Agronin, MD, an adult and geriatric psychiatrist who is medical director for mental health and clinical research at Miami Jewish Health Systems and affiliate associate professor of psychiatry and neurology at University of Miami Miller School of Medicine, both in Florida. He is a contributor to "The Experts" blog for *The Wall Street Journal* at *Blogs.WSJ.com/experts.*

Old age is often portrayed as a time of loneliness, depression and significant cognitive decline. But most research indicates that the opposite is true for most retired people.

Among the common myths about getting older...

MYTH #1: Depression hits. No one loves the physical changes of age, let alone the likelihood of dealing with age-related illnesses. But the emotional prospects are better than you think. The rates of major depression, for example, actually go down with age. A recent study that tracked participants for about 10 years found that their feelings of well-being increased until they reached their 70s. The feelings plateaued at that point but still didn't fall.

People who develop serious medical problems or experience traumatic life events (such as the death of a spouse) obviously will be more likely to suffer from depression than those who have an easier path. But even in the face of adversity, older people are resilient—they've accumulated enough wisdom to help them through hard times.

MYTH #2: You'll be lonely. One of the inevitabilities of aging is the loss of friends and family members. Older people do spend more time alone. But that's not the same as feeling lonely or isolated.

A number of studies have shown that the quality of relationships improves with age. You may have fewer close friends in your 70s than you did in your 50s, but you'll probably find that the connections have matured and become richer and more fulfilling.

Think back to your earlier relationships—how often were they tumultuous and emotionally fraught? Studies have shown that older adults tend to be more positive about their relationships and less likely to experience social tensions.

MYTH #3: Your mind slips. Yes, it will, in some ways—but the typical "slips" that most people experience will be offset by improvements in other mental areas.

Take memory and the ability to concentrate. Both start to decline by middle age. You won't be as quick at math, and your verbal skills won't be quite as sharp. You'll retain the ability to learn, but new information will take longer to sink in.

At the same time, you'll notice improvements in other mental abilities. You'll have a lot of accrued knowledge, along with an edge in reasoning and creative thinking. You won't keep up with the youngsters on cognitive tests, but you may perform better in real-world situations.

To keep your mind active, take up painting or other hobbies. Read challenging novels. Learn another language, or learn to play a musical instrument. People who stretch themselves mentally can improve memory and cognitive skills and possibly slow the rate of subsequent declines.

MYTH #4: No more sex. In surveys, older adults often report more sexual satisfaction than is reported by their younger counterparts. They might have sex less often, but they tend to enjoy it more.

A national survey of sexual attitudes, published in *The New England Journal of Medicine*, found that, on average, the frequency of sexual activity declines only slightly from the 50s to the 70s.

And the sexual attitudes among seniors are sufficiently frisky to make their grandchildren blush. About 50% of people ages 57 to 75 reported engaging in oral sex. More than half of men and about 25% of women masturbated.

Good health (and an available partner) are among the best predictors of a robust sex life. Sex-specific disorders—such as erectile dysfunction in men and vaginal dryness in women—now can be overcome with a variety of aids and treatments. Even when sexual activity does decline (or disappear), older adults enjoy cuddling and other intimacies.

MYTH #5: Falls are normal. Falls are never a normal part of aging...and they're not merely accidents. Anyone who is unsteady on his/her feet has a health problem that needs to be addressed. It could be osteoporosis, reduced muscle strength, impaired vision, disturbed sleep or side effects from medications.

Warning: Falls are the main cause of more than 90% of hip fractures and a leading cause of emergency room visits and deaths.

People who get any kind of exercise—a daily walk, working around the house, digging in the garden—are much less likely to fall or to suffer serious injuries should they have a misstep.

Important: A good night's sleep. We have found that people who don't sleep well tend to have more disorientation and balance problems, particularly if they happen to be taking sleep medications that contain the antihistamine *diphenhydramine.*

Maintain good sleep practices—go to bed and get up at the same times each day...avoid sleep distractions (such as watching TV in bed)...don't drink caffeinated beverages late in the day...and drink a soothing cup of warm milk or chamomile tea at bedtime.

To Protect Your Brain: Hold Off on Retirement

Delaying retirement could protect your brain. For each additional year that a person worked before retiring, dementia risk dropped by 3% in a recent analysis. That means someone who retired at age 60 had a 15% greater chance of developing dementia, on average, than someone who retired at 65.

Theory: The mental stimulation and social connections at work may keep the brain healthy.

Analysis of the records of more than 400,000 retired workers in France by researchers at National Institute of Health and Medical Research, Paris, presented at the 2013 Alzheimer's Association International Conference.

Dating Tips for Seniors

A good way for seniors to find dating partners is to look for friends with shared interests rather than just trying to find someone to date. Meeting people at book clubs, church groups, hobby gatherings and community classes can be a way to find potential dates with similar interests. Online dating can be helpful as well, though only 6% of people ages 55 to 64 have used it compared with 10% of 18-to-24-year-olds.

Roundup of experts on dating among older adults, reported at *USNews.com.*

EASY-TO-DO...

Surprising Mood Booster for Seniors

The Internet prevents depression in older people. After controlling for various factors, researchers found that people over age 50 who used the Internet were one-third less likely to be depressed than nonusers. The reduced rate of depression was greatest among those who lived alone, leading researchers to believe that Internet use counters feelings of loneliness and isolation.

University of California, Berkeley Wellness Letter. BerkeleyWellness.com

13

Travel Talk

Have More Fun Traveling! Save Time, Money and Hassle with These Great Apps

Need to make a last-minute reservation at a hotel? Find your way around an unfamiliar city? Or keep track of a trip itinerary? There are hundreds of travel-oriented apps capable of doing things like these and more—often for free. But which really are worth loading onto your smartphone? *Apps that make travel more enjoyable, affordable and efficient...*

• **Get directions and dodge traffic (and traffic tickets).** There are numerous map apps that can help travelers navigate unfamiliar areas. The well-known *Google Maps* app is one worth having—no app provides more accurate driving and walking directions. Android, iOS or Windows. Free. (*Google.com/mobile/maps*)

Unlike most map apps, *Maps.me* lets you download maps to your digital device and use them offline. It's a good way to avoid the potentially steep international cellular roaming fees sometimes incurred when a conventional map app is used abroad. Just download the *Maps.me* map of the area you're visiting before leaving home or while at a Wi-Fi hot spot. Downloading maps also makes sense if you travel with a digital device that doesn't offer cellular access. Android or iOS. Free. (*Maps.me*)

Waze supplies driving directions like a conventional map app does—but while other apps calculate the fastest route based on distances and speed limits, Waze also gathers real-time traffic data from Waze users and directs drivers

Note: Prices, rates and offers throughout this chapter and book are subject to change.

Christopher Elliott, consumer advocate for *National Geographic Traveler* magazine, author of *The Washington Post* travel section's "Navigator" column and cofounder of the Consumer Travel Alliance. He is author of *How to Be the World's Smartest Traveler (and Save Time, Money, and Hassle)*. *Elliott.org* around traffic tie-ups. Waze also warns drivers when police officers have been spotted on the road ahead. Android, iOS or Windows. Free. (*Waze.com*)

• **Organize your trip.** What's the address of the hotel? What time is your dinner reservation? What's the confirmation number for your car-rental reservation? The *TripIt* app consolidates important trip details like these into an easy-to-understand master itinerary that you can access from your smartphone, even offline. Just forward trip-related confirmation e-mails to *TripIt*, and the app will automatically incorporate the pertinent details. (Trip details can be typed in when there is no confirmation e-mail.) *TripIt* also makes it simple to forward trip details to colleagues or loved ones. Android or iOS. Free unless you upgrade to *TripIt Pro*, which costs $49 a year and provides additional features such as flight-delay alerts and frequent-flier-mile tracking. (*TripIt.com*)

• **Carry a customized digital travel guidebook.** The *Stay.com* app can act as a digital guidebook for more than 150 cities worldwide—without the hassle of lugging around a guidebook. It features insider tips from more than 1,000 local experts...it lets you ask your Facebook friends to suggest their own favorite places in cities you intend to visit, customizing your travel tips in a way that a traditional guidebook cannot...and it allows you to add destinations of particular appeal to you based on your own research. All of these sites then appear together on the app's downloadable city maps. Android or iOS. Free. (*Stay.com*)

• **Avoid unfair rental-car damage charges.** If a car-rental company spots a scratch or ding when you turn in your car, it might stick you with a bill of $500 or more—even if the damage was not your fault. The minor damage might have happened before you ever drove the car but gone unnoticed until you returned it. Some travelers try to avoid this problem by using a smartphone camera to document a rental car's condition. But rental agencies often reject this evidence, arguing that a picture that purports to show a preexisting scuff actually might have been taken after the customer did the damage. And they won't be convinced by the time and location information embedded in the photo showing when you snapped it—that information can be falsified.

An app called *Record360* verifies the precise time and location where video of a rental car was shot in a way that cannot reasonably be questioned by the rental agency, making it much more difficult for the agency to hold you responsible for damage you did not do. The app can be used to record the condition of other rental property, too, including homes, hotel rooms and ski equipment. Or record the condition of your luggage before it is checked and when it's retrieved from the baggage carousel so that you can prove that the airline is responsible for any damage done. iOS only. Free. (*Record360.com*)

• **Locate Wi-Fi hot spots.** The *Boingo Wi-Finder* app can direct you to millions of Wi-Fi hot spots all around the globe, including more than a million that Boingo users can access very quickly—no need to type in a user name and password—with Boingo's ultra-streamlined login process. Boingo's "Virtual Private Network" encryption dramatically reduces security risks. The Boingo app is free, but the service costs anywhere from $4.98 to $39 per month, depending on the plan selected. Remember to cancel Boingo when your trip is over to avoid recurring credit card charges. Android, iOS or Windows. (*Boingo.com/retail*)

• **Find a good hotel.** Many apps provide reviews of hotels (as well as restaurants and tourist attractions) by previous guests. These reviews are not 100% reliable—positive reviews sometimes are written by people paid by the hotel...and negative reviews occasionally are written by owners of competing hotels. That said, most reviews are legitimate, and these apps often do provide a reasonable sense of a hotel's quality. *TripAdvisor* is the most comprehensive of the hotel guest review apps, with more than 200 million total reviews. Android or iOS. Free. (*TripAdvisor.com/apps*)

• **Get help in an emergency.** You know how to summon help when you have an emergency in the US—just dial 911. But foreign countries have different emergency contact numbers. The *Travel Safe* app provides police...fire department...and ambulance emergency contact numbers for more than 200 foreign countries so that travelers can get the help they need as quickly as possible. It costs 99 cents for Android...$1.29 for iOS. (at *LKapps.com.au*, click on "Travel Safe")

• **Get a ride.** It can be difficult to find a taxi in many cities, and taxi rates can be steep. With the app-based *Uber transportation network*, you can use your smartphone to request a ride in more than 200 cities worldwide. Using a map on your smartphone screen, you then can track the driver that Uber designates as he/she comes to pick you up. (Uber says it conducts background checks on all of its drivers, but its screening process has been criticized by lawmakers in many state capitals and various foreign governments. Uber says that it is toughening up background checks and working to do more to improve passenger safety.)

Uber's basic *"UberX" service* tends to be less expensive than conventional taxis—often 10% to 25% less—though savings vary greatly by city, speed of traffic and other factors. *Exception:* Uber can be more expensive than taxis—sometimes much more—during times of peak demand, when Uber increases rates. Watch for warnings on the Uber app that surge pricing is in effect when requesting a ride. You can choose from various payment methods, including credit card or PayPal. Android, iOS or Windows. The app is free. (*Uber.com*)

EASY-TO-DO...

Free App Translates Foreign Languages Instantly

With *Word Lens*, you point your smartphone or iPad video camera at, say, a road sign or restaurant menu. The software replaces foreign words in the live picture on your screen with their English equivalents and vice versa. No Internet connection is needed. Word Lens, which Google has acquired, used to charge $10 per language but now is free for an unspecified limited time for all six languages—French, German, Italian, Portuguese, Russian and Spanish.

Dave Johnson, editorial director of eHow's Tech Channel and author of three dozen books on technology. *Ehow.com/Ehow-tech*

• **Get a deal on a hotel or rental car.** There is no single best app for getting a great last-minute rate on a hotel room or rental car. Instead, check several different apps for the best offer, including *Booking.com* (*Booking.com/apps*)...*Hotwire* (*Hotwire.com/app*)...and *Priceline* (*Priceline.com*). All three apps are free for Android and iOS. The Priceline app is available for Windows as well.

Strong Dollar Creates Travel Bargains

Gabe Saglie, a senior editor at *Travelzoo*, which publishes travel and entertainment deals. *Travelzoo.com*

The strong US dollar has made hotel stays, restaurant meals, entertainment and merchandise in many countries the most affordable they have been in a decade and much cheaper than even a year ago. A lavish 200-euro dinner for two in Paris, for example, recently cost $50 less than a year ago.

Keep the following in mind when you plan your trip...

• **The strong dollar does not save on airfares for flights booked in the US,** which remain high amid strong demand in spite of plunging jet-fuel costs. However, it could save you money on transportation booked in foreign countries.

• **Be careful when booking tour packages that bill you in dollars.** They may not pass through all the currency savings to you, so you might be better off booking everything directly.

• **Look for hotel bargains.** Especially big bargains are available in Portugal and Greece, where in addition to the effects of the strong dollar, hotels are scrambling to attract guests amid a drop in tourism. *Examples:* A room at the highly rated Hotel Herodion in Athens, next to the Acropolis, recently cost as little as $80 per night. In Lisbon, a stay at the posh five-star Pestana Palace Hotel & National Monument, a fairy-tale palace with lush gardens, recently cost $153 per night.

• **Look beyond the eurozone.** Even though the euro receives the most attention, currencies in several other attractive tourist destinations have dropped even more versus the dollar, creating even bigger bargains, including Budapest, Hungary, where the US dollar has gained 25% against the forint...and Oslo, Norway, where the US dollar has gained 25% against the krone.

Aloha Hawaii!

It is possible to lower the cost of a Hawaiian vacation. *Just follow this advice...*

Book early—as early as 11 months before departure. Book a room with a view of a garden or mountain, instead of the ocean, to save $50 or more a night. Choose a hotel designated three-star on *Priceline* or similar sites, such as a Hilton or Marriott, often with rooms on or near the beach for $135 per night or less, instead of a four- or five-star one, where rooms can be $500 or more. Check daily-deal sites such as *Groupon* and *LivingSocial* for special deals. Consider booking a package deal including flights and hotels or ones such as Costco deals that include hotel, rental car and daily breakfast. This can save you up to $300 per person. Travel during off-seasons—spring and fall—to save 50% or more on airfare.

Kiplinger.com

To Spend Less on a Ski Vacation...

Looking to hit the slopes this winter? *Here are ways to save on your trip...*

Fly to a larger, busier airport (book airline tickets at least 14 days in advance)—instead of flying to the closest airport—and drive to the resort. Consider renting a home near a ski resort instead of staying at a hotel—go to *HomeAway.com* and similar sites to find out what is available. Join resorts' mailing lists for discounts on lift tickets, or search for discounted tickets at *Liftopia.com.* Consider buying lift tickets from local ski shops that have rental-and-ticket packages.

For the best deals, avoid the biggest-name resorts and choose less known ones offering high-quality skiing.

Examples: Breckenridge or Arapahoe Basin, Colorado...Park City or Alta, Utah...Lake Tahoe, California.

Roundup of experts on ski vacations, reported at *MarketWatch.com.*

Great Ideas for Vacationing with Teens

Pauline Frommer, editorial director of the Frommer Guidebooks. She is a nationally syndicated radio talk-show host and author of the best-selling *Frommer's EasyGuide to New York City.*

It can be a challenge to choose a place to vacation with hard-to-please teens. *What I recommend...*

• **Belize.** It's a wonderful mix of cultural sites (Mayan ruins) and nature adventures. My family's favorite adventure there was the ATM cave (it stands for a long and unpronounceable Mayan name). You swim into the cave and then clamber through it until you come to a cathedral-like hall where, centuries ago, human sacrifices took place. As you walk around, you'll see ceremonial bowls and actual human skulls calcified to the floor.

• **London.** If you prefer an urban vacation, most teens also enjoy London because there's a great mix of sights and adventures.

More tips for vacationing with teens: In the months leading up to the trip, rent movies about the places you're going, ones that give some insight into the culture and the history of the place. That should help get teens excited about the upcoming trip.

Also, let them take part in the planning. Give each one a guidebook and a day that is theirs to plan for the family, and see what they come up with. You'll likely find yourself on a great adventure, and they'll likely be more patient with the days they didn't plan.

Save on Tickets and Food at Theme Parks

Prices have soared at several theme parks—for example, $99 for one day at Disneyland if you are age 10 or older. Consider buying a season pass, which can pay for itself in a few visits...or multiday tickets. Universal Orlando's one-day ticket for both its parks runs $147, but a four-day pass is $54 a day.

More tips on saving: Buy tickets online, not at the gate...some parks cut prices on weekdays or during late afternoon and evening hours...some have deals for students, military members, in-state residents and other groups...Costco.com and AAA offer park discounts...and the parks' e-mail newsletters and websites often have special deals.

Discounted gift cards are sometimes available for restaurants close to parks, such as McCormick & Schmick's and Rainforest Cafe. And some parks offer dining plans that can save you money. Finally, bring sunscreen, photo supplies and rain gear from home—in-park prices are very high.

The Boston Globe and *MarketWatch.com.*

If Cruises Seem Boring to You...

Pauline Frommer, editorial director of the Frommer Guidebooks. She is a nationally syndicated radio talk-show host and author of the best-selling *Frommer's EasyGuide to New York City.*

Looking for an alternative to the traditional cruise? *Consider these options for adventurers or people who truly want to experience many cultures...*

If you have a long time, say, a few months, for a cruise, you could do Semester at Sea (*SemesteratSea.com*), which is a small boat that carries students and a number of nonstudents (usually seniors) to ports around the world. The participants meet with local experts, tour the sights and delve into the culture they're seeing.

Also, a British company called Swan Hellenic Tours (*US.SwanHellenic.com*), offers cruises that have an educational bent and utilizes smaller ships.

Or you might skip the cruise altogether and go for an overland tour, visiting a number of different cultures (usually in Asia, Africa and Eastern Europe) in a van with a small number of people. The travel agency Adventure Center (*Adventure.com*), in Emoryville, California, acts as a clearinghouse for these sorts of tours.

MONEY SAVER...

Affordable Lodging in Europe

Schools ranging from Oxford University and the London School of Economics to Trinity College in Dublin and Résidence Universitaire Lanteri near Paris rent out student housing to tourists. Prices for a double room typically range from $45 to $120 per night.

Example: A Paris student residence costs $110 a night—an average Paris hotel is $208.

Savings: $98.

To find rooms and availability: *University Rooms.com...LSEVacations.co.uk...TCD.ie/accommodation.*

Reid Bramblett, founder of *ReidsGuides.com*, a budget travel-planning site focused on Europe.

Airlines with the Least-Costly Fees

Airlines just love to tack on fees, but here's a list of the lowest...

Checked-baggage charges: Southwest, two bags free...JetBlue, one bag free.

Unaccompanied minors: Alaska, $25 for ages five to 17...Southwest, $50 for ages five to 11.

Pets: Frontier, $75.

Snacks: Free at Hawaiian, JetBlue and Southwest.

Extra legroom: Frontier, $15.

Seat selection/upgrades: Spirit, $1 to $50... Air Canada, $10 to $40.

Change in nonrefundable ticket: Southwest, free...Frontier, $75.

Roundup of experts on fees for air travel, reported at *GoBankingRates.com.*

Did You Pay *Much More* Than the Person Next to You on the Plane?

An air traveler may pay *eight times* as much as the person sitting in the next seat.

Example: On a recent United Airlines flight from Los Angeles to Las Vegas, one-way coach fares varied from less than $200 to more than $1,600.

Least-varied seat prices: Spirit Airlines, averaging a 5% variation...Virgin America, averaging 15%.

Prices vary less to popular vacation destinations and more to major business locations, such as Washington, DC, and Chicago, because business travelers often have to fly regardless of price.

The Los Angeles Times. LATimes.com

Same Travel Site, Different Prices

Airfares may sometimes be different on the US version and a foreign version of the same website—for example, at *Expedia.com* and the company's English-language Japanese site, *Expedia.co.jp.*

Examples: A recent round-trip from Bogotá to Cartagena on Avianca cost $200 for a listing using the Colombian version of the site...$280 on the US version—for an $80 savings by using the Colombian version. A round-trip from Santiago to Buenos Aires on TAM cost $564 for a listing on the Chilean version of the site...$682 with the US one—for a savings of $118.

Caution: When you use the foreign version of a site, tickets may be sold in that country's currency and your credit card may charge a foreign transaction fee.

Travel+Leisure. TravelandLeisure.com

Lower Airfare Strategy

Lower your airfare by combining two strategies—an extended "fare lock" and a price tracker. For a fee, some airlines let you lock in an airfare for a period before you have to buy the ticket.

Examples: British Airways charges $10 to lock in a price for 72 hours. United Airlines charges $5 to $20 depending on the flight and duration of the lock.

Once you have locked in the fare, you can go to *Yapta.com* to track the price and get an alert if the price drops.

The Wall Street Journal. WSJ.com

"Bargain" Airline Tickets May Cost Your Family *More*

You might spot a bargain price on an airline's website, but when you try to purchase tickets for more than one passenger, the price may jump by 10% or more. That's because there might be just one seat available at the lowest fare. If you request multiple tickets, airline systems will routinely charge you the higher fare for all.

Example: A traveler found an airfare for $708, but when he bought four tickets, it came to $789 per person—more than $300 extra.

Self-defense: Try buying multiple tickets in blocks of just one or two at a time.

AirfareWatchdog.com

CONSUMER SMARTS...

The Best Time to Buy an Airline Ticket Is 54 Days Before the Flight

Statistically, that is when domestic airline tickets are at the lowest price. If you cannot buy at the 54-day mark, purchase your ticket between 29 and 104 days before your trip—tickets typically are within $10 of the lowest price during that time period.

Analyses by *CheapAir.com* and *CheapOair.com*.

Yet Another Airline Fee...

Karen Larson, editor of *Bottom Line/Personal*, 281 Tresser Blvd., Stamford, Connecticut 06901. *BottomLinePersonal.com*

A colleague recently bought tickets on a flight to Denver only to discover that she would have to ante up again to reserve seats. The airline's website sold her economy-class tickets, then wouldn't allow her to select seats—it appeared that all the economy-class seats were taken. "Economy Plus" seats still were available...for an extra $69 each.

This is an increasingly common predicament for air travelers, says George Hobica, founder of *AirfareWatchdog.com*. Many airlines now charge a premium for especially desirable economy seats, such as seats in the roomier exit rows. These pricier seats often are the last ones left to reserve when it looks like the rest of economy is filled up.

Don't be pressured into paying the premium, says Hobica. Call the airline and complain about not being able to select seats. Sometimes you will get premium economy seats at no extra charge—this worked for my colleague. If not, don't select seats at all. You'll be assigned seats when you check in for the flight, which you typically can do up to 24 hours ahead. Here, too, you're likely to receive premium seats at no extra charge.

It's typically worth paying extra to lock in a seat only if you're traveling with a young child and don't want to take any chance that you'll be separated.

Airline seat-assignment fees are likely to become even more widespread in the years ahead, says Hobica. Some carriers, including British Airways, Lufthansa, Virgin Atlantic, Frontier, Spirit and Allegiant, now charge fees to reserve any economy-class seat prior to check-in.

Airlines with the Best/ Worst Economy Seats

The airline with the best economy seats is JetBlue. In a recent poll, when asked which airline had the most comfortable economy-class seats, 21% of people chose JetBlue. JetBlue seats have 33 inches of seat pitch—the standard measurement of distance between seats—more than most other airlines offer.

Other scores: Southwest and AirTran were chosen by 6% as having the most comfortable seats...Allegiant, 8%...Frontier, 13%.

Worst economy seats: It is a tie between US Airways and American Airlines—only 2% of respondents said that their seats are the most comfortable. Just 3% picked United Airlines or Spirit Airlines, and only 5% chose Delta.

Survey conducted by *AirfareWatchdog.com*, reported at *MarketWatch.com*.

Airline Upgrades Disappearing—but Not for You

George Hobica, a travel journalist specializing in consumer affairs and founder of *AirfareWatchdog.com*, a website that reports on travel bargains.

Airline travelers—particularly those who fly enough to earn elite status—used to have a reasonable chance of getting bumped up to business or first class for free if open seats remained at flight time. But free upgrades—and even frequent-flier upgrades—have become extremely rare or nonexistent.

For example: Delta has eliminated complimentary upgrades on most cross-country flights. United has eliminated them on "premium service" flights (such as those with flat-bed seats).

That's largely because the airlines have found a new way to make money—selling upgrades. The upgrade price can be anywhere from $50 to $300 on a domestic flight, and it can top $1,000 on international flights. Some airlines, including American, auction off upgrades.

What to do: Choose flights that business travelers tend not to fly, since business travelers are more likely to spend cash and/or miles for upgrades. Low-business-travel flights include Saturday, Tuesday and Wednesday flights. If you're told that frequent-flier-mile upgrades are not available, try again two to five days prior to departure—airlines sometimes make some additional seats available for mile upgrades during this window. Or if you are willing to wait to purchase a ticket (and risk paying a higher price or no availability), call the airline three to five days prior to your intended departure date and ask if there are any flights to your destination where frequent-flier-mile upgrades are available. If yes, book an upgradable ticket and immediately claim the upgrade.

BETTER WAYS...

More Comfortable Flying

To get a row of seats to yourself on a flight...

Couples should not book side-by-side seats. Choose an aisle and window to improve your chance of having the row to yourselves—middle seats are the last to be booked. If the middle seat becomes occupied, the occupant usually will agree to swap for a window or an aisle seat (so you can sit near your companion). Pick seats toward the rear of the plane—forward seats are chosen first.

If traveling alone, get a sense of how many seats are empty. If there are 15 or more, do not board right away—let others board, then have the gate agent change your booking to a middle seat in an empty row. Sit in that seat—after the doors close and people move around to empty rows, they probably will not sit next to you...and you will have the row to yourself.

ChicagoBusiness.com

Fly First-Class for Economy Prices

George Hobica, a travel journalist specializing in consumer affairs and founder of *AirfareWatchdog.com*, a website that reports on travel bargains.

First-class seats on planes generally are priced 10 to 20 times higher than economy class—but on certain flights, that's no longer so. The airlines seem to have decided that they would rather sell first-class seats at affordable prices than make them available for frequent-flier-mile upgrades.

Example: Recently I flew first-class from New York to Boston for just $140 (one way) on American Airlines, while US Airways was charging $350 that day for economy class.

Unfortunately, cost-conscious travelers tend to assume that first-class is always expensive and rarely investigate first-class fares before booking a ticket. You still will turn up a lot of absurdly high prices in your ticket search, but every now and then, you will stumble onto a first-class bargain.

Exception: Affordable first-class fares are not likely on long international flights. But good deals occasionally are available in business class. Search for business-class bargains when traveling between the US and Europe during the summer or holiday seasons. For summer travel, 60-day advance purchase generally is required.

Virtually all airlines offer cheap nonrefundable advance-purchase business and first-class fares at various times of the year on select routes. You can find them on websites, but it does not hurt to call the airlines, too. Airlines frequently offer last-minute upgrades to first-class and business class, often when you check in for your flight online or even at the airport. I recently was offered a business-class upgrade on a $189 New York to Los Angeles flight on United for $350 one way (for a total ticket cost of $539). If I had bought that seat in advance, it would have cost $2,500. My fare represented a savings of $1,961.

Airlines Do Shortchange Delayed Travelers: Fight Back!

Federal law requires airlines to pay 200% of the ticket price, up to $650, to anyone involuntarily bumped from a flight that results in a delay of original arrival time between one and two hours (between one and four hours for international flights)...and 400% of the ticket price, up to $1,300, for delays of more than two hours (more than four hours for international flights). But airlines often offer restrictive travel vouchers that are worth less and that expire after a year. Read the small-print Contract of Carriage that comes with your ticket. It is a legal agreement that spells out what airlines must do. Don't take airline employees' word about compensation—they are trained to downplay passenger rights. If an airline is not following federal rules, file a complaint with the US Department of Transportation at *DOT.gov/AirConsumer*.

Roundup of experts on airline regulations, reported in *USA Today*.

Better International Travel

You can check out an international airline at *AirlineRatings.com*. The site offers ratings on safety, service and amenities.

Also: Consider the *Smart Traveler Enrollment Program,* free at *Step.State.gov*—it tells the US government when you are traveling and where you will be while abroad, so you can be alerted in case of any difficulties.

Parade.CondeNast.com

Get Paid for Travel Inconveniences

To compensate for mishaps not covered by travel insurance or airlines (or to supplement what is covered), there is *AirCare* from Berkshire Hathaway Travel Protection. It offers a plan for $25 per trip that pays you a set amount for your troubles. Compensation can be deposited into an account that you specify.

What AirCare covers and for how much: $1,000 for a tarmac delay of more than two hours...$1,000 for lost or stolen luggage...$250 for a missed connection due to a flight delay...$500 for delayed luggage (more than 12 hours)...and $50 for a delayed flight (more than two hours). The benefits are cumulative, so if more than one mishap occurs, you are paid for each of them.

AirfareWatchdog.com

Find Out Your Plane's Route

Know your airplane's route before flying if you are concerned about flying over war zones. In the approximately 40 areas in

BETTER WAYS...

Beat Jet Lag Without Drugs

Before leaving on a trip, try to adjust your sleep schedule to that of the time zone you will be visiting—if possible, change your bedtime by one hour a night until it matches that of your arrival time zone. If you are flying from Boston to Los Angeles, there is a three- or four-hour time difference, depending on the time of year. Upon arrival, book a massage or rub your own feet with lavender oil to help you relax and sleep better. If you need more help sleeping, drink California poppy leaf tea or chamomile tea before bedtime. Or take melatonin, valerian or Rescue Remedy supplements—follow directions on the label.

Coleen Murphy, ND, Natural Medicine Works, Orange County, California, writing in *Natural Health*.

the world where fighting is taking place, the conflicts generally are localized, but some groups do have access to surface-to-air missiles. Flight-tracking sites *FlightAware.com* and *FlightRadar24.com* let you enter an airline and flight number to see the path of the latest trip. Flight paths do change because of weather, congestion and other factors, but airlines usually fly the same route each time. Check several days of a flight to find out whether an airline avoids certain areas or countries. If you are concerned about a flight path, book travel on an airline that uses a different one.

The Wall Street Journal. WSJ.com

Air-Travel Health Myths Debunked

Roundup of travel and health experts, reported in *USA Today*.

Misconceptions about air travel abound—here are the facts...

Myth: Cabin air is full of germs.

Reality: Aircraft are equipped with HEPA filters to clean the air. The problems lie on chair upholstery, tray tables, armrests and toilet handles where bacteria such as *MRSA* and *E. coli* can live for up to one week.

Myth: Bagged pillows and blankets are safe to use.

Reality: Pillowcases on bagged pillows are rarely changed, and blankets should be used only on your lower legs—not near your eyes, nose and mouth.

Myth: The aircraft gets cleaned between flights.

Reality: Airplanes typically are wiped down after every 30 days of service or at 100 flying hours, but the FAA doesn't regulate cleaning, so frequency and thoroughness vary.

Myth: There is nothing you can do to protect yourself in an aircraft cabin.

Reality: Use alcohol-based hand sanitizer...wipe the armrest and tray table with disinfectant wipes...stay hydrated...use tissues to open bathroom doorknobs and touch toilet handles...don't touch your eyes because tear ducts are a fast route to the nose and throat.

Best/Worst Airline for Baggage Handling

Airlines you can trust with your luggage...and the airline with the worst rating for luggage handling...

Best airline for baggage handling: Virgin America. It had only 0.97 complaints of lost luggage per 1,000 passengers last year.

Other high-rated airlines for baggage handling: Frontier, 1.78 complaints per 1,000 passengers...JetBlue, 2.08...Hawaiian, 2.20...Delta, 2.44...Alaska, 2.66.

Worst: Envoy Air, formerly American Eagle, had 8.82 complaints per 1,000 passengers.

US Department of Transportation, Washington, DC.

Thieves at the Baggage Carousel

George Hobica, a travel journalist specializing in consumer affairs and founder of *AirfareWatchdog.com*, a website that reports on travel bargains.

Airports and airlines are reducing baggage-carousel security to save money, increasing the risk for theft. Thieves often can simply take a bag off the carousel and walk out of the airport without having to prove to anyone that the bag is theirs.

In the past, air travelers typically had to show a security guard a luggage ticket to prove that they owned the bags they took from the carousel.

Most thieves are not caught—and victims have no way of knowing that their luggage was stolen and not just lost by the airline. But recent arrests of large-scale luggage thieves in Miami and Chicago hint at the scale of the problem.

What to do: If you must check a bag, get to the carousel as soon as possible after landing—it's a poor time for a bathroom stop. Position yourself as close as possible to the ramp or chute where luggage enters the carousel. Purchase distinctive-looking luggage, or put distinctive tags or tape on your bags. Thieves generally shy away from distinctive bags because they can't claim they thought the bag was theirs if they are stopped...and it makes them easy to spot if security camera footage is later reviewed. Avoid checking high-end bags if possible—thieves target these because they often contain expensive goods.

If your luggage does disappear, contact the issuer of the credit card you used to book the trip as well as the airline. Many credit cards now cover luggage losses above reimbursement limits imposed by airlines.

Do not pack jewelry, cash, antiques or electronics in checked bags, because these often are not covered by airline and credit card reimbursement programs.

EASY-TO-DO...

Pack the Perfect Carry-On Suitcase

Start with a soft-sided 21-inch roller suitcase that will fit into most airplanes' overhead compartments. Put the bulkiest items such as jeans and sweaters in first...then tuck shoes and other items around them. Socks and tights can be stashed inside shoes. Tightly roll as many clothes as you can. Pack bras between rolls of clothes, and tuck underwear inside the cups. Fine fabrics go on top with dry-cleaning bags between items to prevent creases. Pack phone and computer chargers in the inside zipper pockets so that they are easy to reach.

Tracy Cristoph, JetBlue flight attendant, writing in *Better Homes and Gardens*.

Stay Fit While You Travel

Find gyms and fitness clubs near more than 50 major US and Canadian airports by checking *AirportGyms.com*. Most are a 10-to-15-minute cab ride from the airport. Listings include hours, phone number, website and cost of a daily pass.

TravelSmart newsletter. *TravelSmartNewsletter.com*

Hotel Scams Now

The latest scams at hotels...and how you can avoid them...

Fake Wi-Fi networks: Scammers set up Wi-Fi networks that use your hotel's name. Ask the front desk what the correct connection is, and never enter your credit card information into a Wi-Fi network that prompts you to do so.

Pizza delivery deal: A fake flyer for pizza or another food is slid under your door. When you place an order, your credit card information is stolen. Check with the front desk for recommendations, or search the Internet for eateries that deliver.

Late-night call from the front desk: Scammers call to say there was a problem with your credit card and ask you to provide it again. Then they steal your account information. Go to the front desk to see if there is a real problem.

Consumerist.com

New Perk from Hotel Loyalty Programs

Even entry-level program members who have no reward points now qualify for free standard Wi-Fi service at several major hotel chains. (*Savings:* About $20 a day.) They include Marriott International, Starwood Hotels & Resorts Worldwide and InterContinental Hotels. Hyatt Hotels Corp. recently started offering free Wi-Fi for all guests.

One notable holdout: Hilton Worldwide, which still requires elite membership status.

Brian Kelly, founder of *ThePointsGuy.com*, which provides consumer information and advice on hotel and airline loyalty-program rewards.

Are You Insured During Overseas Travel?

Find out if your domestic health insurance covers emergency care overseas. Medicare, for example, does not cover any medical costs outside the US.

Self-defense: Consider obtaining a travel health policy for additional coverage.

Check on the coverage for medical evacuations—most insurance plans don't cover emergency transportation costs, which can average $50,000 from Europe to the US and $100,000 from Asia to the US.

Example: Basic insurance coverage may evacuate you to only the nearest "suitable" hospital.

Also, consider a plan with an adventure-sports rider—most policies exclude injuries sustained while scuba diving, parasailing and bungee jumping, which are popular activities for tourists.

Travel + Leisure. TravelandLeisure.com

Forgot Your Charger? The Hotel May Lend You One and Other Items, Too!

Hotels are letting guests borrow helpful items, and some are allowing guests to leave their own belongings behind for use on their next stay. Hotels in all price ranges have widely varying lending programs that may include bicycles, running gear, appliances such as chargers, curling irons, fans, slow cookers, dehumidifiers and office supplies. Some hotels provide places where frequent guests can leave items of their own, such as suits for business meetings.

Roundup of experts on hotel amenities, reported in *The New York Times.*

EASY-TO-DO...

Get a Better Hotel Deal

A half-empty parking lot may indicate that the hotel or motel is not fully booked. Take advantage, and negotiate the price of the room and parking fees.

TravelSmart newsletter. *TravelSmartNewsletter.com*

Fun Finds

How to Watch Movies, Shows and Sports for Free!

Netflix, Hulu and Amazon are the best-known services for streaming great programs and movies to your computer, and often to your TV,* tablet and smartphone. But there are other video-streaming services that are free, and in some cases, they offer programming that you will not find on the big three streaming services.

But which ones are worth your time? *Here's a guide to the best free video-streaming services, all of which are available on computers as well as several other platforms...*

*To stream Internet programming to a TV, you will need either a "streaming box," such as Roku, Chromecast or Apple TV...a "smart TV" that has streaming capabilities built in...or a Blu-ray or video game player that includes streaming capabilities, such as a recent Sony PlayStation or Microsoft Xbox. Programming and platform availability were accurate as of August 2015 but can change. Visit sites for details.

AOL ON

America Online offers about 20 free movies from Miramax at any given time. The movie selection changes each month. These movies generally are not huge hits or new releases, but most feature well-known actors and are from the past few decades.

Some recent examples of AOL On movies include *Doubt* with Meryl Streep...*Robinson Crusoe* with Pierce Brosnan...and *Serendipity* with John Cusak.

The website also offers episodes of original shows made exclusively for AOL On. There are commercial breaks. (Available on many platforms and devices, including Android, iOS and Roku.) *On.AOL.com*

Ryan Downey, founder and editor of *The Streaming Advisor,* a website that provides news, reviews and guidance related to online video content. *TheStreamingAdvisor.com*

CRACKLE

Crackle provides free access to certain movies and TV shows made or owned by Sony. The selection changes frequently, but recently the site offered 10 episodes of *Seinfeld*...12 episodes of *NewsRadio*...and 23 episodes of *The Shield*. Among the movies recently offered were *Step Brothers* with Will Ferrell...*Bad Boys* with Will Smith...*Stand By Me* with Wil Wheaton...and *Air Force One* with Harrison Ford.

Crackle offers original shows, such as *Sports Jeopardy!*, a sports-focused version of the *Jeopardy!* game show. There are commercial breaks. (Available through most major platforms and devices, including Android, iOS, most smart TVs, Roku and Apple TV.) *Crackle.com*

ESPN3

Sports-programming giant ESPN provides sporting events and other programming for free through its ESPN3 online channel. You'll find lots of college football and basketball, plus tennis, golf, soccer, cricket, auto racing, Canadian football, curling and more. Watch live or replay programs later.

Access to ESPN3 is available to consumers who obtain their Internet service through participating Internet service providers, which include most major ones and many smaller ones. (Available on most major platforms and devices, including Android, iOS, Roku, Apple TV, Xbox and more.) For a list of ESPN3 providers, go to *ESPN3.com* and click on "What Is WatchESPN?" To access ESPN3 programming, go to *ESPN3.com*.

PBS

You can stream recent episodes of many PBS shows through its website. Of course, other broadcast-TV networks allow free online viewing of programming, too, but generally only on a computer—PBS lets you stream its programming to a mobile device or TV for free as well.

The shows available for streaming include *Antiques Roadshow*, *Frontline*, *Masterpiece*, *Nature* and *NOVA*, among others. There are commercials. (Many platforms and devices are supported, including Android, iOS, Roku, Apple TV and Xbox.) *Video.PBS.org*

PLUTO TV

This innovative site creates 30- or 60-minute "TV shows" from video clips found on YouTube and elsewhere online. These shows appear on Pluto TV's themed "channels"—there are more than 100 channels in all.

Examples: The Late Night TV channel has shows built from clips of recent episodes of popular late-night talk shows...the Dogs 24/7 and Cats 24/7 channels turn online pet videos into shows...the Classic Toons channel streams old cartoons...and the Food channel features cooking shows and videos. You could track down such videos yourself on the Internet, but Pluto TV transforms watching Internet video clips into a just-sit-and-relax experience that's much more like conventional TV. Advertising is included only if ads were included in the original video clips used to make Pluto's shows. (Platforms include Android and iOS.) *Pluto.TV*

POPCORNFLIX

This website offers free access to hundreds of movies controlled by the film-distribution company Screen Media Ventures. Most of the movies are marginal-quality films of the sort that probably went straight to video—titles like *Birdemic 2: The Resurrection* and *Psycho Shark* abound—but there are some notable films as well. Options recently included *Monster* with Charlize Theron and *Sherrybaby* with Maggie Gyllenhaal. There are a few TV series available, too, including the National Geographic Channel show *Life Below Zero*. There are commercial breaks. (Supported platforms and devices include Android, iOS, Roku, Samsung Smart TV and Xbox.) *Popcornflix.com*

PUBLIC DOMAIN MOVIES

This YouTube service offers access to dozens of movies that have fallen into the public domain. (When a film is in the public domain, no one owns the intellectual property rights anymore, which means anyone is free to sell it, broadcast it or put it on a website.) Most public domain movies are fairly obscure—this site is a great place to find old, campy black-and-white monster movies, for example. But some notable films are in the public domain and available here, including *Beat the Devil* with Humphrey Bogart...*Meet John Doe* with Gary Cooper...and quite a few Charlie Chaplin silent films. (You can watch on any platform/device that provides access to YouTube, including Android, iOS, Roku and Apple TV.) *YouTube.com/user/BestPDMovies*

SNAGFILMS

This site offers thousands of free art-house movies including documentaries and independent films. Recent examples include the award-winning documentary *Capturing the Friedmans* and the Zach Galifianakis comedy *Visioneers*. There are ads—the site splits the ad revenue it generates with the filmmakers. (Available on most major platforms and devices, including Android, iOS, Roku and Xbox.) *SnagFilms.com*

Choose the Best Music-Streaming Service for *You*

Donald Bell, senior editor at *CNET*, a leading consumer technology website now operated by CBS. He is a musician and has extensive experience covering the digital audio sector. *CNET.com*

Instead of depending on compact discs or radio stations, hundreds of millions of people worldwide now listen to music through digital streaming services, often for free. And the field is expanding. The two leading services, Pandora and Spotify, which offer millions of selections, are being joined by new entrants including Beats Electronics, the headphone company that was recently acquired by Apple for $3 billion, and Amazon, which launched a new service called Prime Music. There are important differences among the services, which can be accessed through computers, tablets, smartphones and, in some cases, on TVs and car radios.

How to choose the music-streaming services that suit you best...

IF YOU WANT TO SELECT SPECIFIC SONGS

These "on-demand" services let you listen to exactly the song and/or artist you choose, which is not possible with services such as Pandora. It's like having access to a massive collection of millions of albums. (However, a few notable artists, including the Beatles and Bob Seger, currently are not available through these services.)

• **Spotify** is the most popular of the on-demand services, making it more likely that you can share recommendations with friends or relatives who also use it. It has a catalog of more than 20 million songs to choose from, including the latest hits, and a variety of ways to discover new music, as well as plenty of preset playlists based on musical subgenres or artists when you don't feel like selecting specific songs. But with the free ad-sponsored version, you can select specific songs only on a computer or tablet, not through the smartphone app, although that app allows you to "shuffle play" an assortment of songs from a specific artist or album. Ads tend to pop up every three to six songs and last 15 to 30 seconds or so, as with most free music-streaming services. *Spotify.com*

Upgrade option: Spotify Premium removes the ads, allows you to select specific songs even on the smartphone app, lets users download songs for off-line listening and increases streaming speed for slightly better sound quality. (Sound-quality problems with streaming services often stem from poor Wi-Fi or cellular connections or low-quality speakers, not the services.) $9.99 per month.*

• **Rdio** (pronounced r-dee-oh) is a lot like Spotify and similarly does not allow specific song selection on the smartphone version, but some people find Rdio easier to use and its catalog of more than 25 million songs is slightly larger than Spotify's. Sound quality is comparable, and Rdio offers playlists just like Spotify. *Rdio.com*

Upgrade option: Rdio Unlimited eliminates the ads and includes a download feature for off-line listening. $9.99 per month. Under a family plan, the master account holder pays the full Unlimited rate ($9.99 per month) and

*Prices subject to change.

each subaccount saves 50% off their subscription cost.

• **Beats Music** has more than 20 million songs and tends to be particularly strong with new, hip music such as the latest hip-hop. Beats also offers an impressive range of curated playlists in specific subgenres, many of them put together by musicians rather than based on computer algorithms. The mobile app even has a feature that helps Beats choose appropriate music for the situation. You create a short sentence by clicking on one or more phrases—for example, "I'm in a car"…"I'm on a boat" and feel like "kicking back" or "celebrating," and Beats does the rest. Beats does not offer a free version, but like most paid music-streaming services, it is ad-free. Audio quality is very good—on par with the paid version of Spotify. $9.99 per month or $99.99 per year after a 14-day free trial. *BeatsMusic.com*

• **Google Play Music All Access** offers a catalog of more than 30 million songs and supplies an online music locker where you can store up to 20,000 digital songs that you have purchased through various services so that you can access them from anywhere. It could be a good choice if you want to bring all of your music options together in one place for convenience. It can be accessed through a web browser or by an Android or iOS device. There is no free version, but there is a one-month free trial. $9.99 per month. *Play.Google.com/about/music/allaccess*

• **Amazon Prime Music** recently launched with more than one million songs, a small number compared with what some competitors offer. You will find many big-name musical acts here but often not their full catalogs and nowhere near as many less well-known performers as other services offer. The service provides ad-free listening, allows downloads for off-line listening and is included at no additional cost for members of Amazon Prime, which costs $99 per year. It's worth a try if you have Amazon Prime.

IF YOU WANT TO SELECT TYPES OF SONGS

These free services do not allow you to request specific songs. Instead they create "stations" for you featuring customized playlists based on the artists and/or songs you favor and the feedback you provide about the songs played. Not all of the on-demand services do this, and those that attempt to do it tend not to do it as well as the services listed below. There usually is a way to skip songs you don't like, though this skipping typically has limits.

These services are a great way to discover songs and artists appropriate for your musical tastes and that you haven't necessarily heard before…or rediscover songs and artists you have forgotten.

Which service is best for you depends largely on which does the best job coming up with songs you like. Enter the same song or artist into each of the following as a starting point, and see which best hits the mark.

• **Pandora** employs musicologists to analyze songs in an effort to deliver music well-suited to user tastes. (Competing services generally rely on computer algorithms to select songs.) It's the most popular music-streaming service, with more than 77 million users, in part because those musicologists do an effective job matching songs and listeners. As with most streaming services, ads are sprinkled among the songs if you don't pay for an upgrade.

Pandora listeners can skip up to six songs per hour per "station," up to 24 total each day. But Pandora's sound quality is lower than that of most major competitors, particularly with Pandora's free version. And Pandora's catalog is smaller than most—it claims "more than one million songs" and can be slow to add new music. Pandora offers tracks from comedy albums in addition to music. Some cars and aftermarket car radios now are specifically Pandora-enabled and can stream either the paid or ad-supported version of the service. *Pandora.com*

Upgrade option: Pandora One eliminates ads and improves sound quality somewhat. $4.99 per month.

• **iTunes Radio** has an especially extensive music catalog. There are over 43 million songs in the iTunes music store—though Apple does not disclose precisely how many of these are available through iTunes Radio. This Apple service also gets exclusive access to lots of not-yet-released new music. Listeners can skip up to six songs per station per hour. As with most of these services, you can listen for free

BETTER WAYS...

Best Apps for Organizing Smartphone Photos

Smartphones usually come with a photo-management app installed—but these apps are rarely very good. *Two add-on photo-management apps are available for Android and iOS phones that do a better job organizing images...*

- **Flickr** automatically uploads smartphone photos to a "cloud-based" Flickr account, so you can access them from your computer or tablet, not just your phone. Flickr offers 1,000 GB of free cloud storage, enough for upward of 500,000 digital images. You later can download photos saved on Flickr to your computer if you like. You can add tags and titles to photos so that you can use a keyword search to find them later. The app and the storage are free, and images are stored at full resolution, with no compression. You even can arrange your photos into "collections" or "sets" on Flickr to keep them organized. *Flickr.com*
- **Picturelife** doesn't just automatically upload your smartphone photos to the cloud, it also uploads photos from your computer and social-media pages, consolidating all of your digital images in one place. Only 8 GB of storage is free, however. 25 GB costs $5 per month*...100 GB costs $10 per month...unlimited storage is $15 per month. Uploaded images are saved at full resolution and can be sorted into albums, and you can add keywords ("tags") to them. *Picturelife.com*

Sharon Profis, senior associate editor at *CNET*, a leading consumer technology website. She is author of *Mastering the Galaxy S4*. *CNET.com*

*Prices subject to change.

if you're willing to put up with occasional ads. iTunes Radio comes built into iTunes on Apple computers, iOS devices and Apple TV. It's not available for Android. *Apple.com/itunes/itunes-radio*

Upgrade option: Avoid ads by signing up for iTunes Match, $24.99 per year.

- **iHeartRadio** is a free service that draws on a catalog of more than 20 million songs to deliver ad-free "radio stations" customized to individual listener tastes. It's the best way to listen to digital music that's both free and ad-free. The service also offers digital access to more than 1,500 AM and FM radio stations from around the US. *iHeart.com*

Upgrade option: None available.

MORE STREAMING OPTIONS

Some music-streaming services offer unusual twists on the features provided by more prominent services. These services can be streamed through a web browser, and some offer apps for smartphones.

AccuRadio is a lot like Pandora, but listeners can skip as many songs as they like (free, *AccuRadio.com*). *8tracks* offers playlists designed by fellow 8tracks users (free, *8tracks.com*). *Hype Machine* offers music from more than 800 music blogs (free, *HypeM.com*). Rhapsody's new *UnRadio* service is like Pandora One, Pandora's paid ad-free service, except that you can skip an unlimited number of songs and listen on demand to songs previously played that you marked as favorites, even off-line ($4.99 per month, *Rhapsody.com*).

Hidden Treasures on Your Bookshelf: You May Already Own Books Worth a Lot of Money

Ken Lopez, a dealer in rare books based in Hadley, Massachusetts, who specializes in post–World War II British and American fiction. He has been a book dealer since the late 1970s and is past president of the Antiquarian Booksellers' Association of America. *LopezBooks.com*

There might be a book on your bookshelf that's worth hundreds or even thousands of dollars. Valuable books can turn up at yard sales and book sales, too, where you can buy them for next to nothing.

Even though the most valuable books of the 20th century predate the 1960s, there are a fair number of books published since 1960 that have significant value. Many of these valuable modern books are from early in the careers of authors who only later became widely read.

What to look for: Only first printings of modern books tend to be collectible and therefore valuable (see page 253 for more about first printings). Modern books generally must be in pristine condition—that is, virtually like new—to have significant value.

Here, first printings that have now become collectibles…

Editor's Note: Collectible book values fluctuate, so it's worth checking recent sale prices on *AbeBooks.com* before selling. But don't be fooled into thinking that the highest price asked for a book such as yours on this site is the value of your book. Some sellers ask much more than their books are worth, and even small differences in book condition can have a tremendous impact on value. More telling is the lowest price asked for the book in comparable condition.

• **A Confederacy of Dunces** by John Kennedy Toole (1980). Toole's post-humously published novel won the Pulitzer Prize but was initially printed by a university press in a very small first printing—reportedly just 2,500 copies. *Value:* $3,000 to $4,000.

Helpful: A true first-printing dust jacket should have no reviews on the back, only a blurb from Walker Percy.

• **Americana** by Don DeLillo (1971). DeLillo's first novel received favorable reviews but didn't sell especially well, so first printings are relatively rare. *Value:* $300 to $500.

• **City of Glass** by Paul Auster (1985). Auster was known mainly as a poet and essayist until he wrote this Edgar Award–winning detective novel. *Value:* Around $500.

• **Fear and Loathing in Las Vegas** by Hunter S. Thompson (1971). Thompson's third and most famous book has become a counterculture classic. *Value:* $500 to $750.

• **Heart Songs and Other Stories** by Annie Proulx (1988). Proulx's first book of fiction wasn't as popular as her later best seller *The Shipping News* (1993), but *Heart Songs'* rarity makes it valuable. *Value:* Around $300.

• **Housekeeping** by Marilynne Robinson (1980). Robinson's first novel came out of nowhere to earn a Pulitzer Prize nomination. *Value:* $500 to $750.

• **If I Die in a Combat Zone, Box Me Up and Ship Me Home** by Tim O'Brien (1973). First printings of O'Brien's acclaimed memoir of the Vietnam war are rare. *Value:* Around $2,000.

Also: O'Brien's *Going After Cacciato* (1978) can bring $350 to $500.

• **Lonesome Dove** by Larry McMurtry (1985). *Lonesome Dove* wasn't McMurtry's first novel—far from it—but it was a book people read, not one that just sat on bookshelves. It also is a long book—more than 800 pages—and the spines of fat books tend to age poorly, so few pristine first printings remain. *Value:* Around $350.

Also: McMurtry's first two novels, *Horseman, Pass By* (1961) and *Leaving Cheyenne* (1963), can sell for low four figures. *The Last Picture Show* (1966) can bring $300.

• **Midnight's Children** by Salman Rushdie (1981). Rushdie is a British author, but the first American printing of *Midnight's Children*, his breakthrough second novel, was the true first printing. It preceded the UK edition by a few weeks. *Value:* Around $750.

• **One Hundred Years of Solitude** by Gabriel García Márquez (1970). A first American printing of this hugely important novel is quite valuable—and quite tricky to identify. *Value*: Around $2,000.

Helpful: To confirm that you truly have a first American printing, check the copyright page for the phrase "First Edition." If you find this, flip to the final blank page of the book—if there's a number line (see page 253 for more about number lines), it is not a first printing. (This is a rare case where the number line is published at the back of the book, not on the copyright page.) Finally, check the very end of the first paragraph of the front flap on the dust jacket. On a true "first state" dust jacket, this paragraph will end with an exclamation point, not a period.

• **The Bluest Eye** by Toni Morrison (1970). First printings of Morrison's debut novel are extremely rare and valuable. *Value:* Around $5,000.

Also: First printings of Morrison's second novel, *Sula* (1973), are nearly as rare and worth as much as $1,000.

• **The Godfather** by Mario Puzo (1969). *The Godfather* became a best seller, but it had a relatively modest initial print run. Like *Lonesome Dove*, it is a fat, well-read book, so few first printings survive in pristine condition. *Value:* Around $3,500.

• **The Killer Angels** by Michael Shaara (1974). Shaara's novel about the Civil War's Battle of Gettysburg went on to win the Pulitzer Prize, but the first printing was done cheaply and the binding tended to fall apart. That increases the value of pristine first printings that remain. *Value:* Around $5,000.

• **The Magic Journey** by John Nichols (1978). This book was released in hardcover and paperback at the same time. Most readers opted for the less expensive paperback, so first printings of the hardcover are rare. *Value:* $500 to $750.

Also: Nichols's *Milagro Beanfield War* (1974) can bring around $250.

• **The Orchard Keeper** by Cormac McCarthy (1965). McCarthy's first novel won an award but sold fewer than 3,000 copies. *Value:* Around $3,000. (Even copies in not-quite-pristine condition can be worth four figures.)

Also: First printings of many of McCarthy's other early Random House novels are relatively rare and valuable, too. *Outer Dark* (1968) can bring $2,000 in pristine condition...*Blood Meridian* (1985), around $1,000...and *Suttree* (1979), $500 to $750.

• **The Spy Who Came in from the Cold** by John Le Carré (1963). Le Carré's classic spy novel was first published in England, but the first American printing is valuable, too. *Value:* As much as $500.

Helpful: A true first American printing of this book reads "First Edition" on the copyright page but does not otherwise mention which printing it is.

• **The World According to Garp** by John Irving (1978). The first printing of *Garp*, Irving's fourth novel, was a fairly sizable 35,000 copies. Ordinarily that would make this book too common to have much value—but it was a well-read book and a fat book, so relatively few first printings survive in pristine condition. *Value:* $200 to $300.

EASY-TO-DO...

Bobby Pin Bookmark

You can save your exact place in a book you are reading with a bobby pin. Clip the pin over a few pages so that it stays in place. It won't fall out!

Also: Irving's pre-1978 novels are valuable, too.

• **Welcome to Hard Times** by E.L. Doctorow (1960). Doctorow's debut novel was initially published on cheap, easily damaged paper, so few pristine copies remain. *Value:* Around $1,000. (Even copies in very good but imperfect condition can bring $400 to $500.)

• **Will You Please Be Quiet, Please?** by Raymond Carver (1976). Carver's first book from a major publisher helped reinvigorate the American short story. Its unlaminated dust jacket is easily damaged, increasing the value of pristine copies. *Value:* Around $2,500.

HOW TO IDENTIFY FIRST PRINTINGS

If you have one of the books mentioned in this article, it's only valuable if it's a *first printing*. Not every book identified as a first edition on its copyright page is a first printing. If minor changes were made to the text or dust jacket early in the publication process, only copies printed prior to the changes are first printings.

It can be difficult to tell whether a book is a first printing. In many books published after 1970, there's a "number line" that can be used to identify first printings. Look for a row of numbers up to 10 on the copyright page. These numbers might be arranged in ascending order, descending order or in some other order. If the number one is included in this row, the book is likely a first printing. If not, it probably isn't.

Exception: Random House first printings do not have the number one in their number lines—the lowest number will be two. A Random House first printing also should include the phrase "First Edition" on the copyright page.

If there is no number line, the phrase "First Edition" or "First Printing" on the copyright page suggests that the book could be a first printing, but it is no guarantee. *Book Collecting 2000* by Allen and Patricia Ahearn offers clues for identifying first printings in a wide range of collectible books.

Easy-to-Grow Vegetables You've Never Tried

Eric Toensmeier, appointed lecturer at Yale University who previously managed the Tierra de Oportunidades urban farm project in Holyoke, Massachusetts. He is author of *Perennial Vegetables: From Artichokes to Zuiki Taro, a Gardener's Guide to Over 100 Delicious, Easy-to-Grow Edibles,* which won an American Horticultural Society book award. *PerennialSolutions.org*

Perennials are a real pleasure to grow because they reappear year after year, taking much of the grunt work (and expense) out of gardening. But while many home gardens include perennial flowers, few feature perennial vegetables, aside perhaps from asparagus and rhubarb.

That's a shame. Not only is there no need to replant each spring—but perennials typically require less watering and weeding than annuals...and most are relatively resistant to pests and diseases.

Here are five perennial vegetables that can thrive across much or all of the continental US. If you have trouble finding them, my website, *PerennialSolutions.org,* has a list of plant sources.

• **Sea kale (Crambe maritima).** This perennial looks like a big silvery-gray cabbage, but it sprouts tender, delicious buds similar to small broccoli heads. The leaves of first- and second-year sea kale plants (pick in the fall after growth is completed) are edible and taste like collards.

Sea kale's spring shoots are edible, too—they have a slightly bitter hazelnut flavor. Cut them off when they reach six to nine inches, and prepare them like asparagus. Young sea kale grows slowly, however, so it's wise not to harvest these shoots during the plant's first two years.

Helpful: Cover sea kale's shoots for a few weeks with mulch or upturned flowerpots if you intend to eat them. The less sunlight that reaches these shoots, the better they will taste.

Sea kale is easy to grow across most of the US, except in the hottest parts of the South. It likes full sun and fertile soil—seaweed-based fertilizers are a particular favorite—but can tolerate partial sun.

• **Stinging nettle (Urtica dioica).** The young spring leaves and shoots of stinging nettle are phenomenal to eat once they have been boiled for one to two minutes. The flavor is like a rich nutty spinach. It's extremely nutritious, too.

The plant's green and purple shoots are ready for cooking when they reach a few inches in height. It typically is the first vegetable you can eat from the garden each year, particularly if you live in a cold part of the country. In the Northeast, it often is possible to start harvesting stinging nettle's spring growth while there's still some winter snow lingering on the ground.

Stinging nettle is very easy to grow and is happy in either sun or partial shade. In fact, the biggest challenge for gardeners tends to be controlling stinging nettle's growth. Cutting off seed heads before they ripen should prevent the plant from becoming an annoying weed.

Warning: The word stinging is part of its name for a reason. Wear gloves when touching the leaves (cooking destroys the sting) and stems.

• **Sylvetta arugula (Diplotaxis muralis and Diplotaxis tenuifolia).** These members of the cabbage family can provide edible greens year-round and year after year in mild climates—though in colder northern states, they tend to grow as annuals. The leaves can be harvested starting in year one. Young leaves have a very strong arugula flavor. Older leaves taste best when cooked. The *muralis* variety has a milder flavor than *tenuifolia.*

Sylvetta arugula prefers hot summers and dry soil. It can get weedy if it goes to seed, so it is worth deadheading—removing flowers as they start to die.

• **Welsh onion (Allium fistulosum).** This member of the onion family often is grown as an annual scallion, but it also is a perennial. If you don't harvest the bulb after the first growing season, it will form a perennial clump that will grow new bulbs and stems year after year. When you want onions for your table, just remove a portion of this clump and leave the rest. The flavor is comparable to that of the common onion—and you can use the stalks as chives.

Welsh onion likes full sun and regular watering but will tolerate partial shade and dry soil. It is less susceptible to pests and diseases than the common onion, but some ongoing weeding can be helpful.

Alternatives: Other perennial onions include garlic chives (*Allium tuberosum*)...walking onion (*Allium cepa proliferum*)...and perennial sweet leek (*Allium ampeloprasum*).

• **Wolfberry (Lycium barbarum and Lycium chinense)** is also known as the goji berry. Both the fruit and leaves of this perennial viney shrub are edible. The fruits are small and red with a flavor that suggests cherry tomato mixed with sweet licorice. They can be consumed raw or cooked. The plant's iron- and protein-rich leaves, which can be harvested the first year, are nice either raw or boiled in soups and have a flavor like watercress.

Wolfberry is very tolerant of dry soil. It does struggle in extreme heat, however, and it is somewhat susceptible to mildew—planting it in an area that has good airflow can minimize this risk. Also keep an eye out for slugs.

Caution: People who take blood thinners should not eat this plant.

THE EDIBLE HOSTA

Many gardeners grow hostas, but few realize that they can provide food. In fact, the spring shoots of hosta leaves are not just edible, they're quite tasty. Prepare them as you would asparagus shoots—the flavor is comparable. (The fresh spring leaves of hostas are edible as well.)

There are many varieties of hosta, each with a slightly different flavor. If you don't have hostas in your garden, ask a local nursery if you can cut off shoots and taste a few varieties that grow well in your area before selecting plants. *Hosta montana* and *Hosta sieboldii* often are listed among the best-tasting varieties.

Hostas are easy to grow, and most varieties are shade tolerant. Different varieties have different preferences, so ask your nursery for growing advice.

Caution: Hostas are toxic to dogs and cats.

You're Drinking Wine Wrong! 6 Ways to Maximize Your Enjoyment

Jeff Siegel, the Wine Curmudgeon. He's a wine writer, critic and judge who specializes in inexpensive wine. He is also author of *The Wine Curmudgeon's Guide to Cheap Wine* and oversees the award-winning *Wine Curmudgeon* website, which ranks among the most influential wine sites on the Internet. *WineCurmudgeon.com*

Mishandle wine or select the wrong bottle and you've wasted your money and undermined your meal. *Here are six mistakes that many wine drinkers make...*

MISTAKE: Serving white wines too cold and red wines too warm. Most people serve reds at room temperature and whites at refrigerator temperature—but neither of those temperatures is ideal. Most reds are best consumed at around 64°F, which is cooler than room temperature. Drinking reds too warm means the alcohol covers up the wine flavors in the same way that cold temperatures cover up the flavors in white wine. That's why most whites are best in the 50s. Fridge temperatures, typically in the high 30s, are too cold.

What to do: Use the 20-minute rule of thumb to serve wine at a good temperature—put reds in the fridge for 20 minutes prior to serving, and remove whites from the fridge 20 minutes before serving. If you're in a restaurant and the wine is too cold, cup the glass with your hands, which helps to warm the wine.

If you own a wine fridge, chill whites to 48°F and reds to 58°F. This is slightly cooler than ideal drinking temperature because the wine will warm a bit in the minutes between removing it from the wine fridge and then drinking it.

If your wine fridge has only one thermostat, set it at the lower temperature and store the whites on the bottom and the reds on top (since it's usually warmer at the top).

MISTAKE: Drinking wine from cheap glassware at home. Savvy restaurants have discovered that high-quality wineglasses are worth their price. People's opinions of the wines they drink can be significantly influenced by factors outside the quality of the wine, including the glasses. A study at the University of Tennessee found that glass shape and quality do make a difference in the enjoyment of wine.

Traditional rule of thumb: For every dollar you spend for wine, you should spend $1 for the glass, so a $10 wine works out to a $10 glass. But in my opinion, a $10 glass will work for many more expensive wines.

What to do: Riedel, the leader in high-quality glasses, makes quality crystal stemware for as little as $10 to $12 per glass. Also, the Schott Zwiesel Tritan Forte, a crystal wineglass for about $10 a glass, is unusually difficult to break.

MISTAKE: Judging a wine by sniffing the cork. When a waiter opens a bottle of wine, he typically hands the cork to the customer to sniff. But smelling the cork won't tell you what the wine tastes like, only what the cork smells like.

Instead, you should sniff the wine. An odor of wet cardboard or wet dog indicates that the wine has cork taint, which means that a chemical reaction has occurred in the wine and the wine won't taste the way it should. If the wine smells like brandy, then it has oxidized. You won't get sick from drinking a spoiled wine, but you won't have much fun either.

What to do: The proper way to evaluate wine before drinking it is to pour a little into a glass, then position your nose directly above the glass and inhale deeply as you gently swirl the wine. Swirling amplifies the aroma.

If there's a problem with the wine, point it out to a waiter. If you're drinking at home, set a bottle that exhibits such a smell aside (and later return it to the wine store) and serve your guests something else instead.

MISTAKE: Storing wines in the wrong part of the house. Many people store wine in the kitchen on a rack on top of the refrigerator, which often is the warmest part of the house. Or they store wine in a room that gets lots of sunlight, making the room warm. Wine that gets too hot for too long will lose its flavors and even turn to vinegar.

What to do: The wine refrigerator is one option, but a closet works well, too. And you don't even have to invest in an expensive wine rack. If you're keeping wine in a closet, use the boxes the wine comes in, stacked on their sides.

MISTAKE: Drinking the same wine every time. Many people just buy the wine that they like because it's too much trouble to try something different or they're afraid they'll waste money on a wine they don't like.

What to do: The biggest change in the wine business over the past decade is the increase in quality. It's almost impossible to buy a flawed bottle of wine—most taste more or less like they're supposed to taste, even the least expensive. So you aren't making a big leap of faith when trying something different. If you don't want to stray too far from the tried-and-true, look for wines made with the same grape as the one you like, but from a different part of the world—so chardonnay from France instead of chardonnay from California. Or try something similar. If you like chardonnay, try viognier. If you like merlot, try malbec.

MISTAKE: Paying too much attention to wine-reviewer scores. Wines that earn high grades from respected wine reviewers and magazines tend to be priced accordingly. Plus, they reflect the tastes and prejudices of the reviewers—which may not be yours. Many excellent wines receive less impressive scores simply because they happen not to match the preferences of the expert doing the tasting.

What to do: One way to find wine bargains is to ask wine-store staffers and restaurant sommeliers, "Where's the best value?" Keep track of the success of each of these recommendations, and return to the wine stores and restaurants that consistently seem to hit the mark. A good retailer is a wine drinker's best friend.

5 Things Casinos Don't Want You to Know

Steve Bourie, who has published the *American Casino Guide* annually since 1992. Bourie has more than 70 gambling videos available online at *YouTube.com/AmericanCasinoGuide*. He also has a free *American Casino Guide* app for iPhones, iPads and Android devices. *AmericanCasinoGuide.com*

The odds are stacked against you when you gamble in casinos—the house has an edge on almost every bet. But there are ways that even novice gamblers can greatly improve their odds of winning—or at least reduce the amount they lose. The key is to choose the right games...the right bets...and the right casinos. *Five secrets the casinos don't want you to know...*

TABLE GAMES

• **Casinos are making it harder than ever to win at blackjack.** Hitting a blackjack—that is, getting dealt a two-card opening hand that adds up to 21—traditionally pays the player 3:2 ("three to two"), which is $15 on a $10 bet. But in the past five years or so, many casinos have quietly lowered this payout to 6:5, or just $12 on a $10 bet, greatly reducing players' odds of coming out ahead—even if they play blackjack very well.

Look for a placard at the table that explains the game's payouts. If you don't see this or cannot understand it, ask the dealer, "Is this a 6:5 or 3:2 blackjack game?" If the answer is 6:5, don't play.

Sometimes the only 3:2 blackjack tables in a casino have fairly steep minimum bets—often $20 or higher. If you cannot find a 3:2 table with stakes you feel comfortable with, play a different game.

• **Baccarat is a good table game for novice gamblers.** Many casino goers think of baccarat as a game for high rollers and experienced gamblers. Not so. It requires no skill...many casinos have "mini-baccarat" tables with affordable $5 minimums...and the odds are among the best you'll find in the casino—the house edge is just a little over 1% on each of the two primary bets you can make.

To play mini-baccarat, simply place a bet on either the player or the banker—the dealer will do the rest. (You also can bet on a tie, but the odds against you are much higher if you do.)

The player and the banker hands are marked on the table, and each will be dealt two cards (or sometimes three, for complicated reasons that you don't need to understand to play). Face cards and 10s are worth 0, aces are worth 1 and other cards are worth the number shown. These values are added up after the cards are dealt, and the hand that has the total closest to 9 wins.

Examples: A hand consisting of a 2 and a 6 produces a score of 8. A king and a 4 would create a score of 4 because face cards are worth 0. A 7 and an 8 would result in a score of 5—the cards add up to 15, but only the final digit of this figure matters.

• **Full tables are good for gamblers.** More players at a table slows down the game and results in fewer hands played per hour. That gives you more time to think.

A slower pace of play also can increase the odds that you will be offered free meals and hotel rooms. Casinos award these perks based in part on how much time a gambler spends at the tables. If the pace of play is slow, you can spend more time at the tables without putting additional money at risk.

Helpful: You typically will receive perks only if you join the casino's players club. Players clubs are free to join. Ask a casino employee how to sign up before you begin gambling.

VIDEO POKER AND SLOTS

• **Seemingly identical video poker machines can provide significantly different odds.** A row of video poker machines that all look the same might actually differ in an important way—they might pay different returns for certain winning hands. Compare the "pay tables"—usually displayed on their screens—before playing.

Example: With "Jacks or Better" video poker—a game where players receive a payout if their final hand is a pair of jacks or better—check the payout for full houses and flushes. The best Jacks-or-Better machines pay nine coins for each coin bet if you make a full house and six for a flush. But many others pay only eight coins for a full house and five for a flush—some even less. This reduces your expected return on each hand from 99.5% of the amount you bet to 97.3% or less.

Helpful: Always play five coins per hand at video poker. This will earn you a big bonus if you hit a royal flush.

There are many different varieties of video poker, but Jacks or Better is a good choice for novice gamblers because it is very common and relatively easy to understand.

•**Max bets usually are bad bets on slot machines.** If you make the max bet on a penny slot machine, for example, you might be gambling $3 a spin. If you're going to bet that much, you're better off playing on a $1 slot machine—higher-denomination slots inevitably offer substantially better odds.

Example: On the Las Vegas strip, penny slots return an average of 88% of the money bet on each spin, while dollar slots return an average of 93%.

The best amount to bet when you play slots is the minimum amount that qualifies for any bonuses or progressive jackpots offered by the machine. Or, don't play the slots at all—they offer among the worst odds in the casino.

CASINOS WITH THE BEST ODDS

Where you gamble in Las Vegas can significantly affect your chances of winning. Casinos on the Las Vegas Strip use glitz and prestige to attract out-of-town gamblers. Some casinos in less touristy parts of town, such as North Las Vegas and the Boulder Strip along the Boulder Highway, instead try to attract locals and other savvy gamblers by offering more favorable odds than their better-known competitors.

•**In 2014, the 25-cent slot machines returned, on average, 96.71% of each bet** on the Boulder Strip and 96.61% in North Las Vegas...but just 91.52% on the Vegas Strip and 94.76% downtown.

•**You can find blackjack tables with a $5 minimum bet** on the Boulder Strip and in North Las Vegas, while the minimum bet at blackjack tables in tourist-oriented casinos is rarely below $10.

Examples: The Boyd properties, including Sam's Town on the Boulder Strip (*SamsTownLV.com*) and The Orleans west of the Strip across Route 15 (*OrleansCasino.com*), offer some of the best odds for gamblers and free shuttle buses to and from the Strip. The Station casinos, such as Boulder Station on the Boulder Strip (*BoulderStation.SCLV.com*), are good choices as well.

•**Other cities.** In Atlantic City, the Borgata has the highest slot-machine returns plus high-paying low-denomination video poker machines (*TheBorgata.com*). In Reno, Nevada, the Peppermill offers appealing video poker machine returns (*PeppermillReno.com*), while the Alamo Travel Center, a truck stop that's just outside of town, offers very gambler-friendly, low-limit blackjack rules (*TheAlamo.com*). In Biloxi, Mississippi, IP offers some of the area's best video poker machines and craps table odds (*IPBiloxi.com*), while Treasure Bay offers favorable blackjack rules (*TreasureBay.com*).

BETTER WAYS...

Good Places for a First Date

Going on a first date? *Consider these unique suggestions...*

Museums—which let you compare cultural backgrounds and find out how a person sees the world. Nature—such as hikes or a picnic—offers a relaxing way to be together and gives you a sense of how outdoorsy the other person is. Walking or bus tour—you see things together and get a sense of what is important and interesting to each of you.

Sandy Weiner, dating coach and founder, *LastFirstDate.com*.

15

Car Care

How to Make Your Car Last 300,000 Miles

It used to be that drivers were lucky to get 100,000 miles out of their vehicles. But now it's not uncommon for cars to last 200,000...250,000...or maybe even 300,000 miles. That means car owners can wait much longer before they have to pony up for new autos. *Reasons...*

- **Today's engines suffer much less wear than those made just 15 years ago,** in part because of changes that automakers have made to meet EPA emissions standards.
- **Car bodies and frames are much less susceptible to corrosion and rust.**
- **Today's lubricants and fluids do a great job protecting key automotive components.**

But the number of miles you get with your car depends in large part on how well the vehicle is maintained. *Eight simple ways to avoid the major problems that hurt performance and send cars to the salvage yard sooner that you might hope...*

1. Pay extra for synthetic motor oil and a high-quality filter when you have your oil changed. Synthetic oil can cost much more than conventional petroleum-based motor oil —perhaps $10 for a quart—and it can add $20 to $40 to the cost of an oil change. But it also can extend the life of your engine. Synthetics are less likely to degrade when engine temperatures get very hot, and they remain more fluid in extreme cold.

Caution: Not every motor oil that is labeled "synthetic" is a high-quality product, so choose one that's well-regarded throughout the automotive industry, such as Amsoil or Mobil 1. (Check your vehicle's owner's manual

---

Tom Torbjornsen, who spent nearly two decades as an automotive technician, service manager and auto-service-center manager. He is currently a columnist for *TheCarConnection.com*, host of the syndicated radio program *America's Car Show* and author of *How to Make Your Car Last Forever. AmericasCarShow.com* to confirm that a particular type of oil is appropriate for your car.)

It's worth spending a little extra for a high-quality oil filter, too. These are significantly better than bargain-basement filters at removing particulates from engine oil. They also get oil to the engine faster upon startup. Automaker Kia issued a service bulletin in 2012 warning that it had linked some major engine problems to owners' use of low-quality oil filters.

Ask your mechanic to use either the specific filter recommended in your owner's manual or some other high-quality brand-name filter when changing your oil. (A high-end filter could add perhaps $5 to $15 to the cost of the oil change if it is not included in the price of a synthetic oil upgrade.)

2. Check your coolant every 20,000 miles. Most cars made in the past 15 to 20 years use long-life coolants designed to last for 100,000 miles or more—but that doesn't mean it's safe to ignore your car's coolant for that long.

Open up the coolant reservoir at least once every 20,000 miles, and take a look. Have the coolant replaced if it is dark red rather than orange...feels gritty between your fingers...and/or smells burnt. These symptoms point to rust in the coolant system, which could inhibit coolant flow and lead to engine overheating and failure. If your coolant looks milky, immediately take the car to a mechanic—motor oil is getting into the coolant, and engine work might be needed.

If your car uses traditional green *ethylene glycol* coolant, replace this every two years or 24,000 miles.

3. Check your power steering and brake fluids every 20,000 miles. Take the car to your mechanic to have these fluids examined and, most likely, replaced if the brake fluid is rust-colored or feels gritty...or if the power steering fluid appears dark, smells burnt or feels gritty.

Discolored or gritty fluids could indicate that water has gotten into the system or, in some cases, that the fluid has overheated in the past. Replacing the fluids usually will solve these problems, but in some cases there might be an underlying issue that needs to be addressed. Keep a close eye on these fluids after they are replaced to see if the problem recurs.

4. Replace the transmission fluid and filter every 35,000 miles. Many owner's manuals say that you can wait 100,000 miles or more before replacing transmission fluid. Usually that's true—but not always. If you want to play it safe, replace the transmission fluid at 35,000 to 40,000 miles. It costs $150 to $200 to have transmission fluid replaced—having this done regularly will substantially reduce the odds that you will have to pay $2,000 to $4,000 or more to have your transmission replaced or rebuilt.

Ask the mechanic to use a high-quality synthetic transmission fluid—Mobil 1 and Amsoil are good choices here, too (assuming that these meet the transmission fluid specifications in your car's owner's manual). Synthetic transmission fluid lasts longer and protects better when the transmission gets very hot, such as during prolonged stop-and-go driving or when your vehicle is towing a trailer. The greater slipperiness of synthetic transmission fluid can even slightly boost your vehicle's fuel efficiency.

Also: Immediately check your transmission fluid level if your transmission whines or slips out of gear.

5. Wash away the ravages of road salt. The salt that many states use to melt ice and snow off winter roads can rust away the underside of your car, too. Everything from body panels to brake lines to the frame of the car is at risk.

One way to limit this damage is to take the car to a car wash for an underbody wash after every major snow or ice storm. (Wait until temperatures climb above freezing to do this.)

There are many products and processes that claim to protect against the risk of rust from road salts, but most are either unproved or ineffective, particularly when rust already has a foothold on a car.

6. Have your timing belt inspected regularly. Most modern auto engines have a timing belt that synchronizes the rotation of the crankshaft and the camshaft(s). Your engine could be ruined if this timing belt snaps.

Owner's manuals typically recommend replacing this belt every 50,000 to 100,000 miles. Definitely follow this advice. (If your vehicle's owner's manual does not mention timing belt replacement, it probably means that your vehicle has a timing chain rather than a belt. Timing chains do not generally require regular replacement.)

But if your car has what's called an "interference engine"—an engine where the valves and pistons collide and destroy one another if the timing belt fails—it's worth going a step further. (Your mechanic or dealership should be able to tell you if your car has an interference or noninterference engine.) Ask your mechanic to thoroughly inspect the timing belt every 25,000 miles or so between replacement intervals, particularly after your vehicle's warranty ends.

With most vehicles, this inspection will require removing certain parts at the top of the engine, but this should take the mechanic only around 30 minutes.

7. Give your radiator hoses a squeeze every 20,000 miles. If the hoses feel firm and resilient, all is well. But if they feel mushy and soft or are cracked and brittle, replace all the radiator hoses. If one hose is showing signs of age, the rest likely aren't far behind.

New radiator hoses, which are not expensive and won't take a mechanic very long to install, could save your car from major damage. A blown hose could quickly lead to an overheated and badly damaged—or completely ruined—engine.

8. Frequent a good mechanic. One of the best ways to keep a car running well is to find a mechanic who will help you identify automotive issues before they become serious.

Bring your car to a good mechanic whenever you hear it make a strange sound or notice a change in the way it handles.

Also bring your vehicle to the mechanic when you need an oil change or another basic service. A mechanic might charge a little more for this service than a quick-oil-change place would, but this gives your mechanic an additional opportunity to give your vehicle a once-over.

Choosing a mechanic: It's a good sign if a mechanic has been in the community for many years...offers a relatively clean shop... has a friendly, helpful employee sitting behind the counter...and is AAA-approved (*AAA.com/approved-auto-repair*) and/or ASE-certified (*ASE.com,* select "Car Owners," then "Find an ASE Blue Seal Facility Near You"). Dealerships usually have high-quality mechanics, but they tend to charge a lot if the vehicle is no longer under warranty.

Pothole Protection: Read This Before You Hit the Road Again

Michael Calkins, technical services manager for AAA, the not-for-profit federation of motor clubs that serves more than 53 million members in the US and Canada. Located in Heathrow, Florida, he is certified by the National Institute for Automotive Service Excellence as a Master Automobile Technician. *AAA.com*

Running over a giant pothole can be a bone-rattling, car-crushing and money-draining experience. This past winter's brutal weather resulted in a big increase in potholes in many major cities.

Often that means punctured tires, damaged suspensions, broken shock absorbers and/or misaligned wheels, possibly costing hundreds of dollars—or even more—to fix.

Across the US, repair costs from pothole damage have ballooned to an estimated $6.4 billion this year.

But you can take actions to avoid potholes... reduce the possible damage if you hit one... and lower the cost of repairing damage.

AVOIDING/REDUCING DAMAGE

What to do to lessen the chances of pothole damage...

- **Increase your car's trailing distance behind the car in front of you to at least two car lengths** at slower speeds and four car lengths at faster speeds on pothole-prone roads—the heavily trafficked asphalt ones with signs of previous patch repairs. This allows you more time to react and avoid a pothole or at least brake and decrease your speed before you hit it, which can greatly minimize damage.

Wet-weather alert: Brake before you hit puddles because they can conceal deep, sharp-edged potholes that are filled with water.

• **Don't keep braking as you roll over a pothole that you can't avoid**—instead, release the brakes the moment before your tires reach the pothole, and let your car roll freely through it.

Reason: Braking, especially braking heavily, tilts the vehicle forward and places added stress on the front suspension. This increases the chance that your suspension will be damaged when you hit the hole.

REPAIRING THE DAMAGE

It's pretty obvious very quickly if a pothole has punctured your tire, but it might cause more serious damage that is harder to detect and more costly to fix. *What to do...*

• **Have your vehicle inspected if you notice the following signs...**

• The car pulls to one direction instead of maintaining a straight path. *Likely problem:* The pothole knocked your wheels out of alignment. *Cost:* $75 to $150 for a realignment.*

• You feel a light-to-moderate vibration in the steering wheel. *Likely problem:* A wheel balance weight has been knocked off. *Cost:* $15 to rebalance.

• You notice a moderate-to-heavy vibration from the tire area. *Likely problem:* Your wheel is bent. *Cost:* $75 to $500 to replace the wheel.

• The car sways or rocks during turns and bounces more than normal on rough roads. *Likely problem:* Broken shock absorber or strut. *Cost:* $200 to $400 to replace it, plus the cost of an alignment.

• The steering wheel is no longer centered, and/or there is noise from under the car. *Likely problem:* Damage to the suspension system on the underside of your vehicle. *Cost:* $100 and up, plus the cost of an alignment.

CUTTING YOUR COSTS

You might be able to lessen the cost of recent and/or future pothole damage in various ways...

*Prices subject to change.

• **Purchase a road-hazard warranty from a tire store or repair shop when you buy new tires and wheels.** It is not always available, but the warranty typically lasts for at least a year and costs $10 to $20 per tire, although sometimes it's free. The warranty typically covers the cost to repair the tire/wheel or replace it with a new one for a prorated charge, depending upon how many miles you have driven on the old one.

• **Contact your insurer to determine what it covers.** Most insurers treat pothole damage as an "at-fault" accident. That means you are covered for repair costs above your collision deductible. You generally do not need to file a police report to submit a claim, but the accident likely will remain on your insurance company's records for three years and could affect your premium rates. Damage to tires is generally excluded in insurance policies, but wheels may be covered.

• **See whether the state, city or county government will reimburse you for damages.** It depends on which government body is responsible for the upkeep of the road that you were driving on. *Example:* In 2013, Chicago paid $181,217 on 754 claims, or about $240 per claim. You typically need to submit substantial evidence, including photos of the

CONSUMER SMARTS...

Best-Rated Tires

The incidence of tire problems has fallen by 22% since 2010. The biggest improvements are in tread wear, slow leaks and uneven wear. Satisfaction is measured in four vehicle segments (luxury car, passenger car, performance sport and truck/utility) and according to four factors (wearability, ride, appearance and traction and handling). Michelin ranks highest in the luxury, passenger car and truck/utility segments...Pirelli ranks highest in the performance sport area. The rankings are based on owners' experiences after two years of vehicle ownership. The full report is available at *JDPower.com*.

"J.D. Power 2014 Original Equipment Tire Customer Satisfaction Study."

pothole, the exact location, witness statements and a police report.

Note: Some government bodies accept responsibility only if they had prior notice of a dangerous roadway condition and had sufficient time to repair the problem.

Example: To win a claim against the state of Michigan, there must be a previous record of complaint that is at least 30 days old about the specific pothole you hit.

How to Learn About Car Dangers *Before* a Recall

Sean E. Kane, auto consumer advocate and president of Safety Research & Strategies, Inc., a vehicle-safety research firm in Rehoboth, Massachusetts. His work has prompted numerous federal safety probes, including a report on sudden unintended acceleration in Toyotas that became the foundation for congressional investigations in 2010. *SafetyResearch.net*

An automobile recall notice often is not the best way to find out that there is a problem with your vehicle. Automakers routinely try to avoid or at least delay issuing full-blown recalls. For example, General Motors waited until 2014 to recall 2.6 million small cars worldwide over an ignition-switch defect that was first detected more than 10 years earlier and that has been linked to at least 13 deaths.

You can find out about such problems before there is a recall. Each week, the major automakers send Technical Service Bulletins (TSBs) to their dealership service departments describing fixes that can be made when patterns of possible cosmetic or mechanical problems emerge for particular makes, models and years of vehicles. GM issued its first TSB about the ignition-switch defect 10 years ago.

The fixes often are done for free as long as your vehicle still is under warranty. (In compliance with federal regulations, recall problems must be fixed for free regardless of warranty status.)

Although manufacturers are not required to make TSBs available to the public, you can access them at...

- **SaferCar.gov.** At the website of the National Highway Traffic Safety Administration, you can search for summaries of bulletins about your vehicle's make, model and year. Then, for about 10 cents a page, you can order full copies of the bulletins, which take four to six weeks to arrive by mail. Click on the "Vehicle Manufacturers" tab, then on "Technical Service Bulletins."
- **Your dealership service department or auto-repair shop.** If you have a relationship with someone at the shop, ask if he/she can show you TSBs relating to any problems with your vehicle.
- **Private subscription services.** You can subscribe to *AllDataDIY.com*, which allows you to download full versions of all TSBs relating to your vehicle's make, model and year. A five-year subscription will cost $44.95*...one-year, $26.95.
- **HyundaiTechInfo.com.** Hyundai owners have free access to TSBs.
- **Online forums for car enthusiasts sometimes highlight problems with particular makes and models.** You can use a search engine to track them down.

TSBs can be useful when...

- **You are having a problem with a car you own.** If there is a TSB that relates to the problem you are having, point this out to a mechanic. If the problem is not covered by your warranty, citing the TSB may help you negotiate a reduced charge to fix the problem or even a free fix. Also, citing the TSB might help the mechanic diagnose the problem, especially if it is difficult for the mechanic to replicate the problem.
- **Shopping for a used vehicle.** Check all TSBs for any make, model and year of vehicle you are considering.
- **Making repairs on your own.** TSBs don't just address problems. They often offer step-by-step instructions and diagrams not found in repair manuals on how to fix what's wrong.

*Prices subject to change.

Where to Look Up Car Recalls

Sean E. Kane, auto consumer advocate and president of Safety Research & Strategies, Inc., a vehicle-safety research firm, Rehoboth, Massachusetts. *SafetyResearch.net*

It has become much easier to check on whether a particular vehicle has been subject to any recalls. There is a new, free online search tool offered by the National Highway Traffic Safety Administration for that purpose.

Type in a vehicle's 17-digit vehicle identification number (VIN) at *SaferCar.gov/vinlookup* to check whether a specific car, truck or motorcycle has had any problems that were covered by recalls over the past 15 years and whether recall repairs were made on the vehicle by manufacturer-authorized dealerships or repair shops. That information can be especially useful when you are considering buying a used car or renting a car.

In 2014, more than 46 million cars in the US (nearly one out of every five) were recalled, most notably GM cars with faulty ignition switches that could cut off power to the engine and airbags while driving.

Automakers are required to provide recall repairs for free if a vehicle is 10 years old or less even if it is no longer under warranty. Despite this, 25% of recalled autos have not been repaired 18 months after a recall was first announced. According to Carfax, a service that reports vehicle histories, there are 3.5 million used cars on the market now with unrepaired recall defects. This is a major hidden hazard for consumers because there is no state or federal law requiring that used-car dealerships, private owners or rental-car agencies have the defective cars repaired.

If You're Buying a Certified Pre-Owned Car...

Don't assume that a certified car has been thoroughly inspected. Used-car dealers are supposed to inspect cars under their certification programs, but not all dealers do. There have been a number of recent cases in which certified used cars had been in accidents or had other problems.

Self-defense: Insist on a Carfax or AutoCheck used-car history report from the seller, and contact the company that issued the report to be sure that the report has not been changed. Check the vehicle title to be sure that it does not contain words such as "salvage," "rebuilt" or "flood." Ask the dealer how to contact the former owner—call to verify the car's history. Have the vehicle checked by a mechanic you trust, and ask for a written report—this should cost about $100.

Daniel Blinn, Connecticut-based consumer attorney, quoted in *Consumer Reports Money Adviser.*

Can You Sell a Leased Car Before Lease-End?

You can sell a leased car before the lease is up to a dealer such as CarMax, which will handle the paperwork and pay off the leasing company. This works if your vehicle is worth more than the purchase price in the lease. You can make more by selling privately, but you will have to handle paperwork and ownership transfer requirements yourself.

Alternative: Some dealers offer current lessees good deals on a new leased vehicle if the lessee trades in a current one early. They may offer to waive the last few payments and end-of-lease fees. If you get an offer like this, it means that the dealer wants to sell your car and make a profit.

Do some research—find out your car's value from *Kelley Blue Book* (*KBB.com*) or at *Edmunds.com*, then call your leasing company to find out your payoff amount, the cost to buy the car and the termination fee. Decide whether to take the dealer's offer or sell on your own.

Kiplinger's Personal Finance. Kiplinger.com

MONEYWISE...

How to Lower Your Auto Loan Rate

According to a study, some dealerships mark up interest rates by an average of 2.47%, a hidden charge that costs the average consumer $714. Shop around before finalizing negotiations with the dealer—banks and credit unions may have lower rates. If you decide to use the dealer for the loan, ask for a lower rate—you may get it. If that doesn't work, offer to increase your down payment...shorten the term of the loan...and/or set up automatic payments. Also, ask the dealer about available financing incentives. And be prepared to go to another dealer if you do not get an acceptable loan rate.

GoBankingRates.com

Winter Survival Kit for Your Car

To put together a winter survival kit for your vehicle, pack a sturdy duffle bag with a flashlight, first-aid kit, warm clothes, boots, a hat, old blankets, chemical heater packs and snacks that won't spoil. Also have in the vehicle a small shovel and clumping cat litter or something else that can double as a traction aid in case your car gets stuck in the snow. And be sure to carry your cell phone and a car charger for it.

Car and Travel (C&T), a monthly AAA magazine.

Please Put Away That Cell Phone!

Rebecca Shannonhouse, editor, *Bottom Line/Health*, 281 Tresser Blvd., Stamford, Connecticut 06901. *BottomLineHealth.com*

The next time you see your doctor, don't be surprised if you get asked whether you use your cell phone while driving. Sound far-fetched? More and more doctors are starting to include this question when they ask their patients about their diets, exercise routines, smoking and other lifestyle habits.

Research has shown that in-office discussions about tobacco can improve the odds that patients will quit smoking. Maybe a discussion about cell phone use while driving can also affect patients' behavior. *Why it matters...*

- **Up to 80% of car accidents involve driver distraction.** Studies show that chatting on your cell phone (hands-free or not) is more distracting than talking to a passenger or listening to music.
- **Drivers are fooling themselves.** Nearly 90% of drivers agree that talking on a cell phone while driving is a dangerous practice, yet about three-quarters admit that they do it!

Fact: Your risk of getting in a crash is four to eight times higher when you're dialing or talking on a cell phone...and your risk is 23 times higher when you text. Think you can text and pay attention? Forget it. Texters spend 400% more time with their eyes off the road.

It doesn't matter if you're a great driver or a natural multitasker. You put everyone at risk the second you start chatting or texting.

Ask yourself this: Would you want to fly with a pilot who spent the whole flight chatting? Get an operation from a surgeon who can't put the phone down? Didn't think so!

New Ways to Set Limits on Your Teen Driver

Ford models equipped with the MyFord Touch system (available with Ford's Sync system, which costs $60 per year*) let you set the maximum speed, give beeper reminders as the vehicle reaches designated speeds and put limits on the volume of the audio system. And the radio will not turn on if seat belts are not fastened. General Motors Family Link, a $3.99 per month add-on to the GM OnStar service—which costs $20 to $30 a month—lets you stipulate where a teen can drive, providing text messages if he/she leaves the area.

CBSNews.com

*Prices subject to change.

INTERESTING FINDING...

Driving with a Hangover Can Be as Bad as Driving Drunk

People who got behind the wheel after drinking about 10 alcoholic drinks the night before—but who had no alcohol in their bloodstreams while driving—showed increased weaving and an inability to maintain attention on the road.

Study by researchers from Utrecht University in the Netherlands and University of the West of England in the UK, presented at a meeting of the Australian Professional Society on Alcohol and Other Drugs.

One Drink Too Many...

Even small amounts of alcohol may be too much if you're driving. Adults over age 55 who drank roughly the equivalent of one glass of wine had worse driving skills—such as more difficulty controlling the wheel—in a simulated test than sober peers and younger drivers who drank the same amounts of alcohol. *Reason:* Alcohol is more potent in older adults.

Sara Jo Nixon, PhD, chief, addiction research, University of Florida College of Medicine, Gainesville.

Loan Your Car and Not Get Sued

Mary Randolph, JD, editor in chief of Nolo, a publisher of do-it-yourself legal guides. Based in San Francisco, she specializes in inheritance and wealth-transfer issues. *Nolo.com*

Say you have a vehicle that you're willing to lend to a relative for an extended period—perhaps a daughter going off to college or a brother whose new job involves a lengthy commute. You make sure that he/she is covered under your automobile insurance policy and hand over the keys.

But it's not that simple. Loaning a car exposes you to a slew of legal liabilities and financial uncertainties. For example, who pays for repairs if the car breaks down? What if the family member lends the car to a friend who wrecks it? Are you covered? Who pays the deductible if the family member has an accident? And how much will your insurance premiums rise after an accident? *To protect yourself...*

- **Have the family member sign and notarize a permission letter detailing your arrangement.** In that letter, specify who is responsible for repairs and who pays the insurance deductibles...and include a promise that the borrower will pay traffic- and parking-related tickets promptly, since delays could result in the car being towed. Keep a copy of the agreement in the vehicle in case the police ever question the family member about ownership issues.

- **Request that the family member take out his/her own insurance policy on the car.** Inform the insurance company or companies that the family member will be the primary driver and will have the primary policy—the first to cover liability in the event of an accident.

You should still maintain your own insurance on the car even if the family member gets insurance. Also consider getting a general umbrella policy.

Reason: In the event of an accident, other drivers can sue you for damages if the dollar amount exceeds your family member's policy limits or if the family member fails to maintain coverage.

- **Give the car to the family member as a gift if you no longer need it.** If you do this, you save money by canceling your own insurance coverage on the vehicle, and it's the easiest way to protect yourself from liability and financial responsibilities. Unless the vehicle's value is more than $14,000 (for 2015), you won't have to file a gift-tax form with the IRS, and even then, it's unlikely that you would owe any tax, since the overage will be applied to your lifetime estate-tax exemption.

Important: Carefully review state guidelines before transferring the title to your car, because these can vary significantly. For example, in most states, if a person gifts a vehicle to an immediate family member, he typically doesn't have to pay an excise or a sales tax. But there are exceptions.

Family First

Say This, Not That: Words That Can Transform Your Marriage

Just a few simple changes in what you say to your spouse can turn an unhappy marriage into a happy one. That's because most marital discontent actually isn't caused by serious differences between spouses, but by small breakdowns in communications—and these communication problems can be corrected, often quite quickly. *Five ways to do it...*

• **Compliment your spouse's character, not just his/her actions.** Commend his kindness, honesty, dependability or thoughtfulness, for example. Our studies have found that 84% of married people value compliments about their character more than other types of spousal praise (though virtually any compliment is likely to be well-received to some degree). Character compliments make spouses feel validated and appreciated on a deep level. They aren't just about something that the spouse has done or how he looks, but who he truly is at his core.

Strategy: When you compliment a deed by your spouse, link it to a positive character trait. Offer these character compliments even when you are not the direct beneficiary of his actions. This encourages your spouse to consider you the one person in the world who sees and appreciates who he is.

Example: "It was nice of you to make coffee for me this morning. You are a very thoughtful person."

Laurie Puhn, JD, a couples' mediator in private practice in New York City. She previously served on the board of the Harvard Mediation Program. She is author of *Fight Less, Love More: 5-Minute Conversations to Change Your Relationship Without Blowing Up or Giving In,* which is the basis for the virtual online *Fight Less, Love More* course for couples that you can take from your home. *LauriePuhn.com*

BETTER WAYS...

Need to Have a Heart-to-Heart with Your Spouse? Best Time to Do It...

Don't discuss a sensitive issue with your spouse on an empty stomach. It's better to do so after you've eaten, a recent study advises.

Details: For three weeks, 107 couples were asked to check their blood sugar before bed and then note their level of anger toward their spouses for that same day.

Outcome: Spouses of both genders were found to be more hostile on evenings when their blood sugar was lowest.

Brad Bushman, PhD, professor of communication and psychology, The Ohio State University, Columbus.

• **Ask yourself, "Does this affect me?" before making a critical comment.** Sometimes the secret to healthy marital communication is understanding that you don't need to say anything.

Strategy: If your partner's action does not directly involve you, do not get involved. Ask yourself, "Does this affect me?" before offering your input.

Example: Your spouse shares a story with you about a disagreement he had with a coworker—and you think the coworker was right. Saying this will make your spouse feel like you are not his teammate. Instead, just express sympathy for the unpleasant interaction your spouse endured and let the moment pass. If you are desperate to share your opinion, ask permission first. Show respect with, "Would you like my thoughts on this?" If you get a no, then move on. However, showing respect by seeking permission first will make you more likely to get a yes and actually be heard.

• **Provide truly meaningful apologies if you are in the wrong**—don't just say, "I'm sorry." You made a mistake, but you said, "I'm sorry"—so why is your spouse still upset? As most married people already know, spouses often are not quick to forgive even when they receive a quick apology.

Strategy: A detailed apology can greatly reduce the odds of lingering anger. Say, "I'm sorry for..." then describe what you've done and why your spouse has a right to be mad about it. This establishes that you understand that you have caused pain and are not just saying "sorry" to end the conversation. Also say, "In the future, I will..." and describe how you will handle things better the next time the situation arises. If you are unsure of how to prevent the problem from recurring, seek your mate's input—"I want to make sure that this doesn't happen again. Can you help me think of a way to prevent it?" This helps rebuild your spouse's shaken trust in you. If there's something you can do to set the current situation right, say that you will do this as well.

Example: "I'm sorry for mentioning your health condition to my sister. That was something personal that you had a right to keep private. I'm going to call my sister and ask her not to share it with anyone else. And in the future, I will never discuss your medical condition with anyone without getting your permission first."

• **Figure out why the mildly annoying things your spouse does trigger more than mild annoyance in you.** We all do things that are potentially annoying to our partners. It might be leaving clothes on the bedroom floor or turning up the TV volume too loud or any of a million other missteps. But think back to early in the relationship when you felt enamored with your partner. Chances are he did annoying things then, too—only back then you probably didn't get excessively annoyed by them.

Excessive anger at a spouse's minor foibles and faux pas usually stem from feeling alone in the relationship. Your mind is making a big deal out of a small matter because it now views this small annoyance as a sign that your spouse is not truly your teammate.

Strategy: Stop pestering your partner about minor mistakes—that's only deepening the sense of distance between you. Instead, if you and/or your spouse are making a big deal about small stuff, consider it a sign that the two of you need to become teammates again. First, refocus your radar on noticing and praising the positive things your mate does, such as emptying the dishwasher. Then look for the times when your mate doesn't do the thing that annoys you and praise that, as in, "It was great to come home today and see the clean floor in our bedroom. Thank you for putting away your laundry. It made me smile." What you praise is reinforced and will be repeated more often.

Also, find time to do things that you both enjoy. Communicate with each other in positive ways, as described in this article. Feeling like teammates won't get your spouse's socks into the hamper, but it should make those socks seem like the minor matter that they really are.

• **Stop saying, "Whatever you want."** Some people imagine that letting a spouse have his way will avoid marital conflict, whether it's what to have for dinner or buying a new car. In reality, your spouse could grow resentful about always having to take full responsibility for the decision making...while you are likely to grow resentful about rarely getting what you want. And if your spouse senses your resentment, he is likely to be angry that he's getting blamed for not doing what you want when you never told him what it is you wanted.

Strategy: Both partners should offer their opinions when a decision needs to be made. When you don't have a strong opinion or truly wish to let your spouse choose, say that you're happy to do whatever he wants to do, then add, "But let me know if you would like my input." Do this only if you truly can accept your spouse's choice without second-guessing it later.

If you disagree on a decision, then be a detective and ask your mate neutral questions such as, "Why do you think that?" "What are your reasons for that choice?" Listen first, then share your thoughts. By seeking to learn new information from your mate, rather than assuming that you know his thoughts, you are showing respect. Once you have both aired your perspectives, follow up with additional questions and then brainstorm possible solutions together.

How to Argue with Your Spouse

Laurie Puhn, JD, a couples' mediator in private practice in New York City. She previously served on the board of the Harvard Mediation Program. She is author of *Fight Less, Love More: 5-Minute Conversations to Change Your Relationship Without Blowing Up or Giving In*, which is the basis for the virtual online *Fight Less, Love More* course for couples that you can take from your home. *LauriePuhn.com*

You can argue and still have a happy marriage—if your arguments lead to solutions rather than lingering bitterness. *Four ways to encourage this...*

• **Alter argument patterns.** Many couples have fallen into argument patterns that lead to more anger instead of a peaceful resolution. Maybe she criticizes, he gets defensive, she dredges up an old disagreement, he insults her, then she storms off—again and again.

Making even a minor change near the outset of an argument could prevent this pattern from recurring, improving the odds of a positive outcome.

Example: As soon as an argument begins, stop and say, "Let's sit down at the kitchen table and talk this through." Sitting is a particularly useful suggestion because it helps the brain remain calm and rational during arguments rather than shifting into panic-driven fight-or-flight mode.

• **Ask neutral questions when you feel wronged by your spouse.** Married people sometimes see nefarious intent in their spouses' missteps where none truly exists.

When you feel you have been wronged, ask calm, nonaccusatory questions that encourage your spouse to explain his/her actions. Imagine that you're a dispassionate detective trying to get to the bottom of the situation, not the aggrieved party.

Example: Your spouse is an hour late for dinner. Rather than explode in anger about how he takes your time for granted, calmly say, "What happened? You are an hour later than we had planned," or "I tried calling you on your cell, but there was no answer." There might be an innocent explanation. Perhaps

INTERESTING FINDING...

Affairs Typically Start Two Years into Marriage

And an average affair lasts six months, costing the cheating spouse more than $2,600 for hotels, dinners, gifts and other items.

Survey by *VoucherCloud.net* of 2,645 people, age 25 or older, who had been married to their current partners for at least five years.

your partner lost track of time...or perhaps there was a lot of traffic and his phone battery was dead.

- **Stop arguing about pointless stuff.** Don't argue about what your adult children should do or over any fact that you easily can check on. These are pointless arguments. Your adult children probably are not going to do what you want them to do anyway, so it makes no difference if you and your spouse disagree over what that should be. And if a fact can be looked up, just agree to look it up when you can, rather than let the disagreement become a full-blown argument. Alternatively, you could turn the disagreement into a lighthearted low-stakes bet—"I bet you a dollar that I've got this one right!"

- **Team up to find a solution.** People are more likely to live up to the terms of an agreement when they feel that they had a role in crafting it. Thus the best way to prevent a problem from recurring in a marriage isn't thinking up a solution—it's sitting down with your spouse to think up a solution together.

Example: Don't tell your spouse, "Keep a cell phone charger in your car so you can call the next time you're going to be late." Ask your spouse, "What could be done to avoid this happening again?" If your spouse doesn't think up the car-charger solution, raise it yourself in the form of a question—"How about we keep cell phone chargers in our cars?"

I'm Dating Again (My Husband Is Thrilled!)

Karen Larson, editor of *Bottom Line/Personal*, 281 Tresser Blvd., Stamford, Connecticut 06901. *BottomLine Personal.com*

As someone who's been married a long time, I love hearing the secrets of happy marriages. Recently, I learned a secret that surprised me—treat marriage as if it were a lifetime date.

That came from Cornell University gerontologist Karl Pillemer, PhD, author of *30 Lessons for Loving: Advice from the Wisest Americans on Love, Relationships, and Marriage*. Dr. Pillemer learned it from a 70-year-old woman, Leigh. Leigh and her husband had each been married before and agreed to treat their marriage together as a lifetime date.

Here's why it works: When you go on dates, you do your best to be interesting, upbeat, attractive and attentive. You try to make the person you are with feel special.

When people have been married for a long time, they take their partners for granted. We don't feel the need to make an effort, because, after all, we know they love us, so why do we need to? But you do need to, explained Dr. Pillemer. When you make an effort, you fuel the spark that makes a marriage thrive.

Another aspect of dating is that it's exciting because it offers an element of the unknown. Married couples who try new things...take spontaneous trips...and give surprise gifts increase their chances of remaining happily married.

Treating a marriage like a date doesn't mean that there won't be plenty of trying times. The trick is to view the difficult days of a marriage like the time between dates—not as a problem with the relationship but as an unavoidable intermission from it. Then we look forward to when we can resume the date of our lifetime.

When Anger Separates Family Members: Here's How to Connect

Douglas Stone, a lecturer on law at Harvard Law School and founder and managing partner of Triad Consulting Group, a global corporate education and communications consulting firm based in Cambridge, Massachusetts. He is coauthor with Sheila Heen of *Thanks for the Feedback: The Science and Art of Receiving Feedback Well (even when it is off-base, unfair, poorly delivered, and frankly, you're not in the mood). StoneandHeen.com*

Do you have a family member you no longer see or talk to? It could be a brother, sister, grown child, cousin, parent, in-law, aunt or uncle. Maybe it was something he/she said or something you did, but no matter the cause, there is a sense of loss.

Here is my proven five-step plan for bringing an estranged family member back into the fold...

STEP 1: See his side. Family members who cut off contact often do so because they believe that it's the only way they can protect themselves and their sanity. From this person's point of view, he is acting reasonably while you and/or other members of the family have treated him unreasonably. Try to understand what might have led this person to think and feel this way.

Example: The estranged family member always complained that no one in the family listened to his wife or respected her. At the last family gathering, the wife got so angry, she walked out. Perhaps he thinks cutting off contact is the only way to maintain his wife's sense of self-worth.

You do not have to agree with this perception, but it's important to try to understand it from that person's point of view.

In addition, we often have an impact on others that we may not be aware of. It's useful to ask yourself what you have said or done that might have impacted an alienated family member in ways that did not reflect your actual intentions.

STEP 2: Send the right kind of letter. If you have been out of touch for a long period, a handwritten letter can be a useful way to attempt to reconnect. Handwritten letters have become rare, so sending one signifies a special effort.

This letter should describe the impact on you of the current state of the relationship and express a desire to repair it. Acknowledge that this will be difficult, but write that you think it is worth trying and propose a first step.

Example: "I miss you. My life and our family life aren't the same without you. Maybe we could see if there's a way for us to start the process of trying to fix things. I'll be in town on the 12th. Maybe we could get together for coffee."

Resist the urge to defend your past actions (or the actions of other family members) in this letter. Do not apologize, either, even if you recognize that you played a role in the rift. Estranged family members are so predisposed to expect troublesome interactions with their families that it's easy for them to see ulterior motives in apologies. This person might conclude, *He's trying to seem like "the good one" by apologizing, but he's not.*

If efforts for reconciliation with this family member have failed multiple times in the past, you might suggest setting aside old issues rather than trying to solve them. Here you could write, "Let's leave the past in the

TAKE NOTE...

Movies That Help You Heal After Divorce

Ten divorce movies that can help you cope after ending a marriage...

The First Wives Club...The War of the Roses... Along Came Polly...Prime...Shirley Valentine... One Fine Day...Kramer vs. Kramer... Mrs. Doubtfire...It's Complicated...The Odd Couple.

All provide meaningful messages while looking at the ending of a marriage, and most provide plenty of laughs, too.

Lois Tarter, divorce blogger and divorce party planner, Los Angeles and New York City, and author of *The Divorce Ritual: Get Up, Get Out and Get On with Your Life.*

past and come up with a way where we can have some sort of relationship."

STEP 3: Acknowledge without agreeing. When you meet with the estranged family member, encourage him to speak his mind first—and brace for the worst. There's a good chance that this person's words will be full of blame and righteousness. Resist the urge to contradict—that would only deepen the rift. Instead, let the person know you are working hard to understand him—"I can see how hurt you are by what I said. Were there other things I said or did that contributed to how you've been feeling?" After you've spent time seeking to understand, you can express remorse (if you genuinely feel remorse)—"I'm so sorry that things I said and did caused you this pain." And you can take responsibility for your contribution to the problem—"I see now that I was contributing in important ways to the strain in our relationship."

You may find yourself getting angry while your family member is talking, but resist the urge to lash out. Instead, prompt him to keep talking: "I see this so differently. We have such different perceptions. But I'm working really hard to understand your view."

STEP 4: Transition gently to your viewpoint. When the estranged person is done explaining his views, thank him for doing so and explicitly turn the conversation to the topic of how you've been feeling.

Example: "Thanks for explaining that. I know how hard it must have been to open up to me. But it really did help me to understand how you experienced what happened, and it helped me to see what I've been contributing to the problem. I want to share how I've been feeling as well."

State your thoughts in a calm and blame-free way, even if the estranged family member was aggressive and abrasive when he spoke.

Avoid attributing motives to this estranged family member. Instead, describe the impact of his actions on you.

Example: Rather than, "You didn't invite me to your Christmas party because you take every opportunity to exclude me," say, "When you didn't invite me to your party, I felt left out and upset."

STEP 5: Defuse future missteps in advance. If the estranged family member agrees to reestablish contact, there are likely to be some bumps in the road. Make sure everyone is aware that stress and misunderstandings are normal. Ask each family member in advance what he thinks will help and whether he has any specific requests of others. Also, set up a time to check back in to discuss how people are feeling

Example: "We're bound to get on each other's nerves every now and then, but let's not let things fall apart when we do. Let's agree that whenever either of us says something that the other considers out of bounds, we can just say 'time out' and agree to talk about it later."

How to Deal with Birth-Order Disharmony

Kevin Leman, PhD, a Tucson, Arizona–based psychologist and author of *The Birth Order Book: Why You Are the Way You Are.*

The oldest sibling in a family often is considered bossy by younger siblings and the youngest frequently feels as if he/she is treated dismissively—and these feelings can last into adulthood. Ironically, the best way to get past birth-order disharmony often isn't to try to set birth-order differences aside but rather to embrace them.

Older siblings tired of being called bossy might assume that the smart strategy is to sit back and let younger siblings take the reins. But many younger siblings are so preconditioned to let firstborns lead that they reflexively cede responsibility—then accuse the older siblings of taking over.

Instead, older siblings should use their natural leadership skills to put younger siblings in charge. You might ask one of your siblings to plan the family's next gathering, then add,

"Just tell me how I can help." Doing this regularly can forge a new sibling dynamic.

Younger siblings struggling to be seen as adults should take advantage of their natural interpersonal and diplomacy abilities. Rather than come right out and accuse older siblings of unfair treatment, you can stroke a firstborn's considerable ego by saying how thankful you are for everything he did for you during childhood. Then add, "Sometimes I still feel like I'm not treated like your equal. I would love to have a relationship where we see each other as peers." If your older sibling protests that he does treat you as an equal, say that you are probably oversensitive on the subject, but that it's important to you. That should do the trick.

How to Prevent a Nut Allergy in Your Baby

Eating nuts while pregnant may lower the child's chances of having a nut allergy.

Recent finding: The more peanuts, walnuts, almonds, pistachios, cashews, pecans, hazelnuts, macadamia nuts and/or Brazil nuts a woman ate during her pregnancy, the less likely her child was to have a nut allergy.

Study of more than 8,200 children of nearly 11,000 mothers who took part in the Nurses' Health Study II by researchers at Harvard Medical School, Boston, published in *JAMA Pediatrics.*

Common Painkiller Linked to ADHD

Acetaminophen may be tied to *attention-deficit/hyperactivity disorder* (ADHD). Pregnant women who took Tylenol and other medications with acetaminophen were 13% more likely to have children diagnosed with ADHD in a recent study.

Study of more than 64,000 Danish mothers and children by researchers at University of California, Los Angeles, Fielding School of Public Health, published in *JAMA Pediatrics.*

Dogs Help Protect Babies Against Allergies and Asthma

When mice were exposed to dust from households with dogs that were allowed outdoors, the mice's gut microbes changed significantly and they had reduced allergic responses to well-known allergy triggers.

Theory: Children in homes with dogs that are allowed outside develop intestinal bacteria that provide better immunity against many allergens.

Animal study by researchers at University of California, San Francisco, published in *Proceedings of the National Academy of Sciences.*

Surprising Protection from Benign Breast Disease—but Start Early

Young girls who eat peanut butter may reduce their risk of developing *benign breast disease.* Eating peanut butter or nuts three days a week between the ages of nine and 15 lowered the risk for breast disease by 39% 15 years later in a recent study. Benign breast disease—noncancerous changes in the breast tissue—affects about one-fourth of all women and is considered a risk factor for later development of breast cancer.

Graham Colditz, MD, DrPh, associate director for cancer prevention and control, Alvin J. Siteman Cancer Center and professor of surgery, Washington University School of Medicine, both in St. Louis, and leader of a study of 9,039 schoolgirls, published in *Breast Cancer Research and Treatment.*

Why Kids Hate Veggies

Most children are wary of plant foods—which stems from our ancestors, who had to be cautious because many plants were poisonous or covered with spines or thorns. This may explain why children have a natural aversion to vegetables.

Study of 47 children 18 months old to age eight by researchers at Yale University, New Haven, Connecticut, published in *Cognition*.

Small Amounts of Caffeine May Harm Children

Even low doses of caffeine—the equivalent of what is found in a half can of caffeinated soda or a half cup of coffee—actually slow children's heart rates and increase their blood pressure. It is not yet known what the long-term effects of repeated exposure to caffeine would be.

Study of 52 children, ages eight and nine...and 49 children, ages 15 to 17, by researchers at University at Buffalo School of Public Health and Health Professions, New York, published in *Pediatrics*.

Long-Term Effects of Being Bullied

The ramifications of bullying last far beyond school years. Researchers found that men who were bullied as children made less money and were more likely to be unemployed. Adults who suffered from childhood bullying had greater physical and mental health issues, lower levels of education and more social awkwardness when compared with those who were not bullied.

Best: Keep an open dialogue with your child so that there is a greater chance that he/she will tell you if he is being bullied. Anti-bullying awareness and laws are more common now but can help only if the bullying is reported.

The National Child Development Study, which followed almost 8,000 children born in England, Scotland and Wales, led by researchers at Kings College London, published in *The American Journal of Psychiatry*.

Abuse Linked to Dyslexia

Children who suffered abuse in childhood were six times more likely to have dyslexia, according to recent research. It's not clear if abuse leads to dyslexia or if dyslexic children are more likely to be abused.

Journal of Interpersonal Violence.

Protect Your Kids from Cell Phone Radiation

Cell phones pose greater risks to children than to adults. Children absorb more radiation from cell phones because their brain tissue is more absorbent than that of adults and their skulls are thinner.

Self-defense: Teach children to hold cell phones six inches from their ears. And children should not keep cell phones on their bodies when phones are not in use...or under their pillows, as 75% of preteens and early teens do—the phones give off microwave radiation all the time when turned on. Also, keep cell phones away from a pregnant woman's abdomen...and do not use a cell phone while nursing.

Analysis by researchers at Environmental Health Trust, Teton Village, Wyoming, published in *Journal of Microscopy and Ultrastructure*, with additional reporting from *WebMD.com*.

BEWARE...

Little-Known Danger to Children

10,000 children were poisoned by laundry and dishwasher detergent packs last year.

Many of the single-dose detergent capsules look like candy. When ingested, they can cause digestive and breathing problems, especially in young children.

The New York Times. NYTimes.com

Identity Theft and Kids

Child identity theft can follow children into their adult lives and affect student loans, employment and housing. *To prevent this...*

Do not carry your child's Social Security number with you, and don't give it out unless there is reason to do so—usually for tax reasons. Provide your child's full name, address and birth date only when necessary. Limit personal information about your child on social media. At doctors' offices, write down personal details instead of saying them out loud for others to hear. Lock up your child's birth certificate and passport in a safe-deposit box. Watch for credit card applications, bills for unfamiliar services or unexpected notices in your child's name. If you think your child's identity has been compromised, ask for credit reports from Equifax, Experian and TransUnion.

Bankrate.com

What You *Must* Tell Your Kids About Drinking

Teens whose parents told them they were against underage drinking are more than 80% less likely to drink than teens whose parents didn't give them a clear message. Only 8% of teens whose parents said that underage drinking was not acceptable were active drinkers. Nearly 50% of teens whose parents thought that underage drinking was acceptable or somewhat acceptable were active drinkers.

Online survey of 663 high school students by *MADD.*

College Aptitude Tests Don't Predict a Student's Success...

Students who opted out of the ACT and/or the SAT tests had virtually the same grades and graduation rates as students who chose to take one or both tests, according to a recent study. High school grades were the best predictor of a student's success in college.

"Defining Promise: Optional Standardized Testing Policies in American College and University Admissions," a study of students at nearly three dozen schools by William Hiss, former dean of admissions at Bates College, Lewiston, Maine.

TAKE NOTE...

Most Kids Watch Way Too Much TV

About 7% of kids watch TV for *five hours or more* a day and 5% use a computer for five hours or more. Only 27% of children ages 12 to 15 follow the recommendations of the American Academy of Pediatrics, watching TV and using the computer for a total of two hours or less each day.

Study by researchers at National Center for Health Statistics, Hyattsville, Maryland, published by the Centers for Disease Control and Prevention.

No More "Bad Dog": How to Break Your Pet's Bad Habits

Victoria Schade, author of *Bonding with Your Dog: A Trainer's Secrets for Building a Better Relationship* and *Secrets of a Dog Trainer: Positive Problem Solving for a Well-Behaved Dog.* Based in Bucks County, Pennsylvania, she was the featured trainer on the Animal Planet TV show *Faithful Friends. LifeontheLeash.com*

Does your dog ignore you when you call its name? Does it jump on you when you walk in the door? Does it pull at its leash when you go for a walk?

Before you blame your dog, consider that the way you train and interact with your dog could be at the heart of the problem. Many widely used, seemingly sensible dog-training strategies are not very effective—some actually are counterproductive.

Here, nine dog-training mistakes...

MISTAKE: Calling your dog to you by yelling its name. Dog owners say their dogs'

EASY-TO-DO...

Track Your Family on Your Smartphone

Apps that allow you to keep tabs on family members can be helpful if you want to keep an eye on children or an elderly relative. The free *Connect* app for iPhone or iPad uses data from your family's updates on social-media sites such as Facebook, Twitter, Instagram and LinkedIn to show where they are on a map. *Find My Friends!*, free for iPhone and Android, sends an invitation to the contact you would like to track. Once he/she accepts the invitation, you can see where he is on a map. *Phone Tracker* for iPhone and Android lets you follow the movements of friends and family members, $3.99.*

Roundup of experts on smartphone tracking software, reported at *MarketWatch.com*.

*Price subject to change.

names so often and for so many different reasons that dogs can become uncertain what to do when they hear their names. Some dogs start ignoring their names entirely.

Better: Select a word like "Here" or "Come" that you will call to your dog only when you want it to return to you. Call out this word in a friendly tone, not a stern command as many dog owners do. A stern voice could make your dog think you're angry, discouraging it from rushing to your side. Reward the dog with a treat when it responds properly to your recall word. (You can phase out these treats once your dog responds reliably, but don't do so too quickly. Coming when called takes time to cement.)

Do not use this recall word only to call your dog for things that it doesn't like, such as going back inside when playtime ends. Your dog is much more likely to come when called if it often receives something nice when it does, such as praise or food.

MISTAKE: Pulling back when your dog pulls at its leash...or letting yourself get pulled along. This teaches the dog that straining at a taut leash is normal and acceptable.

Better: When you walk your dog, carry dog treats and a "clicker"—a small device available in pet stores that makes a clicking sound. Immediately sound this clicker whenever the dog walks next to you with a slack leash as it is supposed to, even if it's just for a few steps, then quickly reward with a treat. The clicking sound marks the good behavior in the dog's mind, and the treat is a powerful reward for a job well-done.

When your dog pulls at its leash, stop and don't budge until the dog either turns around to see what's wrong or just stops in its tracks. Continue this process until your dog is reliably walking by your side, and then slowly wean down from the frequent click and treating. Because the great outdoors is filled with distractions, you'll probably have to use the clicker and treats for several weeks before you can begin weaning.

MISTAKE: Chasing a dog that grabbed something it shouldn't have. If you chase your dog when it picks up something that it isn't supposed to have in its mouth, you increase the odds that the dog will engage in this misbehavior again. Dogs love to have a game of chase with their owners.

Better: Get a dog treat, squat down to the dog's level, and call the dog to you. When the dog approaches for the treat, place it in front of your dog's nose and say, "Drop it." Reward the dog with the treat when it does drop it.

Similar: If your dog gets loose, don't chase after it—your dog can probably outrun you and likely will enjoy the chase. Instead, get the dog's attention, then run away from it. This might cause the dog to change its game from running away from you to chasing after you, making it easier to calmly take hold of your dog when it catches up to you.

MISTAKE: Giving a jumping dog attention. Dogs that jump up and put their front paws on people crave attention. They will continue jumping as long as their owners give them attention—even if the attention they're receiving is just hearing their owners tell them, "Get down."

Better: Walk away from the jumping dog without making eye contact or saying a word to it.

Later, when the dog is calm, start to teach it to sit when you cross your arms across your chest. Many dogs tune out verbal commands when they get excited, but most still notice body language.

To teach your dog to respond to a crossed-arm sit command, start by combining the verbal sit command with crossed arms. Provide treats when the dog responds. Then eliminate the verbal command and use the crossed-arm signal alone, still rewarding with treats.

Once your dog masters the crossed-arm sit command, instruct houseguests to use it, too. Otherwise they might accidentally give the dog attention when it jumps up, undermining the training.

MISTAKE: Letting your dog use older household items as chew toys. If you let your dog chew on an old flip-flop or towel, don't blame the dog when it chews up your new flip-flops or towels, too. Dogs generally can't figure out the difference.

Better: Never let your dog chew on anything that could be mistaken for something you don't want it to chew on. Limit your dog to products made for dogs, including toys and bones.

MISTAKE: Failing to notice that a puppy is about to go to the bathroom inside.

Better: If you can hustle the puppy outside before it relieves itself, this will help the puppy figure out that outdoors is the proper place to do its business.

What to do: When your puppy becomes distracted and wanders away from people, dog toys and/or other dogs, quickly take it outside—there's a good chance that the puppy is about to heed nature's call.

When the puppy must go to the bathroom inside—when you're away all day at work, for example—provide grass-textured pet potties, not smooth-surfaced potty pads. The feeling of the artificial grass underfoot can help the puppy learn that it is supposed to use the yard to relieve itself.

MISTAKE: Yelling at a barking dog to get it to quiet down. Making noise is not an effective way to convince a dog to stop making noise. Your dog might think that you're joining in on the fun.

Better: Look for the reason behind the barking and address it. *Examples...*

- If your dog barks to defend its territory against animals and people that it sees nearby, block its view. You could do this with curtains, fencing, landscaping or opaque window privacy film, available in home centers, that temporarily adheres to windows. You don't have to cover the entire window, just the lower section that is in the dog's sight line. You can gradually lower the privacy film until you don't need it at all.
- If your dog barks to get your attention, ignore the dog until the barking stops, wait a few beats and only then see what it wants. Eventually the dog will figure out that barking will not get it attention, though you might have to put up with considerable barking until this message gets through. Stay strong—many dogs try barking louder just before they finally give up on barking. You also can teach your dog the "hush" command. Say, "Hush," and when the dog stops barking, give it a treat.

MISTAKE: Waiting for misbehavior to become entrenched before acting to correct it. The longer you tolerate a dog's misbehavior, the harder it will become to alter.

Better: Correct misbehavior when you notice the dog doing it a second time. Once could be a fluke...twice suggests that this is a habit.

MISTAKE: Using pain to train. Choke chains and other training tools that hurt dogs might suppress misbehavior, but they don't change the way the dog thinks. If your dog lunges at other dogs, for example, a correction from a choke collar might convince it not to, but your dog still might feel antagonism toward other dogs and react when you're not around.

Better: Provide treats when the dog behaves properly, rather than pain when it does not.

EASY-TO-DO...

Give Your Dog the Sniff Test

The following odors may indicate that your dog needs medical attention...

Sweet-smelling breath can indicate diabetes. Urine that smells like sour or rotting fish can indicate a urinary tract infection. A sickly fermented smell from a dog's ear can be a sign of a yeast infection. Exceptionally foul-smelling diarrhea can mean the life-threatening *parvovirus* could be present. Strong and foul-smelling breath can be a sign of an oral tumor or severe periodontal disease. A musty odor coming from your dog's skin can indicate *pyoderma*, a bacterial infection.

Your Dog. TuftsYourDog.com

Hardest Dogs to Housebreak

The hardest dogs to housebreak are small and toy breeds. It can take a year to housebreak some small and toy dogs, such as pugs, dachshunds, beagles, basset hounds, most terriers and Chihuahuas—and males tend to be harder to train than females.

Theory: These small breeds are genetically the furthest from the primitive dog. Dog breeds that have remained close to the primitive dog tend to stay clean almost instinctively and keep the area they consider their den very clean as well. Wild dogs never use their dens as bathrooms—the smell might attract predators.

CanineInformationLibrary.com

Pets Get Food Poisoning, Too

Like humans, dogs and cats are susceptible to getting sick from foods contaminated with bacteria, especially *Salmonella* and *Listeria monocytogenes*. Symptoms include vomiting, diarrhea and fever.

Best: Don't feed your dog raw food, not even store-bought raw pet food that is marketed as safe.

US Food and Drug Administration in Silver Spring, Maryland.

Natural Arthritis Cures for Dogs and Cats

Jeff Feinman, VMD, CVH, a certified veterinary homeopath and integrated veterinary practitioner with a private practice in Weston, Connecticut. He is president of the nonprofit Academy of Veterinary Homeopathy Foundation. *HomeVet.com*

Arthritis is no more fun for pets than it is for people. The symptoms (and treatments) are similar, but there's a big difference—your pets can't tell you when they're hurting.

Dogs and cats actually try to hide their pain because animals in the wild know that weakness makes them a target. You have to be a bit of a detective to recognize the signs—a stiff walk...a favorite couch that they no longer use...a groan when they lie down.

About 20% of middle-aged dogs and cats have arthritis in at least one joint, and nearly all will be affected at some time in their lives. The good news is that arthritis often can be prevented—and pets that already have it can get relief without taking drugs. *Steps to take...*

• **Check your pet's weight.** A recent study found that 53% of dogs are overweight or obese. Among cats, the percentage is even higher.

Why it matters: Those extra pounds accelerate degenerative joint disease, the breakdown of cartilage that surrounds the joints. Cartilage damage triggers the release of inflammatory chemicals that cause pain and stiffness.

You don't need a scale to know if your pet is overweight. You have to look and feel. When you look down at your dog or cat, you should see a pronounced waist behind the rib cage. Viewed from the side, the abdomen should be tucked up and not hanging down. You should be able to feel the ribs under a thin layer of fat.

If your pet is overweight, there won't be much of a waist...you'll barely feel the ribs... and the abdomen will be rounded rather than tucked.

Because dogs and cats come in different sizes, you can't count on the portion guides that are listed on food labels.

In general: If your pet is overweight, start by reducing food amounts by about one-fifth. Keep at that amount for a few weeks. If your pet still seems heavy, decrease the portions again.

• **More exercise.** Along with weight loss, exercise is the most effective way to prevent and treat arthritis. Regular exercise increases *synovial fluid*, the natural lubricant that allows joints to glide rather than grind. Exercise also reduces pressure by strengthening the muscles that surround the joints.

It's usually easy to get dogs to exercise—just snap on a leash and take a walk. Cats need more encouragement—or at least something that engages their interest such as a ball or a moving piece of string. Walk/play with your pet for at least 10 to 15 minutes a few times a day.

BETTER THAN DRUGS

The standard arthritis treatments for dogs and cats include *nonsteroidal anti-inflammatory drugs* (NSAIDs) prescribed by veterinarians. I recommend drugs only as a last resort. You usually can treat arthritis with natural—and safer—remedies. *Best choices...*

• **Homeopathy.** This is a system of medicine that uses extremely small doses of natural substances to alter the body's energy. I have found it to be quite effective in my practice. It's my first treatment choice because it causes no side effects and can help reduce cartilage damage and inflammation.

Homeopathy is complicated because there are hundreds of potential remedies and doses and because the treatments vary widely from one pet to the next. You can give the remedies at home, but only after they've been chosen by a veterinary homeopath.

Examples: If your pet limps when it first gets up, but the stiffness improves with movement, your veterinarian might recommend *Rhus toxicodendron.* Arthritis that gets worse in cold/damp weather might respond better to *Calcarea carbonica.*

To find a veterinary homeopath near you, go to *TheAVH.org/referrals.*

• **Physical therapy.** Moving the limbs in certain ways can markedly reduce pain and improve your pet's ability to stand, walk and run. When your pet is lying on its side, for example, you can gently grip the knee and move the leg through its full range of motion. Your veterinarian can recommend exercises for different joints. You might be advised to work with a veterinary physical therapist who might use specialized equipment (such as underwater treadmills) to get your pet moving.

• **Gelatin.** Over-the-counter joint supplements such as *glucosamine* and *chondroitin* are effective but expensive. I usually recommend an unflavored *gelatin* such as Knox, available in any grocery store. Gelatin contains collagen, one of the materials used by the body to manufacture cartilage and bone. Studies have shown that it improves flexibility and can relieve joint pain. Add about one teaspoon of the gelatin powder to your pet's food every day.

• **Bone broth.** This soup offers the same bone-building effects as gelatin, and pets love the taste. You can make it yourself by slow-simmering chicken, pork or beef bones until they're soft and fall apart. (It might take up to two days—using a slow cooker is best, as it can stay on safely for that length of time.) Strain the broth carefully so that no bone bits remain. Store the broth in the refrigerator, and give your pet a little taste with each meal.

• **Acupuncture.** Stimulating the acupuncture points can increase circulation and boost painkilling chemicals in the body. Use the Internet to find a certified veterinary acupuncturist in your area. A session typically costs between $30 and $50.* Your pet may improve after a single session, but you'll probably be advised to schedule two sessions a week for a few weeks, followed by occasional maintenance sessions.

• **Orthopedic beds.** Who doesn't like a cozy bed? Large dogs in particular do better when

*Prices subject to change.

they sleep on a firm mattress. You can buy orthopedic pet beds in pet stores and online that make it easier to stand up...have memory foam for extra support...and are heated to keep joints limber.

Also: Elevated food and water bowls, which are available at pet stores and online, can help pets with neck or back problems.

TAKE NOTE...

Easier Ways to Medicate Your Cat

Ask your veterinarian if any of the following could work for administering pills to your reluctant kitty without affecting potency, absorption or effectiveness—splitting the pill for easier swallowing...using a pill gun (a long device that looks like a syringe and lets you position the pill at the back of the cat's mouth) or pulverizing it...switching from a three-times-a-day dose to a twice-daily dose...or hiding the pill in a piece of cheese or meaty treat.

Helpful: Prevent your cat's escape by administering meds in a room with the door shut...hold the cat firmly (wrapping the animal in a towel may prevent scratching).

Catnip. TuftsCatnip.com

Grieving for a Beloved Pet—Be Patient

Pet owners can have a difficult time getting over the death of a beloved animal.

Example: A friend of mine lost her dog a year ago, but still misses him deeply and is having trouble moving on.

Pets provide unconditional love and companionship, so it's only natural to grieve the loss of this beloved family member. There is no timetable for the grieving process—when a pet dies, be patient with yourself during the time it takes to heal.

Sometimes when we experience a loss, it can bring up feelings about other losses, such as the death of a parent, sibling or friend. If you think that old grief might be adding to what you're feeling about losing a pet, you might want to work with a grief therapist. To find a qualified therapist in your area, go to *GoodTherapy.org*.

Phyllis Kosminsky, PhD, clinical social worker in private practice in Pleasantville, New York, and author of *Getting Back to Life When Grief Won't Heal.*

17

Household Helpers

Declutter Your Home Forever: A Psychiatrist's Surprising Tricks

A cluttered home is more than simply unsightly—living in the midst of a mess actually can take a toll on our mood and on our quality of life.

A home is supposed to be a peaceful, joyful retreat. A disorderly home instead makes us feel anxious and unsettled. It's hard to relax when surrounded by chaos.

Here's a strategy for decluttering each room in your house that also can boost your mood...

DINING ROOM

The dining room table serves as a multi-purpose space in many homes. It's a craft table where we pursue hobbies...a library where we read newspapers...a game room where we play cards with friends...and a workstation where our kids do their homework. (In some homes, the kitchen table serves this multipurpose role.)

That wide range of uses can lead to a very cluttered table. Half-completed projects pile up, making it difficult for the family to gather for a peaceful meal.

When the table is cleared, this clutter typically gets stacked in a corner of the dining room—where it serves as a mealtime distraction and source of stress, with potentially significant consequences to our health.

Distractions in dining areas increase the odds that we will overeat because our minds are not focused on our meal. And it increases the odds that we will indulge in unhealthy comfort foods in an attempt to make ourselves feel better.

What to do: Make a list of each project and activity that regularly occur on your din-

Melva Green, MD, psychiatrist and expert on the A&E program *Hoarders*. She is coauthor of *Breathing Room: Open Your Heart by Decluttering Your Home*. *DrMelvaGreen.com* ing room (or kitchen) table, aside from eating. Purchase a stackable plastic container for each of these, and label these containers appropriately. Before meals, put everything on the table into its container, then place these containers somewhere that they cannot be seen from the dining room.

KITCHEN

Many of us have kitchens that serve our unfulfilled dreams, not our reality. They are stocked with lots of specialized cooking tools for making meals that we never actually prepare...or fancy glassware and china for dinner parties that we never actually throw.

These items don't just clutter up our kitchen cabinets, making it hard to find the things that we do use. They also serve as an unpleasant reminder of the life we don't have—the one where we throw parties and have hours to devote to cooking.

What to do: Imagine that you are going to throw that fancy dinner party. Write up the menu (this is the first step to actually having that dinner party), then take out all the dishes, glassware, utensils and cooking tools you would need. Now scan whatever remains in your kitchen cabinets with a critical eye. Anything that you don't need for your dream party and that you don't use regularly likely is something you don't really need in your kitchen at all.

Donate these unneeded items to a secondhand store run by a charity. Donating things to a good cause helps overcome guilt about getting rid of possessions you paid good money for but never used. Plus, your donation may be tax-deductible.

Helpful: If it makes you anxious to give away things that you might need someday, remind yourself that you are not really giving them away. Instead, you're trading them for something better—an uncluttered kitchen where you feel at peace.

LIVING ROOM

A living room should be a place for relaxing and enjoying life's blessings. It should feature comfortable seating and decor that makes us feel joy. Scan your living room for things that do not serve this purpose or, worse, that stand in the way of your relaxation and joy.

Examples: Is your living room full of furniture that looks nice but is not comfortable? Is there a stack of magazines blocking your view of pictures of your kids or grandkids?

What to do: Remove anything from your living room that doesn't make you feel relaxed and joyful. Select living room furniture that's comfortable, not stiff and formal.

STUDY

The study is where we pay our bills, do our taxes, make investment decisions and wade through all the other important paperwork that comes into the home. (In some homes, this might occur at a desk located in a bedroom or kitchen.)

The trouble is that many of the responsibilities and decisions that await our attention in the study are tedious or, worse, frightening. If this leads to procrastination, we're likely to end up with a cluttered room choked with piles of paper.

What to do: Sort all of the paperwork that requires your attention into 10 stacks. Stack number one is for things that you can deal with without any anxiety. Stack number two is for things that trigger a very slight twinge of anxiety...on through stack 10, which is for things that you're terrified to confront.

Today, deal with only stack number one...tomorrow tackle only stack two...and so on for 10 days. This strategy allows us to get through most of the clutter in our studies—and feel good about having accomplished so much—before we come to a terrifying task that could bring our progress to a halt.

It also enforces a slow-and-steady 10-day pace, reducing the odds that we try to do everything at once—which usually results in burnout and bad decisions.

BEDROOM

Clutter in the bedroom can interfere with our ability to feel at peace, costing us sleep. When we don't get enough sleep, it becomes especially difficult to be happy, healthy and productive.

What to do: Clear all clutter from the bedroom. Everything that doesn't absolutely need to be in this room must go. The only exception is objects and artwork that give you a sense of peacefulness and love—for example, your framed wedding photo.

Take special care to clear out anything that causes your mind to relive old wounds. If your relationship with one of your family members currently is strained, for example, temporarily remove photos of that family member from your bedroom.

BATHROOM

Many of us have bathrooms full of various products that stoke our insecurities. A jar of wrinkle cream might remind us that we're not young anymore. A bathroom scale might remind us that we're not as thin as we would like to be.

What to do: Consider each beauty and grooming product in your bathroom one by one. Do you feel better about yourself when you use that hair-coloring product? That skin cream? Or does this product only remind you of your physical imperfections? Throw away anything that makes you feel bad about yourself. Such things have no place in your home.

Tricks to Make a Small House Feel Bigger (No Renovations Required)

Maxwell Ryan, an interior designer in the New York metropolitan area and founder of *ApartmentTherapy.com*, a popular interior design website. His books include *Apartment Therapy: The Eight-Step Home Cure.*

In a recent survey, 80% of home owners had at least one major regret about their home. Among the most common regrets—nearly 16% said their home was too small. But you can make a small home look and feel bigger. *Here's how....*

GO FOR LIGHT

It's not the size of a room that gives a sense of space but how your eyes travel through it. The eye is drawn to light and open space, so use both of these to make your small space feel bigger.

- **Use curtain rods that are wider than your window.** Install rods that extend a few inches beyond the window so that, when the curtains are open, the entire window is exposed. You'll have more light, and your windows will seem larger.
- **Use at least three light sources, of varying heights, in every room.** One light source should be low and indirect (such as a table lamp). The second could be a standing floor lamp, which is space-efficient and great for reading. Your third source could be a pendant, which both illuminates and adds visual depth to a space.
- **Put dimmers on all the lights.** Being able to adjust light intensity to suit the time of day and occasion can make a small room more inviting. Dimmers make your home feel cozy.
- **Clean windows twice a year so you'll have more natural light.** Few people do this, but it makes a huge difference. It is one of

EASY-TO-DO...

Select Your Best Paint Color

With so many options available, choosing the right paint color can be daunting. *How to get it right...*

Look in your closet—the colors you favor in your wardrobe can help you pick a color for your walls. Consider how and when you will be using a room most—the time of day that the room will be used most often and for what type of activity may help you decide between darker and lighter colors (e.g., dinners may dictate darker tones in a dining room than brunches). Connect your rooms with colors that flow—use colors that are similar to your favorite color, maybe with a lighter hue or varying textures such as fabric or wallpaper. Don't tape your swatch to just one spot in the room—move it around, and place it next to furniture or other design elements in the room. View your potential color throughout the day to see how it changes in different lighting. Don't date your home by sticking to off-white or taupe—if you want a fresh look, you can go neutral with gray tones, which are very popular now.

Miles Redd, interior designer and author of *The Big Book of Chic.*

the easiest, most powerful things you can do. Shiny, clean windows bring in tons of natural, beautiful sunlight while inviting the eye to travel beyond the boundaries of your home to the outdoors.

• **Place light outside your windows.** With nice clean windows, adding some lighting outside your windows (in the yard, on the deck or on the windowsill) will draw the eye out the window and provide the visual feeling of more space. Simply being able to see something outside will feel very expansive. I like to put votives in lanterns outside my windows at night when giving dinner parties. This is particularly stunning in the snow!

• **Install lighting in closets.** Closets can be one of the darkest and most cluttered areas of the home, but they are improved dramatically when there is light inside of them. You can find things more easily and organize the space much more effectively. In the old days, all closets had light fixtures, but today you often have to add them. It's not expensive to do and even a battery-operated light makes a difference.

CONSIDER WALLS AND FLOORS

To keep the walls from feeling like they are closing in, try these tricks...

• **Use mirrors.** Mirrors enlarge a space by making walls melt as your eye travels through them while also brightening up a room by multiplying light. Hanging a big mirror on a wall facing a window doubles its light, brightens the entire space and allows you to enjoy the view from more than one place. A mirror also can be fabulous in a dining room at night, with candlelight.

• **Paint walls bright, light colors—but choose whites with care.** Painting walls with light, bright colors expands your space. Avoid pure white or "photographer's" white (cold!). Instead, choose whites that have a hint of color. My favorites are China White in flat for the wall and White Dove in semigloss for the trim—both by Benjamin Moore. For the ceiling, use a pure "ceiling white" to draw the eye upward by providing contrast.

• **Use paint as camouflage.** Paint things that you'd rather not accentuate, such as radiators and shelves, the same color as the wall. They'll disappear into the wall.

• **Opt for dark floors.** With light walls, a dark floor makes your walls feel brighter by contrast and gives a warm, grounded feeling to a room (dark-stained floors are very warm in their effect...blond floors are colder). Dark floors also have a more earthy feeling underfoot and seem to disappear beneath you as you enter a room. This will make your walls seem taller.

• **Get rid of interior doors that you don't need.** Removing unnecessary doors—such as a door between the dining room and living room—lets the eye travel without interruption. Leave doors for bedrooms and bathrooms. Remove all the other doors.

CLEAR OUT CLUTTER

Most people can easily get rid of a quarter to half of their stuff. Keep necessities and things that enhance your life—lose the rest. *Also...*

• **Create a "welcome home" landing strip.** Every home benefits from a hospitable entry that conveys calm and order while also keeping unwanted and unnecessary stuff from creating disarray in your home. *Your "foyer" should include the following...*

• Doormat for wiping shoes (and I suggest taking them off).

• Coat hook or tree to hang outerwear, bag, umbrellas, dog leash, etc.

• A flat surface (I call it a "landing strip") where you can lay down your wallet and keys and sort the mail. This can be a small table or bookshelf. If space is very limited, look for a shelf or photo ledge to mount directly on the wall.

• Basket for recycling. This makes it easy to dump unwanted mail at the door.

• **Plan your empty space, too.** This may sound counterintuitive, but don't use every nook and cranny for storage—you'll just keep more stuff! Allow open space for the eye to rest by keeping at least 10% of your space (walls, doors, tabletops, shelves) empty. Visual breathing room makes rooms feel spacious.

• **Try long, lean shelving.** A bookshelf (but just one!) that goes all the way up the wall draws the eye to the ceiling and creates an illusion of a bigger space. Or go long and low

TAKE NOTE...

Home Renovations for Better Winter Comfort

For better warmth this winter, consider making these changes...

Install a new heating appliance in an old fireplace—traditional fireplaces pull more heat out through the chimney than they deliver from the fire. Add south-facing windows to help catch the sun's energy. Add a covered porch—it keeps snow out of the house and moisture away from the doorsill. Insulate your home, especially if it was built before 1970—older homes often have little or no insulation. Open up your interior—an open plan spreads heat more evenly.

Andrew Schuster, AIA, registered architect, New York State, and outreach director, American Institute of Architects Central New York Chapter, writing at *Syracuse.com*.

with console-style shelves for a smart use of otherwise wasted space, such as underneath windows.

• **Use shelving inside your closet.** To maximize your closet space and keep it more organized, install hanging shelving (such as Elfa, available at The Container Store) in at least one section of your closet. Instead of trying to get a dresser in your closet or simply giving it all over to hanging clothing, a number of solid shelves that run from the floor up to the top of the closet will give you a great new useful space with easy access for clothes, shoes or accessories.

CHOOSE FURNITURE CAREFULLY

Get rid of furniture that you rarely use. For example, if there is a chair that no one sits in because it is uncomfortable, give it away. *Then...*

• **Go big.** It's a common misconception that small spaces can't handle large furnishings. A great sectional that accommodates all seating in one swoop actually can make a small room feel more gracious. It multitasks by defining space, providing space to stretch out for a nap and accommodating guests with plenty of seating for everyone. To keep the space open, choose small nesting tables instead of a big coffee table.

• **Embrace multifunctionality.** Try to use pieces that serve two or three purposes. The more multifunctional a piece is, the less you'll have to buy or bring in to your home.

Examples: Storage bed...dining table/office desk...sleeper sofa...trunk/coffee table...ottoman/storage unit.

• **Look for legs.** When choosing furniture, it will help to keep the room visually light if your sofa, chair or even bed is lifted up off the floor on legs that you can see. This idea works particularly well in small spaces because air (or "negative space") provides the visual illusion of spaciousness.

• **Be crystal clear.** Create a feeling of spaciousness by choosing glass or acrylic tables instead of wood, which blocks your view of the space.

The 8 Worst Things You Can Do to Your Lawn

John (Trey) Rogers III, PhD, professor of turfgrass management at Michigan State University, East Lansing. He was a turf consultant and project leader for the 2004 and 2008 Summer Olympic Games and 2008 UEFA World Cup and is author of *Lawn Geek: Tips and Tricks for the Ultimate Turf from the Guru of Grass. Turf.MSU.edu*

Americans spend $40 billion each year on lawns—but money isn't their only contribution. The typical home owner also devotes 73 hours to yard care every year, the equivalent of nearly two full workweeks.

That massive investment of time, effort and money could go to waste if you make any of these eight common lawn mistakes...

1. Skipping a weekly mowing. This seems harmless but can cause lasting damage. Extended gaps between mowings allow lawns to grow tall and shaggy rather than thick and dense. If done repeatedly, fewer blades of grass will grow because tall grass will block out the sun. When that tall grass finally is mowed, the gaps between the blades will be large enough for weeds to take hold.

When grass is allowed to grow tall, there also is a good chance that the subsequent mowing will "scalp" the lawn. Mowing a lawn too low is not the only scalping danger—cutting off more than one-third of the height of grass in any single mowing also is very stressful and damaging to lawns.

If you let your grass grow to about four inches and then mow it down to two, for example, you may open the door to disease or further weed growth—even if two inches is the proper height for the grass.

What to do: Mow at least once a week. Even a 10-day gap between mowings is too long. If a gap of more than a week does occur, adjust your mower's blade height to avoid clipping off more than one-third of the grass height in the next mowing, then mow again a few days later to bring the lawn down to the preferred height.

Tip: Mowing twice a week will yield an even lusher lawn—frequent mowing is the single biggest reason why golf courses and professional baseball diamonds tend to look lusher than yards.

2. Overfertilizing. Excess fertilizer could seriously dehydrate grass, something known as "burning" the lawn. And even if a lawn escapes this fate, the excess fertilizer could make the grass grow faster than normal, potentially leading to scalping of the lawn when it is mowed, as discussed earlier.

What to do: The amount of fertilizer recommended on the packaging is the maximum amount that's safe to use. Spend a little extra for a "timed-release," or "slow-release," fertilizer that supplies nutrients to the lawn slowly over a period of weeks, not all at once.

Choose a fertilizer that has about 50% of its total nitrogen as slow-release nitrogen. To determine this, find the overall percentage of "slowly available nitrogen" (indicated in small print on the package) and make sure that it is about half the overall percentage of "total nitrogen" (which is the first of a set of three numbers joined by hyphens on the package).

3. Not knowing what type of grass you have. Grass is not just grass. Many different turfgrasses are grown in US lawns—Kentucky bluegrass, fescue and ryegrass are common in cold climates...Bermuda and St. Augustine grass are found in warmer parts of the country, to name just a few. But the vast majority of home owners do not know what type of grass is growing in their lawns. So they often buy the wrong seed (or seed mixture) to spread over areas of the lawn that have thinned. This results in patches of grass that look and feel noticeably different from the rest of the lawn or that grow at a noticeably different pace.

Not knowing what type of grass you have also means that you can't care for your grass the way that it prefers to be treated. For example, different types of grass thrive at different heights.

What to do: Bring a sample of your grass to your local garden center, home center or hardware store—wherever grass seed is sold—and ask what type of grass you have. You can enter the name of this grass into a search engine to find websites from university extensions and other sources that provide mowing-height recommendations and other care tips for your specific lawn. (Add the word "mow" to this search if the initial search fails to turn up mowing recommendations.)

Examples: Kentucky bluegrass does best when its height is kept between two inches and three inches, while zoysia grass tends to flourish at one to two inches.

4. Buying off-brand grass seed. Bargain-brand grass seed is inexpensive for a reason—most often it failed to pass an inspection because there was weed seed mixed in with the grass seed. So if you plant bargain seed, there's a good chance that you are introducing weeds to your lawn.

What to do: Pay a bit more for grass seed that is at least 99.5% weed-seed free. By law, this statistic should be listed on grass-seed packaging.

5. Overwatering. Overwatering a lawn isn't just wasteful, it also puts your lawn at risk. In fact, more lawns are damaged by overwatering than by underwatering. Overwatering increases the odds of getting lawn diseases… it can wash away fertilizer…and it can cause a lawn to grow faster than normal, increasing the odds that it will be scalped during a subsequent mowing.

What to do: Purchase a soil moisture meter so that you don't have to guess when your lawn needs water. Simple meters are available in garden and home stores and online for as little as $10. If you are willing to spend much more and you have an irrigation system, opt for the UgMO PH100 (*UgMO.com*), which uses underground soil sensors to automatically inform the irrigation system when watering is needed.

6. Bagging grass. Grass clippings provide much needed nutrients to your lawn. Contrary to widely held belief, leaving clippings on a lawn does not increase the odds of thatch problems—thatch is a layer of decomposing grass roots, not grass clippings.

What to do: If your current mower has a mulching mode, that's the way to use it. If not, make your next mower a mulching mower. These are specifically designed to finely chop clippings and return them to the lawn. Mulching is easier, faster and better for your lawn than bagging.

7. Ignoring a new home's special lawn needs. When a home is built, the surrounding land often is reshaped to encourage water to run away from the structure. One unintended consequence when the lawn is first planted is that it might be planted in soil that until very recently was subsoil, not topsoil. Subsoil has not had plants growing in it—then dying and decaying in it—so it lacks the nutrients that grass needs to thrive.

What to do: Be a bit more aggressive with the fertilizing schedule when you move into a newly built home—apply fertilizer in both May and June rather than waiting until July for the second application. However, do not increase the amount of fertilizer that is used per treatment.

8. Mowing with dull blades. Dull mower blades rip grass blades apart rather than making a clean cut. This rough treatment can make grass more susceptible to drought and disease. It also can make the grass appear white.

What to do: Sharpen your mower blades at least once a year—potentially several times a year if your lawn has lots of rocks or roots that often nick your blade.

EASY-TO-DO…

4 Uncommon Uses for Deodorant

Quiet squeaky doors—apply it to door hinges. *Break in a new pair of shoes comfortably*—apply gel deodorant on the sides and tops of dry feet to prevent rubbing. *Deodorize your closet*—place your favorite scented version, cap off, inside. *Deodorize feet*—apply a thin layer of clear deodorant to the bottoms of your feet at bedtime for next-day protection.

Reader's Digest. RD.com

26 Whodathunk Household Tricks That Save You Money

Julie Edelman, also known as "The Accidental Housewife," is a rich source of everyday tips to maintain your home, family, health and sanity. Based on Florida's Gulf Coast, she is author of *The New York Times* best seller *The Accidental Housewife: How to Overcome Housekeeping Hysteria One Task at a Time. JuliesTips.com*

You can save hundreds and potentially thousands of dollars a year with these helpful money-saving household tips and tricks…

CLEANING TRICKS

- **Clean silver jewelry using toothpaste.** Squirt a small amount of regular nongel toothpaste onto your jewelry (gel toothpaste is too slippery to scrub away dirt and tarnish). Brush with a toothbrush, then rinse with warm water and blot dry with a soft towel. This works great and is easier and cheaper than silver polish.

- **Wash inside vases and thermoses with eggshells.** For hard-to-clean objects such as vases and thermoses, rinse with warm water, then add two crushed eggshells. Fill with warm water and a squirt of dishwashing soap. Shake thoroughly, and rinse with hot water.

Before cleaning your vases and thermoses, wash the eggshells with hot water to remove any remaining egg or residual membrane. You can store cleaned, air-dried shells in a cool, dry place.

• **Remove dust and debris from artificial plants and silk flowers with salt.** Dust can adhere and be hard to remove. Pour one cup of salt into a paper shopping bag. Place the plant in the bag, and shake vigorously for 30 seconds to remove dust and dirt. Use a pastry brush to remove remaining debris.

• **Clean tarnished copper pots and silver with ketchup.** Apply a thin coat of ketchup to the item. (First test on a small inconspicuous area to be sure that it doesn't cause any discoloration.)

Leave for 15 minutes. For nooks and crannies, work the ketchup in with a toothbrush. Rinse off with warm water, and dry. Due to its high acidic composition (vinegar and tomato paste), ketchup is a nontoxic alternative to store-bought cleaners and less expensive.

• **Prevent mold and bacteria in sponges with binder clips.** Sponges are havens for mold and bacteria growth if they don't dry out thoroughly. Use an office binder clip or a butterfly hair clip to make a sponge stand. Clip the sponge with the clip, then let it stand to dry on your kitchen counter.

• **Clean with lemon and baking soda.** If you don't like to use chemical cleaners, sprinkle baking soda on a nonporous surface, such as stainless steel, quartz or laminate, and buff with half a lemon. Then wipe with a damp cloth. For tougher messes or burnt-on gunk, coat the halved lemon in salt—this makes it a more abrasive scrubber. Make sure not to use lemon on porous surfaces such as marble and limestone because the citric acid can cause damage. And to be ultrasafe, test on an inconspicuous area before using to ensure that this won't harm the surface you're cleaning.

CLEVER FIX-ITS

• **Hide wood furniture scratches with coffee grinds.** Rub a cotton swab in steeped grounds, and dab on scratches to make them less noticeable. Test this first in a hard-to-see area to make sure the coffee works with the color of your wood furniture.

• **Avoid overwatering potted plants by using packing peanuts.** Place a one-inch layer of Styrofoam peanuts at the bottom of gardening pots before adding soil. Styrofoam peanuts won't decompose or absorb the water, and they prevent water buildup, bacteria, fungus and root rot.

• **Unstick zippers with pencils.** Place the item on a newspaper or paper towel to catch the lead debris. Rub a pencil on both sides of the teeth of the zipper where it is stuck. Repeat until you can move it up and down. The graphite in the pencil acts as a dry lubricant. Wipe away any excess graphite with a slightly damp cloth or paper towel.

• **Prevent dogs from destroying furniture with cayenne pepper.** Use a 1:10 ratio of cayenne pepper to water in a spray bottle. Shake well. Apply to wood legs or the wood base of furniture. (Test on an inconspicuous area to make sure that it does not damage your furniture.) Dogs will be put off by the burning taste. You also can spray your pet's favorite potty spots in the house to deter the pet from peeing and marking the area as its territory.

• **Cut cheese and cakes with dental floss.** Softer cheeses and delicate desserts can get squished or fall apart when you use knives. Plain (not minty!) dental floss is gentle enough to cut cheeses such as mozzarella and Brie and soft rectangular loglike cakes without having a special cheese or cake knife.

Be sure to use a piece of floss that is long enough to extend an inch and a half to two inches beyond each end you are cutting to make it easier to cut and minimize mess.

• **Remove water-stained suede with stale bread.** Gently rub the dried stain with a piece of stale bread or unseasoned bread crumbs. When using bread crumbs, use a toothbrush to work the crumbs into the stain and lift the fibers. An emery board will also do the trick.

MAKING THINGS LAST LONGER

• **Get more servings from near-empty condiments with vinegar.** Vinegar is a common ingredient in many of our most common condiments, including ketchup, mustard and barbecue sauce. Add two teaspoons of white vinegar to your near-empty bottles, and shake.

• **Squeeze more out of tube products.** When you feel you can't squeeze any more out of the tube, snip the other end and you'll have a few more applications. Seal with a binder clip.

• **Remove pills in sweaters with a pumice stone.** Gently rub the stone in one direction until the pills are removed.

• **Prevent mold on cheese with oil.** Apply a light film of vegetable oil or soft butter with a pastry brush or paper towel (or use cooking spray) to the outside of the cheese, and store in an airtight container in the fridge. This prevents airflow to the cheese. If mold begins to grow on the film, simply wipe off with a paper towel.

• **Keep flowers fresh using vodka and sugar.** Add a few drops of vodka and a teaspoon of sugar to the vase water. Both agents help reduce bacteria growth, keeping flowers fresher longer.

• **Fix DVD scratches with bananas.** Gently rub a freshly cut banana in a circular motion to coat and fill in scratches. Use the inside of the peel to clean and polish. Wipe with a clean, soft cloth.

STAIN REMOVERS

If you don't have stain stick or stain spray handy, try these remedies...

• **Use aspirin to remove sweat stains.** Crush and dissolve four to six aspirins in warm water. Submerge the stained areas into the solution. Let soak for two to three hours, then launder.

• **Remove ink and lipstick stains with rubbing alcohol.** Place a clean cloth or a paper towel under the stained area to prevent bleeding. Gently dab the stain with a cotton ball that has been dampened with rubbing alcohol. Repeat until the stain is gone. Let dry, and launder as usual.

• **Get out grass stains with vodka.** Gently rub the stain with a clean cloth saturated with vodka. Rinse with cool water and launder.

NATURAL BUG REPELLENTS

• **Create flea repellent with apple cider vinegar.** After bathing your dog, spray the animal lightly with a 50/50 solution of vinegar and water. Reapply after every bath.

• **Build a roach trap with apples.** Fill the bottom of an empty, 12-ounce jar with apple peels to lure roaches in with the scent. Then coat the inner rim of the jar with double-sided tape or petroleum jelly, which will prevent the roaches from climbing back out. Place in areas of the kitchen where roaches consistently are present, such as near refrigerators and small appliances such as microwaves, blenders and toasters.

• **Catch garden slugs with old beer cans.** Leave out a beer can with enough beer to drown the slug (about one inch). You also can pour beer in a saucer. Slugs are attracted to beer's yeasty smell.

• **Deter ants with lemons.** Put lemon juice in a spray bottle, and take aim at entryways, windowsills, between kitchen cabinets and other spots where bugs enter. Lemon juice destroys the scent trails that ants follow. This also deters fleas and roaches.

• **Repel spiders with vinegar.** Fill a spray bottle with a 50/50 mix of white vinegar and water. Spray evenly on windowsills, doorjambs and other areas where spiders make their entrance. Do this weekly. Spiders are repelled by the taste of vinegar, and since they taste with their legs, the spray solution will deter them.

Beware: Shampooing Your Carpet Can Make It *Dirtier*

Shampooing carpets too frequently can leave behind a buildup of detergent that can attract more dirt.

Better: Vacuum thoroughly daily or every other day. Vacuum up and down the length of the carpet, then from left to right and then right to left. If you really need to shampoo, focus on areas with a lot of foot traffic, not the entire carpet, and be sure to rinse well, taking care not to overwet the carpet.

Heloise, writing in *Good Housekeeping.*

Quick Fix for Scratches on a Glass Table

To remove scratches from a glass tabletop, sprinkle with baking soda, add a little white toothpaste and rub with your finger in circles. Wipe with a towel dampened with water, then dry. If this starts to help, repeat.

For deeper scratches: Buy a windshield-scratch repair kit at an auto store. The kit contains resin that will fill the cracks.

Heloise, writing in *Good Housekeeping.*

The Smart Eater's Kitchen—5 Must-Have Foods That Are Often Overlooked

John La Puma, MD, a board-certified specialist in internal medicine. Dr. La Puma and Michael Roizen, MD, are the first physicians to teach cooking and nutrition in a US medical school. A trained chef who has a private nutritional medical practice in Santa Barbara, California, Dr. La Puma is a cofounder of the popular *ChefMD* video series and author of *Refuel: A 24-Day Eating Plan to Shed Fat, Boost Testosterone, and Pump Up Strength and Stamina. DrJohnLaPuma.com*

Take a quick look around your kitchen. If you pride yourself on eating healthfully, chances are you'll find plenty of veggies, fruits, whole grains, fish, lean meat, olive oil and nuts. Pat yourself on the back… then go to the grocery store!

Even the most health-conscious among us are likely to be missing out on the "secret" foods that allow us to turn a nutritious—but sometimes boring—dish into something fantastic. These are the healthful foods that add zing to the basics.

EASY-TO-DO...

Neater Way to Clean Grout

Use a bleach pen, such as the one sold by Clorox, to trace light or white grout lines without getting bleach all over your tiles. Wait 10 minutes and rinse. You may need two tries to get really mildewed grout clean. Be sure to run the bathroom fan, and avoid contact with skin.

The Family Handyman. FamilyHandyman.com

For advice on the items that you need to keep your taste buds popping, we spoke with John La Puma, a medical doctor and a trained chef. *His favorite must-have foods that may be missing from your kitchen…*

- **Beef broth.** This is an ingredient that most chefs would never do without—but that many people never buy or make. Chicken broth—which is much more popular with home cooks—is OK, but beef broth (also called stock) is far more flavorful.

If you're a vegetarian: Try mushroom stock (available in natural-food stores or online).

How to use broth: A rich broth is the secret to good soups—or even a plate of beans. Use it in place of water to cook brown rice…to braise inexpensive cuts of beef, pork or poultry…or to moisten leftovers when reheating them.

To make your own stock: Roast leftover beef bones for 30 minutes in a 400°F oven, and then simmer them for four hours with onions, carrots, celery and herbs (usually thyme, bay leaves and parsley).

But boxed stocks are also good—they're virtually calorie-free and are available in low-sodium, fat-free and organic versions.

Hint: Bouillon cubes or powders work in a pinch, but high-quality, ready-made liquid stocks taste much better.

Tasty shortcut: A demi-glace sauce or stock from *MoreThanGourmet.com.* Just add water and heat.

- **Dijon mustard.** Usually made with white wine and mustard seeds, Dijon mustard is more flavorful than the classic yellow version and adds a nice "bite" to leftovers.

How to use it: A good-quality Dijon mustard is more than just a sandwich spread. You can mix it with olive oil, vinegar and a little lemon juice to make salad dressings...mix it with a touch of honey and plain yogurt for a tangy vegetable dip...or spread it on chicken to deepen the flavor and brown the skin during roasting.

• **Ground turkey.** Assuming that you eat meat, it's a good idea to keep some antibiotic-free ground meat in the freezer. Ground turkey is an excellent choice. It defrosts in minutes in the microwave, and it cooks quickly on the stove. Compared with ground beef, it's also a little higher in protein.

How to use it: Because ground turkey highlights the flavors of other foods more readily than ground beef, it's great in casseroles, meatloaf and chili. You can add it to just about anything—even canned beans or frozen or canned vegetables.

• **Hot sauces.** These high-octane condiments include old favorites like Tabasco Pepper Sauce (at grocery stores) and newer-to-the-market specialty products such as Acid Rain Hot Sauce or Captain Spongefoot Sriracha Table Sauce, both available at *HotSauceWorld.com*...and Third-Degree Burn Hot Sauce, at *PepperPalace.com.*

Capsaicin, the chemical compound that puts the "hot" in hot sauces, is not only a natural flavor-enhancer but also causes the body to burn more calories.

How to use it: Try hot sauce on eggs, meats and otherwise bland-tasting foods, such as cottage cheese and macaroni and cheese. Hot sauce also goes well with cooked carrots or on popcorn.

• **Parmigiano-Reggiano cheese.** I might be biased (I am a third-generation Italian-American), but I think that finely grated Parmigiano-Reggiano gives foods a better flavor than any other cheese and that it's worth its price compared with cheaper, less flavorful versions of Parmesan cheese. Parmigiano-Reggiano is nearly lactose-free, helpful for people who have trouble digesting this sugar found in milk and other dairy products.

How to use it: The slightly nutty taste of Parmigiano-Reggiano goes well with practically all types of vegetables, fresh salads and even bean dishes. It makes an attractive, delicious garnish—and because it fluffs up when it's grated, one-half cup is only about 121 calories and has just 1 gram (g) of carbohydrates and 8 g of fat.

TAKE NOTE...

You're Probably Cooking Chicken Wrong!

Forty percent of people undercook chicken.

Best: Always use a meat thermometer—slicing through the meat is not a good guide to whether chicken is properly cooked to 165°F.

Also: Do not wash chicken before cooking it—washing uncooked chicken can spread bacteria around the kitchen.

And: Wash your hands for at least 20 seconds before handling anything else after you touch raw chicken. Use a separate cutting board exclusively for chicken, and clean that board in the dishwasher.

Christine Bruhn, PhD, director, Center for Consumer Research, University of California at Davis.

Follow Microwave Cooking Instructions!

Frozen meals need standing time to finish cooking. When researchers investigated a *Salmonella* outbreak that was caused by frozen entrées, they found that 12% of the people infected did not follow the package directions and skipped the standing time before eating. Letting the meal rest after taking it out of a conventional oven or a microwave allows it to finish cooking properly.

Morbidity and Mortality Weekly Report by the Centers for Disease Control and Prevention.

What to Do with Lettuce (Besides Make a Salad!)

Linda Gassenheimer, an award-winning author of several cookbooks, including *Simply Smoothies: Fresh & Fast Diabetes-Friendly Snacks & Complete Meals.* She also writes the syndicated newspaper column "Dinner in Minutes." *DinnerinMinutes.com*

Do you just love lettuce? *Here are three delicious ways to use those greens...*

What I do: Start with the freshest greens possible (usually found in a farmers' market). Fresh lettuce will keep three to four weeks. Store-bought lettuce will keep six to nine days. Separate the lettuce into individual leaves. Then air-dry leaves on paper towels if there is any moisture on them. Wet a dish towel under cold water, and wring it out so that it's wet but not dripping. Roll the lettuce in the damp towel, and place it in the crisper drawer. Every three to four days, use a mister to moisten the towel. Wash the lettuce before using it.

CHINESE PORK IN LETTUCE PUFFS

Wrap savory pork, slivers of cool cucumber and tangy scallions in large lettuce puffs for a crisp Chinese treat. You can substitute chicken for pork if you choose.

1 Tablespoon low-sodium soy sauce
1 Tablespoon dry sherry
2 medium garlic cloves, crushed through a garlic press
1 Tablespoon chopped fresh ginger
1 Tablespoon honey
¾ pound pork tenderloin (or skinless, boneless chicken breasts), visible fat removed, cut into half-inch pieces
2 scallions
½ medium cucumber
2 teaspoons sesame oil
Salt and freshly ground black pepper
4 large iceberg leaves, washed
3 Tablespoons hoisin sauce

Mix the soy sauce, sherry, garlic, ginger and honey together in a bowl. Add the pork to the marinade while you prepare the garnishes.

To prepare garnishes: Wash and remove the root end and damaged leaves from the scallions. Cut into four-inch pieces. Slice each piece lengthwise into long slivers. Place in a small bowl. Peel and cut the cucumber into four-inch pieces, then cut lengthwise into thin slivers. Place in a small bowl.

Heat the sesame oil in a wok or skillet over high heat until smoking. Add the pork and any extra marinade to the wok. Separate any pieces that cling together. Cook without moving the pork for one minute. Turn and stir-fry for two more minutes. Sprinkle with salt and pepper to taste. Spoon into a small bowl.

To serve, place the bowls with scallions, cucumber, lettuce, hoisin sauce and pork on the table. To make the puffs, take one lettuce leaf and spoon a little hoisin sauce onto it. Add a few scallions and cucumber slivers and some pork pieces. Roll up and eat. The recipe makes two servings.

CREAM OF LETTUCE SOUP

This tasty soup is a great way to use up wilted lettuce leaves. Serve the soup at room temperature in the summer or serve it hot as the weather gets colder. You can freeze it for up to three months.

1 Tablespoon canola oil
2 cups chopped yellow onions
2 cups milk
4 packed cups thinly sliced romaine lettuce leaves
1½ Tablespoons flour
Salt and freshly ground black pepper
¼ cup chopped walnuts
2 Tablespoons thinly sliced chives or the green tops of scallions

Heat the oil in a large saucepan over medium-high heat. Add the onions, and sauté one minute. Add water just to cover the onions. Cover the saucepan with a lid, and cook for 10 minutes or until the water is evaporated and the onions are soft and clear. While the onions cook, bring the milk to a simmer in a separate pan. To the saucepan with the onions, add the lettuce. Stir until the lettuce is wilted, about two minutes. Stir in the flour. Add the hot milk, and stir well. Add salt and pepper to taste. Bring to a simmer, and cook for 20 minutes. Cool the soup, and purée in a blender or food processor or use an immersion blender. Add more salt and pepper to taste. Finally, sprinkle the walnuts and chives/scallions on top. Makes two servings.

SAUTÉED LETTUCES OVER CHICKEN

Quick-sautéed radicchio, romaine and Bibb lettuce add color and flavor to chicken cutlets.

¾ pound boneless, skinless chicken breast cutlets (one-half-inch thick)
¼ cup balsamic vinegar
Vegetable oil spray
Salt and freshly ground black pepper
2 teaspoons olive oil
4 medium garlic cloves, crushed through a garlic press
4 cups (about 5 ounces) washed, ready-to-eat greens, including radicchio, romaine and Bibb lettuce

Remove any visible fat from the chicken. Pour vinegar into a bowl or resealable bag, and add the chicken. Let the chicken marinate for 10 minutes, turning once during that time. Remove the chicken from the vinegar, and wipe dry with a paper towel. Discard the vinegar. Heat a medium-sized nonstick skillet over medium-high heat, and spray with vegetable oil spray. Cook the chicken for three minutes, then turn and cook the other side for three more minutes. A meat thermometer inserted in the chicken should read 165°F. Add salt and pepper to taste. Remove to a plate.

Heat the olive oil in the same skillet. Add the garlic, and sauté for one minute. Add the lettuce, and toss it in the pan about 30 seconds to one minute. The lettuce should be warm but remain firm.

Add salt and pepper to taste, and divide evenly over the chicken cutlets. Makes two servings.

What 7 Tricky Terms on Egg Labels Really Mean

Bonnie Taub-Dix, RDN, CDN, a registered dietitian and director and owner of BTD Nutrition Consultants, LLC, on Long Island and in New York City. She is author of *Read It Before You Eat It. BonnieTaubDix.com*

Now that research has settled the big controversy about eggs—eating them does *not* affect cholesterol levels significantly in most people, as once believed—you may assume that the case is closed on these popular protein-rich foods. Not so.

It is true that Americans are buying more and more eggs. The reasons are simple—eggs are inexpensive and can be prepared in minutes. But they're also great sources of key nutrients such as *choline*, a micronutrient that is vital for brain and liver health...and *lutein* and *zeaxanthin*, carotenoids that help prevent cataracts and other eye diseases.

The problem is, *shopping* for eggs now requires hefty label-decoding skills, thanks to new categories of "designer" eggs and often-confusing terms used to market them. *What terms on egg labels really mean...*

- **Brown.** Surprise! There is no reason to choose brown eggs over white, unless you find the hue more appealing. The shell color is usually a reflection of the feather color of the chicken. *Impact on nutrition?* None. *More humane?* No.

- **Cage-free or free-range.** These eggs come from hens that are not confined to cages, but thousands of them may be crowded into a barn or warehouse. Free-range hens have access to the outdoors. However, there is no independent auditing of these practices unless the eggs are also certified organic (see next page). *Impact on nutrition?* None. *More humane?* Mildly.

- **Certified Humane.** If a carton bears an official-looking seal such as "Certified Humane," "Animal Welfare Approved" or "Food Alliance Certified," it means that the manufacturer's claim of "cage-free," "free-range" or "pasture-raised" has been verified by an independent third party. This labeling has everything to do with humane treatment and nothing to do with nutritional content.

There are multiple third-party certifiers, and each one has its own requirements. For a list of trustworthy certifiers, go to *GreenerChoices.org/eco-labels*, a website sponsored by *Consumer Reports,* and search "egg certifiers." *Impact on nutrition?* None. *More humane?* Yes—to varying degrees, depending on the certifier.

• **Omega-3–enriched.** These eggs are from hens that are fed a diet rich in algae, flaxseed, chia seeds and/or fish oil—all good sources of healthful omega-3s.

How does this diet affect the eggs? A conventional egg contains 37 milligrams (mg) of omega-3s...but an omega-3–enriched egg has about 225 mg. To put those amounts in perspective, the American Heart Association recommends at least two 3.5-ounce servings of fatty fish per week for heart health, which is a total of about 3,500 mg of omega-3s.

Vegetarians who avoid fish may want to try omega-3–enriched eggs. Look for hens fed vegetarian diets (see next column). They are also a good choice for people with fish allergies. However, if you eat fatty fish several times a week and/or take a daily omega-3 supplement, you might as well skip omega-3–enriched eggs and save yourself some money. *Impact on nutrition?* Yes. *More humane?* No.

• **Organic.** This label means that the USDA has certified that these eggs come from hens raised on feed that is free of pesticides, commercial fertilizers and animal by-products. Organic also means that the hens weren't given antibiotics and are cage-free with some amount of access to the outdoors. Eggs from hens treated with antibiotics cannot be labeled antibiotic-free even though the eggs do not contain antibiotic residue. Hormones are generally not used in any form of egg production.

If you're concerned about pesticides and fertilizers, you might want to buy organic. But no research indicates that organic eggs are more healthful than conventional eggs.

The Cornucopia Institute, a nonprofit group that conducts research on sustainable and organic agriculture, has an organic egg scorecard that rates individual organic brands based on the amount of outdoor access and indoor space their birds receive, farming practices and other criteria. The scorecard is available at *Cornucopia.org/organic-egg-scorecard. Impact on nutrition?* Possibly. *More humane?* Mildly.

• **Pastured/pasture-raised.** If you do not mind paying extra (about twice as much), these eggs could be the ideal choice for anyone seeking both enhanced nutrition and humane treatment. Pastured hens move about freely outdoors, have an organic diet and are allowed to eat grass, worms and bugs, all of which produce a deeper-colored yolk, creamier texture and richer flavor.

A recent study found that eggs produced by pasture-raised hens contained more than double the omega-3s and twice as much vitamin E as conventionally raised eggs. *Impact on nutrition?* Yes. *More humane?* Yes.

• **Vegetarian.** Eggs are considered vegetarian if the feed a chicken consumes doesn't contain animal by-products. But chickens are omnivores by nature, not vegetarians—wild chickens eat bugs and worms. If your eggs are labeled vegetarian and free-range, they might not be real "vegetarian" eggs, as roaming hens probably eat a bug or two. There is no nutritional difference between vegetarian and nonvegetarian eggs. *Impact on nutrition?* None. *More humane?* No.

BETTER WAYS...

Make Perishables Last Longer...

Herbs: Fill an ice-cube tray two-thirds full with chopped herbs, cover with olive oil or melted butter. Freeze, then transfer cubes to a resealable bag and store for up to one month.

Mushrooms: Store in the fridge in a paper bag to absorb excess moisture and maintain crispness.

Cookies: Put a slice of bread in an airtight container with the cookies to keep them moist.

Produce: Veggies that are wrapped tightly in aluminum foil will stay crisp for up to four weeks in the fridge.

Cheese: Smear a bit of butter onto the cut side of the cheese to keep it from drying out.

Reader's Digest. RD.com

18

Life Lessons

A Surprising Way to Handle Difficult People

When you are faced with difficult behavior at work or with family and friends, most people tend to revert to automatic reactions. They cave in…get defensive or aggressive…or dig in their heels and refuse to budge.

None of these reactions produces satisfying results, but they are the only alternatives most of us are aware of.

A more effective way to deal with difficult people is to *surrender*—to let go of the need to control a situation and let go of the illusion that you can compel someone to change. Surrendering means accepting a person or situation as is—if you have done everything possible to create change and nothing is budging. This is very different from caving in, which means giving up your needs simply to make peace without any effort to try to create positive change.

This may sound surprising. Many people equate surrender with defeat or weakness. However, surrender is not the same as failure or defeat. It takes great strength of character.

Surrender is an active choice to accept what life brings you, to be flexible rather than rigid and to see past a momentary block to a greater breakthrough beyond. Surrendering will allow you to let go of overthinking and second-guessing.

PRACTICING SURRENDER

Surrender doesn't come naturally to most people. It needs to be learned and practiced.

Surrendering is easier to do when you are only mildly stressed. With practice, you can learn to let go even in more challenging encounters. *Simple ways to practice…*

Judith Orloff, MD, assistant clinical professor of psychiatry at UCLA. She is author of *The Ecstasy of Surrender: 12 Surprising Ways Letting Go Can Empower Your Life*, upon which this article is based. *DrJudithOrloff.com*

• **Drink a glass of water or juice—slowly.** Savor the sensation of quenching your thirst. Enjoy the fact that there is nothing you have to do but sip and be refreshed.

• **Take a deep breath.** Inhale deeply, and then release your breath fully. This counteracts the stress-induced impulse to clench muscles and breathe shallowly, both of which increase resistance and tension.

• **Change what you say to yourself.** Any time you notice yourself dwelling on regrets about the past or fears about the future, bring yourself back to the present. Say, *I can handle the here and now. I don't have to worry about three weeks ago or 10 years from now.*

• **Observe water.** Watch the water in a fountain or creek. Notice how water doesn't keep bumping into the same boulder over and over again—it flows around the obstacle. Water can teach you how to flow.

• **Appreciate your body's natural joyful responses.** Let out a hearty laugh. Put on your favorite music, and dance around the living room. Don't choke off those urges—enjoy them.

• **Let yourself feel awe.** Look up at the night sky, and notice the vastness of the galaxy and universe around you. Like a child, allow yourself to surrender to this mystery and awe.

DIFFICULT SITUATIONS

In most cases, difficult people aren't trying to make your life miserable—they are just preoccupied with their own frustrations and needs. *Guidelines for dealing with difficult behavior...*

• **Pause.** If you feel yourself getting angry or tense, don't say anything. Let go of the urge to express your immediate reaction. Instead, take a few slow breaths to calm your stress. Count to 10 or 20 if it helps you to postpone action.

• **Listen without interrupting.** When we are upset about what someone is saying, we typically want to cut the person off in order to stop our discomfort and express our disagreement or anger. However, interruption just escalates hostility. Let go of the need to direct the discussion. Hear the other person out.

Exception: If the person is being verbally abusive, cut off the abuse at once. Verbal abuse includes personal attacks that target your worth—such as *You're a terrible mother* or *You can't do anything right.* In cases like these, break in and set boundaries in a calm voice.

Example: "That kind of statement is unacceptable. If you continue like this, I will leave the room."

• **Don't argue.** You may have the strong desire to state all the evidence that shows you are right, but defensiveness in charged situations doesn't change anyone's mind—it just fuels the conflict.

• **Empathize.** Make a genuine effort to see the situation from the other person's point of view. People who behave badly are suffering in some way. This doesn't excuse their behavior, but once you recognize that they are trying to avoid pain or anxiety, letting go becomes easier.

• **Be willing to concede a point.** Even if you agree with only 1% of what the person is saying, acknowledge that point of agreement. You can say, "That's a good point, and I'm going to think about it."

Also be willing to apologize for your own difficult behavior.

Example: "I'm sorry I snapped at you. I didn't act with love." Too many relationships disintegrate because no one will give ground. Let go of the need to protect your turf. Look at the larger picture—which is more important, this battle or the relationship?

• **Use a pleasant, neutral tone.** No matter how carefully you choose your words, they will get you nowhere if your voice has an edge of irritation, condescension or sarcasm. Practice a neutral tone by role-playing with a friend until you are able to keep the edge out of your voice.

THREE DIFFICULT TYPES

Here's how to deal with three common types of difficult people...

• **The Guilt Tripper.** Blamers and martyrs activate your insecurity to get what they want. Their sentences often start with, "If it weren't for you..." or "I'm the only one..." ***What to do...***

> **GOOD TO KNOW...**
>
> **When People Are More Likely to Lie**
>
> People are 50% more likely to be dishonest in the afternoon than in the morning.
>
> ***Reason:*** Our ability to exhibit self-control to avoid cheating or lying is reduced over the course of a day.
>
> David Eccles School of Business, Salt Lake City, published in *Psychological Science*.

• Be compassionate with yourself. When you feel bad about any area of your life, work on being compassionate with yourself. By understanding your own guilt triggers, you will be better able to keep your balance when someone tries to activate them.

• Make a matter-of-fact statement. Tell guilt trippers that those comments hurt your feelings and that you would be grateful if they would stop making them. If you don't get emotional, most guilt trippers will lose interest in baiting you.

• **The Control Freak.** Control freaks micromanage, give unsolicited advice, voice strong opinions relentlessly and are rarely satisfied. *What to do...*

• Let go of needing the controller to see things your way. Don't try to control a controller or win over the person to your way of thinking—it's a waste of time. Say, "Thank you for your input. I'll take it into consideration" or "I value your advice, but I want to work through this myself."

• Be patient. Control freaks don't give up easily, so repetition is key. Continue to be calm and pleasant even when you have to repeat the aforementioned statements many times.

• **The Anger Addict.** Rage-aholics intimidate by accusing, yelling or cursing. *What to do...*

• Let go of the impulse to cower or to lash out in return. The more impulsively you react to someone else's rage, the more you reinforce the anger addict's aggressive behavior. Even if you are upset, stay as neutral as you can. Get centered before you respond.

• Use imagery. Picture a martial artist who finds a balanced, grounded stance and then transforms the opponent's energy by flowing with the person's movements instead of resisting them. Imagine that the person's anger can flow right through you and that you are breathing the anger out with every breath.

• If the anger addict is your boss, acknowledge the person's point of view. Say, "I can see why you would feel that way." Then bring the discussion back to a solution focus. Say in a calm tone, "I have a different take that I'd like to share" or "That's fine—tell me what you need, and I'll do it."

Look for another job if you can, because being the recipient of chronic anger takes a physical and mental toll. In the meantime—or if changing jobs is not possible—remind yourself that the rage is about the other person, not you.

• If the anger addict is a spouse or family member, set limits. Say, "Your anger is hurting me. We have to find a better way to communicate" or "I care about you, but I shut down when you raise your voice. Let's talk about this when we can hear each other better." Later, when you are both calm, request a small, doable change. *Example of a small, doable change*: "When we are in the midst of a disagreement, I propose that we each wait five seconds before saying anything. Would you be willing to try that?"

If the person doesn't try to change, observe how your health is affected. You may need to let go of the relationship to protect your well-being.

Stand Up to Rudeness!

Amy Alkon, author of *Good Manners for Nice People Who Sometimes Say F*ck.*

It's a common scenario—a person seated next to you in a theater keeps checking his/her cell phone as the show starts. When you ask him to please turn off the phone, he gives you a withering glare in return.

I consider rudeness a form of theft. Rude people steal our attention, time and peace of mind. If we don't stand up to them, they'll go right on stealing from us. But when we get angry at rude people, they tend to become defensive and angry in return...and sometimes even ruder.

What's more effective...

• **Enlist support.** Ask someone to chime in with, "Actually, that was bothering me, too." Rude people are more likely to back down when confronted by more than one person. If you want to confront a teenager blasting a car stereo, for example, first call a neighbor and ask him to stroll by as you say your piece and agree that the music was bothering him, too.

• **Write a note.** A note gives the recipient a chance to simmer down before responding, which might allow him to consider the possibility that he was wrong. Open with, "I'm sure you didn't know this was happening, but..." and close with a smiley face. Smiley faces seem silly but can diffuse tension.

• **Use pseudo-pity as a weapon.** Respond to a cutting remark by saying in a sympathetic voice, "You must be having a very bad day to say something like that. I hope you feel better tomorrow."

EASY-TO-DO...

Touch a Plant to Reduce Stress

In a recent study, men who touched plant leaves for two minutes felt calmer and had less cerebral blood flow to the brain areas associated with stress than men who touched metal or other materials.

Study by researchers at Chiba University, Chiba, Japan, published in *Journal of Physiological Anthropology*.

Though it may seem that there's anger all around us—think angry drivers!—many of us shy away from anger if we need to confront a person we know. To increase the odds of a positive outcome, preface angry comments with, "I'm feeling uncomfortable right now, which means it's not the best time for me to be expressing myself. But under the circumstances, it's important for me to say..." The person will feel empathy for you rather than react defensively.

The Upside of Anger

Todd Kashdan, PhD, professor of psychology at George Mason University and coauthor of *The Upside of Your Dark Side.*

Many people hate to get angry. They're almost always sorry when they do. It makes them uncomfortable and tends to spark anger in return. But it turns out that maybe they should get angry more often. "Negative" emotions such as anger can produce positive results. Anger helps us deal with people and things that get in the way of the things we care about.

Researchers have found that when we express anger, we increase our level of optimism...our chances of success during negotiations...our ability to motivate other people...our overall performance...our overall health...and—perhaps most surprisingly—our creativity. When we get angry, there is increased activity in the region of the brain that appreciates action and exploration. Then ideas collide in unique ways, and that's where creativity comes from.

How to Break the 6 Big Bad Habits

Richard O'Connor, PhD, a psychotherapist in private practice in Canaan, Connecticut, and New York City. He is also former executive director of the Northwest Center for Family Service and Mental Health and author of *Rewire: Change Your Brain to Break Bad Habits, Overcome Addictions, Conquer Self-Destructive Behavior. UndoingDepression.com*

Nearly everyone has at least one bad habit that he/she would just love to be rid of—maybe it's eating too much, losing your temper or putting things off. But why is it so hard to break a bad habit even though you clearly know that the behavior is harmful to you?

A POWERFUL FORCE THAT RESISTS CHANGE

Undesirable habits are often developed by unconscious motives, beliefs and feelings. Of course, you can make a conscious effort to stop these practices, but that won't help when the powerful unconscious or automatic part of your brain makes you reach for another helping or tells you to tailgate that driver who isn't going as fast as you'd like. The unconscious brain holds on to what has always been done and reacts, over and over again, without thinking about consequences.

The good news: The unconscious mind can be rewired so that making the right choices and withstanding temptation become second nature. Then you don't have to struggle to do what's good for you—you just do it because it has become your new habit. The key is to engage in behaviors or practices that reprogram the unconscious brain. *How to break common bad habits...*

RULE-BREAKING AND RISK-TAKING

Why it happens: These bad habits, which can include overeating, overspending, gambling or driving too fast, can be triggered by feelings of self-entitlement. Deep down these people feel that they are special and that the usual rules don't apply to them. They also may lack empathy and act boastful and pretentious.

How to rewire your brain: Practice empathy. Scientists used to think that empathy was an innate characteristic—you either had it or you didn't. But recent research has shown that people can improve their ability to sense—and share—other people's emotions.

Helpful: When you interact with people, watch their body language and facial expressions. Maintain eye contact, and listen closely to what they say rather than anticipating your own response. Look for clues that tell you how they are feeling. And ask questions to be sure you understand them.

Also: Stop judging. If you have a harsh thought about someone, remind yourself to think of something kind.

PROCRASTINATION

Why it happens: Procrastination is particularly common in people who have a fear of failing and unrealistically high personal standards. They tell themselves that they would have succeeded had they completed a task.

How to rewire your brain: Learn to tolerate the fear and anxiety of failing without getting overwhelmed by it. Meditation can help.

What to do: Sit in a quiet place, and breathe slowly and deeply while focusing on your breath. You can't stop the thoughts that will flit in and out of your mind, but you can learn to simply observe all these thoughts without worry or judgment and let them float away. I recommend trying to meditate for a half-hour daily for a month. After this intense practice, you can scale back to shorter daily sessions.

Also helpful: Narrow your focus. If you have so much to do that you feel overwhelmed, start anywhere. Don't worry about priorities. Just pick an item on your list and dig in. Plan to work for five minutes on that task only. Take a short break, then work five minutes more. Keep going with this cycle as long as you can.

QUICK TO ANGER

Why it happens: Many people who have a problem with anger management resent authority and lash out when questioned by an authority figure. "Rage-aholics" also may feel helpless or shortchanged by life. Expressing anger makes them feel powerful and less like victims.

How to rewire your brain: If you resent authority, take time to understand what the rules are. It may help you gain new perspec-

TAKE NOTE...

Better Body Language

For better body language, be careful with your hands. Pointing can seem aggressive...placing hands on hips shows arrogance or impatience... and playing with your hair reveals nervousness. Also, do not cross your legs—in women wearing a dress or skirt, this can reveal too much thigh, and in men, it can show distracting skin above the ankle. Finally, know what your standard face looks like. If it is stern or severe, this can make people angry or defensive—try to relax facial muscles, and smile more often when meeting new people.

Vivian Giang, former lead entrepreneurship editor, *PolicyMic*, a news site for millennials, based in New York City, writing at *AmericanExpress.com*.

tive. If you are angry because life isn't giving you what you want, ask yourself if what you want is possible or practical. Some disappointments must be accepted, and others can be compensated for in different ways. Daily meditation (discussed earlier) also can help minimize outbursts of anger because it teaches you how to calm yourself.

In addition: You can learn how to be assertive in more appropriate ways. Calmly state, without personal attacks, how you are hurt by another person's behavior. Listen carefully to the other person's response and be ready to negotiate.

WATCH OUT FOR SELF-HATRED

Self-hatred is behind numerous bad habits and addictions, including overworking, overeating, smoking and drinking too much alcohol. It often arises from unconscious feelings of guilt and shame that were acquired early in life and causes frequent negative thoughts and feelings of unworthiness.

How to rewire your brain: Don't wallow in negativity. Pay attention to your negative thoughts and remind yourself that you do not deserve the harshness that you heap upon yourself. If you feel guilty about something you did recently, apologize. If that's not possible, find symbolic ways to make amends—by giving to charity, working with the disadvantaged, etc.

TO BREAK ANY BAD HABIT...

- **Spend a few days studying a bad habit you want to change.** Take note of the triggers of this habit—time of day, level of hunger, something someone has said, a memory, etc. Ask yourself what you can do about these triggers. Can you avoid some? Prevent some? Knowing your triggers can help you take positive actions (such as starting a new project) rather than negative actions (such as overeating).
- **Practice daily meditation** (see previous page) to calm yourself and help you shut out negative thoughts.
- **Practice willpower.** This is a skill, not a trait. Imagine it as a muscle in your brain that gets strengthened each time you use it.

How to Stop Worrying So Much

Do you tend to worry a lot? *Helpful strategies to try...*

- **Tone down extremes by writing your worries down and rewording them**—instead of "Nobody likes me," you might write, "My boss does not like my report."
- **Think of worries as trains posted on the departure board at a station**—they all are there, but you need not board any of them, and as they depart, you can let them go.
- **Set aside 20 "worry minutes" a day, and refuse to think about troubling matters at any other time**—when your thoughts do drift toward something that causes anxiety, write the concern down and come back to it at the scheduled time.
- **Make monotony your friend by slowly repeating worrying notions to yourself**—expressing a negative to yourself over and over should soon make your mind wander to more enjoyable thoughts.

Psychology Today. PsychologyToday.com

Better Treatment for Social Anxiety

Cognitive behavioral therapy (CBT) was more effective than antidepressants and other drugs and types of psychotherapy in treatment of social anxiety disorder (fear and avoidance of interacting with others) in an analysis of research spanning 25 years.

Why: CBT focuses on making permanent changes to destructive thought patterns and behaviors.

Evan Mayo-Wilson, DPhil, assistant scientist, department of epidemiology, Johns Hopkins Bloomberg School of Public Health, Baltimore.

6 Clever Ways to Get More Done in Less Time

Daniel J. Levitin, PhD, the James McGill Professor of Psychology and Behavioural Neuroscience at McGill University in Montreal and dean of The College of Arts & Humanities at the Minerva Schools at Keck Graduate Institute, Claremont, California. He is author of *The Organized Mind: Thinking Straight in the Age of Information Overload. DanielLevitin.com*

Of course, it's not a secret that the modern world can be an overwhelming place. The average American is confronted by at least five times as much information each day as he/she was in 1986. The typical supermarket now stocks more than four times as many items as in 1976, greatly increasing the number of decisions faced during a chore as seemingly simple as grocery shopping. And this kind of information and choice overload permeates our culture.

Yet the human brain has not evolved to effectively cope with this deluge of information and decisions.

However, there are various ways to cope that will reduce stress, save time and bring your life back into balance. Here are six practical strategies rooted in cutting-edge neurological and psychological research that can help you thrive and be happier in today's overloaded world...

• **Write down everything that's on your mind to clear your mind.** When something is nagging at your mind, it significantly reduces your ability to focus on anything else—the brain's capacity for attention is limited.

To clear your mind of distractions, jot down every idea, doubt and responsibility that is competing for your attention before turning to an important project or at any other time that you feel overwhelmed.

The human mind's desire to hold on to thoughts is greatly reduced when we know that those thoughts have been written down (or typed into a smartphone or computer). It's the neurological equivalent of downloading computer files onto a backup storage device to clear up space on the computer's hard drive.

Two more ways to "offload memory" from your brain...

• Use a smartphone calendar app to remember deadlines and responsibilities. Your brain won't feel that it has to keep track of everything you need to do and everywhere you need to be if your smartphone is remembering these things for you.

Some smartphone apps, including *Google Now iPhone Reminders*, even feature "location-based" reminders that provide a helpful nudge when you're in the location where this information is most useful. Many smartphones have this function built in.

Example: Set a location-based reminder to remind you to pick up a gallon of milk next time you are in or near the grocery store.

• Each evening, place a note about any items that you need to remember the next morning somewhere that you will see it at the start of your day, such as by your front door or on the driver's seat of your vehicle.

• **Assign everything a precise place.** Start with anything that you chronically misplace. Choose a specific hook for your keys...and a specific spot in a specific drawer for your reading glasses. The brain has a structure called the *hippocampus* that does a wonderful job of remembering where things are—but only if things are always in the same spot. The hippocampus is relatively ineffective at locating things that lack a fixed location.

Also, choose one or two locations in your home to serve as an all-purpose storage location for items that lack any other obvious storage spot. This might be a "junk drawer" in the kitchen for small items...and a specific "miscellaneous" corner of an attic or a basement for larger items.

Junk drawers and miscellaneous storage areas are a triumph of cognitive economy. It would be inefficient to devote time and mental resources to deciding where to store each hard-to-sort item and remembering where to find these things later.

• **Store items by usage, not by type.** People tend to store items together with other similar items. All household paperwork often is stored together in a single file cabinet...all tools together on a tool bench. But while that seems sensible, it actually can make things more challenging to find in some circumstances.

If an item is always used in a particular place, it probably should be stored near that place, even if various other, similar items are stored elsewhere. If an item is used only at one particular time of year, it should be stored with various other items that are used at that time of year. *Examples...*

• That little tightening tool that comes with a piece of Ikea furniture can get lost among larger tools. Instead, tape or strap it to an out-of-sight spot on the Ikea furniture itself.

• Kitchen tools used only for cooking (as opposed to, say, serving) should be stored as close as possible to the stove—I hang mine right over the stove—not necessarily with other kitchen implements.

• Holiday cookie cutters should be stored with holiday items, not with everyday baking items.

• Invoices from a child's summer day camp should be filed with tax paperwork, not with child-activity–related paperwork, because summer day camp expenses might be tax-deductible and so the invoices would be needed when completing a tax return.

• **Assign each project its own location.** Your memory can be greatly aided by location and context. That's why people often experience a flood of old memories when they return to a place where they haven't been in years. It's also why students do better on exams if they study in the same room where the exam will be given.

Of course, this can be a detriment when you are trying to remember something *out of* its natural location or context...or when trying to focus on just one thing in a place where you pursue multiple projects. Famed neurologist and best-selling author Oliver Sacks, MD, has a strategy for coping with this challenge—he chooses a different spot in his home or office for each project that he is currently pursuing. This spot might be a particular room in the home or a particular table or desk in the office.

Stepping into a project's designated space triggers the memories he has formed in that specific location, improving his ability to focus his mind on only that project so that he can think more productively and creatively about it. Any other projects that he currently is pursuing are tackled elsewhere, so his mind is somewhat less likely to drift to them.

Similarly, if you struggle to maintain focus while using your computer, you could set up a different user account on your computer for each project. Select a different computer-screen background picture and/or color for each of these user accounts. You may find it easier to focus on a particular project or task when using its user account.

• **Don't let unimportant e-mails distract you.** The *prefrontal cortex,* the part of the brain responsible for complex thinking such as decision-making and problem-solving, has a novelty bias—it is easily distracted by anything new.

That's why e-mail can be such a productivity killer. Every time a new message arrives, your prefrontal cortex nudges you to stop whatever you're doing and see what it is.

The best solution is to keep your e-mail account closed most of the time, opening it to check for new messages only when you take breaks from a project. But if you cannot do this because you sometimes receive e-mails that require immediate attention, at least re-

BETTER WAYS...

How to Perform Well Under Pressure

Getting excited before an anxiety-producing event is more beneficial to performance than trying to calm down, say several studies from Harvard.

Details: When volunteers were told to say either, "I am calm" or "I am excited" before making a public speech, those in the "excited" group gave longer, more persuasive speeches.

Explanation: Whenever people try to calm down, they tend to think about things that could go wrong. But when they get excited, they think about how things could go well.

Alison Wood Brooks, PhD, assistant professor of business administration, Harvard Business School, Boston.

duce the number of e-mails that interfere with your focus. *Two potential ways to do this...*

• Open a new e-mail account, and give its address to only your most important contacts. Keep this e-mail account open on your computer desktop, but leave other e-mail accounts closed most of the time.

• Use your e-mail program's filter settings to automatically sort e-mails by categories into subfolders rather than into your main e-mail inbasket.

• **Double up on supplies.** Buy duplicates of inexpensive supplies that you use in multiple places. This additional piece of advice might seem like overkill, but it is surprisingly helpful for increasing productivity.

People are especially likely to misplace small items when they use those items in more than one room in the home or workplace. Items used in multiple rooms often are not returned to their designated storage spots, and it is difficult to remember where they were used last.

Such items might include scissors, Scotch tape, staplers, tape measures, screwdrivers and reading glasses.

Purchase multiple copies of all of these (and similar) items. Assign each of these copies to a specific storage spot in each room where it often is needed. You'll never have to search for any of these items again.

Edison's Problem Solver

Barbara Oakley, PhD, an engineering professor at Oakland University in Michigan and author of *A Mind for Numbers: How to Excel at Math and Science (Even If You Flunked Algebra).*

When Edison couldn't crack a tough problem, he reportedly put a metal plate on the floor alongside a comfortable chair, then relaxed in the chair with a ball bearing held in his hand dangling over the plate. When he drifted off to sleep, the ball bearing would fall from his hand, clatter onto the plate and rouse Edison—who would wake full of fresh ideas.

Edison was tapping into what I call "diffuse-mode thinking." The human brain has two radically different modes of thought. There's focused mode, where attention is directed intensely at a specific topic...and diffuse mode, where attention drifts, allowing the brain to make new connections and discover creative solutions.

Diffuse mode is useful when you've been focused on a problem for some time, can't find a solution and feel your frustration level rising. The trouble is, shifting out of focused mode can be difficult.

Focusing on a completely different task might do the trick. Listening to music, meditating, exercising or taking a bath or shower can be effective.

Approaching a sleeping state can be a surer way to enter diffuse mode. You could try Edison's trick or take a nap, setting an alarm for 10 minutes in. Problem solved!

For Better Decisions, Turn Down the Lights

Room lighting affects decision making, a recent study reports. Brighter lights tend to promote more intense emotions, positive or negative. Volunteers were asked to rate a wide range of things including the spiciness of a chicken wing sauce, the aggressiveness of a fictional character and their feelings about specific words. Volunteers exposed to bright light tended to make stronger judgments. They wanted a spicier wing sauce...thought the fictional character was more aggressive...and felt better about positive words and worse about negative words than people in dimmer light.

Recommended: Turn down room lighting before making big decisions so that those decisions are less driven by intense emotion.

Study by researchers at University of Toronto Scarborough, Rotman School of Management, also part of University of Toronto, and Northwestern University in Evanston, Illinois, published in *Journal of Consumer Psychology.*

6 Foods Proven to Make You Happy

Tonia Reinhard, MS, RD, a registered dietitian and professor at Wayne State University in Detroit. She is the program director for the Coordinated Program in Dietetics, course director of clinical nutrition at Wayne State University School of Medicine and a past president of the Michigan Academy of Nutrition and Dietetics. She is author of *Superfoods: The Healthiest Foods on the Planet* and *Superjuicing: More Than 100 Nutritious Vegetable and Fruit Recipes.*

You can eat your way to a better mood! Certain foods and beverages have been proven to provide the raw materials that you need to feel sharper, more relaxed and just plain happier. *Best choices...*

HAPPY FOOD #1: Chocolate. Chocolate can make you feel good—to such an extent that 52% of women would choose chocolate over sex, according to one survey.

Chocolate contains chemical compounds known as *polyphenols*, which interact with neurotransmitters in the brain and reduce anxiety. An Australian study found that men and women who consumed the most chocolate polyphenols (in the form of a beverage) felt calmer and more content than those who consumed a placebo drink.

Chocolate also boosts *serotonin*, the same neurotransmitter affected by antidepressant medications. It triggers the release of *dopamine* and stimulates the "pleasure" parts of the brain.

Then there's the sensual side of chocolate—the intensity of the flavor and the melting sensation as it dissolves in your mouth. The satisfaction that people get from chocolate could be as helpful for happiness as its chemical composition.

Recommended amount: Aim for one ounce of dark chocolate a day. Most studies used dark chocolate with 70% cacao or more.

HAPPY FOOD #2: Fish. Fish has been called "brain food" because our brains have a high concentration of *omega-3 fatty acids*—and so does fish. These fatty acids have been linked to memory and other cognitive functions. In countries where people eat a lot of fish, depression occurs less often than in countries (such as the US) where people eat less.

The omega-3s in fish accumulate in the brain and increase "membrane fluidity," the ability of brain-cell membranes to absorb nutrients and transmit chemical signals.

A study in *Archives of General Psychiatry* looked at patients diagnosed with depression who had not responded well to antidepressants. Those who were given 1,000 mg of EPA (a type of omega-3 fatty acid) daily for three months had significant improvements, including less anxiety and better sleep.

Recommended amount: Try to have at least two or three fish meals a week. Cold-water fish—such as sardines, mackerel and salmon—have the highest levels of omega-3s. Or choose a supplement with 1,000 mg of EPA and DHA (another omega-3 fatty acid) in total.

HAPPY FOOD #3: Dark green veggies. Dark green vegetables such as spinach, asparagus, broccoli and Brussels sprouts are loaded with *folate*, a B-complex vitamin that plays a key role in regulating mood. A Harvard study found that up to 38% of adults with depression had low or borderline levels of folate. Boosting the folate levels of depressed patients improved their mood.

Dark green vegetables are particularly good, but all vegetables and fruits boost mood. Researchers asked 281 people to note their moods on different days. On the days when the participants consumed the most vegetables and fruits, they reported feeling happier and more energetic. Folate certainly plays a role, but self-satisfaction may have something to do with it as well. People feel good when they eat right and take care of themselves.

Recommended amount: The minimum you should have is five servings of vegetables and fruits a day.

Bonus: Middle-aged men who had 10 servings a day showed reduced blood pressure.

HAPPY FOOD #4: Beans (including soybeans). Beans are rich in *tryptophan*, an essential amino acid that is used by the body to produce serotonin, the neurotransmitter that affects feelings of calmness and relaxation.

Beans also are loaded with folate. Folate, as mentioned in the veggies section, plays a key role in regulating mood.

In addition, beans contain *manganese*, a trace element that helps prevent mood swings due to low blood sugar.

Recommended amount: For people not used to eating beans, start with one-quarter cup five days a week. Build up to one-half cup daily. This progression will help prevent gastrointestinal symptoms such as flatulence.

HAPPY FOOD #5: Nuts. Nuts are high in *magnesium*, a trace mineral involved in more than 300 processes in the body. People who don't get enough magnesium feel irritable, fatigued and susceptible to stress.

The elderly are more likely than young adults to be low in magnesium—because they don't eat enough magnesium-rich foods and/or because they tend to excrete more magnesium in their urine.

Also, many health problems can accelerate the depletion of magnesium from the body.

Examples: Gastrointestinal disorders (or bariatric surgery), kidney disease and sometimes diabetes.

Recommended amount: Aim to get one ounce of nuts a day. Good choices include almonds, walnuts, cashews, hazelnuts and peanuts (the latter is technically a legume). If you don't like nuts, other high-magnesium foods include spinach, pumpkin seeds, fish, beans, whole grains and dairy.

HAPPY FOOD #6: Coffee. The caffeine in coffee, tea and other caffeinated beverages is a very beneficial compound. One study found that people with mild cognitive impairment were less likely to develop full-fledged Alzheimer's disease when they had the caffeine equivalent of about three cups of coffee a day.

Caffeine can temporarily strengthen your memory and performance on tests. It enhances coordination and other parameters of physical performance. When you feel energized, you feel happier. Also, people who feel good from caffeine may be more likely to engage in other happiness-promoting behaviors, such as seeing friends and exercising.

Recommended amount: The challenge is finding the "sweet spot"—just enough caffeine to boost mood but not so much that you get the shakes or start feeling anxious. For those who aren't overly sensitive to caffeine, one to three daily cups of coffee or tea are about right.

WHAT NOT TO EAT

Some people turn to food and/or drink for comfort when they're feeling down. *Here's what not to eat or drink when you've got the blues...*

- **Alcohol** is a depressant of the central nervous system. When you initially consume alcohol, it produces a euphoric effect and you become more animated and much less inhibited. But as you continue drinking and more alcohol crosses the blood-brain barrier, the depressant effect predominates.
- **Baked goods.** When you eat high-sugar, high-fat carbs such as cookies, pastries and donuts, you tend to want more of them. The food gives you a temporary "good feeling," but the excess food intake that typically results causes drowsiness and often self-loathing.

Dwelling on Negative Memories? What to Do...

To cope with negative memories, think about circumstances, not feelings. People who focus on how sad, hurt or embarrassed they felt during an event feel worse than those who think about nonemotional elements associated with the event—such as the weather or a friend who was present. Remembering nonemotional details helps your mind wander away from negative feelings and makes it easier to get past them.

Florin Dolcos, PhD, assistant professor, Cognitive Neuroscience Group, Beckman Institute, University of Illinois at Urbana-Champaign, and leader of a study published in *Social Cognitive and Affective Neuroscience.*

Banish a Bad Mood—in Just Minutes!

Pierce Howard, PhD, managing director of research and development at the Center for Applied Cognitive Studies in Charlotte, North Carolina, a firm that provides consulting services in leadership development and personality testing. He is author of *The Owner's Manual for the Brain: The Ultimate Guide to Peak Mental Performance at All Ages. CentACS.com*

Depression is serious business, and it should be treated by a professional. But what if you're not depressed—perhaps just feeling a little blue or in a funk?

With the steps below, most people can escape a bad mood in a matter of minutes instead of toughing it out for hours or even an entire day or more. *To get started...*

CHECK IN WITH YOURSELF

• **How's your physical state?** Are you hungry? Thirsty? Tired? You may not think to ask yourself these questions, but any of these conditions can make you feel out of sorts.

• **Do a gut check.** Once your physical needs are taken care of, take a minute to ask yourself *why* you might be feeling down. An honest assessment of what's bugging you may reveal a way to actively address the problem.

Even if you identify the cause of your bad mood—maybe you're overworked, for example, or worried about a loved one's health—and can take steps to address the issue, your dark cloud might not lift immediately. *Other steps you can take to boost your mood...*

QUICK FEEL-GOOD TRICKS

• **Turn on some minor-key tunes.** Research shows that people who are bordering on depression tend to feel better after listening to music in a *minor* key—perhaps because happier, major keys prove too jarring to their emotional state.

Good choices: "Hey Jude" by The Beatles... "Bad Romance" by Lady Gaga...and Piano Concerto in A Minor by Edvard Grieg. If you find that this type of music doesn't lift your mood, switch to some up-tempo music such as Aaron Copland...most big-band music... and "Born to Run" by Bruce Springsteen. According to recent research, people are happier in both the short term and long term after listening to up-tempo music.

> **EASY-TO-DO...**
>
> **Walk Happily to Feel Happier**
>
> Happy people walk more quickly and in a more upright position than sad or depressed people—and they swing their arms more while swaying less from side to side.
>
> ***Recent finding:*** Deliberately walking this way made people feel better—while walking as a depressed person made them feel sad.
>
> Study of 39 people by researchers at Witten Herdecke University, Witten, Germany, published in *Journal of Behavior Therapy and Experimental Psychology*.

• **Take a brisk, five-minute walk outdoors.** Brisk walking gets your blood moving, which means more oxygen and energy-boosting glucose are getting to your brain. Five minutes is the minimum time needed, according to research, to produce mood-enhancing changes.

Walking *outside* helps most. That's because sunlight suppresses the production of the sleep hormone *melatonin* (making you feel less sluggish and more alert) and gives you a dose of energy-boosting vitamin D. The fresh air also may contain negative ions that attach themselves to particles in the atmosphere and act as air purifiers, allowing you to get more oxygen to your brain with each breath.

• **Eat a hamburger (really!).** The "Comfort foods," such as ice cream, chocolate, cheese and pasta, produce a quick mood boost by encouraging the release of the neurotransmitter *serotonin.* But if you overdo it, you'll end up feeling bloated and tired.

What works better: When you're feeling down, eat some protein or complex carbohydrates. Good protein choices include a hamburger (without the bun)...nuts...eggs...and beans. Good complete carbohydrates include dark berries...bananas...and a salad full of vegetables.

• **Use your words.** Using language triggers the pleasure pathway in the brain, but you don't need to have a gabfest if that's not in your nature. While some people find that having a conversation with a friend elevates their mood, others might prefer writing in a journal or composing a letter. Research has shown that the act of using language is soothing whether you're focusing on whatever is causing your bad mood or something unrelated.

• **Tweak your posture.** If you're slouching in your chair or staring down at the sidewalk while walking, you may be inadvertently prolonging the blues by inhibiting the blood and oxygen circulation in your body.

What to do: Pull your shoulders back and balance your head over your spine. When you are in perfect alignment, your ear, shoulder, hip, knee and ankle should form a vertical line when viewed from the side.

• **Ditch the alarm clock.** Most people sleep in cycles lasting around 90 minutes, progressing from a light to deep sleep and back again. If you have your alarm set to go off in the later stages of your cycle, chances are you'll awaken in a disoriented, grumpy mood.

What to do: Try experimenting with your bedtime so that you wake naturally without using an alarm. If you go to bed early enough, you'll wake up on your own feeling refreshed after having an optimal number of complete sleep cycles.

EASY-TO-DO...

Can't Remember Someone's Name? Fast Trick...

If you forget someone's name, say so—with a bit of humor.

Example: "I am so sorry. I am having one of those days. I even forgot my own name."

Always state your name when greeting people you don't see often—they may have forgotten it. And never put someone on the spot by asking, "Do you remember me?"

Susan RoAne, professional speaker and best-selling author of a number of books, including *How to Work a Room*.

A Good Laugh Can Help You Focus

When study participants watched funny videos, their brains showed similar activity patterns to those generated during yoga meditation sessions. Scientists found that the gamma wave activity generated from joyous laughter provided the brain with a type of mental clarity and an ability to focus that typically are experienced after a yoga session.

Study by researchers at Loma Linda University's School of Medicine, Loma Linda, California, presented at the Federation of American Societies Experimental Biology Meeting in San Diego.

Quick Memory Booster: Grab a Cup of Joe

Study participants who had 200 milligrams (mg) of caffeine in a tablet form—the amount of caffeine contained in a strong cup of coffee—performed better on a memory test than people who were not given caffeine. In the test, participants had to identify pictures that were slightly different from ones they had seen the day before.

Study of 160 people, ages 18 to 30, none of whom consumed caffeine on a regular basis, by researchers at Johns Hopkins University, Baltimore, published in *Nature Neuroscience*.

Why a Daily Alcoholic Drink May Help Your Memory

Light-to-moderate drinking in later life may keep memory strong, according to a recent study. Consuming up to one drink a day was associated with better *episodic memory*—the ability to remember specific events. Episodic memory is the type that usually diminishes in dementia.

Theory: Alcohol may help preserve the *hippocampus*, a brain area that shrinks in people with dementia.

Faika Zanjani, PhD, associate professor, University of Maryland School of Public Health, College Park, and leader of a study of 664 people, average age 75, published in *American Journal of Alzheimer's Disease & Other Dementias.*

Yoga Makes You Smarter!

In a recent eight-week study, adults over age 55 who took an hour-long class of hatha yoga (the most commonly practiced form of yoga worldwide) three times a week had significantly better memory and attention than adults who simply did stretching and toning exercises.

Possible reason: The focus required to hold poses and control breathing during yoga may result in better attention to mental tasks as well.

Neha Gothe, PhD, assistant professor of kinesiology, Wayne State University, Detroit.

A Little Stress Can Actually Be Good for You

Rats under stress for three hours released *fibroblast growth factor 2* (FGF2), which triggers the development of new nerve cells in the part of the brain needed for memory.

Caution: Too much stress can lead to obesity, depression, heart disease and brain-cell damage.

Animal study by researchers at Helen Wills Neuroscience Institute at University of California-Berkeley, published in *eLife.*

Don't Talk About It Before You're Ready

Charles Figley, PhD, founder of the Traumatology Institute (now at Tulane University), and coauthor of the army vet study discussed below.

"I don't want to talk about it." That's a very common reaction after a traumatic event. Many people would wonder if that was a "healthy" response. Isn't opening up about our pain the only way we can come to terms with trauma and move on with our lives?

Not necessarily. In a study I coauthored that was published in *The Journal of Nervous and Mental Diseases*, we discovered that US Army veterans who repressed traumas rather than talked about them suffered no additional health problems and lived just as long as other vets. And the vets who repressed were less likely to exhibit symptoms of post-traumatic stress disorder.

What people call repression is really a form of self-regulation. It's the ability to compartmentalize information in a way that you can handle.

When people discuss traumas before they feel ready, it can lead to even deeper suffering. They might hear troubling words coming out of their mouths that they are not yet able to confront or refute, for example. A combat vet might label himself a murderer. A rape victim might tell herself that she was somehow to blame for the crime.

If you suffer a trauma, you'll know if you are ready to open up about it—it suddenly will feel safe to do so. Do not let anyone pressure you into talking if you don't want to. If a loved one suffers a trauma, make yourself available to discuss it, but do not push for this conversation or push this person into therapy.

How to Live and Die with No Regrets: You Can Change Your Life Before It's Too Late...

Neil A. Fiore, PhD, a psychologist in private practice in Albany, California, and CEO of Fiore Productivity, Inc. A cancer survivor, Dr. Fiore worked as an economist before training to become a psychologist. He is also an executive coach and author of several books, including *The Now Habit*. Dr. Fiore has several videos available at *YouTube.com/fioreproductivity*.

What is your greatest fear? For many people, it's death...and the possibility of physical suffering as the body shuts down. But along with that, there often is a deep emotional fear of ending our lives with regrets.

Most of us have an idea of what it means to live a fulfilled life, but oftentimes people don't even realize until they're approaching their final days what exactly their regrets might be.

Psychologist Neil A. Fiore, PhD, has come close to dying twice—while fighting in the Vietnam War and from having "terminal" cancer. As a result, he decided to alter the course of his own life and now motivates people to make significant changes in their lives. *Here's Dr. Fiore's advice on how to make changes (no matter what your age) so that you won't be left wishing you'd lived your life differently...**

REGRET #1: I wish I hadn't worked so hard. If you find yourself consistently overworking, you may be a perfectionist trying to avoid criticism by working harder and longer than you need to.

To avoid this regret: You've probably heard that you should break up projects into smaller segments rather than trying to do everything at once. Most people think this approach simply gives you more control over what to do when, but it also helps you avoid getting bogged down in perfectionism...and prevents you from getting overwhelmed by trying to finish projects in one shot. Instead of saying, I must finish all this work perfectly, say, I choose to begin this project by working on an outline or making some calls for 15 or 30 minutes. It doesn't have to be perfect!

*The regrets in this article first appeared in *The Top Five Regrets of the Dying* by Bronnie Ware.

If you tend to work too much, you probably don't make much time for fun.

Solution: Schedule fun. Earmarking time specifically for fun allows you to avoid any guilt during your time off.

REGRET #2: I wish I'd had the courage to live a life true to myself, not the life others expected of me. Being your own person—whether it's in your personal relationships or in your professional life—takes courage. You must be willing to deviate from society's expectations...and to overcome fear of criticism.

To avoid this regret: Pay attention when your actions aren't in sync with your true beliefs.

Helpful: Recognize when you act in a habitual—but false—way by saying to yourself, I'm reacting this way out of fear. But I am now strong enough that I can choose to stand up for my true beliefs. Then make a conscious decision to act in a way that supports your true beliefs. Even if you're not sure of what your true self is, you know when you're acting falsely to fit in. When you start acting in new ways, others may try to pressure you to conform to their rules for your life, but resist.

REGRET #3: I wish I had stayed in touch with friends and loved ones. All of us have friends or family members we've lost touch with.

To avoid this regret: Make a list of friends or relatives you'd like to reconnect with, then schedule specific times every week when you will call, text, e-mail or visit. Instead of saying, "I should call Amy," put Amy on your calendar for, say, Wednesday at noon. After a few weeks, keeping in touch will be automatic because it's so rewarding to have these warm, supportive connections.

REGRET #4: I wish I'd had the courage to express my feelings. It's often scary to express our true emotions—so much so that we may feel that we don't even know how.

To avoid this regret: Start by keeping an emotions journal where you can vent all your emotions privately and promptly.

If you decide to share your feelings with someone, write a "script" so you don't have to hunt for words during the conversation.

Example: You can start a difficult message with, "Our relationship is important to me, so I'm anxious about telling you something that upset me." Don't blame the other person. Rather, focus on your own feelings.

For people who have a difficult time saying "no," a great trick is to start with "yes"...followed by a statement that expresses your true feelings. For example, "Yes, I would love to organize the fund-raiser...thank you for asking me, but unfortunately, I have other commitments right now." The beauty is you never have to utter the word "no" but still get the benefit of not agreeing to something you don't want to do.

REGRET #5: I wish I had let myself be happier. Bad things happen to everyone.

Here's a secret, though: You can learn to be compassionate toward yourself even when having difficult emotions such as depression. And you can enjoy yourself even when lonely. Remember that you are the one who chooses how you respond to tough situations.

Writing about one's negative emotions has been shown to reduce stress hormones and lessen the intensity of negative feelings. You also can be active—dance or sing, for example—to help deal with negative emotions. Recognizing your strengths and joys can promote happiness as well.

Important: Be sure to consult your doctor if you have depression for a few weeks or longer. You may need therapy and/or medication.

If you've suffered emotional trauma, such as being brought up by an abusive parent, it helps to write about this as well. I also advise a burial ritual in which you bury a symbol of the trauma, such as a photo or letter, marking that day as the end of this issue in your life. When new thoughts of the trauma return, recall the burial ritual and say to yourself, *This is over. I let go of it on this date.* If negative emotions persist, consult a mental-health professional.

A word about mistakes: All people make mistakes. Errors don't have to diminish your worth—they simply define you as human. If you have moments of feeling bad about a decision, give yourself no more than 10 to 30 seconds to feel regret, then focus on what you can do to fix the situation and move on.

Why You Should Dump Your Bucket List

Chris Guillebeau, author of *The Happiness of Pursuit.*

Chris Guillebeau, speaker and best-selling author, hates the word "bucket list"—too death evoking. He prefers to call it a "life list." You write down what you want to accomplish during your life. Why bother? Because it helps you think through what you really want and goes beyond career goals.

Guillebeau has come across life lists that have included such interesting things as "win a watermelon seed–spitting contest"..."hug a panda"...and "drive a Zamboni" (that's the ice-conditioning machine used at hockey rinks).

Guillebeau is a particular fan of life-list entries that aim to do good in a creative and engaging way—"sponsor a child in need in as many different countries as possible," for example. Not long ago, Guillebeau himself reached one of his own life goals—he visited every country on Earth.

Guillebeau's tips for crafting a life list...

- **Goals should be specific.** "Visit Vienna" or "visit every country in Asia" is better than "travel." Vague goals can lead to inaction.
- **Goals should fall into multiple categories.** Some might be educational, others altruistic, adventuresome, professional, personal or quirky. A varied list encourages you to stretch yourself. It also is more likely to hold your interest as the years pass.
- **Goals should differ in scale.** Some should be major undertakings that will take years to achieve, but others should be easily checked-off items so that you can feel progress is being made.
- **Goals shouldn't be constrained by your present circumstances.** Set aside any restrictions that currently hold you back, and think about what you really would like to do.

19

Business Brainstorm

Want Your Business to Really Grow? The *One Thing* You Must Do

An Indianapolis man ran a valet service parking cars for fancy restaurants. The business was profitable, but its growth potential was very limited. To boost profits, he offered to clean and detail cars while their owners dined, but the stiff competition in the auto-detailing sector constricted growth here, too.

Then the man was asked to clean a plane, and he noticed that the private-plane cleaning business offered little competition and great growth potential. He quickly switched gears and now has a thriving business cleaning planes at airports around the world. His company even cleaned Air Force One.

The man uncovered this opportunity because he wasn't satisfied with modest success. His goal was huge growth, and he kept searching for new opportunities until he achieved it.

All small-business owners who desire to make it big need to stop targeting 10% growth and start targeting 10-times growth instead. Setting ultra-aggressive goals might seem unrealistic, but it actually is the most practical option. When business owners target relatively modest growth, their brains look for ways to do what they already are doing, only a little better. They conclude that they just need to work a little harder or a little longer—which is the path to burnout, not success. By instead targeting 1,000% (10-times) growth, they force their brains to search outside of what they currently are doing for completely new opportunities. It isn't possible to achieve 10-times growth by just working harder.

Dan Sullivan, cofounder and president of The Strategic Coach Inc., an entrepreneurial coaching practice with offices in Toronto, Chicago and London. He is author of *How the Best Get Better: The Art and Science of Entrepreneurial Success. StrategicCoach.com*

Here are three key ways to achieve 10-times growth…

HIRE SMART

Most entrepreneurs are rugged individualist types who think that they alone must make all the decisions and perform all the important tasks for their businesses. When they hire employees, they tend to view them as support staff for their personal efforts. But it usually is impossible to grow a business to 10 times its current size with just one person tackling all the key roles.

Better: Consider what your unique abilities are and what you truly enjoy doing, then hire teammates, not support staff, to do everything else.

To hire great employees…

- **Hire candidates who are passionate about your business.** To identify true passion, mention and praise a book that you consider crucial to your business philosophy or goals during your initial interview with a promising candidate. Then ask questions about this book during a subsequent interview. A candidate who has true passion for your business should have read the book after you mentioned it.

- **Hire team players.** It isn't easy to identify teamwork skills during job interviews, because candidates are on their best behavior. But once someone joins your company, it soon will become apparent whether he/she works well with others. Let go of employees who are self-centered or dishonest.

- **Hire employees who embrace change.** Mention a new idea that you're considering to potential hires during job interviews—something very different from the way things normally are done, perhaps the idea of using a new system or technology. A good candidate will seem energized by the idea of trying something different, not apprehensive.

- **Hire help for design and/or marketing.** New businesses need to get noticed and look professional—but marketing, creation of logos and product-packaging design are not areas of strength for many entrepreneurs. Consider making a marketing pro one of your first hires. And use websites such as *99Designs.com* and *Guru.com* to obtain high-quality graphic design help for as little as $300 per project, compared with thousands of dollars or more.

LEVERAGE YOUR TOP 20% CLIENTS

It's no secret that treating existing clients well can be good for business. Happy customers are loyal customers, and they sometimes refer new customers. But to achieve 10-times growth, an entrepreneur often must make the difficult decision not to lavish extensive attention on every client. Each hour you devote to one client is an hour you can't devote to another. Dividing up your time evenly may not be the wisest solution.

Better: While you serve your clients, also analyze them. If your business is like most, approximately 80% of your clients will never grow significantly larger than they are now… will never provide you with significantly more business than they currently do…and will never refer profitable new clients to you. Your goal is to identify the other 20%—the clients most likely to feed your growth—then lavish most of your time and attention on them. Wow them time and again, even if that means you don't always have time to wow your other clients.

When you're considering which of your clients fall into this crucial 20%, consider not just their size and growth potential but also how well-connected they are in the business community at large.

Example: An intellectual-property attorney in Silicon Valley gave his most promising small, high-tech clients the sort of high-end patent-protection assistance that young companies usually cannot afford. Some of these young clients became very big, successful companies—one of them was Facebook. The attorney now is in huge demand—and the shares of the young tech companies he received as part of his compensation have earned him a fortune.

MANAGE YOUR CALENDAR LIKE AN ENTERTAINER

Don't work more to grow your business—work less.

Entrepreneurs often pour virtually every waking hour into their businesses. But working nonstop eventually wears them down.

Mental fatigue leads to uncreative thinking, and a lack of creativity means certain death for entrepreneurs.

Better: Learn a lesson from entertainers and athletes. These professionals typically divide their time between *performance days*, when they need to be on their game...*preparation days*, which are devoted to rehearsing or practicing...and *free days*, when they don't work at all. Each of these days can play a crucial role in success—if handled properly.

- **Free days** should be completely and truly free. Don't even answer e-mails, take business calls or fret about work for the entire day. Don't feel guilty. You're not slacking off—you're giving your mind the downtime it requires. You also are giving your family the time it needs with you. Ignoring your spouse and children can lead to family problems that undermine an entrepreneur's ability to focus on business.
- **Preparation days,** or what I call "Buffer Days," are for meetings, interviewing potential employees, organizing the office and doing the other backstage stuff necessary to keep a business running. Dedicating certain days to this prevents these tasks from distracting your focus on performance days.
- **Focus days are performance days**—doing only what makes money for you. Any distractions should be set aside for the next preparation day.

TAKE NOTE...

Best Cities for Work-Life Balance

The five best cities for work-life balance are all university towns—Bloomington, Indiana...Provo, Utah...Gainesville, Florida...Eau Claire, Wisconsin...Tuscaloosa, Alabama.

All of these cities have relatively short average workweeks, easy commutes and things for people to enjoy when not working—outdoor activities, sports events, museums, theaters and more.

Analysis by *NerdWallet.com*.

Turn Your Bright Idea into Cash: Mistakes New Investors Make

Edith G. Tolchin, founder of EGT Global Trading, a company that specializes in coordinating the offshore manufacturing of textiles and sewn items, household goods and other products in Hillsborough, New Jersey. She is contributing editor of *Inventors Digest* and editor of *Secrets of Successful Inventing: From Concept to Commerce. EGTGlobalTrading.com*

A once-in-a-lifetime idea for a wonderful new invention could make you a fortune...or cost you your savings. By most estimates, fewer than 1% of patented inventions ever make money. But some novice inventors do become hugely successful.

Examples: Sara Blakely cut the feet off a pair of panty hose and invented Spanx—it made her a billionaire. Scott Boilen put sleeves on a blanket and created the Snuggie—and made hundreds of millions of dollars. More recently, David Toledo and Paul Slusser designed PowerPot, a portable cooking pot that uses heat from cooking to generate electricity, which is useful for both campers and people in developing nations—billionaire Mark Cuban invested $250,000 in the young company in 2014.

How do you boost your chances of success? *By avoiding the key mistakes that novice inventors often make...*

PLANNING MISTAKES

Many costly inventor mistakes occur while inventions are still just ideas...

MISTAKE: Launching your crowdfunding campaign or laying out big bucks before truly analyzing profit potential. It can cost well into five figures to have a prototype built... and that much again to hire a lawyer to secure a patent. Inexperienced inventors sometimes get so caught up in the excitement of their big ideas that they dip into their savings or start crowdfunding campaigns at websites such as *Kickstarter* and *Indiegogo* before taking an in-depth, objective look at their idea's true moneymaking potential. Crowdfunding sites let people finance projects by soliciting small contributions from large numbers of supporters, but more than half of these projects fail to reach their monetary goals.

Better: Before investing in an invention or trying to get others to invest...

- **Use the search tool** on the US Patent and Trademark Office website (*USPTO.gov*) to see if similar ideas already have been patented. If so, it might be difficult for you to get a patent...or it could suggest that others have already attempted similar ideas without commercial success.
- **Identify the competition.** Which companies are selling products that will compete with yours? If these competitors have huge marketing budgets, well-established distribution networks and/or other advantages, your product could be better but still fail.
- **Consider the gatekeepers.** Who decides which new products reach the market in the sector? How will you convince these people that your product deserves a shot? The fact that your product is slightly better than competing products might not be enough. Gatekeepers can be major obstacles if you expect to sell your product through large retail chains, for example—the executives who do the buying for these chains often are hesitant to stock products from small, unproven companies.

Helpful: SCORE, the nonprofit organization previously known as the Service Corps of Retired Executives, can provide a retired businessperson with relevant experience to serve as your volunteer mentor (*SCORE.org*). SCORE has been around for a long time, but surprisingly few people take advantage of this excellent resource.

MISTAKE: Trusting the wrong people to help you develop your idea. If you visit invention-related sites on the Internet or watch late-night cable TV, you are likely to come across advertisements from companies that claim to assist inventors. Do not work with these companies. Most will ask for big payments—sometimes $10,000 or beyond—then provide very little help.

Better: A wiser way for novice inventors to obtain insight and assistance is to join an inventor's club. These groups typically have guest speakers at their meetings who discuss inventing-related topics. The clubs also are a great way to meet other inventors who have overcome challenges similar to the ones you're facing...and they are a great way to get referrals to trustworthy patent attorneys and prototypers.

You can find inventor's clubs through the US Patent and Trademark Office (visit *USPTO.gov/inventors*, then select "State Resources" from the menu, followed by your state) or the Inventor's Alliance (visit *InventorsAlliance.org*, select "Resources," then "United States Map"). Or enter the terms "inventor," "club" and the name of your state or city into a search engine. Legitimate clubs should not charge more than a modest annual fee—generally less than $100. Many clubs will let you attend one meeting for free before deciding whether to join.

MISTAKE: Inventing without any outside input. Savvy inventors seek input from their potential customers...and from other inventors throughout the invention process. The feedback they receive helps them identify potential problems with their ideas and make any necessary adjustments.

But inventors often are worried that their ideas could be stolen if they reach the wrong ears. That is a legitimate concern—but there are ways around it.

To reduce idea-theft risk...

- **Discuss the problem your product is meant to solve without mentioning your breakthrough idea for overcoming it.** This can at least help you confirm that other people consider this a significant problem, too...that they are not satisfied with the solutions to the problem currently on the market...and that they would be willing to pay what your invention would cost.
- **Share your idea with people who have signed nondisclosure agreements.** Legitimate inventor's clubs usually insist that everyone who attends meetings sign these, for example.

Helpful: You can find nondisclosure forms online by entering the terms "nondisclosure," "agreement" and "template" into any search engine.

PRODUCTION MISTAKES

Two things that novice inventors get wrong as their inventions start down the path to becoming products...

MISTAKE: Ignoring or delaying US Consumer Product Safety Commission (CPSC) testing. First-time inventors tend to be more concerned with designing their products than with government regulations. But if you fail to pay sufficient attention to consumer-safety regulations early in the invention process, you might end up with a product that you cannot legally sell in the US. The safety rules governing children's products are especially strict.

Better: Go to the CPSC website to determine which consumer-safety rules apply to your product before having a prototype made (*CPSC.gov*, then select "Testing & Certification" from the "Business & Manufacturing" pull-down menu). As soon as you have a prototype made, submit it to a lab for a "Product Design Evaluation" report. The report will include a list of mandatory testing that needs to be done. You can find a lab at the website above.

MISTAKE: Working with a manufacturer with whom you have communication issues. Difficulty communicating leads to larger problems down the road.

Better: Do not agree to work with a manufacturer if...

- **It is slow to respond to your questions.** Manufacturers that are slow to answer questions early in the process tend to be slow to deliver products later.
- **It cannot communicate in easy-to-understand English.** Most products are made overseas these days, leading to language barriers. If you find it difficult to understand the people with whom you exchange e-mails or speak on the phone, there's a good chance they are struggling to understand you, too—which greatly increases the odds that they will miss some crucial detail.

Time to Try a Fab Lab?

Fab labs allow people who have ideas for inventions to create prototypes using digital tools, such as laser cutters and computer-controlled routers and milling machines. The inventors pay a monthly fee, generally less than $100, to be allowed hands-on fabrication time. The labs—a form of what is being called public "makerspace"—exist worldwide. They offer classes to teach inventors how to use design software and fabrication tools, so prototypes can be made for a fraction of the cost of hiring a machine shop or engineering firm.

To find fab labs in your area, go to: *FabFoundation.org.*

The Trends Journal. TrendsResearch.com

Why You Should Do Something Stupid

Tobias van Schneider, product designer and art director with digital music service Spotify USA. *Spotify.com*

What's the difference between the side project that turns into a successful business and the one that never gets off the ground? Often it's how seriously that side project is taken by its creator. But...surprise! It's the projects that are taken less seriously that are more likely to blossom.

The massively successful classified-ad website Craigslist was just a hobby for founder Craig Newmark before he started treating it like a business. Post-it Notes were created by a 3M employee who just wanted a bookmark that wouldn't fall out of his hymnal when he sang in his church choir.

It's wise to keep side projects "stupid" because when we try to smarten them up, they often stall. When we use "smart" business practices with side projects, two things happen. First, the side project starts to seem a lot less compelling and fulfilling and a lot more like a job with no paycheck. And second, we start to uncover reasons why the side project

DID YOU KNOW THAT...

Most People Would Like to Switch Careers

A whopping 86% of employees feel that they are not in their dream career. About half of them would like to be their own boss.

Poll of 1,616 US adults, age 18 or older, by Harris Interactive on behalf of University of Phoenix.

might not be the great idea we initially thought it was.

Result: The side project is set aside, never to be pursued again.

Our financial future is not on the line with a side project, and we don't have to explain our missteps to a boss or a board, so skip the market research...skip the financial planning...and just dive in. If your initial idea is off-target, you can change course on the fly. Just trust your intuition. That's the path to somewhere interesting.

Rejection Proof: How to Change a "No" into a "Yes"

Jia Jiang, founder of the popular blog and video series *100 Days of Rejection* and author of *Rejection Proof.* His story has been covered by dozens of news outlets, including *Bloomberg Businessweek, The Huffington Post* and *Forbes.* A native of Beijing, China, Jiang came to the US as a teenager to pursue his dream of becoming an entrepreneur. Jiang holds an MBA from Duke University and a bachelor's degree in computer science from Brigham Young University.

A Texas businessman named Jia Jiang was devastated in 2012 when a potential investor decided not to back his company. But Jiang soon realized that the greatest obstacle to his long-term success was his deep-seated fear of further rejection.

Jiang's solution? He resolved to make absurd, sure-to-be-rejected requests each day for 100 days and post videos of his rejections on his blog. Jiang reasoned that this would forever inoculate him against rejection.

But then something unexpected occurred—people began saying yes. A Krispy Kreme employee agreed to custom-make him a special "Olympic ring" of doughnuts—and then didn't charge him. A stranger agreed to film Jiang playing soccer—in the stranger's backyard.

Here's what Jiang found works to transform a "no" into a "yes"...

- **Ask why you were rejected.** The answer could help you reshape your request.
- **Quickly make a second request of the same person.** Second requests often are accepted—people don't like to reject two requests in a row for fear it will make them appear mean.
- **Don't argue when you hear "no"**—offer to help. Asking, "Is there anything I can do to help you say 'yes' to this?" casts you as a collaborator working toward a common goal.
- **Don't reject yourself.** It may seem that not making a request spares you pain, but the pain of knowing you never tried lingers longer than the rejection.

Borrowing Options for Internet-Based Businesses

Online retailers often don't have the necessary collateral to get traditional bank loans, so companies such as *Amazon.com, PayPal.com* and *Kabbage.com* now provide loans to these online sellers. Paypal says it allows businesses that sell on eBay to borrow amounts up to 8% of their annual sales and repay with a percentage of each sale made. E-commerce loans typically are for six months to one year, come with higher interest rates than bank loans and have more restrictions.

Scot Wingo, CEO of ChannelAdvisor, which provides e-commerce advice, Morrisville, North Carolina. *ChannelAdvisor.com*

Looking for a Job? Surefire Ways to Get Your Foot in the Door

Deborah Brown-Volkman, a Professional Certified Coach (PCC) and president of Surpass Your Dreams, a career-coaching company based on Long Island, New York. She is also author of several best-selling books including *Don't Blow It: The Right Words for the Right Job. SurpassYourDreams.com*

The recent positive employment statistics hide a troubling truth—many of the jobs being created in this economic recovery are not very desirable. There are plenty of openings if you're willing to work for minimum wage in retail or fast food, but far fewer if your career goals are at all ambitious.

At the same time, many very desirable employers are taking on temps—in fact, temporary positions account for nearly 9% of the job growth of the past five years. And becoming a temp worker can be a great way to find a very good full-time job. Temp assignments typically last only a few weeks or months. But temping lets you get a foot in the door with a desirable employer...acquire in-demand job skills...and make valuable professional contacts. This is true if you're just starting out...or are in that hard-to-find-a-job 50-and-older age group...or somewhere in between. You even may be retired and looking for a way to use your skills in the workplace. *Here's how to use temping to reach your goal...*

BECOMING A TEMP

Settle on your goal for temping before you start. Without a specific goal, it's easy to just drift from one low-paying temp position to the next without ever getting your career on track. This goal might be as specific as "Get in the door with either Smith Co. or Jones Co."... or as general as "Make a few dollars, and explore different companies and sectors until I find work I enjoy." If your goal is to work for a particular employer (or one of a small group of employers), scan that company's website for temp openings or contact its human resources department.

If you don't have a specific company in mind, sign up with a temp agency. You can find agencies in your area by typing "temp agency" and the nearest city into an Internet search engine. If you live in an area with multiple temp agencies, choose one that regularly works with people in your profession or with companies in sectors that appeal to you. Temp agencies' websites often list the professions and sectors they work with. If not, call and ask.

WEIGHING ASSIGNMENTS

When a temp assignment is offered to you, ask yourself...

- **Does this seem like a great place to work?** If not, politely decline. Tell the temp agency that you are anxious to work, but that this particular position or company is not a great fit for you.
- **Is this employer growing?** A temp job at a company that is increasing its revenue and adding permanent staff as well as temps is much more likely to lead to a permanent position than one at a company that is stagnant or shrinking. A temp job at a company that is laying off permanent employees and hiring temps instead is especially unlikely to lead to a full-time job.

To find out whether a company is growing, enter its name into a search engine and look for recent news stories covering its financial state...network with anyone you know in the sector...read the company's recent SEC filings if it has stock that trades on a stock exchange (these filings should be available on the com-

INTERESTING FINDING...

College Graduates Who Majored in Business Are the Most Bored with Their Jobs

Business is the most popular course of study at US universities—but it comes in last in terms of how interested graduates are in the work they end up doing. Those most interested in their work are in social sciences and education.

Survey of 30,000 graduates of all ages by Gallup and Purdue University, reported in *The Wall Street Journal*.

EASY-TO-DO...

Get Pumped Before a Job Interview

To boost your confidence before a job interview, listen to the right music. People who listened to two minutes of throbbing, up-tempo, bass-heavy rap and rock tunes felt more confident and in control than people who listened to lower-power pop songs.

Study by researchers at Northwestern University, Evanston, Illinois, published in *Social Psychological and Personality Science.*

pany's website)...and search job websites to see if the company is adding permanent staff in any capacity.

• **Is this temp assignment likely to put you in direct contact with the company's decision makers?** Your odds of landing a permanent position increase dramatically if an executive who has the power to offer you a job is impressed by you in person.

• **Is the position described as "temp to perm"?** That means the employer specifically expressed an interest in offering a permanent position to a temp who excels. (But don't reject a position just because it is not listed as temp to perm.)

• **Will you be able to do this job well from day one without much training?** Employers may not always invest much time in training temps, nor will they have time to spend answering temps' questions. The best way to impress is to jump right in and do the job well with minimal hand-holding.

• **How many employees does this company have?** Obamacare rules can make it expensive for companies to grow from 49 to 50 employees. Companies approaching this threshold sometimes hire temps rather than permanent staff to avoid reaching 50. Such companies are very unlikely to offer a temp a permanent job. If there is a staff list on the company's website, count the names to see if this is a potential issue.

JOIN THE CULTURE

Once you accept a temp assignment, the best way to boost the odds that it will lead to the offer of a permanent position is, of course, to exceed performance expectations. But there is a second way to improve these odds that temps often overlook—become part of the company's culture. If colleagues and company decision makers see you as a member of the family, they won't want to see you go.

Examples: Bring in coffee or pastries for coworkers. Attend office parties. Put a few dollars in the kitty when a collection is taken for a gift. Join the office softball team, and/or sign up for company-sponsored volunteer activities. Dress the same way that permanent employees dress. Ask colleagues to lunch. If the company offers employee-training programs, ask if you can sign up. This shows commitment and can provide valuable skills.

When the end date of a temp assignment nears, meet with your boss and ask if there are any opportunities to extend the employment. If this boss seems at all receptive, suggest specific roles you could realistically fill for the company.

WHAT TO DO WHEN A TEMP JOB ENDS

All is not lost if a permanent job is not immediately offered. *As the temp position's end nears...*

• **Tell all the people you know at the company that you enjoyed working with them but that your final day is coming soon.** Someone other than your current supervisor might have a position to offer—but he/she might not realize you will soon be available.

• **Ask your boss for permission to list him among your references on future job applications.**

• **Ask your colleagues if you can connect with them on LinkedIn.** Keep track of their careers—they might later be in a position to offer you a job or put in a good word for you with someone who can.

• **Lump all of your temp assignments together in a single entry on your résumé.** Label this entry "Temporary work." Listing each temp assignment as a separate entry could make it look like you jump rapidly from job to job—a red flag for potential employers.

Help Recruiters Find You on LinkedIn

Recruiters look for keywords such as *won, sold, built* and *achieved* on LinkedIn. They respond negatively to buzzwords such as *maven, guru* and *prophet*. Recruiters also look for thoughtful recommendations from well-respected peers or ex-employers. They are not interested in jobs or accomplishments more than a decade old. Recruiters join and follow LinkedIn groups—where members discuss industry-specific topics—and look for job candidates who contribute regularly and provide significant, useful information. Any complaints and criticisms are a turnoff—avoid them.

Roundup of experts on recruitment using LinkedIn, reported at *MarketWatch.com*.

Warning Signs of a Job Scam

Here are some helpful indicators that a job opening is a hoax...

Few details—the job description is short on details and skills required.

Complaints—before applying for a job, do a web search using the name of the company and the word "scam." If it is a bogus job, you likely will find complaints.

Requires cash up front—unless you are buying a franchise, you shouldn't have to pay to get paid.

Requires personal information—you should not need to provide your Social Security, driver's license or a credit card number on a job application. It is a red flag for identity theft.

CBS News.

To Explain Extended Unemployment During an Interview...

You can be sure a job interviewer will ask about any period of extended unemployment. *What to do...*

Think about what you learned, perhaps from volunteering or taking a class. Explain how the time off reenergized you so that you now are ready for a transition back to your line of work. Keep your explanation brief—overexplaining can make you seem nervous. It is best to bring up the gap in employment yourself instead of waiting for the interviewer to discuss it—make it part of your opening statement when asked to tell something about yourself.

Roundup of experts on careers and job interviews, reported at *USNews.com*.

BETTER WAYS...

Quick Tips to Get More Organized and Focused

Get more organized and focused by eliminating the open-door policy—if employees can come in anytime, you will be constantly distracted. Instead, set aside an hour every day for a team meeting.

Also: Automate small digital tasks, such as posting tweets and sending invoices so that these tasks do not distract you. Tackle similar activities all at once every week or month to avoid breaking your concentration when they come up at various times.

Additionally, you can try a service known as *ScheduleOnce* that lets you share a public calendar for setting up meetings—all contacts can see it and pick a time that works for everybody (it offers a 14-day free trial, and plans range from $5 to $49 after that*).

Fortune. Fortune.com

*Prices subject to change.

EASY-TO-DO...

Fight Fatigue in Meetings

Drink iced tea during long meetings to stay awake and involved. Sipping anything keeps your energy up, but iced tea also contains caffeine and the amino acid *theanine*, which helps make the brain more alert.

Study by researchers at Unilever Food and Health Research Institute, the Netherlands, published in *Asia Pacific Journal of Clinical Nutrition*.

What You *Don't* Want to Hear After an Interview

Two things you don't want to hear at the end of a job interview...and what to do if you hear them...

• **Can I give you some advice?** This question usually means that you won't get the job. But say yes and listen politely. Then say that you may not be a perfect fit but will give the job your all if offered a chance.

• **We have a number of interviews to go through.** This means that they are looking for a candidate they consider better. Ask what it is that you don't have that makes them reluctant to hire you—that should keep the conversation going and perhaps provide an opportunity for you to show that you are the best candidate.

Tim Sackett, executive vice president, HRU Technical Resources, contingent-staffing firm, Lansing, Michigan.

Send a Thank-You Note Even If You Don't Get the Job

If you liked the organization and want to be considered for a future opening, a thank-you note after a rejection will set you apart from other applicants. If the newly hired person does not work out, the firm may reach back to other finalists. Your note should thank the company for letting you know the outcome of the search...express your disappointment in not getting the job...repeat your interest in working there...and request that they contact you the next time a position is available.

Susan P. Joyce, president of NETability, Inc., and editor and chief technology writer for *Job-Hunt.org* and *WorkCoachCafe.com*.

How to Reduce E-Mail Overload

To cut down on the number of e-mails you send and receive, instead of trying to solve problems with coworkers by e-mail, get together in person for 15 minutes at the same time every day or week. You will resolve matters with less back-and-forth communication.

Also: Use specific subject lines in e-mails so that recipients easily can find messages if they need them later...insist that most e-mails be kept short, like Twitter messages...require one topic per e-mail...and when replying with a thank-you or simple yes or no, put your response in the subject line followed by (EOM) for "End of Message."

Verne Harnish, CEO, of the executive-education firm Gazelles Inc., Ashburn, Virginia, writing in *Fortune*.

Avoid E-Mail Burnout

People who checked their e-mail only three times a day reported less stress than those who checked it more frequently, reports a recent study.

The University of British Columbia.

To Be a Better Public Speaker...

The position you stand in while speaking to a group can put people at ease and make them more receptive to what you are saying...or stress them out and make them want to leave.

Best: Stand with your hands at your waist or higher, palms facing up and spread out so that they are six inches away from each hip bone. This pose opens you up to the group, allowing people to relax and be more attentive.

Nick Morgan, speech coach and author of *Power Cues: The Subtle Science of Leading Groups, Persuading Others, and Maximizing Your Personal Impact.*

Shy? How to Stand Out at Work

If you're shy, consider trying these strategies to be more successful at work...

Use social media—write a blog to build an online network. *Connect one-on-one* rather than in large groups—ask one person from a department other than your own to have lunch each week. *Use nonverbal clues* to indicate your expertise—hang certifications and accolades on the walls in your office.

Harvard Business Review. HBR.org

How to Say What You Do (in 10 Words or Less)...

When you are at a party, a conference or other event and someone asks what you do, use the following template as a guide: "I + [verb] + [people I help] + [achieve their desired result]."

Examples: I connect entrepreneurs with the funding they need...I help my grandchildren enjoy the world.

Clay Hebert, a marketing strategist, keynote speaker and crowdfunding expert. *ClayHebert.com*

When "Friending" the Boss Can Be a Good Idea

If your company encourages workers to use social media and others are connected to the boss, friending the boss on Facebook is probably all right. It can give you some helpful personal information that you can use when meeting him/her in a situation calling for small talk—his vacation or restaurant preferences, for example.

Caution: Even in companies that approve of social-media use, some bosses may not welcome friend requests. Also, be sure to use privacy settings and friend lists to control what your manager sees—and watch your posts carefully.

Money. Money.com

TAKE NOTE...

Better Negotiating for a Raise...

Ask human resources for your position's salary range before negotiating for a raise. The range includes the low-to-high amounts that your company pays for a specific job. Knowing where you are in the range can make negotiating easier—and may show how you can benefit by getting more training. (Just remember that your company's human resources department is not obligated to answer this question.)

Jean Chatzky, AARP financial ambassador, quoted in *AARP Bulletin*.

Open-Office Floor Plans Mean More Sick Days

Open-office floor plans result in more sick days.

Possible reasons: Greater risk of infection from shared space...lack of privacy and control, leading to higher stress.

Study of almost 2,000 people by researchers at Stockholm University, Sweden, published in *Ergonomics*.

Refresh Yourself During the Workday

Take mini-sabbaticals from your job to refresh yourself physically and emotionally throughout the workday.

Examples: While commuting, set your cell phone to Do Not Disturb and listen to an audiobook or some mood-boosting music. During the workday, get some physical distance from a problem—when you feel stuck, stand up...get some water...and disconnect from the task before returning to the problem, hopefully with a fresh perspective.

On weekends, eliminate work-related communication for at least one full day.

Roundup of experts on renewing workplace enthusiasm, reported in *Natural Health*.

INTERESTING FINDING...

Most People Go to Work Sick

Nearly 90% of office workers go to work when they are sick.

But: Productivity drops by almost 60% when you are unwell...and you risk infecting coworkers.

Survey of office workers and facility managers for the fourth annual Flu Season Survey by Staples.

Getting a Raise Has Become Easier

Forty-three percent of companies say that they offered raises in the second quarter of 2014, compared with 19% a year earlier. And 54% of global firms say that they are struggling to keep their best workers. If you are not ready to ask for a raise, consider requesting something to make your work life easier—for example, the right to telecommute twice a week. Offer a trial period of a few months to increase the chance of a positive response.

Surveys by Towers Watson, a global benefits consultancy, and the National Association for Business Economics, quoted in *Money*.

If You Can't Afford to Give Raises...

Help employee salaries go further even if you can't afford raises...

Run an efficient company—let people leave on time to save on child-care costs and reduce stress. *Provide on-site budgeting classes*—free ones may be available through credit unions or nonprofit groups. *Consider offering memberships in warehouse clubs* or local food co-ops as a benefit—the cost to the company is low, and reductions to employees' food costs can be significant. *Let employees have five or more paid days off a year* to boost their income with freelance projects.

Fortune.com

Perks That Help Keep Employees Motivated

A news-media-analysis company in Omaha offers Free Beer Fridays and soda for those who do not want alcohol. A seller of Internet equipment in Amherst, New York, allows employees to bring nondisruptive pets to the office. Some companies give employees time off every year to do volunteer work or participate in causes. A consulting firm in San Francisco gives workers $400 a year to spend on technology. An insurance brokerage in Los Angeles offers summer internships to employees' children. A digital ad agency in Denver provides an hour of yoga every Friday.

If you own a business: Consider what perks would best motivate your workforce.

Roundup of executives of companies that provide workplace perks, reported in *The Wall Street Journal.*

More Workplace Perks

Four percent of companies let their employees work wherever and whenever they want—as long as the projects that the employees are responsible for are done on time. A few companies offer on-site car care, pay for home cleaning or provide at-work haircuts. Twenty-five percent of employers provide financial advice, and 23% offer legal help. Some even provide workers with art—University of Minnesota lets staff members display works from the campus's museum collection in their own homes for $40 a year.

Psychology Today. PsychologyToday.com

Conduct "Stay Interviews"

Many employers conduct exit interviews, but by then an employee has decided to take another job. In informal one-on-one meetings, ask employees why they stay in their jobs so that you can reinforce those positive elements. Also, ask if there are any things that have made them consider leaving, if only for a moment—again, so that you can deal with those issues before someone has already decided to take another job.

John Sullivan, professor of management, San Francisco State University, quoted at *ERE.net.*

DID YOU KNOW THAT...

Workers Don't Use Their Vacation Days

Workers lost 169 million vacation days in a recent year. They gave up vacation time that could not be paid out, banked or substituted for another benefit—likely because of concerns about keeping their jobs or falling behind after missing work.

CBSNews.com

To Make Someone Accountable...

When a project is not done, ask the person responsible what his/her next step is to get it done...when he is going to take that step...and whether you can count on him to do it. If the person is noncommittal, explain that he must give you a solution that will get the task done. If he says that he will try to do it, say that you understand that he will try—but what you want to know is whether you can count on him for the necessary results.

Mike Scott, founder and principal, Mike Scott and Associates, a consulting company based in Etowah, North Carolina, that helps organizations create an efficient and accountable workplace. *TotallyAccountable.com*

Are Your Employees Stealing?

Steven Nicokiris, CPA, managing director in the New York office of CBIZ MHM, LLC. He provides consulting, auditing and accounting services to privately held and family-owned companies. *CBIZ.com*

Small businesses face big risks from employee fraud. They often lack the resources or know-how to implement extensive fraud-prevention safeguards. The outcome can be devastating—in a recent study, the median loss among victimized small companies was $147,000. *To reduce the odds of fraud...*

• **Set up a fraud tip box or hotline.** Most fraud isn't uncovered by fancy accounting techniques—it's uncovered because one employee becomes suspicious of another and tips off the boss.

• **Segregate financial responsibilities.** The employee who sends out your company's bills should not be the one who receives its incoming payments. The bookkeeping and the actual handling of cash should be segregated.

• **Insist that employees take vacations.** The dedicated employee who never takes a day off actually might be a thieving employee unwilling to leave his/her post for fear that his fill-in will uncover his crimes.

• **Add fraud coverage to your business insurance.** Most small-business insurance policies do not cover any losses due to employee theft—but it usually is possible to add a fraud endorsement for as little as $500 or so a year for up to $500,000 in coverage.

• **Have your bank and credit card statements sent to a post office box or your home address.** This prevents a dishonest employee from hiding these statements before you can see them. Or you could monitor these statements online.

• **Conduct background checks on potential employees.** For less than $50, you can find out if an applicant has a criminal history. Type "background check" into a search engine to find companies that do these searches.

• **Secure sensitive documents.** Blank checks and documents containing account numbers or Social Security numbers should be locked up.

• **Tag and secure valuable business equipment.** Any portable, valuable business equipment in your office should be locked up when not in use. Pay a service to etch ID numbers into each piece of business equipment so that you easily can determine which item is missing if one disappears.

• **Take an actual physical inventory at least once a year.** Some companies track inventory only digitally—they never confirm that the things their computer says they have really are on warehouse or store shelves. That makes it very easy for employees to get away with theft.

EASY-TO-DO...

Boost Employee Productivity

Adding plants to a bare-bones workplace improves worker satisfaction and increases productivity by 15%.

University of Exeter, Devon, UK.

Tricks to Get Customers to Open Your E-Mails Right Away!

To get customers to open your e-mails, keep the subject lines short but not too short. Marketing e-mails with six-to-10-word subject lines were opened by 21% of recipients, which is higher than industry average. E-mails with subject lines of five or fewer words had a 16% open rate. Those with 11 to 15 words had only a 14% open rate.

Best: Adding a personalized touch, such as the recipient's first name, increases the open rate by 2.6%.

RetentionScience.com

Make Your Workplace Safer

The Occupational Safety & Health Administration (OSHA) will inspect small and midsized companies to identify safety concerns and offer advice about work-site problems. The inspection is free. No penalties or citations will result from the inspection, but OSHA does make the government aware of any work-site problems that could trigger future penalties.

Barbara Weltman, Esq., Vero Beach, Florida, author of *J.K. Lasser's 1001 Deductions & Tax Breaks* and publisher of *Big Ideas for Small Business*, a free monthly e-letter. *BarbaraWeltman.com*

20

Safety Survey

Hackers Could Ruin Your Life: Changing Passwords Isn't Enough to Stop Them

When Russian hackers stole over 1.2 billion passwords from almost 420,000 websites, it sent shudders through computer users. But what dangers do you really face as a result of these kinds of increasingly common data breaches?

Unfortunately, the risks can be far greater than most people realize. Stolen passwords can result in financial devastation...or even medical disaster. The risks vary greatly depending on the type of account involved.

Here's a look at the real dangers you face when criminals steal your online IDs and what you can do to reduce those risks...

INVESTMENT ACCOUNTS

Financial institutions in general provide investors with some sort of written security guarantee—but these guarantees are designed primarily to protect the institution's interests rather than yours. They typically promise to refund stolen money only if the investor has followed a list of Internet security precautions—it can be difficult for most people to understand these lawyer-crafted high-tech requirements, much less follow them. And an investment company could, in theory, still decide not to make good on the losses, knowing that it would be very expensive for an individual investor to challenge a big financial company in court.

Firms generally—though not always—have compensated investors who have had money

---

John Sileo, president and CEO of The Sileo Group, a Denver-based data-security think tank that has worked with the Department of Defense and Federal Reserve Bank of New York, among other clients. He is author of *Privacy Means Profit: Prevent Identity Theft and Secure You and Your Bottom Line. Sileo.com* stolen by cybercriminals, but that's often because they conclude that it's better to compensate a few investors for losses than risk losing the confidence of thousands—a decision that may not apply in all situations.

What to do: Set up "two-factor authorization," also known as "multifactor authentication," with your investment companies so that they send a code to your cell phone via text or voice message whenever you or someone else tries to log into your account. You must enter this code into the website to gain access. (Three-factor authorization, which also uses a fingerprint or voice scan to confirm identities, is becoming available.)

Of course, always read account statements carefully and contact the financial institution immediately if you spot any activity that you don't recognize.

CREDIT CARD AND BANK ACCOUNTS

There's a major gap in the federal laws that restrict your potential losses if cybercriminals run up fraudulent charges on your credit cards or drain money from checking or savings accounts at a bank or credit union—business bank accounts are not covered. *The rules...*

- **With personal and business credit cards, your out-of-pocket losses are limited** by federal law to no more than $50. Many card issuers now have zero-liability policies and do not make cardholders responsible even for this $50.

- **With personal bank savings and checking accounts**—and the debit cards linked to them—you generally are not liable for unauthorized debits stemming from cybercrime as long as you report the debits within 60 days of the date on the first bank statement that lists the unauthorized transactions. Fail to report the unauthorized transactions within 60 days, however, and you could be responsible for all of the losses.

Note: Your liability is slightly different if someone is able to steal money from your bank account by getting your physical debit card. If that occurs, you are liable for as much as $50 if you report the loss of the card to the bank within two days...up to $500 if you report it within three to 60 days...or potentially for all of your losses if you report it after 60 days. Some debit card issuers offer zero-liability policies—that is, they will cover any cardholder losses to fraud even if federal law says that the cardholder could be liable for some portion of them—but these generally do not cover ATM and PIN-based transactions. However, MasterCard is extending its zero-liability policy to include these.

- **With business bank accounts, you could be saddled with all of the losses.** Cybertheft from bank accounts has driven some small businesses out of business. Your bank is likely to be held liable for business account losses only if it failed to offer "commercially reasonable" security procedures. *What to do...*

- Monitor bank and credit card accounts closely for unauthorized activity.

- Update your account passwords in the wake of the recent data breach.

- If you have a business bank account, keep the number of employees who have access to the account information to a minimum. Make sure that you have a password that you can use when making transactions over the phone in addition to Internet passwords. And ask your bank if it can recommend additional security procedures to maximize the account's security. *Example:* It might be possible to restrict anyone from making sizable online withdrawals or transfers out of the account from any computer other than the one that you normally use.

- Ask your insurance agent if your coverage protects you against cybertheft from your business bank accounts or if such coverage is available.

HEALTH INSURANCE

Few people give much thought to the security of their health insurance policies—but

EASY-TO-DO...

Trick to Protect Your Password

When signing up for a website, do not answer the security questions honestly—such as your mother's maiden name or your birthplace. You'll actually better protect your account and identity if you always use the same *wrong* answers.

Keith Bradford, author of *Life Hacks*.

this can be a matter of life and death. If a cybercriminal gets hold of your health insurance account information, he/she could sell a replica of your insurance ID card to someone in need of medical services. Bills for the uncovered portion of these medical treatments would then be sent to you.

You would not be legally liable for these bills, but convincing health-care providers and insurance companies that the bills are not yours could be a long and frustrating process.

The greater danger is that someone else's medical information could be added to your medical files. If the person who poses as you has a different blood type than you, for example, you might be given the wrong blood type if you need a transfusion.

What to do: Read all "explanation of benefits" statements that you receive from your insurer to make sure that you really used those benefits. If you suddenly stop receiving statements and other mailings from your health insurer, call to make sure that the mailing address on your policy hasn't been altered.

E-MAIL ACCOUNTS

A cybercriminal who learns your e-mail account's user name and password could parlay this information into access to your financial accounts.

Example: A cybercriminal might search through your e-mails for messages from financial companies that you work with, then send you e-mails that appear to be from these companies. If you click a link in one of these e-mails, you'll be routed to what appears to be the financial company's site—but if you enter your user name and password into this page as prompted, you actually will divulge your private account information to the criminal.

What to do: If you get an e-mail with what appears to be a link from your financial institution, do not click this link. Instead, go to the institution's website as you normally would. If you cannot find the page related to the e-mail on the website, call the investment company and ask for directions—and confirmation that the e-mail was genuine.

The Safest Password Today

William Poundstone, author of *Rock Breaks Scissors: A Practical Guide to Outguessing & Outwitting Almost Everybody.*

First Target and Home Depot, then Anthem! It's very clear that hackers are all around us. What can we do? Fight back with a secure password for your accounts.

The challenge is that just about any password you can think up, the bad guys can guess with the help of password-hacking software.

One strategy—turning a memorable phrase into an obscure password by combining the first letter of each word in the phrase—has become so popular that the hacking software now can guess some of these seemingly secure passwords as well. Trouble is, people tend to gravitate to the same phrases. Star Wars fans use MTFBWY (May The Force Be With You)... Shakespeare fans, TBONTBTITQ (To Be Or Not To Be...).

If you want a truly strong password for your most important accounts, use one created by the free "Password Generator" on *Random.org* or a similar site. But the challenge with truly random passwords is remembering them.

The secret is for you to mentally convert these random passwords into phrases. The random password RPM8T4KA might be remembered as Revolutions Per Minute Eight-Track for KAthy, for example. The human mind is very good at remembering phrases, even odd ones that include a lowercase letter, a number or a symbol. Keep trying the random password generator until you get a password that you can convert into a phrase that you can remember.

Identity and Privacy Defense for Wi-Fi

When using Wi-Fi, make sure that you have two-step verification enabled (for directions, search for "two-step verification" and the service you want to use, such as Google or Facebook). This means that signing into an account will require two forms of identity verification—usually a password you create and a code sent to you through a text message or with a special app. So even if your user name and password are stolen, the thieves cannot get to your account because they will not receive the additional required code.

For the system to work properly, you need separate sign-ins and passwords for every online account and need to enable two-step authorization for all of them. Since this may significantly increase the number of passwords you have, consider using a password manager such as *1Password* or *LastPass*.

The New York Times. NYTimes.com

Warning: Cyberthieves May Have Your Social Security Number

John Sileo, president and CEO of The Sileo Group, a Denver-based data-security think tank that has worked with the Department of Defense and Federal Reserve Bank of New York, among other clients. He is author of *Privacy Means Profit: Prevent Identity Theft and Secure You and Your Bottom Line. Sileo.com*

Massive data breaches at giant companies have become so commonplace that consumers now tend to shrug them off. But high-tech criminals have ratcheted up the danger—and the steps required to safeguard consumer finances and identities—to a whole new level.

The biggest and most recently revealed example of a much more dangerous hacking incident involves the health insurance provider Anthem. Similar and less publicized invasions have occurred at other companies, but the Anthem breach makes the possible fallout from incidents of credit card and password theft seem mild in comparison.

We asked security expert John Sileo to explain why the dangers are so high now and what consumers can do to protect themselves...

SOCIAL SECURITY NUMBERS ARE KEY

Unlike the hacking incidents at such companies as Target and The Home Depot, the Anthem breach could lead to long-lasting and even life-altering identity theft for many of the up to 80 million current and former customers potentially affected. That's because the hackers who invaded Anthem's computers stole data including names, employment and contact information, health insurance IDs, addresses, birth dates and Social Security numbers.

Social Security number breaches are especially dangerous because they don't just help crooks gain access to your accounts, the way a credit card breach does. A Social Security breach allows the crook to pose as you in myriad ways that could wreck your life. Victims might spend the rest of their lives fending off bill collectors about purchases they never made...fighting to remove inaccurate and potentially lethal information from their medical files...explaining to police that it was really someone else who was arrested and skipped bail...and praying that no one steals their tax refunds.

That's far worse than having your credit card information stolen—credit cards can be quickly canceled, passwords can be changed and any losses generally are covered by the issuer.

If you become a victim of a corporate data breach, don't be fooled into thinking that you're safe just because...

• **Months have passed and your credit reports remain fine.** A 2012 survey by consulting company Javelin Strategy & Research found that 22.5% of people who receive a notice informing them that they were the victim of a data breach later become victims of identity theft—but it doesn't always happen fast. Data thieves sometimes wait years to use stolen data.

• **You have never been an Anthem customer.** There have been other comparable data breaches, and more are sure to follow.

Examples: Community Health Systems, a network of more than 200 hospitals across 29 states, had approximately 4.5 million patient records breached. Experian, which maintains confidential credit files, was breached, exposing an unknown number of files.

Possible consequences for victims of the Anthem breach—and other similar breaches—and what to do about each...

PHONY DEBTS IN YOUR NAME

An identity thief who has your Social Security number might open new credit accounts in your name or even borrow against the value of your home. You would not be held legally responsible for these debts ultimately, but it could take decades to clear up the mess. In the meantime, your damaged credit score could mean higher interest rates on loans... higher auto insurance rates...and even rejections from potential employers.

What to do: Place a security freeze on your credit files. The usual advice is to put a fraud alert on your files, but that does not provide sufficient protection. Alerts generally expire in 90 days, and while lenders are supposed to take added precautions when an alert is in place, these precautions can fail. A freeze completely blocks your credit report from being accessed and credit from being issued until the freeze is lifted.

Contact all three credit bureaus by phone or online to establish this freeze (*Experian.com*, *Equifax.com* and *TransUnion.com*). You will have to contact the bureaus again and provide a password whenever you wish to temporarily lift the freeze to apply for credit. Costs vary by state, but expect to pay $3 to $10* to each reporting agency each time the freeze is lifted. In some states, there also is a fee to establish or reestablish a freeze.

Helpful: Ask lenders and credit card issuers which credit-reporting agency or agencies they use, and then lift the freeze only with those—generally only mortgage lenders check all three. In some states, you will be exempt from the fees cited above if you are 65 or older (62 or older in Louisiana and North Carolina) and/or can provide a police report showing that you are a victim of ID theft.

If you are not willing to place a security freeze on your credit—perhaps because you are in the process of applying for loans or jobs—at least sign up for an ID-theft-monitoring service. These services do not prevent ID theft, but they can notify you quickly of certain signs of trouble and help you navigate the often frustrating recovery process.

Warning: The ID-theft-monitoring services provided to the victims of large-scale data breaches for free usually are badly lacking, possibly monitoring credit reports with only one of the three major credit bureaus, for example.

Instead, consider spending around $250 per person a year for a high-quality ID-theft-monitoring service. Choose one that monitors credit reports from all three credit-reporting agencies plus address-change requests, court records, driver's license activity, payday loan applications and websites where stolen identities are bought and sold. Services that use the underlying monitoring technology of a company called CSID tend to be among the most robust. These include IDT911 and LifeLock.

PHONY DEBTS IN KIDS' NAMES

If your children are covered through your health insurance, they also could be at risk for identity theft if your insurer or one of your medical providers is breached. This was not a risk with retailers such as Target and The Home Depot that do not normally have minors' confidential information on file.

ID theft can be especially troublesome for minors because it frequently is not noticed for years. One frustrating twist for parents—you generally cannot place a fraud alert or a security freeze on a young child's credit file. If the child doesn't yet have credit, he/she probably doesn't yet have a credit file. If you try to set up a fraud alert or credit freeze for such a child, it could trigger the creation of a credit file, which in some ways makes it easier to steal the child's identity.

What to do: An ID-theft-monitoring service that includes family protection can monitor databases for signs that the child's Social Security number is being used by identity thieves. Even the free monitoring product being offered by Anthem likely can do this, though a higher-quality service offered by a pay service probably could do it better.

*Prices subject to change.

PHONY HEALTH INSURANCE BILLS

Someone could use your health insurance ID number to obtain health services in your name, leaving you to battle health-care providers and bill collectors about co-pays and other fees that you don't owe. What's more, your medical records could become corrupted with someone else's information, leading to a potentially lethal misdiagnosis.

What to do: Read every "Explanation of Benefits" statement you get from your insurer. If any don't correspond to a medical visit you made or treatment you had, contact the provider and the insurer immediately to alert them to potential medical identity theft. If you have access to your medical records through a health-care provider's online patient portal, check this every month or so.

STOLEN TAX REFUNDS

An identity thief who has your Social Security number and date of birth could file a phony tax return in your name to claim a tax refund. Not only could this greatly complicate your own tax filing, it might mean that you can't receive the refund you are due until the situation is cleared up, which could take years.

If you filed taxes last year in Florida, Georgia or Washington, DC—the places with the highest rates of tax-refund identity theft—you can apply for an identity-protection personal identification number, or IP PIN, through the IRS website. On *IRS.gov*, enter "IP PIN" into the search box, then select "The Identity Protection PIN (IP PIN)." Once you receive your six-digit IP PIN, enter it on your tax return to confirm that the return actually is from you. IP PINs also are available to the approximately 1.7 million taxpayers who received a letter offering them this safeguard because the IRS identified what it considered suspicious activity in their accounts. IP PINs cannot be used on state tax returns, however. For more information on eligibility and rules, go to *IRS.gov*.

SHOULD YOU GET A NEW SOCIAL SECURITY NUMBER?

The Social Security Administration allows people to request new Social Security numbers when other measures fail to stop identity thieves. To request this, complete form SS-5, *Application for a Social Security Card* (*SocialSecurity.gov/forms*) and bring proof of your identity and proof of a serious ID-theft problem—such as letters from bill collectors or credit-reporting agencies—to your local Social Security office.

But this generally is worth doing only in the most extreme cases. Replacing a Social Security number inevitably leads to years of headaches as lenders and other legitimate companies try—and often fail—to make sense of the unusual situation. Worse, it won't necessarily solve your problem. Every company that has your current Social Security number on file will add a note in its system linking your new Social Security number to it. The old number could continue to be abused—and perhaps the new one, too.

How to Stop Online Spies

Robert Siciliano, a security analyst and the CEO of *IDTheftSecurity.com*. He has more than 30 years of experience in cyber and real-world security and is author of *99 Things You Wish You Knew Before...Your Identity Was Stolen*.

It is not a secret that your online activity is not very private. Cyber criminals and government agencies have ways of reading your e-mails and discovering where you go on the Internet. Websites you visit can figure out who you are, where you live and what your interests are, then sell that information to marketing companies or anyone else who wants to know.

Two of the latest options for improving online privacy...

• **A device called Safeplug keeps your Internet activity private.** Plug *Safeplug* ($49,* *PogoPlug.com/safeplug*) into your Internet router, and it can conceal your IP address—a unique number that can be used to identify your computer. It also can route your Internet traffic through random computers around the

*Price subject to change.

BEWARE...

College Students at High Risk for Identity Theft

Students are five times more likely than the general public to have their personal information stolen.

Reasons: Living spaces, like dorm rooms, tend to be very close quarters, and keeping personal documents hidden can be tricky...students often download free music, videos and apps and use free Wi-Fi in public places, which makes them especially vulnerable to malware...college students' social-media postings often provide too much detail about personal likes and dislikes and may give away password hints and security questions...and college students tend to use the same password, such as the name of their pet, for all of their devices and accounts.

Steve Weisman, lawyer and founder of *Scamicide.com* and author of *Identity Theft Alert*.

globe, making it extremely difficult for high-tech snoops to figure out where you live.

This added security can slow down your Internet speeds, however, sometimes noticeably. Consider loading more than one web browser onto your computer—both *Chrome* and *Firefox*, perhaps—and activating Safeplug with only one of these. Use the browser that is not Safeplug-enabled when fast Internet speeds are more important than privacy, such as when streaming a movie from Netflix or another reputable site.

- **A service called ShazzleMail keeps your e-mails private.** When you send a regular e-mail, your e-mail provider stores a copy of the message on its computers. Those stored messages could later be read by a government agency or a cybercriminal who hacks the e-mail provider's system. Your e-mail provider itself might examine your e-mails in order to target advertisements to your interests. You would never tolerate eavesdropping on your phone calls—but that's what this is like.

ShazzleMail lets you send e-mails from your smartphone or tablet to your e-mail recipients. These messages are never stored on an e-mail provider's computers, increasing the odds that they will remain private (free, iOS or Android, *ShazzleMail.com*). You have to use a special ShazzleMail e-mail address to send these messages, however, and using this service won't keep your e-mails secure if a criminal has loaded spyware onto your device or onto the phone or computer of the person who receives the message. ShazzleMail works best if both sender and recipient have ShazzleMail accounts. You can send messages to non-ShazzleMail users, too, but they will have to take a few extra steps to access them.

The Very Best Identity Theft Protection

Putting a freeze on your credit reports at the three major bureaus—Equifax, Experian and TransUnion—prevents anybody from getting access to your credit data.

But: It also prevents legitimate inquiries—for credit applications, mortgages, cell phone contracts, an apartment lease, a new job and other purposes. And a freeze costs $5 to $10 per credit bureau* to set up and as much as $12 each time you want it lifted to allow a credit search.

Roundup of experts on identity theft, reported at *Time.com*.

*Prices subject to change.

Hidden Dangers in Online Ads

Rahul Kashyap, head of security and research at Bromium, a cybersecurity firm, Cupertino, California. *Bromium.com*

Even the "safest" corners of the Internet are no longer safe. ***Latest scam that could harm you:*** Cybercriminals have been placing hidden land mines in legitimate online ads on high-profile, trusted websites. When computer users click on the ads, they unknowingly download destructive software, called malware, to their computers. That allows hackers to steal financial account information or even to lock up your files until you pay a ransom to free them.

The malicious practice has been dubbed "malvertising" because the malware hides in online advertising. Malvertising has invaded extremely popular sites including *Amazon, Answers.com, Yahoo* and *YouTube*.

Even if you don't click on an infected ad, just having the ads on your screen can put you at risk because the malware can exploit security holes in your Internet browser and download itself to your computer.

Malvertising is especially difficult for computer users or security software to spot or trace because of the nature of online advertising now. Big ad networks, such as the one owned by Google, often automatically and instantaneously insert ads when you visit a website, based on your interests, location and previous visits to other websites. Most malware is designed to be stealthy and goes undetected by traditional defenses such as antivirus software.

Self-protection: Keep your computer's operating system, web browsers and browser plug-ins, such as Java and Adobe Flash, up to date by either setting them for automatic update or regularly checking if updates are available. Updates often are able to close security holes reported by previous malvertising victims. Also consider using a free ad-blocking plug-in with your browser, such as Adblock Plus (*AdblockPlus.org*).

DID YOU KNOW THAT...

Android Phones Are Less Secure Than Others

Android phones are tied to a completely open operating system that is not well-policed. It is easier to place an app containing malware in the Google Play Store, formerly called the Android Market, than in Apple or Microsoft app stores. And the many variants of the Android operating system and devices using it can make it difficult for users to be sure that their downloads are safe.

Self-defense for Android users: Download only from developers you know and trust... and carefully look at the extent of permissions that each app has on your device to be sure that you are comfortable granting access.

Roundup of security experts reported at *InfoWorld.com.*

Watch Out for Cryptolocker!

Cryptolocker virus infects your hard drive and encrypts it, making it impossible for you to retrieve files. Then a message appears on your screen demanding payment to repair the damage. Cryptolocker is spread like other malware through phony websites, Facebook videos and e-mail.

Best: Regularly back up all data...keep security software up to date...never click on unfamiliar links.

If your computer is infected, you will have to erase your hard drive and reinstall your data from a backup.

MarketWatch.com

Tech-Support Con

Tech-support scammers get your name and phone number from public databases, then call and say that they represent a well-known company, such as Microsoft. The scammer warns you about malware on your computer and asks you to perform some tests. Then he/she requests remote access to your computer, which allows him to install malware...or tries to enroll you in a phony maintenance program...requests credit card information so he can bill you for phony services...or directs you to websites that will install malware or steal personal information.

Self-defense: Never allow any person who contacts you out of the blue to direct you to websites or to links or to control your computer remotely—and do not rely on caller ID to point out frauds, because scammers know how to get around it.

OnGuardOnline.gov

Hotel Business-Center Security Risk

Hackers have been installing keystroke-logging malware on many hotel computers so that they can monitor users' sessions and steal passwords, financial information and identities. Thieves use stolen credit cards to register as hotel guests, then go to business centers to install the tracking malware.

Self-defense: Use hotel and other public computers only for web browsing, not for anything personal or password-protected. If you need to print something from an e-mail account on a public computer, create a free throwaway address at either *YOPMail.com* or *10MinuteMail.com*. Use a mobile device to forward the file or e-mail to the throwaway account, and use the public computer to print from the throwaway address.

KrebsonSecurity.com

Beware of Fake Companies on Google

Audri Lanford, PhD, cofounder of *Scambusters.org*, a website that has educated more than 11 million people about scams and cons.

If you ever use Google to search for a nearby business, scammers may be targeting you. That's because it's easy to set up a fake company, address and telephone number on the Google Maps site using online tools.

How the scam works: Say that you get locked out of your home and look for a locksmith near you by searching in Google the word "locksmith" and the name of your town or your zip code. You pick one of the locksmiths from a list, call and get a very attractive quote. But the number you call actually may be forwarded to a boiler-room operation, possibly in some other state, that dispatches an unscrupulous and most likely unlicensed person to help you. There is no legitimate local business. When the person arrives, he/she charges a huge premium over what a licensed locksmith would or he does expensive, unnecessary work. It is difficult for you to argue after the work is done.

By flooding Google Maps with hundreds of fraudulent listings in a city or town, scammers can swindle consumers with a variety of low-quality, overpriced emergency service providers, including supposed plumbers, electricians, tow services and taxis.

Self-defense: Go to a trusted source instead of Google for a recommendation. Ask a neighbor…try AAA…or check Angie's List if you are a member. Google the information that you

EASY-TO-DO...

Free Ways to Boost Home Security

Ask the local police to send an officer to walk through your home, pointing out areas of vulnerability and suggesting fixes. Also, join your local Neighborhood Watch program or start one, and get to know your neighbors so that everyone keeps an eye on one another.

Additional free strategies: Use locks at all times on every exterior door and every window, even if you live in a safe neighborhood…keep foliage well-trimmed to avoid creating hiding places…never open the door to uninvited strangers, and teach your kids not to open it as well…and stay home when workers are in or near your house.

To be sure your home looks lived-in: Rotate lights on timers when you are away…have mail held by the postal service if you will be gone for a few days…and have friends drop by to water plants or just walk around.

Roundup of experts on home security, reported at *DailyFinance.com*.

BETTER WAYS...

How to Protect Against a Smartphone Loss

Write down the serial number and model number of your smartphone, and store them safely in case you need to report a lost or stolen phone. Also set up password protection so that a thief can't gain access to your data, and back up your information online, including photos, account settings and app data. You can use the GPS function built into Android phones and iPhones to help track down a missing phone.

If all else fails, report the missing phone to your carrier—it will shut the phone down, rendering it unusable even if you find it.

Roundup of experts on mobile phones, reported at *DailyFinance.com*.

get from your initial Google search—for example, type in the name of the supposed locksmith company and the word "scam." Call the phone number you find on Google Maps, but watch out for red flags, including individuals who answer the phone without mentioning the company's name or who offer a quote that seems too low. When the person arrives, ask for a written estimate and state licensing number before any work begins.

Beware Social-Media Investment Fraud

Be careful about responding to unsolicited investment offers that arrive on your Facebook wall or in a tweet.

Helpful: Watch for affinity fraud—investment pitches through online groups to which you belong...look for red flags, such as claims of guaranteed returns that come with no risk...and learn the privacy and security settings at every site that you use, and set them to limit access by people you do not know.

Best: Always ask questions about any investment proposed to you by anyone—research the idea carefully on your own, not through people or sites recommended by the person proposing it. And look into the person as well as the investment proposal, and invest only if you are thoroughly comfortable with both.

US Securities and Exchange Commission, *Investor.gov*.

Before Giving Away Your Computer...

Before you give away or dispose of a computer, be sure that private data is deleted. Use a disk-wiping tool if you run Windows 7...then reinstall the operating system from scratch. In Windows 8, the *Reset your PC* feature has an option called *Fully clean the drive* that deletes data. For external drives, perform a *full format* to erase data.

To check whether you have deleted everything, use a recovery tool such as the free *Recuva* program to scan internal and external drives. If you wiped everything, the program should find no files for recovery.

Roundup of experts on data destruction and recovery, reported at *PCWorld.com*.

Missed-Call Phone Scam

Crooks use computers to call thousands of numbers per hour, letting each phone ring only once. The computer hangs up before you can answer, but your phone will notify you that you have missed a call. The number looks like a US number but is a disguised international one. If you call back, you will be charged several dollars to connect the call and several more for each minute you are on hold or remain in conversation with a scammer.

Self-defense: Do not call back a number that you do not recognize. If you are unsure, Google the number and be sure that the area code is a legitimate US one. Watch your phone bill, and request reversal of any scam-related charges.

Roundup of experts on telephone scams, reported at *TechCrunch.com*.

Index

D

E

F

G

H

I